D0260841

**select
editions**

Reader's
Digest

Reader's
Digest

The names, characters and incidents portrayed in the novels in
this volume are the work of the authors' imaginations. Any
resemblance to actual persons, living or dead,
events or localities is entirely coincidental.

The condensations in this volume
are published with the consent of the authors
and the publishers © 2010 Reader's Digest.

www.readersdigest.co.uk

The Reader's Digest Association Limited
11 Westferry Circus Canary Wharf London E14 4HE

For information as to ownership of
copyright in the material of this book,
and acknowledgments, see last page.

Printed in Germany
ISBN 978 0 276 44439 5

select
editions

THE READER'S DIGEST ASSOCIATION LIMITED, LONDON

contents

author in focus

In *Present Danger*, **Stella Rimington**, ex-Director General of MI5, has come up with her fifth and best novel to date. Set in Northern Ireland and the South of France, it provides a fascinating glimpse into the risky, high-tension work of an intelligence agent, and stars her sympathetic heroine, Liz Carlyle. Observing Liz in action, it's not hard to imagine the young Stella Rimington, when she joined MI5 in 1965, full of determination to make her way in what was then a very male-dominated world. It's no wonder, perhaps, that Judi Dench is said to have drawn inspiration from Dame Stella when playing James Bond's boss, 'M', in 007 films.

in the spotlight

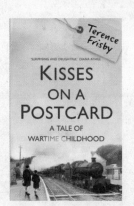

Kisses on a Postcard is a happy recollection of years spent away from home during the Second World War, but author Terence Frisby would be the first to say that of the 3.5 million British evacuees, not all children were so lucky. Now, seventy years on, the Evacuees Reunion Association is gathering funds for a national memorial to be cast in bronze. It will show children holding hands with gas masks and luggage labels round their necks, but facing different directions as they leave home to escape the Blitz. It is hoped the monument will stand outside St Paul's Cathedral, where, on September 1, 2009, a commemorative service was held. For more details, go to www.evacuees.org.uk.

NINE DRAGONS

MICHAEL CONNELLY

Detective Harry Bosch has built his career

solving cases on the streets of Los Angeles.

But a sudden and unexpected call for help is

about to draw him across the world to

crowded, neon-lit Kowloon, where the Triad

gangs hold sway.

He has just twenty-four hours to find and

protect the person he loves more than anyone

else in the world.

ONE

From across the aisle, Harry Bosch looked into his partner's cubicle and watched him conduct his daily ritual of straightening the corners on his stacks of files, clearing the paperwork from the centre of his desk and finally placing his rinsed-out coffee cup in a desk drawer. Bosch checked his watch and saw it was only 3.40. It seemed that each day, Ignacio Ferras began the ritual a minute or two earlier than the day before. It was only Tuesday, the day after Labor Day weekend and the start of a short week, and already he was edging towards the early exit. This routine was always prompted by a phone call from home. There was a wife waiting there with a brand-new set of twins. She watched the clock like the owner of a candy store watches the fat kids. She needed the break and she needed her husband home to deliver it. Even across the aisle from his partner, Bosch could usually hear both sides of the call. It always began with, 'When are you coming home?'

Everything in final order at his workstation, Ferras looked over at Bosch. 'Harry, I'm going to take off,' he said. 'Beat some of the traffic. I have a lot of calls out but they have my cell. No need waiting around for that.'

Ferras rubbed his left shoulder as he spoke. This was also part of the routine. It was his unspoken way of reminding Bosch that he had taken a bullet a couple of years before and had earned the early exit.

Bosch just nodded. The issue wasn't about whether his partner left the job early or what he had earned. It was about commitment. Ferras had gone through nine months of rehab before reporting back to the squad room. But in the year since, he had worked cases with a reluctance that was wearing Bosch thin. He wasn't committed and Bosch was tired of waiting on him.

Ferras stood up and locked his desk. He was taking his jacket off the back of the chair when Bosch saw Larry Gandle step out of his office on the far side of the squad room and head towards them. As the senior man in the partnership, Bosch had been given the first choice of cubicles a month earlier when Robbery-Homicide Division, RHD, moved over from the decrepit Parker Center to the new Police Administration Building, the PAB. He could have taken a cubicle facing the windows that looked out on City Hall, but Bosch had chosen the cube that let him watch what was happening in the squad room. Now he saw the approaching lieutenant and he instinctively knew that his partner wasn't going home early.

Gandle was holding a piece of paper torn from a notepad and had an extra spring in his step. It had been four weeks since they'd drawn a case and Bosch could tell the wait was over. The fresh kill. He started to rise.

'Bosch and Ferras, you're up,' Gandle said when he got to them. 'Need you to take a case for South Bureau.'

Bosch saw his partner's shoulders slump. He ignored it and reached out for the paper Gandle was holding. He looked at the address written on it. South Normandie. He'd been there before.

'It's a liquor store,' Gandle said. 'One man down behind the counter. Patrol is holding a witness. That's all I got. You two good to go?'

'We're good,' Bosch said before his partner could complain.

But that didn't work. 'Lieutenant, this is Homicide Special,' Ferras said, turning and pointing to the boar's head mounted over the squad-room door. 'Why are we taking a rob job at a liquor store? You know it was a gang member and the South guys could wrap it up—or at least put a name on the shooter—before midnight.'

Ferras had a point. Homicide Special was for complex cases, an elite squad that went after the tough cases with the relentless skill of a boar rooting for a truffle. A liquor-store holdup in gang territory hardly qualified.

Gandle, whose balding pate and dour expression made him a perfect administrator, spread his hands in a gesture offering a complete lack of sympathy. 'I told everybody last week. We've got South's back this week. They've got a skeleton crew on while everybody else is in homicide school. They caught three cases over the weekend and one this morning. So there goes the skeleton crew. You guys are up and the rob job is yours. That's it.'

'We're good, Boss,' Bosch said, ending the discussion.

'I'll wait to hear from you, then.'

Gandle headed back to his office. Bosch pulled on his coat and opened the middle drawer of his desk. He took the leather notebook out of his back pocket and replaced the pad of lined paper in it with a new one. A fresh kill always got a fresh pad. That was his routine.

Ferras stood with his hands on his hips, looking up at the clock on the wall. 'Shit,' he said. 'Every time.'

'What do you mean, "every time"?' Bosch said. 'We haven't caught a case in a month.'

'Yeah, well, I was getting used to that.'

'Well, if you don't want to work murders, there's always a nine-to-five table like auto theft.'

'Yeah, right.'

'Then let's go.'

Bosch headed towards the door. Ferras followed, pulling his phone out so he could give his wife the bad news. On the way out of the squad room, both men reached up and patted the boar on its flat nose for good luck.

BOSCH DIDN'T NEED to lecture Ferras on the way to South LA. His driving in silence was his lecture.

Finally, his young partner opened up. 'This is driving me crazy,' he said.

'What is?' Bosch asked.

'The twins. There's so much work, so much crying. It's a domino effect. One wakes up and that starts the other one up. Neither of us is getting any sleep and my wife is going crazy. Calling me all the time, asking when I'm coming home. So I come home and then it's my turn and I get the boys and I get no break. It's work, kids, work, kids, work, kids every day.'

'What about a nanny?'

'We can't afford a nanny. Not with the way things are, and we don't even get overtime any more.'

Bosch didn't know what to say. His daughter was thirteen and ten thousand miles away. He had never been directly involved in raising her. He saw her four weeks a year—two in Hong Kong and two in LA—and that was it. What advice could he give a full-time dad with three kids, including twins?

'Look, I don't know what to tell you,' he said. 'You know I've got your back. I'll do what I can when I can. But maybe it's more than just the twins. Maybe it's you, Ignacio.'

'Me? What are you saying?'

'I'm saying maybe it's you. Maybe you came back too soon.'

Ferras did a slow burn and didn't respond.

'Hey, it happens sometimes,' Bosch said. 'You take a bullet and you start thinking that lightning might strike twice.'

'Look, Harry, I'm fine that way. I'm good. This is about sleep depriva- tion and being exhausted all the time and not being able to catch up because my wife is riding my ass from the moment I get home, OK? Believe me, I get it enough from her. I don't need it from you, too.'

Bosch nodded and that was enough said. He knew when to quit.

The address Gandle had given them was in the seventieth block of South Normandie Avenue, just a few blocks from the infamous corner of Florence and Normandie where some of the most horrible images of the 1992 riots had been captured by news helicopters and broadcast around the world.

But Bosch quickly realised he knew the area and the liquor store that was their destination from a different riot and for a different reason.

Fortune Liquors was already cordoned off by yellow crime-scene tape. A small number of onlookers were gathered but murder in this neighbourhood was not that much of a curiosity. The people here had seen it before—many times. Bosch parked their sedan and after going to the trunk to retrieve his briefcase, he headed towards the tape.

Bosch and Ferras gave their names and serial numbers to a patrol officer with the crime-scene attendance log and then ducked under the tape. As they approached the front door of the store, Bosch put his hand into his jacket pocket and pulled out a book of matches. It was old and worn. The front cover said 'Fortune Liquors' and it carried the address of the building before them. He thumbed the book open. There was only one match missing, and on the inside cover was the fortune that came with every matchbook: *Happy Is the Man Who Finds Refuge in Himself*.

Bosch had carried the matchbook with him for almost twelve years. Not so much for the fortune, though he believed in what it said. It was because of the missing match and what it reminded him of—a case a long time ago.

Several patrol officers and a sergeant were standing inside the store, which was long and narrow and essentially three aisles wide. Bosch could see down the centre aisle to a rear hallway and an open back door leading to a parking area behind the store. The cold-beverage cases ran along the wall on the left aisle and then across the back of the store. The liquor was on the right aisle while the middle aisle was reserved for wine.

Bosch saw two more patrol officers in the rear hallway and he guessed they were holding the witness in what was probably a rear storage room or office. He put his briefcase down and from the pocket of his coat he pulled out two pairs of latex gloves. He gave a set to Ferras and they put them on.

The sergeant noticed the arrival of the two detectives and broke away from his men. 'Ray Lucas,' he said by way of greeting. 'We have one vic down behind the counter. His name is John Li, spelled L-I. Happened, we think, less than two hours ago. Looks like a robbery where the guy didn't want to leave a witness. A lot of us here in the 77th knew Mr Li. He was a good guy.'

Lucas signalled Bosch and Ferras over to the counter. Bosch squeezed into the small space behind the counter and squatted down like a baseball catcher to look closer at the dead man.

The man on the floor was Asian and looked to be almost seventy. He was on his back, eyes staring blankly at the ceiling. His lips were pulled back from clenched teeth, almost in a sneer. There was blood on his lips, cheek and chin, coughed up as he died. The front of his shirt was soaked with his blood and Bosch could see at least three bullet entry points in his chest. His right leg was bent at the knee and folded awkwardly under his other leg. He had obviously collapsed on the spot when he was shot.

'No casings that we can see,' Lucas said. 'The shooter cleaned those up and then he pulled the disc out of the recorder in the back.'

'Unless it was a revolver,' Bosch said. 'Then there would have been no casings to clean up.'

'Maybe,' Lucas said. 'But you don't see too many revolvers down here. Nobody wants to be caught in a drive-by with just six bullets in their gun.'

Lucas wanted Bosch to know that he knew the lay of the land down here. Bosch was just a visitor.

'I'll keep that in mind,' Bosch said.

He studied the scene silently. He was pretty sure the victim was the same man he had encountered in the store so many years before.

He noticed that the victim's right hand had blood smeared on it. This was not unusual. From earliest childhood you touch an injury to try to protect it and make it better. It's a natural instinct. This victim had done the same here, most likely grabbing at his chest after the first shot hit him.

There were at least four inches separating the bullet wounds. Bosch knew that three quick shots from close range would usually have made a tighter cluster. This led him to believe that the victim had been shot once and then fell to the floor. The killer had probably then leaned over the counter and shot him two more times.

The slugs tore through the victim's chest, causing massive damage to the heart and lungs. The blood expectorated through the mouth showed that death was not immediate. The victim had tried to breathe. After all his years working cases Bosch was sure of one thing. There was no easy way to die.

Bosch took his eyes off the body and looked around from his low angle. His eyes immediately held on a gun in a holster attached to the underside of the counter, located for easy access in case of a robbery or worse.

'We've got a gun under here,' Bosch said. 'Looks like a .45 in a holster, but the old man never got the chance to pull it.'

'The shooter came in quick and shot the old guy before he could reach for his piece,' Ferras said. 'Maybe it was known in the neighbourhood that the old man had the gun under the counter.'

Lucas made a noise with his mouth, as if he was disagreeing. 'The gun's gotta be new,' the sergeant said. 'The guy's been robbed at least six times in the past five years. This is the first I knew about a gun.'

Bosch nodded. It was a valid observation. 'Tell me about the witness.'

'Uh, she's not really a witness,' Lucas said. 'It's Mrs Li, the wife. She came in and found her husband when she was bringing him in his dinner. We've got her in the back room but you'll need a translator. We called the AGU, asked for Chinese to go.' Lucas was referring to the Asian Gang Unit.

Bosch took another look at the dead man's face and then stood up, both his knees cracking loudly. The decision to call in an additional investigator of any stripe should have been left to Bosch as lead investigator.

'You speak Chinese, Sarge?'

'No, that's why I called AGU.'

'Then how did you know to ask for Chinese and not Korean or maybe even Vietnamese?'

'Once a day I stop by here to pick up one of those energy drinks. I got to know Mr Li a little from that. He told me he and his wife came from China.'

Bosch nodded and was abashed at his effort to embarrass Lucas. 'Did Mrs Li call nine-one-one?' he said.

'No, like I said, she'd doesn't have much English. From what I got from dispatch, Mrs Li called her son and he's the one who called nine-one-one.'

Bosch stepped out and around the counter. Ferras lingered behind it, squatting to get the view of the body and the gun that Bosch had just had.

'Where is the son?' Bosch asked.

'He works up in the Valley. Should be here anytime now.'

Bosch pointed to the counter. 'When he gets here, you and your people keep him away from this.'

The sergeant took his officers out of the store. Finished behind the counter, Ferras joined Bosch near the front door, where he was looking up at the camera mounted on the ceiling at the centre of the store.

'Why don't you check out the back?' Bosch said. 'See if the guy really pulled the disc and look in on our witness.'

'Got it.' Ferras headed down the centre aisle.

Bosch looked back to take the scene in as a whole. The counter was about twelve feet long, with the cash register set up at the centre. On one side of the register were racks of gum and candy. On the other side were other point-of-purchase products like cheap cigars and a lotto display case.

Behind the counter were shelves where high-end liquors were stored, and which had to be asked for by customers. Bosch saw six rows of Hennessy. He knew the expensive cognac was favoured by high-rolling gang members. He noticed two things and stepped closer to the counter.

The cash register had been turned askew. Bosch reasoned that the killer had pulled it towards him while he took the money from the drawer. This meant that Mr Li had not opened the drawer and given the robber the money. It probably also meant he had already been shot. Ferras's theory that the killer had come in shooting could be correct. And this could be significant in proving intent to kill. More importantly, it gave Bosch a better idea of what kind of person they were looking for.

Without touching anything, Harry leaned over the counter to study the cash register's keyboard. He saw no button that said OPEN or any other obvious indication of how to open the cash drawer. He wondered how the killer knew how to open the register.

He straightened up and looked at the bottles behind the counter. The Hennessy was front and centre, the rows flush. No bottle was missing.

Again Bosch leaned forward across the counter. This time he tried to reach across to one of the bottles of Hennessy. He realised that if he put his hand on the counter for balance he would be able to reach a bottle easily.

'Harry?'

Bosch straightened back up and turned to his partner.

'The sergeant was right,' Ferras said. 'The camera system records to disc. There's no disc in the machine. Either it was removed or the camera was just for show.'

'Are there any back-up discs?'

'There's a couple back there but it's a one-disc system. It just records over and over on the same disc. I worked robbery way back when and we saw a lot of these. They last about a day and then it records over it.'

'OK, make sure we get those extra discs.'

Lucas came back in through the front door. 'AGU is here,' he said. 'Should I send him in?'

'No, don't send him in. I'll be right out.'

Bosch stepped out of the store into the late summer heat. The dry Santa Ana winds were blowing down out of the mountain passes and he could feel the sweat drying on the back of his neck. He was met by a plain-clothes detective.

'Detective Bosch?'

'That's me.'

'Detective David Chu, AGU. Patrol called me down. How can I help?' Chu was short and slightly built. There was no trace of an accent in his voice.

Bosch signalled him to follow as he ducked back under the tape and headed to his car, taking off his suit jacket as he went. He took the match-book out and put it in his trouser pocket, then folded the jacket inside out and put it in a clean cardboard box he kept in the trunk of his work car.

'Hot in there,' he told Chu.

'Hot out here, too,' Chu said. 'The patrol sergeant told me to wait until you came out.'

'Yeah, sorry about that. OK, what we've got is the old man who runs this store dead behind the counter. Shot at least three times in what looks like a robbery. His wife, who does not speak English, found him. She called their son, who was the one who then called it in. We obviously need to interview her and that's where you come in. We may also need help with the son when he gets here. That's about all I know at the moment.'

They headed back to the tape.

'Do you know which dialect Mrs Li speaks?' Chu asked.

'Nope. Is that going to be a problem?'

'I am proficient in Cantonese and Mandarin. These are the two dialects we most often encounter here in LA.'

Bosch held the tape up for Chu so he could go back under.

'Which are you?'

'I was born here, Detective. But my family is from Hong Kong and we spoke Mandarin at home.'

'Yeah? I have a kid who lives in Hong Kong with her mother. She's getting good at Mandarin.'

'Good for her. I hope it will be useful to her.'

They entered the store. Bosch gave Chu a quick view of the body behind the counter and then walked him to the rear of the store. They were met by Ferras; then Chu was used to make introductions to Mrs Li.

The newly widowed woman appeared to be in shock. Bosch guessed she was waiting for her son to arrive, and then the tears would fall. Chu was gentle with her and conversational at first.

After a few minutes he broke away to report to Bosch and Ferras.

'Her husband was alone in the store while she went home to prepare their supper. When she came back she found him behind the counter. She saw no one in the store when she came in. She had parked in the rear and used a key to open the back door.'

Bosch nodded. 'Ask her what time it was when she left the store.'

Chu did as instructed and turned back to Bosch with the answer. 'She leaves at two thirty every day to pick up the supper. Then she comes back.'

'Are there other employees?'

'No, I asked that already. Just her husband and Mrs Li. They work every day eleven to ten. Closed Sundays.'

A typical immigrant story, Bosch thought. They just weren't counting on the bullets coming at the end of it.

'Ask her about the son. Was he at home when she called?'

'I already asked. There is another store. It's in the Valley. He was working there. The family lives together in the middle. In the Wilshire district.'

It seemed clear to Bosch that Chu knew what he was doing. He didn't need Bosch to prompt him with questions.

'OK, we're going back up front. You deal with her and after her son arrives it might be better to take everybody downtown. You OK with that?'

'I'm fine with it,' Chu said.

'Good. Tell me if you need anything.'

Bosch and Ferras went down the hall to the front of the store. A team from the medical examiner's office had arrived to document the death scene and collect the body, and the forensics team had already started work.

Bosch and Ferras decided to split up at that point. Bosch would stay on scene to monitor the collection of forensic evidence and the removal of the body. Ferras would go knock on doors in an effort to find someone who had heard or seen something related to the killing. Both knew this would likely be fruitless, but it needed to be done. A description of a car or a suspicious person could be the piece of the puzzle that would eventually break the case.

Two minutes after Ferras left, Bosch heard loud voices coming from outside the store. He stepped out and saw two of Lucas's patrol officers trying to physically detain a man at the yellow tape. The struggling man was Asian and in his mid-twenties. Bosch quickly stepped towards the problem.

'OK, stop it right there,' he said forcefully, so no one would doubt who was in charge of the situation. 'Let him go,' he added.

'I want to see my father,' the young man said.

Bosch nodded to the two patrolmen. 'I'll take care of Mr Li now.'

They left Bosch and the victim's son alone. 'What's your full name, Mr Li?'

'Robert Li. I want to see my father.'

'I understand. I'm going to let you see your father if you really want to. But you can't until it's clear. I'm the detective in charge and I need you to calm down. The only way you will get what you want is if you calm down.'

The young man looked down at the ground.

Bosch reached out and touched him on the shoulder. 'OK, good,' he said.

'Where's my mother?'

'She's inside in the back room being interviewed by another detective.'

'Can I at least see her?'

'Yes, you can. I just need to ask you a few questions first. Is that OK?'

'Fine. Go ahead.'

'First of all, my name is Harry Bosch. I'm the lead detective here. I'm going to find whoever killed your father. I promise you that.'

'Don't make promises you don't intend to keep. You didn't even know him. You don't care. He's just another—Never mind.'

'Another what?'

'I said never mind.'

Bosch stared at him for a moment before responding.

'How old are you, Robert?'

'I'm twenty-six and I would like to see my mother now.'

He made a move to turn and head towards the back of the store but Bosch grabbed him on the arm with a strength that surprised the young man. Li stopped and looked down at the hand on his arm.

'Let me show you something, then I'll take you to your mother.'

Bosch let go of Li's arm, then pulled the matchbook from his pocket. He handed it over.

Li looked at it with no surprise. 'What about it? We used to give these away until the economy went bad and we couldn't afford the extras.'

Bosch took the matchbook back. 'I got it in your father's store twelve years ago,' he said. 'We almost had a riot in this city. Right here at this intersection.'

'I remember. They looted the store and beat up my father. He should never have reopened here. My mother and me, we told him to open a store up in the Valley but he wouldn't listen to us. Now look what's happened.' He gestured helplessly towards the front of the store.

'Yeah, well, I was here that night, too,' Bosch said. 'A riot started but it ended pretty quick. Right here. One casualty.'

'A cop. I know. They pulled him right out of his car.'

'I was in that car with him but they didn't get to me. And when I got to this spot I was safe. I needed a smoke and I went into your father's store. He was there behind the counter but the looters had taken every last pack of cigarettes in the place.' Bosch held up the book of matches. 'I found plenty of matches but no cigarettes. Then your father reached into his pocket and pulled out his own. He had one last smoke left and he gave it to me.'

That was the story. That was it.

'I didn't know your father, Robert. But I'm going to find the person who killed him. That's a promise I'll keep.'

Robert Li nodded and looked down at the ground.

'OK,' Bosch said. 'Let's go see your mother now.'

TWO

The detectives didn't get back to the squad room until almost midnight. Bosch decided not to bring the victim's family to the PAB for formal interviews. After appointments were made for them to come in the next morning, he let them go home to grieve. Bosch also sent Ferras home so he could attempt to repair any damage with his family. Harry stayed behind alone to organise the evidence and contemplate the case without interruption.

While Ferras's canvas of nearby businesses had proved fruitless, as expected, the evening's work had produced one possible suspect. Three days before his murder, Mr Li had confronted a young man he believed had been routinely shoplifting from the store. According to Mrs Li and as translated by Detective Chu, the teenager had angrily denied ever stealing anything, claiming Mr Li had accused him only because he was black. This seemed laughable since 99 per cent of the store's business came from neighbourhood residents who were black. But Li did not call the police. He simply banished the teenager from the store, telling him never to return. Mrs Li told Chu that the teen's parting shot was to tell her husband that the next time he came back it would be to blow the shopkeeper's head off. Li in turn had pulled his weapon from beneath the counter and pointed it at the youth, assuring him that he would be ready.

This meant the teenager was aware of the weapon Li had beneath the counter. If he were to make good on his threat he would have to enter the store and act swiftly, shooting Li before he could get to his gun.

Mrs Li would look through gang books in the morning in an effort to find a photo of the threatening youth.

They would have to run the lead down and talk to the kid, but Bosch wasn't fully convinced it was a viable lead or that the kid was a valid suspect. There were things about the crime scene that didn't add up to a revenge killing.

Off the captain's office in the squad room there was a meeting room with a long boardroom-style table. Bosch had commandeered the room and spread several crime-scene photographs, fresh from forensics, across the table in a disjointed mosaic that as a whole created the entire crime scene.

Looking at the photos now while sipping from a mug of black coffee, Bosch was first drawn to the same things that had hooked him while he had been at the scene. Front and centre were the bottles of Hennessy standing untouched just across the counter. Harry had a hard time believing that the killing could be gang-related because he had difficulty believing that a gang member would take the money and not a single bottle of Hennessy. The cognac would be a trophy and it was right there within reach.

Bosch's conclusion was that they were looking for a shooter who didn't care about Hennessy. A shooter who was not a gang member.

The next point of interest was the victim's wounds. For Bosch, these alone excluded the mystery shoplifter as a suspect. Three bullets in the chest left no doubt that the intention was to kill. But there was no face shot and this seemed to put the lie to this being a killing motivated by anger or revenge. Bosch knew that when there was a face shot, the killing was most likely personal and the killer was someone known to the victim. Therefore the opposite could be held true. Three in the chest was not personal. It was business. They were looking for someone who was possibly a complete stranger to John Li, someone who had coolly walked in and put three slugs into Li's chest, calmly emptied the cash register and then gone to the back room to grab the disc out of the camera-recorder.

Bosch knew it was likely that this was not a first-time crime. In the morning he would need to check for similar crimes in the Los Angeles area.

Looking at the image of the victim's face, Bosch suddenly noticed something new. The blood on Li's cheek and chin was smeared. The teeth were clean. There was no blood on them. He held the photo up closer. He had assumed the blood on Li's face was expectorant—blood that had come up from his destroyed lungs in his last gasps for air. But how could that happen without getting blood on his teeth?

He put the photo down and moved across the mosaic to the victim's right hand. It had dropped down at his side. There was blood on the fingers and thumb, a drip line to the palm of his hand.

Bosch looked back at the blood smeared on the face. He suddenly realised that Li had not touched his wound out of some natural instinct to soothe the injured area. He had touched his bloody hand to his mouth. This meant a double transfer had taken place. Li had touched his hand to his chest, getting blood on it, and had then transferred blood from his hand to his mouth.

The question was why. Were these movements part of the final death throes, or had Li done something else?

Bosch pulled out his cell and called the investigators' line at the medical examiner's office. He checked his watch as the phone rang. It was ten past midnight.

'Coroner's.'

'Is Cassel still there? It's Bosch.' Max Cassel was the ME investigator who had worked the scene at Fortune Liquors and collected the body.

The call was put on hold and then Cassel picked up.

'I'm out the door, Bosch. I just came back for my coffee warmer.'

Bosch knew Cassel lived at least an hour's commute out in Palmdale.

Coffee mugs with warmers you plugged into the cigarette lighter were required kit for downtown workers with long drive times.

'You put my guy in a drawer already?'

'Nope, all the drawers are taken. He's in icebox three. But I'm done with him and going home, Bosch.'

'I understand. I just have one quick question. Did you check his mouth?'

'What do you mean, check his mouth? Of course I checked his mouth.'

'And there was nothing there? Nothing in the mouth or throat?'

'No, there was something there all right.'

Bosch felt the adrenaline start to kick in. 'What was it?'

'His tongue.' Cassel chuckled.

'Very funny. What about blood?'

'Yes, there was a small amount of blood on the tongue and in the throat. It's noted in my report, which you will get tomorrow.'

'But three shots. His lungs must've looked like Swiss cheese. Wouldn't there be a lot of blood?'

'Not if he was already dead. Not if the first shot blew up the heart and it stopped beating. Look, I gotta go, Bosch. You're on the sked tomorrow at two with Laksmi. Ask her these questions.'

'I will. But I'm talking to you now. I think we missed something. I think Mr Li put something in his mouth.'

There was a pause while Cassel considered this. 'Well, if he did, I didn't see it in the mouth or throat. If it was something he swallowed, then that is not my jurisdiction. It's Laksmi's and she'll find it—whatever it is—tomorrow.'

'Would you make a note so she'll see it?'

'Fine, whatever, I'll make a note. You know nobody's gettin' overtime around here anymore, Bosch.'

'Yeah, I know. Same over here. Thanks, Max.'

Bosch closed the phone and turned to the plastic evidence envelopes that contained the two discs found next to the recorder. Each was in a flat plastic case, marked with a date. One was marked 9/01, exactly a week earlier, and the other was dated 8/27. Bosch took the discs over to the AV equipment at the far end of the room and put the 8/27 disc into the DVD player.

The images were contained on a split screen. One camera angle showed the front of the store, including the cash-register counter, and the other was on the rear of the store. A time and date stamp ran across the top.

Bosch pulled a chair over, and moved the playback speed to four times real time. He figured it would take him less than three hours to knock off the first disc. He would then go home, get a few hours' sleep and be back at the same time as everybody else in the morning.

'Sounds like a plan,' he said to himself.

BOSCH WAS ROUGHLY DRAGGED out of sleep and opened his eyes to see Lieutenant Gandle staring down at him.

'What are you doing in my office, Bosch?'

Bosch sat up on the couch. 'I . . . I was watching a video in the board-room and it got so late it wasn't worth going home. What time is it now?'

'Almost seven but that still doesn't explain why you're in my office. When I left yesterday, I locked my door.'

'Really?'

'Yes, really.'

Bosch acted like he was still clearing his head. He was happy he'd put his picks back in his wallet after he'd opened the door. Gandle had the only couch in Robbery-Homicide Division.

'Maybe the office cleaners came by and forgot to lock it,' he offered.

'No, they don't have a key. Look, Harry, I can't have people opening my door after I've locked it.'

'You're right, Lieutenant. I get the point.' Bosch stood up. 'I'm going back to work now.'

'Not so fast. Tell me about this video that kept you here all night.'

Bosch briefly explained how John Li had unintentionally left behind what looked like a solid lead on the two discs.

'You want me to set it up for you in the conference room?'

'Why don't you wait till your partner's here? We can all look at it together.'

Bosch left Gandle and walked through the deserted squad room. Gandle was always the first man in. He liked to set the precedent for the squad.

Harry went down to the cafeteria, which had opened at seven but was empty because the bulk of the police department's personnel were still working out of Parker Center. The move to the new Police Administration Building was progressing slowly. First some detective squads, then admin-istrators and then the rest. Bosch got the cop's breakfast: two doughnuts and a coffee. He also picked up a second coffee for Ferras. He ate the doughnuts quickly and then took the elevator back up. As expected, when he got back to the squad room his partner was at his desk. Bosch put one of the coffees down in front of him and walked over to his own cubicle.

'Thanks, Harry,' Ferras said. 'Hey, you wore that suit yesterday. Don't tell me you've been working all night.'

Bosch sat down. 'I got a couple of hours on the lieutenant's couch. What time are Mrs Li and her son coming in today?'

'I told them ten. Why?'

'I think I've got something we need to pursue. I watched the extra discs from the store's cameras last night. Grab your coffee and I'll show you what I found. The lieutenant wants to see it, too.'

Ten minutes later Bosch was standing with the remote control in front of the AV equipment while Ferras and Gandle sat at the boardroom table. He cued the disc marked 9/01 to the right spot and then froze the playback.

'OK, our shooter took the disc out of the recorder, so we have no video of what happened in the store yesterday. But what *was* left behind were two extra discs marked August the 27th and September the 1st. This is the disc from September the 1st, one week prior to yesterday. You follow?'

'Follow,' Gandle said.

'So what Mr Li was doing was documenting a tag team of shoplifters. The commonality between these two discs is that on both days these same two guys come in. One goes to the counter and asks for cigarettes while the other goes down the liquor aisle. While Li's getting smokes for the guy at the counter the other guy slides a couple of flasks of vodka into his trousers, then takes a third to the counter to purchase. The guy at the counter pulls out his wallet, sees he left his money at home or whatever and they leave without making a purchase. It happens on both these days with them alternating their roles.'

'This is your lead?' Gandle said. 'You worked through the night for this?'

'This is not the lead,' Bosch said impatiently. 'I'm only telling you the reason why Li pulled these two discs out of the camera. Inadvertently, he also preserved this on the September the 1st tape.'

Bosch hit the playback and the image started to move. On the split screen the front door opened and a customer entered the empty store. He waved casually to Li at the counter and proceeded to the rear of the store. The image was grainy but it was clear enough for the three viewers to tell the customer was an Asian man in his early thirties. He was picked up on the second camera as he went to one of the cold cases at the rear of the store and selected a single can of beer. He took it forward to the counter, said something to Li and the store owner reached up to the overhead storage rack and pulled down a carton of Camel cigarettes. He put them on the counter and then put the can of beer into a small brown bag.

The customer was imposing. Though short and squat, he had thick arms and heavy shoulders. He dropped a single bill on the counter and Li took it, opened the cash register, put the bill in the last slot of the drawer, then handed the change across the counter. The customer took his money and pocketed it. He put the carton of cigarettes under one arm, grabbed the beer and with his remaining free hand pointed a finger like a gun at Li. He pumped his thumb as if shooting the gun and then left the store.

Bosch stopped the playback.

'What was that?' Gandle asked. 'Was that a threat with the finger? Is that what you've got?'

Ferras didn't say anything but Bosch was pretty sure his young partner saw what Harry wanted them to see. He started to replay the video.

'What do you see, Ignacio?'

Ferras stepped forward so he could point to the screen. 'First of all, the guy's Asian. So he's not from the neighbourhood.'

Bosch nodded. 'What else, Ignacio?'

'Watch the money,' Ferras said. 'He gets back more than he gives. Look, Li puts the guy's money in the drawer and then he starts giving him money back, including what the guy gave him in the first place. So he gets the beer and smokes for free and then all the money. It's a payoff.'

Bosch nodded. Ferras was good.

'How much does he get?' Gandle asked.

'I slowed this down last night,' Bosch said. 'He puts the customer's bill in the fourth slot. A carton of smokes and a beer, we assume that is the slot for twenties. If that is the case, he gives him a one, a five, a ten and then eleven twenties. Ten twenties if you don't count the one the customer put in first.'

'Two hundred and thirty-six dollars?' Gandle asked. 'Seems an odd payoff.'

'Actually,' Ferras said, 'two-*sixteen* if you subtract the twenty the customer gives in the first place.'

'Right,' Bosch said.

The three of them stared at the frozen screen without speaking.

'So, Harry,' Gandle finally said. 'What's it mean?'

Bosch pointed to the time stamp on the top of the screen. 'The payoff was made exactly one week before the murder. This Tuesday at about three Mr Li gets shot. Maybe this week he decided not to pay.'

'Or he didn't have the money to pay,' Ferras offered. 'The son told us yesterday that business has been way down and opening the store in the Valley has nearly bankrupted them.'

'So the old man says no and gets popped,' Gandle said. 'Isn't that a bit extreme? You kill the guy and you've lost your funding stream.'

Ferras shrugged. 'There's always the wife and the son,' he said. 'They'd get the message.'

'They're coming in at ten to sign statements,' Bosch said. 'We find out what it's about then.'

Gandle's usually dour expression brightened. He was pleased with the progress of the case. 'OK, gentlemen, I want to know,' he said, leaving the room.

'Nice going, Harry. You made him happy,' Ferras said.

'He'll be happier if we clear this thing.' Bosch turned the screen off and ejected the disc. 'I'm going to go have a talk with Detective Chu before the Li family gets here.'

'You think he held something back on us?'

'That's what I'm going to find out.'

THE AGU was part of the Gang and Operations Support Division, from which many undercover investigations and officers were directed. The GOSD was located in an unmarked building several blocks away from the PAB.

'Good morning, Detective Bosch. I wasn't expecting to see you here,' Chu said when Bosch entered the small squad room. 'I was planning to come by RHD at ten when Mrs Li comes in. What can I do for you?'

'I got something I want to show you. Do you have an AV room here?'

'Yeah, this way.'

The AGU had four interview rooms at the back of the squad room. One had been converted to an AV room with the standard rolling tower of television stacked on top of DVDs. Bosch saw that the stack also had an image printer, something they didn't have yet in the new RHD squad room.

Bosch handed Chu the DVD from Fortune Liquors and he set it up. Bosch took the remote and fast-forwarded to 3 p.m. on the time stamp.

'I wanted you to take a look at this guy who comes in,' he said.

Chu watched silently as the Asian man entered the store, bought a beer and a carton of cigarettes and got the big return on his investment.

'What did you see there?' Bosch asked, after the customer had left the store.

'A payoff of some kind. He got much more back than he gave.'

'Yeah, two hundred and sixteen on top of his own twenty. We counted it.' Bosch saw Chu's eyebrows rise. 'What's it mean?' Bosch asked.

'Well, it probably means he's Triad,' Chu said matter-of-factly.

Bosch nodded. He had never investigated a Triad murder before but he was aware that the so-called secret societies of China operated in most large American cities. Los Angeles, with its large Chinese population, was one of the strongholds, along with San Francisco, New York and Houston.

'What makes you say he's a Triad guy?'

'You said the payoff was two hundred and sixteen dollars, correct?'

'That's right. What's it mean?'

'The Triad extortion business relies on weekly payments from small shop owners seeking protection. The payment is usually one hundred and eight dollars. Two-sixteen is a multiple of that. A double payment.'

'Why one-oh-eight? They charge tax on top of the tax? They send the extra eight bucks to the state or something?'

Chu did not register Bosch's sarcasm and answered as if lecturing a child. 'No, Detective, it has nothing to do with that. Let me give you a brief history lesson that hopefully will give you some understanding.'

'By all means,' Bosch said.

'The creation of the Triads goes back to the seventeenth century in China. There were one hundred and thirteen monks in the Shaolin monastery. Buddhist monks. Manchu invaders attacked and killed all but five of them. Those remaining five monks created the secret societies with the goal of overthrowing the invaders. The Triads were born. But over the centuries, they dropped politics and patriotism and became criminal organisations, engaged in extortion and protection rackets. To honour the slaughtered monks, the extortion amounts are usually a multiple of one hundred and eight.'

'There were five remaining monks, not three,' Bosch said. 'Why are they called Triads?'

'Because each monk started his own Triad. *Tian di hui*. It means heaven and earth society. Each group had a flag in the shape of a triangle symbolising the relationship between heaven, earth and man. From that they became known as the Triads.'

'Great. And they victimise their own people?'

'For the most part, yes. But Mr Li was religious. Did you see the Buddhist shrine in the storage room yesterday?'

'I missed that.'

'I talked to his wife about it. Mr Li was very spiritual. He believed in ghosts. To him, paying the Triad might have been like an offering to a ghost. To an ancestor. You see, if all you knew from day one was that part of your money went to the Triad, just as simply as money goes to the IRS, then you would not view yourself as a victim. It was simply a part of life.'

'But the IRS doesn't put three slugs in your chest when you don't pay.'

'Do you believe that Li was murdered by this man or the Triad?' Chu asked. 'What about the lead we developed through Mrs Li? The gang member who threatened her husband on Saturday.'

Bosch shook his head. 'Things don't match up there. The kid said he would come back and blow Mr Li's head off. Mr Li was shot in the chest. It wasn't a crime of rage. It doesn't fit. But don't worry, we'll still run it down, even if it's a waste of time.' Bosch pointed to the time stamp on the screen. 'Li was killed at the same time on the same day of the week. We have to assume that he made regular payoffs. We have to assume that this man was there when Li was killed. I think that makes him the better suspect.'

The interview room was very small and they had left the door open. Bosch now stepped over and closed it, then looked back at Chu.

'So tell me you didn't have any idea about this yesterday.'

'No, of course not.'

'Mrs Li didn't say anything about making payments to the local Triad?'

Chu stiffened. 'Bosch, what are you suggesting?'

'I'm suggesting that this is your world and you should have told me. I found this by accident.'

They were now facing each other from less than two feet away.

'Well, there was nothing before me yesterday that even suggested this,' Chu said. 'I was called out there to translate. You didn't ask me my opinion about anything else. You deliberately shut me out, Bosch. Maybe if you had included me, I would have seen or heard something.'

'You're a detective, Chu. You don't need an invite to ask a question.'

'With you I thought I did.'

'And what's that supposed to mean?'

'It means I watched you, Bosch. How you treated Mrs Li, her son . . . me.'

'Oh, here we go.'

'What was it, Vietnam? You served in Vietnam, right?'

'Don't pretend you know anything about me, Chu.'

'I know what I see and I've seen it before. I'm not from Vietnam, Detective. I'm an American. Born right here like you.'

'Look, can we just drop this so we can get on with the case?'

'Whatever you say. You're the lead.'

Chu put his hands on his hips and turned back to the screen. Bosch tried to back his emotions down. He had to admit Chu had a point. And he was embarrassed that he had been so easily pegged as someone who had come back from Vietnam with a racial prejudice.

'All right,' he said. 'Maybe the way I dealt with you yesterday was a mistake. I'm sorry. But you're in now and I need to know what you know.'

Chu relaxed, too. 'I just told you everything. The only other thing I was thinking was about the two hundred and sixteen. It's a double payment. Like maybe Mr Li missed a week. Maybe he was having trouble paying.'

'And so maybe that's what got him killed.' Bosch pointed to the screen again. 'Can you make me a hard copy?'

'I would like one myself.'

Chu moved to the printer and pushed a button twice. Soon two copies of the image of the man turning from the counter were printing.

'Do you have mug books?' Bosch asked. 'Intelligence files?'

'Of course,' Chu said. 'I will try to identify him. I would like to get a print of the tattoo as well,' he added.

'What tattoo?' Bosch asked.

Chu took the remote from Bosch and tapped the rewind. He eventually froze the picture at the moment the man was reaching his left hand out to take the cash from Mr Li. Chu used his finger to trace a barely visible outline on the inside of the man's arm. Chu was right. It was a tattoo, but the marking was so light on the grainy image that Bosch had missed it.

'What is that?' he asked.

'It looks like the outline of a knife. A self-administered tattoo.'

'What does it mean to you?'

'Knife is *kim*. There are at least three Triads that have a presence here in Southern California. *Yee Kim, Sai Kim* and *Yung Kim*. These mean Righteous Knife, Western Knife and Brave Knife. They are offshoots of a Hong Kong Triad called Fourteen K. Very strong and powerful.'

'Fourteen K? Like fourteen-carat gold?'

'No, fourteen is a bad-luck number. It sounds like the Chinese word for death. K is for kill.'

Bosch knew from his daughter and his frequent visits to Hong Kong that any permutation of the number four was considered bad luck. His daughter lived with his ex-wife in a condominium tower where there was no floors marked with the numeral four. The fourth floor was marked P for parking and the fourteenth was skipped in the way the thirteenth floor was skipped in most Western buildings.

Bosch gestured to the screen. 'So you think this guy could be in one of the Fourteen K spin-offs?' he asked.

'Perhaps,' Chu said. 'I will begin to make enquiries as soon as you leave.'

Bosch looked at Chu and tried to read him again. He believed he understood the message. Chu wanted Bosch out of there so he could go to work. Harry ejected the DVD. 'Stay in touch, Chu,' he said.

'I will,' Chu responded curtly.

'Good, and I'll see you at ten with Mrs Li and her son.'

FERRAS HAD the cash register from Fortune Liquors on his desk and had run a wire from its side into the side of his laptop. 'Forensics are through with this. No prints other than the victim's. I'm just getting into the memory now. I can tell you the take for the day up until the murder was under two hundred bucks. The victim would have had a hard time making a payment of two hundred and sixteen dollars, if that's what you think happened.'

'Well, I've got some stuff on that to tell you,' Bosch said, putting the print-outs on the desk. 'Anything else from forensics?'

'Not much. They're still processing every—Oh, the GSR on the widow came back negative. But I guess we were expecting that.'

Bosch nodded. Since Mrs Li had discovered her husband's body it was routine to test her hands and arms for gunshot residue to determine if she had recently discharged a firearm. Bosch was pretty sure she could now be scratched from the list of potential suspects.

'How deep is the memory on that thing?' he asked.

'It looks like it goes back a whole year. I ran some averages. The gross income on that place was slightly less than three thousand a week. You figure in overheads and cost of goods, insurance and stuff like that, and this guy was lucky if he was clearing fifty a year for himself. That ain't no way to make a living.'

'Yesterday the son said business was down lately.'

'Looking at this, I don't see where it was ever up.'

Bosch told Ferras what he had learned from Chu and that he was hoping the AGU could come up with an ID. They both agreed that the focal point of the investigation was shifting towards the man in the grainy print-out from the store's surveillance camera. The Triad bagman. Meanwhile, the possible gang member who had argued with John Li the Saturday before his murder still needed to be identified and interviewed.

They went to work on the statements and other voluminous paperwork that accompanied every murder investigation. Chu arrived at ten o'clock.

'Mrs Li isn't here yet?' he asked by way of greeting.

Bosch looked up from his work. 'Not yet. You come up with anything over there?'

'I checked through our photo albums. Didn't see our guy. But we're making enquiries within the community about who this man is and what Mr Li's affiliation was.'

'Affiliation?' Ferras asked. 'He was being extorted. His affiliation was that he was a victim.'

'Detective Ferras,' Chu said patiently, 'you are looking at it from the typical Western point of view. As I explained to Detective Bosch, Mr Li may have had a lifelong relationship with a Triad society. It is called *quang xi*, in his dialect. It has no direct translation, but it has to do with one's social network and a Triad relationship would be included in that.'

Ferras just stared at Chu for a long moment. 'Whatever,' he finally said. 'The vic had lived here almost thirty years. I don't care what they call it in China. Over here it's extortion.'

Bosch admired his young partner's adamant reaction. He was contemplating joining the fray when the phone on his desk rang. He picked it up.

'Bosch.'

'This is Rogers downstairs. You've got two visitors, both named Li.'

'Send them up.'

Bosch hung up. 'OK, they're on their way up. This is how I want to play this. Chu, you take the old lady into one of the interview rooms and go over her statement and have her sign it. After she signs it I want you to ask her about the payoff and the guy on the video. Show her his photo. Ferras and I will talk to the son. I want to find out if he's paying protection at the store up in the Valley. If so, that could be where we grab our guy.'

Bosch looked across the squad room and saw Mrs Li enter, but not with her son. She was with a younger woman. Bosch waved them over.

'Chu, who is this?'

Chu turned round as the two women approached. He didn't say anything. He didn't know. As the two women got closer Bosch saw that the younger woman was Asian, in her mid-thirties and attractive in an understated hair-behind-the-ears sort of way. She walked half a step behind Mrs Li with her eyes cast down on the floor, like a maid pressed into service.

Chu spoke to Mrs Li in Chinese. After she responded, he translated.

'This is Mr and Mrs Li's daughter, Mia. She drove her mother here because Robert Li is delayed.'

Bosch was immediately frustrated by the news. 'Great,' he said. 'How come we didn't know there was a daughter? Ask Mia where she lives.'

The young woman cleared her throat and looked up at Bosch. 'I live with my mother and father,' she said. 'Or I did until yesterday. I guess now I live with just my mother.'

Bosch felt embarrassed that he had assumed she spoke no English and she had heard and understood his annoyed response to her showing up.

'Sorry. It's just that we need all the information we can get.' He looked at the other two detectives. 'OK, Detective Chu, why don't you take Mrs Li into an interview room to go over her statement? I will interview Mia and, Ignacio, you wait for Robert to show up.' He turned back to Mia. 'Do you know how long your brother is delayed?'

'He should be on his way. He said he was going to leave the store by ten.'

'OK, Mia, why don't you come with me and your mother can go with Detective Chu.'

Mia spoke in Chinese to her mother and they proceeded towards the bank of interview rooms at the back of the squad room.

Bosch led the victim's daughter to a small, windowless room with a table in the middle. They sat down on either side of it.

'OK, Mia,' Bosch said. 'Let's start over. I am Detective Bosch. I am assigned as lead investigator on the case involving the murder of your father. I am very sorry for your loss.'

'Thank you.' She had her eyes cast down to the tabletop.

'Can you tell me your full name?'

'Mia-Ling Li.'

'When is your birthday?'

'February the 14th, 1980.'

'Valentine's Day.'

Bosch smiled. He didn't know why. He was just trying to start the relationship over. Then he wondered if they even had Valentine's Day in China. He moved on with his thoughts and did the maths. He realised that Mia was younger than she looked, and only a few years older than her brother.

'You came here with your parents? When was that?'

'In 1982.'

'You were only two.'

'Yes.'

'Are there any other brothers or sisters besides you and Robert?'

'No, just us.'

'OK, good. Now, how long have you been living with your parents?'

She looked up briefly and then back down. 'My whole life. Except for about two years when I was younger.'

'Were you married?'

'No. What does this have to do with who killed my father? Shouldn't you be finding the killer?'

'I'm sorry, Mia. I just need to get some basic information and then, yes, I will be out there looking for the killer. Have you talked to your brother? Did he tell you I knew your father?'

'He said you met him one time. That's not knowing him.'

Bosch nodded. 'You're right. That was an exaggeration. I didn't know him but because of the situation we were in when I . . . met him, I feel like I sort of knew him. I want to find his killer, Mia. And I will. I just need you and your family to help me wherever you can. Don't hold anything back because you never know what might help us.'

'I understand. I won't.'

'OK, what do you do for a living?'

'I take care of my parents.'

'You mean at home? You stay home and take care of your parents?'

Now she looked up and right into his eyes. Her pupils were so dark it was hard to read anything in them. 'Yes. It is the tradition in my family for the daughter to care for her parents.'

'Did you go to school?'

'Yes, I went to university for two years. But then I came home. I cook and clean and keep the house. For my brother, too.'

'So as of yesterday, everybody was living together.'

'Yes.'

'When was the last time you saw your father alive?'

'When he left for work yesterday morning. About nine thirty.'

'And your mother left then, too?'

'Yes, they always go together.'

'And then your mother came back in the afternoon?'

'Yes, I make the supper and she comes for it. Every day at three o'clock.'

Bosch knew that the family home was at least a half-hour drive from the store. 'How long before she took the supper back to the store?'

'She stayed about a half-hour and then she left.'

Bosch nodded. Everything was tallying with the mother's story.

'Mia, did your father talk about anybody at work he was afraid of? Like a customer or anybody else?'

'No, my father was very quiet. He didn't talk about work at home.'

'Did he like living here in Los Angeles?'

'No, I don't think so. He wanted to go home to China but he couldn't.'

'Why not?'

'Because when you leave you do not come back. They left because Robert was coming. In our province you could have only one child. They already had me, and my mother would not put me in the orphanage. My father wanted a son and when my mother became pregnant we came to America.'

Bosch was aware of China's one-child policies. It was a population-containment plan that resulted in a higher value being placed on male births. Newborn females were often abandoned in orphanages or worse. Rather than giving up Mia, the Li family had left the country for the USA.

Bosch decided that he had gathered enough information in this regard. He opened the file and removed the print-out of the image from the store camera. He placed it in front of Mia. 'Who is that, Mia?'

Her eyes narrowed as she studied the grainy image. 'I don't know him. Who is he? Did he kill my father?'

'We don't know yet. But we'll find out. Did your father ever talk about the Triads? About having to pay them?'

She seemed very nervous about the question. 'I don't know about this. We didn't talk about it.'

'Did you ever hear your parents talking about it?'

'No, they didn't. I don't know about this.'

'OK, Mia, then I think we can stop now.'

'Can I take my mother home?'

'As soon as she's finished talking to Detective Chu. What do you think will happen with the store now? Will your mother and brother run it?'

She shook her head. 'I think it will be closed. My mother will work in my brother's store now.'

'What about you, Mia? Will anything change for you now?'

She took a long moment to consider this, as if she had not thought about it before. 'I don't know,' she said finally. 'Perhaps.'

THREE

Back in the squad room, Mrs Li had already finished her interview with Chu and was waiting for her daughter. There was still no sign of Robert Li, and Ferras explained that he had called and said he could not get away from his store because his assistant manager had called in sick.

After escorting the two women out to the elevator, Bosch checked his watch and decided he had time to go out to the Valley and speak to the victim's son and then get back downtown for the scheduled 2 p.m. autopsy. He would take Chu with him.

Bosch drove his Crown Vic with 220,000 miles on the clock. Along the way, Chu reported that Mrs Li had signed her statement and had had nothing new to add. She had not recognised the man from the store video and claimed to know nothing about paying off the Triad. Bosch then relayed what little information he had gleaned from Mia-Ling Li and asked Chu what he knew of the tradition of keeping an adult daughter at home to care for her parents.

'She's a *chin*derella,' Chu said. 'Stays home and does the cooking and cleaning, stuff like that. Almost like a servant to her parents.'

'They don't want them to get married and leave the house?'

'No, man, why would they want her to get married? Then they'd have to hire a maid and a chef and a driver.'

Bosch drove silently for a while after that, thinking about the life Mia-Ling Li lived. He doubted anything would change with the death of her father. There was still her mother to care for.

The traffic was rough and it took them forty-five minutes to get to Sherman Oaks. Fortune Fine Foods & Liquor was on Sepulveda, just a block south of Ventura Boulevard. This put it in an upscale neighbourhood of apartments and condominiums below the even more upscale hillside residences. Bosch parked on the street and flipped down the visor, which had a card clipped to it showing a city vehicle identification code.

Bosch and Chu had worked out a plan during the long ride up. They believed that if anyone knew about the Triad payoffs besides the victim, it would be the son and fellow shop manager, Robert. Why he had not told the detectives about this the day before was the big question.

Fortune Fine Foods & Liquor was completely different from its counterpart in South LA, at least five times bigger and brimming with high-end touches that befitted its neighbourhood. There was a do-it-yourself coffee bar. The cold cases were well lit with open shelves instead of glass doors. There were aisles of speciality foods and hot and cold counters where customers could order fresh steaks and fish or precooked meals. The son had taken his father's business and advanced it several levels.

There were two checkout stations and Chu asked one of the women behind them where Robert Li was. The detectives were directed to a set of double doors that led to a stockroom. To the far left was a door marked office. Bosch knocked and Robert Li promptly answered the door.

He looked surprised to see them. 'Detectives, come in,' he said. 'I am so sorry about not getting downtown today. My assistant manager called in sick and I can't leave the place without a supervisor. I'm sorry.'

'It's OK,' Bosch said. 'We're only trying to find your father's killer.'

Bosch wanted to put the kid on the defensive. Interviewing him in his own surroundings put him at an advantage. Bosch wanted to bring some discomfort to the situation. Then maybe he'd be more forthcoming.

'I am sorry. I thought all I needed to do was sign my statement anyway.'

'We have your statement but it's a little more involved than signing papers, Mr Li. It's an ongoing investigation. Things change. More information comes in.'

'All I can do is apologise. Have a seat, please.'

The office was narrow and Bosch could tell it was shared. There were two desks side by side against the right wall. Two desk chairs and two folding chairs, probably for sales representatives and job interviews.

Li picked up the phone on his desk, dialled a number and told someone he was not to be disturbed. He then made a gesture signalling that he was ready to go.

'First of all, I'm a little surprised that you are working today,' Bosch said. 'Your father was murdered yesterday.'

Li nodded solemnly. 'I am afraid that I have no time to grieve. I must run the business or there will be no business to run.'

Bosch nodded and signalled to Chu to take over. He had typed up Li's statement. As he went over it with Li, Bosch looked around the office. On the wall over the desks were framed licences from the state, Li's 2004 diploma from the business school at the University of Southern California and an honourable mention certificate for Best New Store of 2007 from the American Grocers Association.

Bosch reached across and straightened the cock-eyed frame of the USC diploma, thinking about how Robert got the opportunity to take his father's business and turn it into something bigger and better, while his older sister stayed home and made the beds.

Li signed his statement and when he was finished looked up at a wall clock hung over the door. Bosch could tell he thought they were done.

But they weren't. Now it was Bosch's turn. He opened his briefcase and removed a file. From it he took the photo print of the bagman who had collected money from Li's father. Bosch handed it to Li.

'Tell me about this guy,' he said.

Li held the print-out in both hands and knitted his eyebrows as he looked at it. Bosch knew that people did this to show they were concentrating, but it was usually a cover for something else. Bosch knew that he had probably taken a call in the past hour from his mother and had known that he would be shown the print-out.

'I can't tell you anything,' Li said after thirty seconds. 'I don't recognise him. I've never seen him.'

He handed the print-out back to Bosch but Harry didn't take it.

'But you know who he is, don't you?'

'No, actually, I don't,' Li said, mild annoyance in his voice.

Bosch smiled at him but it was one of those smiles that carried no warmth or humour. 'Mr Li, did your mother call you and tell you we would be showing you that picture?'

'No.'

'We can check the phones, you know.'

'So what if she did? She didn't know who it was and neither do I.'

'You want us to find the person who killed your father, right?'

'Of course! What kind of question is that?'

'It's the kind of question I ask when I know somebody is holding something back from me and that it—'

'What? How dare you!'

'—could be very useful to my investigation.'

'I am holding nothing back! I don't know this man. I don't know his name and I have never seen him before! That is the goddamn truth!'

Li's face grew flushed. Bosch waited a moment and then spoke calmly.

'You may be telling the truth. You may not know his name and maybe you've never seen him before. But you know who he is, Robert. You know your father was making payoffs. Maybe you are, too. If you think there is any danger involved in talking to us, then we can protect you.'

Li shook his head and smiled like he couldn't believe the situation he had found himself in. He started breathing heavily. 'My father just died—he was killed. Can't you leave me alone? Why am I being badgered? I'm a victim here, too.'

'I wish we could leave you alone, Robert. But if we don't find the party responsible, nobody else will. You don't want that, do you?'

Li seemed to compose himself and shook his head.

'Look,' Bosch continued. 'Whoever killed your father took the disc out of the recorder in the back but left the old discs. This guy was on one of them. He took a payment from your father at the same time and on the same day a week before the murder. The guy is Triad and I think you know it. You have to help us out here, Robert.'

Bosch waited. Li put the print-out on the desk.

'OK, yes, my father paid the Triad,' he said.

Bosch breathed slowly. They had just made a big step.

'For how long?' he asked.

'I don't know, all his life—all my life, I guess. It was just something he always did. To him, it was part of being Chinese. You paid.'

Bosch nodded. 'Thank you, Robert, for telling us this. Now, yesterday you told us that things were not going so well at the store. Do you know, was your father behind on his payments?'

'I don't know, maybe. He didn't tell me. We didn't see eye to eye on that.'

'What do you mean?'

NINE DRAGONS | 39

'I didn't think he should pay. I told him a million times. This is America, Pop, you don't have to pay them.'

'But he still paid.'

'Yeah, every week. He was just old school.'

'So you don't pay here?'

Li shook his head but his eyes darted to the side a moment. An easy give-away. 'You do pay, don't you?' Bosch said.

'No.'

'Robert, we need the—'

'I don't pay because he paid for me. He paid for both stores. Now, I don't know what will happen.' Li rubbed his sweating palms on his pants.

'The payment covered both stores.'

'That's right. Last week.'

Li nodded and Bosch thought he saw tears welling in his eyes. Harry knew the next question was the most important one.

'What happened this week?'

'I don't know.'

'But you have an idea, right, Robert?'

He nodded again. 'Both stores are losing money. We expanded at the wrong time—right before the downturn. I told my father we couldn't keep paying. I told him we were going to lose the stores if we didn't stop. Eight hundred dollars a month is a lot in a business like this. My old man, he thought he could find other ways of saving money. He became obsessed with catching shoplifters. He thought if he stopped the losses he'd make a difference. He was from a different time. He didn't get it.'

Bosch leaned back in his chair and looked over at Chu.

They had got Li to open up. It was now Chu's turn to move in with specific questions relating to the Triad. 'Robert, you have been very helpful,' Chu said. 'I want to ask you a few questions with regard to the man in the photo.'

'I was telling the truth. I don't know who he is. I never saw him before.'

'OK, but did your father ever talk about him when, you know, you were discussing the payments?'

'He never used his name. He just said he would be upset if we stopped the payments.'

'Did he ever mention the name of the group he paid? The Triad?'

Li shook his head. 'No, he never—Wait, yes, he did once. It was like the name came from a kind of knife or something. But I don't remember it.'

'Are you sure? That could help us narrow it down.'

Li frowned and shook his head again.

'OK, Robert.'

Chu continued the interview but his questions were too specific and Li continually answered that he didn't know. All that was OK with Bosch. They had made a big breakthrough.

After a while Chu finished up and passed the baton back to Bosch.

'OK, Robert,' Harry said. 'Do you think the man or men your father was paying will now come to you for the money?'

The question prompted a deep frown from Li. 'I don't know,' he said.

'Well, if someone shows up, cooperate. Promise him the money.'

'I don't have the money!'

'That's the point. Promise him the money but say it will take you a day to get it. Then call us. We'll take it from there.'

'What if he just takes it out of the cash registers? You told me yesterday that the cash drawer was empty in my father's store.'

'If he does that, then let him and then you call us. We'll get him when he comes back the next time.'

Li nodded and Bosch could see he had thoroughly spooked him.

'Robert, do you have a gun in the store?'

It was a test. They had already checked gun records. Only the gun in the other store was registered.

'No, my father had the gun. He was in the bad area.'

'Good. Don't bring a gun into this. If the guy shows up, just cooperate.'

'OK.'

'By the way, why did your father buy that gun?'

'The last time he was robbed, they hurt him. Two gang members. They hit him with a bottle. I told him if he wouldn't sell the store, then he had to get a gun. But it didn't do him any good.'

'They usually don't.'

'When will my father's body be released to us?'

'Probably tomorrow,' Bosch said. 'The autopsy is today.'

Li looked crestfallen. 'My father was a very spiritual man. Do they have to desecrate his body?'

Bosch nodded. 'There's an autopsy after any homicide. It's the law.'

Li nodded in acceptance. 'Please don't tell my mother this was done. Will they call me when I can have his body?'

'I'll make sure they do.'

The detectives thanked Li then and left him, a twenty-six-year-old who somehow seemed a couple of decades older now.

BOSCH DROPPED CHU OFF at the AGU office and then headed over to the county coroner's office on Mission Road. By the time he had checked in, gowned up and got into suite three the autopsy was well under way.

John Li's body was lying naked on the cold stainless-steel autopsy table. The chest had been opened and the vital organs removed. Dr Sharon Laksmi was working at a nearby table, putting tissue samples on slides.

'Afternoon, Doctor,' Bosch said.

Laksmi turned from her work and glanced at him. 'You're late, Bosch. I started without you.'

Laksmi was small and dark. What was most noticeable about her was that her eyes were heavily made up behind the plastic shield of her mask. It was as if she realised that her eyes were the only feature people saw behind all the safety garb she wore most of the time.

'Yes, sorry. I was with the victim's son and it ran kind of long.'

'Here's what you are probably looking for.'

She tapped the blade of her scalpel on one of four steel specimen cups lined up to her left on the counter. Bosch stepped over and looked down into them. Each held one piece of evidence extracted from the body. He saw three deformed bullets and a single bullet casing.

'You found a casing? Was it on the body?'

'In it, actually.'

'In the body?'

'That's right. Lodged in the oesophagus.'

Bosch thought of what he had discovered while looking at the crime-scene pictures. Blood on the victim's fingers, chin and lips. But not his teeth. He had been right about his hunch.

'It appears you are looking for a very sadistic killer, Detective Bosch.'

'Why do you say that?'

'Because either he shoved a bullet casing down your victim's throat or the ejected casing somehow landed in his mouth. Since the latter would be a million-to-one shot, I would go with the former.'

Bosch nodded. But not because he subscribed to what she was saying. He was thinking of a scenario Laksmi hadn't considered. One of the casings from the shooter's gun had landed on or near John Li as he lay dying. He saw the shooter collecting the casings and knew they might be valuable evidence in the investigation of his murder. In his last moment he had grabbed the casing and swallowed it, to keep it from the shooter. John Li's final act was an attempt to provide Bosch with an important clue.

'Did you clean the casing, Doctor?' he asked.

'Yes, blood had backed up into the throat and the casing acted like a dam, keeping most of it out of the mouth. I had to clean it to see what it was.'

'Right.'

Bosch knew that the possibility of there being fingerprints on the casing was negligible anyway. The explosion of gases when a bullet fired almost always vaporised fingerprints on the casing. Still, the casing was most likely a good solid piece of evidence. The marks made by the weapon's extractor, firing pin and ejector could be useful in identifying and matching the gun if it were ever found. The casing would link the victim to the gun.

'You want to hear my summary and then be on your way?' Laksmi asked.

'Sure, Doctor, run it down.'

While Laksmi gave a preliminary report on her findings, Bosch grabbed clear plastic evidence envelopes and bagged the slugs and casing separately. The casing looked like it had come from a 9mm round but he would wait for confirmation from ballistics on that. He marked each envelope with the case number and then put them in his coat pocket.

'The first shot was to the upper-left chest, the projectile piercing the right ventricle of the heart and impacting the upper vertebrae, severing the spinal cord. The victim would have immediately dropped to the floor. The next two shots were to the right and left lower sternum. The right and left lobes of the lungs were pierced and the projectiles lodged in the lower back musculature. The result of the three shots was instant loss of cardiopulmonary function. I'd say he lasted no more than thirty seconds.'

'With the spinal-cord damage could he have had any hand and arm movement?'

'Not for very long. Death was almost instantaneous.'

Bosch's theory still worked. Li could have quickly grabbed the casing with his last ounce of strength and put it in his mouth while the shooter moved around the counter to look for the casings.

Bosch felt a growing excitement. The casing was a significant find. He wanted to get the evidence over to ballistics as soon as possible.

'OK, Doctor, what else is there?'

'There's something you might want to look at now rather than wait for the photos. Help me turn him.'

They moved to the autopsy table and carefully rolled the body over. Rigor mortis had come and gone and the procedure was easy. Laksmi pointed to the ankles, where two or three small Chinese symbols were tattooed at the back of Li's feet, on either side of the Achilles tendon.

'Anybody around here who can translate these?'

'I don't think so.'

'OK, can we slide him down a bit so I can take a picture?'

Laksmi helped him move the body down the table. The feet hooked over the edge so the Chinese symbols were in a line across. Bosch reached under his gown, pulled out his cellphone and took two photos of the tattoos. He put the phone down and they turned the body back over and moved it back up into place on the table.

Bosch took off his gloves and threw them into the medical waste receptacle, then picked his phone back up and emailed the photos to Chu, asking him what the symbols meant. He was ready to get moving again.

'Thank you, Doctor,' he said. 'For your records, I'm taking the ballistic evidence over to the Scientific Investigation Division.'

'Did you sign for it?'

She pointed to a clipboard on the counter. Bosch signed the line acknowledging he was now in possession of the evidence listed.

'Give me a couple of days on the hard copy,' Laksmi said. Meaning the formal autopsy report.

'You got it,' Bosch said as he headed towards the autopsy suite's door.

ON THE WAY to SID Bosch called Chu and asked about the tattoos.

'I haven't translated them yet,' Chu said. 'I'm trying to find somebody who can. All my schooling was in English. I spoke Chinese at home. Never read it.'

'Chu, it is the *Asian* Gang Unit, isn't it? There must be somebody that can get me a translation.'

'Yes, there are people here who can do it, but they don't happen to be here right now. As soon as I have it I will call you.'

'Great. Call me.'

Bosch hung up. He was frustrated by the delay. A case had to move like a shark. It could never stop its momentum because that could be fatal. He checked his watch. It was just past three o'clock in LA. His daughter was fifteen hours ahead and sleeping. He pulled to the kerb and sent the photo of the ankle tattoos to her in an email. She would get it on her phone when she got up for school in about an hour.

Pleased with himself, Bosch pulled back into traffic. He was becoming more adept at digital communication, thanks to her. She had insisted that they communicate on all modern levels: email, text, video—she had even tried unsuccessfully to get him on to something called Twitter. He insisted in return that they also communicate the old-fashioned way—verbal conversation. He made sure that their phones were covered by international call plans.

He made it back to the PAB a few minutes later and went straight to the Tool Marks and Ballistics Unit on the fourth floor. He took his four plastic evidence bags to a technician named Ross Malone. His job was to take bullet slugs and casings and use them to attempt to identify the make and model of the firearm they came from.

Malone began with the bullet casing, using tweezers to take it from its packaging and then hold it under a high-powered magnifying glass with a lighted rim. He studied it for a long moment before speaking.

'Cor Bon 9mm,' he said. 'And you're probably looking for a Glock.'

Bosch was expecting him to confirm the size of the round and identify the brand, but not to name the make of weapon that had fired the bullet.

'How do you know that?'

'Take a look.'

Bosch looked over his shoulder through the magnifying glass. He could read the words 'Cor Bon' stamped into the outer edge of the cap. At the centre was a depression made when the gun's firing pin had struck the primer, firing the bullet.

'You see how the impression is elongated, almost rectangular?' Malone asked. 'That's Glock. Only Glocks have the rectangle because the firing pin is rectangular. So you are looking for a 9mm Glock.'

'OK, that helps. What about the slugs?'

Malone put the casing back in its plastic bag and one by one took out the slugs and studied them under the glass. Then he shook his head.

'These aren't much use. They're not in good shape. The casing is going to be your best bet for comparison. Bring me the weapon and I think I'll be able to match it up.'

Bosch realised that John Li's last act was growing in importance. The last desperate act of a man who knew he was dead.

Bosch's quiet contemplation prompted Malone to speak up.

'Did you touch this casing, Harry?'

'No, but Dr Laksmi at the ME's sprayed blood off it with water. It was found inside the victim's throat. He tried to swallow it.'

'Oh. So Laksmi would have been gloved up when she found it.'

'Right. What's up, Ross?'

'Well, I was thinking. We got a flyer about a month ago from latents. It said they had some new state-of-the-art method of raising prints on brass casings, and they were looking for test cases. You know, to get it into court.'

Bosch stared at Malone. He had never heard of fingerprints being raised on a casing that had been fired in the chamber of a gun.

'Ross, you sure you're talking about spent casings?'

'Yeah, that's what it said. Teri Sopp is the tech over there handling it. Why don't you go see her?'

Fifteen minutes later Bosch was with Sopp in the latent fingerprints lab. Sopp had been around nearly as long as Harry and they had an easy comfort with each other, but Bosch still felt he had to lead her to the water.

'Harry, what's the story?' It was how she always greeted Bosch.

'The story is I caught a case yesterday down south and today we recovered a single bullet casing from the shooter's gun.' Bosch held out the evidence bag with the casing in it.

Sopp took it and studied it through the plastic. 'Fired?'

'Yup. I know it's a long shot but I was hoping maybe there'd be a print on it. I don't have much else going on the case at the moment.'

'Well, let's see. Normally, you'd have to wait your turn but seeing how we go back about five police chiefs . . .'

'That's why I came to you, Teri.'

Sopp sat down at an examination table and, like Malone, used a pair of tweezers to pull the casing from the evidence bag. She first fumed it with cyanoacrylate and then held it under an ultraviolet light.

'You have a smear here. Looks like somebody handled it after it was fired. But that's all. Sorry, Harry.'

Bosch's shoulders sagged. He knew it was a long shot, but he was hoping to convey to Sopp how much he had counted on getting a print.

Sopp started to put the casing back into the evidence envelope. He could tell she was thinking about something.

'Harry, tell me about the case. Give me the parameters.'

Bosch summarised the case but left out the detail about the suspect they had pulled out of the surveillance video. It made it sound like the investigation was hopeless. No evidence, no suspect, no motive. *Nada, nothing.*

'Well, there's one thing we might be able to do,' Sopp said. 'We're gearing up for electrostatic enhancement. This might be a good first case for us.'

'What the hell is electrostatic enhancement?'

Sopp smiled like the kid who still had candy after you were all out. 'It's a process developed in England with the Northamptonshire Police by which fingerprints can be raised on brass surfaces using electricity.'

'How's it work?'

'OK, here's the deal. When you load bullets into a revolver or a magazine for an automatic, you hold each bullet between your fingers and you push it in. You apply pressure, leaving prints, right? A latent print is essentially a deposit of the sweat that builds up between the grooves of your fingerprint. The problem is that when a gun is fired the latent print usually disappears in the explosion.'

'All this I know,' Bosch said. 'Tell me something I don't know.'

'OK, OK. Well, this process works best if the gun is not immediately fired. In other words, if the bullet has been loaded into the gun but then allowed to sit in there for at least a few days, so that the sweat that forms the latents reacts with the brass. You understand?'

'You mean there's a chemical reaction.'

'A microscopic chemical reaction. Your sweat is made up of a lot of different things but mostly sodium chloride—salt. It reacts with the brass—corrodes it—and leaves its mark. But we just can't see it.'

'And the electricity lets you see it.'

'Exactly. We run a twenty-five-hundred-volt charge through the casing, dust it with carbon and then we see it.'

Bosch was growing excited. 'Then why don't we do it?'

Sopp spread her fingers in a calming gesture. 'Whoa, hold on, Harry. We can't just do it. This kind of evidence and procedure has not been introduced in a California court yet. We have to think of the future. The first time we use this process as evidence will set the precedent. If it's not the right case, we'll blow it and it would really set us back.'

'Well, maybe this is the case. Who decides that?'

'Brenneman will pick the case and then he'll take it to the DA.'

Chuck Brenneman was the commander of the Scientific Investigation Division. Bosch realised the process of choosing the first case could take weeks.

'Teri, I need this. The killer's print might be on that shell.'

Sopp seemed to realise that she had been cornered by someone who was not going to go away. 'All right, listen. The next set of experiments are not scheduled till next week. I'll see what I can do.'

'Thanks, Teri.'

Bosch filled the chain-of-evidence form out and left the lab. He was excited about the possibility of using the new science to get the killer's print. It almost felt to him as if John Li had known about electrostatic enhancement all along.

As he stepped out of the elevator on the fifth floor he checked his watch and saw that it was time to call his daughter. She would be walking down Stubbs Road to the Happy Valley Academy. If he didn't get to her now, he would have to wait until after school was out. He stopped in the hallway outside the squad room, pulled out his phone and hit the speed dial.

'Dad! What's with the picture of a dead person?'

He smiled. 'Hello to you, too. How do you know he's dead?'

'Um, let's see. My dad investigates murders and he sends me bare feet on a steel table. It's so gross. I have a dead guy's feet on my phone.'

'Well, you can delete it as soon as you tell me what the tattoo on the ankles mean. I know you study that stuff in school.'

'I won't delete it. I'm showing my friends. They'll think it's cool.'

'No, don't do that. It's part of a case I'm working on and nobody should see it. I sent it to you because I thought you could give me a quick translation.'

'You mean in all of the LAPD you don't have one person who can tell you? You have to call your daughter in Hong Kong for such a simple thing?'

'At the moment, that's about right. You do what you have to do. Do you know what the symbols mean or not?'

'Yes, Dad. They were easy. It's like a fortune. On the left ankle the symbols are *Fu* and *Cai*, which mean luck and money. Then on the right side you have *Ai* and *Xi*, which are love and family.'

Bosch thought about this. It seemed to him the symbols were the things that were important to John Li. He hoped that these things would always walk with him. Then he thought of the symbols being located on either side of Li's Achilles tendons. Perhaps Li realised that the things he hoped for also made him vulnerable. They were also his Achilles heel.

'Well, does it help? Did I crack the case?'

Bosch smiled but immediately realised she couldn't see this. 'Not quite but it helps.'

'Good. You owe me.'

Bosch nodded. 'You're a pretty smart kid, aren't you? Your mother must be doing something right.'

'Not much.'

'Hey, that's no way to talk about her.'

'Dad, you don't have to live with her. I do. And it's not so much fun. I told you when I was in LA.'

'She's still seeing somebody?'

'Yeah, and I'm yesterday's news.'

'It's not like that, Maddie. It's just that it's been a long time for her.' A long time for me, too, Bosch thought.

'Dad, don't take her side. To her I'm just in the way all the time. But when I say, fine, I'll live with Dad, she says no way.'

'You should be with your mother. She's raised you. Look, in a month I'll be coming over for a week. We can talk about all of this then.'

'Whatever. I gotta go. I'm here at school.'

He closed the phone and let her go. It seemed to him that the weeks and months between seeing Maddie were getting more difficult. As she became her own person and grew more bright and communicative, he loved her more and missed her all the time. She had just been out to LA in July, taking the long flight for the first time on her own. He'd taken time off work and they'd enjoyed two weeks of doing things together, exploring the city. It had been a wonderful break for him and at the end it was the first time she had ever mentioned wanting to live in Los Angeles. With him.

Bosch was smart enough to realise that these sentiments were expressed after two weeks of full-time attention from a father who began each day by asking what she wanted to do. It was far different from the full-time commitment of her mother, who raised her day by day while making a living for them. Still, the toughest day Bosch had ever had as a part-time father was the day he put his daughter on the plane home. He'd felt a hollowness inside ever since.

FOUR

Bosch got home at eight that night, coming through the door with a 'to go' bag from the In-N-Out down on Cahuenga.

'Honey, I'm home,' he called out as he struggled with the key, the bag and his briefcase.

He smiled to himself and went directly into the kitchen. He grabbed a bottle of beer out of the refrigerator and went out to the deck. Along the way he turned on his CD player, leaving the sliding door open so the music could mingle with the sound of the 101 freeway down in the pass.

The deck was positioned with a northeasterly view stretching across Universal City, Burbank and on to the San Gabriel Mountains. Harry ate his two hamburgers and watched the dying sun change the colours on the mountains. He listened to 'Seven Steps to Heaven' off Ron Carter's *Dear Miles* album. Carter was one of the most important bassists of the past five decades. Whether on his own recordings or on somebody else's, his work always stood out. Harry believed this was because as a bassist he could never really be a sideman. He always drove the beat, even if it was behind Miles Davis's horn.

The song now playing had an undeniable momentum to it. Like a car chase. It made Bosch think about his own chase. He was satisfied with his own momentum, but uncomfortable with the realisation that he had moved the case to a point where he was now reliant on the work of others. He had to wait on somebody to call. Bosch was most at home in a case when he was pushing the action himself. He wasn't a sideman. He had to drive the beat.

He started thinking about his next moves and the options were few. He could start hitting Chinese-owned businesses in South LA with the photo of the Triad bagman. But he knew it would probably be an exercise in futility. The cultural divide was wide. No one would willingly identify a Triad member to the police. Nevertheless, he was prepared to go down that route if nothing else broke soon.

His cell rang as he was chewing his last bite.

'Bosch.'

'Harry, David Chu. I'm in Monterey Park. We got him!' His voice was tight with excitement. 'Our guy. The suspect.'

Monterey Park was a city in the east county where much of the population was Chinese. Fifteen minutes from downtown, it was like a foreign country.

'You mean you got an ID?' Bosch asked.

'We got more than an ID. We got him. We're looking right at him.'

There were several things about what Chu was saying that immediately bothered Bosch. 'First of all, who is *we*?'

'I'm with the MPPD. They IDed our guy off the video and then took me right to him.'

Bosch could feel the pulse pounding in his temple. No doubt, getting the ID of the Triad bagman—if it was legit—was a big step in the investigation. But bringing another police department into the case and moving in on the suspect were potentially fatal mistakes, and should never even have been considered without the lead investigator's approval. But Bosch knew he had to stay calm and do his best to contain a bad situation.

'Detective Chu, listen to me. Did you make contact with the suspect?'

'Contact? No, not yet. He's not alone right now. We're across the street. We can see him with the binoculars.'

Thank God for that, Bosch thought but didn't say. The situation might be salvageable. 'OK, I want you to stay where you are and tell me exactly where we're at. How did you get to Monterey Park?'

'The AGU has a strong relationship with Monterey Park's gang detail. Tonight after work I took the photo of our guy by to see if anybody recognised him. I got a positive ID from the third guy I showed it to, Detective Tao. I'm with him and his partner right now.'

'OK, give me the name you got.'

'Bo-Jing Chang.' He spelled the name out.

'So the last name is Chang?' Bosch asked.

'Right. And according to their intel, he's in *Yung Kim*—Brave Knife. It fits with the tattoo.'

'OK, what else?'

'That's it at the moment. He's supposedly a low-level guy. All of these guys have real jobs. He works at a used-car lot here in MP. He has been here since 1995 and has dual citizenship. No arrest record—over here at least.'

'And you got a twenty on him right now?'

'I'm watching him play cards. Brave Knife is mostly centred here in MP.

And there's a club here where they like to get together at the end of the day. Tao and Herrera took me.'

Bosch assumed Herrera was Tao's partner. 'OK, listen, I'm coming out there. I want you to back away until I get there. Move at least another block away.'

There was a long pause before Chu responded. 'We don't need to move back. If we lose track of him, he might get away.'

'Listen, Detective, I need you to back away. If he gets away, that will be on me, not you. I don't want to risk him seeing a police presence.'

'We're across the street,' Chu protested. 'Four lanes.'

'Chu, you're not listening. If you can see him, then he can see you. Back away and wait for me. I'll be there in less than thirty minutes. What's the name of the place?'

After a pause Chu answered in a sulky voice. 'It's called Club 88. It's on Garvey about four blocks west of Garfield. Take the ten out to—'

'I know how to get there. I'm on my way.'

He closed the phone to end the debate. If Chu didn't back off, then his ass would belong to Bosch in an internal complaint process.

HARRY WAS OUT through the door within two minutes. He drove down out of the hills and then took the 101 back through Hollywood into downtown. He hooked up with the 10 and headed east. Monterey Park was another ten minutes in light traffic. Along the way Bosch called Ignacio Ferras at home, apprised him of what was happening and offered him the opportunity to meet up in Monterey Park. Ferras declined, saying it might be better if one of them was fresh in the morning.

Bosch agreed and closed the phone. He had expected his partner to decline the invitation. His fear of the streets was becoming more and more evident. Bosch had done his best to give him time to recover, but it had reached a point where he had to consider the victims who were not getting what they should get. It was hard to conduct a relentless investigation when your partner was tethered to a desk chair.

Monterey Park could easily pass for a ground-level district neighbourhood in Hong Kong. The neon, the colours, the shops and the language on the signs were geared towards a Chinese-speaking populace. The only things missing were the towers rising high above. Hong Kong was a vertical city. Monterey Park was not. He turned left on Garvey and pulled out his phone to call Chu.

'OK, I'm on Garvey. Where are you?'

'Come down and you'll see the big supermarket on the south side. We're in the lot. You'll pass the club on the north side before you get here.'

'Got it.'

Bosch closed the phone and kept driving, his eyes scanning the neon on the left. Soon he saw the red '88' glowing above the door of a small club. Seeing the numeral prompted a realisation. Bosch knew from his daughter that 8 was a lucky number in Chinese culture. Apparently, the members of Brave Knife were hoping for double luck by putting '88' over their door.

As he drove by he could see light behind the front window. The slotted blinds were slightly open and Bosch could see about ten men either sitting or standing round a table. Harry kept going and three blocks later pulled into the parking lot of the Big Lau Super Market. He saw a government model Crown Victoria at the far end and pulled into the space next to it.

Everybody put their windows down and Chu made introductions from the back seat. Herrera was behind the wheel and Tao was riding shotgun. Neither of the Monterey Park officers was close to thirty years old.

'You IDed Chang?' Bosch asked Tao.

'That's right,' Tao said. 'I pulled him over six months ago. When Davy came round with the photo, I remembered him.'

'Where was this?'

While Tao spoke, Herrera kept his eyes on Club 88 up the street.

'I ran across him in the warehouse district down at the end of Garvey. It was late and he was driving a panel van. Looked like he was lost. He let us look and the van was empty but I figure he was going to make a pick-up or something. A lot of counterfeit goods go through those warehouses. It's easy to lose your way in there because there's so many of them and they all look the same. Anyway, the van was registered to Vincent Tsing. He lives in Pasadena but he's pretty well known to us as a member of Brave Knife. He has a car lot here in MP and Chang works for him.'

Bosch understood the procedure. Tao had pulled the van over, but with no probable cause to search it or to arrest Chang, he was reliant on Chang's volunteerism. They filled out a field interview card with information he provided and checked the back of the van after being given permission.

'And what, he just volunteered that he was in Brave Knife Triad?'

'No,' Tao said indignantly. 'We noted his tattoo and the ownership of the vehicle. We put two and two together, Detective.'

'That's good. You have the shake card with you?' he asked.

Tao handed a three-by-five card out of the window to Bosch. Harry read the information handwritten on the card. Since field interviews had been challenged repeatedly over the years by civil rights groups as unwarranted shakedowns, the information forms were referred to as shake cards. Tao had conducted a very thorough interview with Bo-Jing Chang. There was a cellphone number written on the card. It was a watershed moment.

'This number is good?'

'I don't know about now—these guys dump phones all the time. But it was good then. I called it right on the spot to make sure.'

'OK, we have to confirm it. No, you're going to. Block your ID and call the number in five minutes. If he answers, tell him you've got a wrong number. Let me borrow the binocs and, *Davy*, you come with me.'

'Wait a minute,' Tao said. 'What are we doing fucking with the phones?'

'If the number's still good, we can go for a wire. Give me the glasses. You call while I'm watching and we confirm, get it?'

'Sure.'

Bosch handed the shake card back to Tao and took the binoculars in return. Chu got out of their car, came round to Bosch's ride and got in.

Bosch pulled out onto Garvey and headed towards Club 88. He pulled into a space in a parking lot across the street from the club.

'Which one is Chang?' he asked.

'He's at the left end, next to the guy in the hat.'

'Take the glasses and see if he answers his phone,' he told Chu.

As Chu zeroed in on Chang, Bosch checked his watch. Tao should've made the call. He was growing impatient.

'What are we doing, anyway?' Chu asked.

'We're building a case, Detective. We confirm that number; then we get a warrant for a wire. We start listening to him and we find things out. Who he talks to, what he's up to. Maybe we spook him and we see who he calls. We start closing in. The point is, we take our time and do it right.'

Chu didn't respond. He kept the binoculars locked on his eyes.

'Tell me something,' Bosch said. 'Do you trust Tao and Herrera?'

Chu didn't hesitate. 'I trust them. You don't?'

'I don't know them so I can't trust them. All I know is that you took my case and showed everything all around that police department.'

'Look, I was trying to make a break in the case and I did. We got the ID.'

'Yeah, we got the ID and hopefully our suspect doesn't find out about it.'

Chu lowered the binoculars and looked at Bosch. 'Man, don't you trust anybody?'

'Just watch the club,' Bosch responded sternly.

Chu put the binoculars back up as instructed. 'I just wonder if this is something to do with me and Tao. Whether that's the issue.'

Bosch turned towards him. 'Don't start that shit again, Chu. You can go back to AGU and stay the hell out of my case. I didn't call you out—'

'Chang just took a call.'

Bosch looked at the club. He thought he saw the man Chu had identified as Chang with a phone to his ear. He then dropped his arm.

'He put it away,' Chu said. 'The number's good.'

Bosch backed out of the space and started back to the supermarket.

'Why don't we just go pick the guy up?' Chu asked. 'We got him on tape. Same day, same time. We use it to break him.'

'And what if he doesn't break? We need more, Chu. That's what I'm trying to teach you.'

'OK, so we do it your way. What's next?'

'We go back to the parking lot and cut your friends loose. Tell them we'll take it from here. It's our case, not theirs.'

'They're not going to like that.'

'I don't care if they like it or not. That's the way it's going to be. You figure out a way of letting them down nice.'

'Me?'

'Yeah, you. You invited them in, you invite them out.'

'Thanks, Bosch.'

'Anytime, Chu. Welcome to homicide.'

BOSCH, FERRAS AND CHU sat on one side of the meeting table across from Lieutenant Gandle and Captain Bob Dodds, commander of the Robbery-Homicide Division. Spread across the polished surface between them were the case documents and photographs, most notably the shot of Bo-Jing Chang from the Fortune Liquors security camera.

'I'm not convinced it's the way to go,' Dodds said.

It was Thursday morning, just six hours after Bosch and Chu had ended their surveillance of Chang with the suspect going to an apartment in Monterey Park and apparently retiring for the night.

'Surveillance is fine. But a wire is a lot of work for long-shot results.'

Bosch understood. Dodds had to find ways of doing more with less and never allowing a dip in the statistics of arrests made and cases closed. That made him a realist and the reality was that electronic surveillance was very expensive. Once permission for a wire was granted by the court, a wiretap room had to be staffed twenty-four hours a day with a detective monitoring the line. Often a single number tap led to other numbers needing to be tapped and under the law each line had to have its own monitor. Such an operation quickly sucked up overtime like a giant sponge. Dodds was reluctant to give any of the RHD's seriously constrained OT budget up for what amounted to an investigation of the murder of a southside liquor-store clerk.

'This is the tip of the iceberg, Captain,' he said. 'We're not just talking about a liquor-store shooting. We could take down a whole Triad before this is over. What if we did it without overtime?' Bosch asked.

The captain shook his head. 'You know I can't ask you to do that,' he said. 'I can't even know about that.' It was true. The department had been sued so many times for unfair labour practices that no one in administration would ever give even tacit approval to detectives working off the clock.

Bosch's frustration with bureaucracy finally got the best of him. 'Then what do we do? Bring Chang in. We all know he's not going to say a word to us and the case will die right there.'

'Bosch, you know what the alternative is. You work the case until something breaks. You work the witnesses. You work the evidence. There's always a link. Find it. A wiretap is a long shot and you know it. Legwork is always the better bet. Now, is there anything else?'

Harry felt his face growing red. The captain was dismissing him. What burned was that deep down Bosch knew Dodds was right.

'Thanks, Captain,' he said curtly and stood up.

The detectives left the captain and the lieutenant in the conference room and convened in Bosch's cubicle. Bosch threw his pen down on the desk.

'Guy's an ass,' Chu said.

'No, he's not,' Bosch said. 'He's right and that's why he's the captain.'

'Then what do we do?'

'We stay with Chang. I don't care about overtime and what the captain doesn't know won't hurt him. We watch Chang and we wait for him to make a mistake. I don't care how long it takes.' Bosch looked at the other two, expecting them to decline to participate.

To his surprise, Chu nodded. 'I'm already detached to this case. I can do it.'

Bosch nodded and at first considered that he had been wrong to be so suspicious of Chu. His next thought, however, was that Chu's commitment to stay with the case was just a means of monitoring the investigation.

Harry turned to his partner. 'What about you? Are you in or out?'

Ferras reluctantly nodded. 'I'm in, but with a limit. I've got a family, man. I'm not sitting on surveillance all night, especially for nothing.'

'All right, fine,' Bosch said, even though his tone communicated his disappointment with Ferras. 'You do what you can. You handle the inside work and Chu and I will stay with Chang.'

Noting Bosch's tone, Ferras protested in his own tone. 'You don't know what it's like, Harry. Three kids . . . You try selling it at home. That you're going to watch some Triad guy all night and your pay cheque is going to look the same no matter how many hours you're gone.'

Bosch put his hands up as if to say, *Enough said*.

'You're right. I don't have to sell it. I just have to do it. That's the job.'

FROM BEHIND THE WHEEL of his own car, Bosch watched Chang as he performed menial chores at Tsing Motors in Monterey Park. Bosch was parked half a block away on busy Garvey Avenue and was in no danger of being spotted. Chu was in his own car half a block past the car lot in the other direction. Using their personal cars for the surveillance was a violation of departmental policy but there were no undercover vehicles available. Bosch didn't mind breaking policy because he had a six-CD stack in his car loaded with music from his latest discovery, Thomasz Stanko, a Polish trumpeter who sounded like the ghost of Miles Davis. His horn was sharp and soulful. It kept Bosch alert.

For almost three hours they had watched their suspect handle his mundane duties on the lot. Then at 4 p.m. Chang went into the small office and changed his shirt. When he stepped out he was finished for the day. He got into a 1989 Mustang and drove by himself off the lot.

Bosch's phone immediately buzzed. Harry killed the music.

'You got him?' Chu asked. 'He's moving.'

'Yeah, I see. I'll take the lead and then you be ready to move up.'

Bosch followed five car lengths behind and then caught up as Chang headed west on the 10 towards downtown. He was not going back to the apartment in Monterey Park—also owned by Vincent Tsing—that they had followed him to the night before. He was heading into LA and Bosch's instincts told him he was carrying out Triad business. Bosch sped up and passed the Mustang, holding his cellphone up to his ear so Chang wouldn't get a look at his face. He called Chu and told him he was now on point.

Bosch and Chu continued to trade off the point while Chang connected to the 101 freeway and headed north through Hollywood towards the Valley. It took him nearly an hour to get up to Sherman Oaks, where he finally exited on the Sepulveda Boulevard ramp. Bosch called Chu.

'I think he's going to the other store,' he told his surveillance partner.

'I think you're right. Should we call Robert Li and warn him?'

Bosch paused. It was a good question. He had to decide whether Robert Li was in danger. If so, he should be warned. But a warning could blow the whole operation.

'No, not yet. Let's see what happens. If Chang goes into the store, we go in with him. And we'll step in if things go wrong.'

'You sure, Harry?'

'No, but that's how we'll play it. Make sure you make the light.'

They held the connection. The light at the bottom of the ramp had just turned green. Bosch was four cars behind Chang but Chu was at least eight behind. The traffic moved slowly and Bosch crept along, watching the light. It turned yellow just as he hit the intersection. He made it but Chu wouldn't.

'OK, I got him,' he said into the phone. 'No worries.'

Bosch closed the phone. Just then he heard a siren from directly behind him and saw flashing blues in the rear view.

'Shit!'

He looked ahead and saw Chang proceeding south on Sepulveda. He was four blocks from Fortune Fine Foods. Bosch pulled to the kerb. He opened his door and quickly got out. He was holding his badge up as he approached the officer on the motorcycle who had pulled him over.

'I'm on a surveillance! I can't stop!'

'Talking on a cellphone is illegal.'

'Write it up and send it in. I'm not blowing a surveillance for this.'

He turned round and went back to his car. He bulled his way back into the traffic and looked ahead for Chang's Mustang. It was gone.

The traffic was moving slowly and Bosch wasn't panicked because the road was so clogged with vehicles that he knew Chang could not have got too far ahead. He stayed in his lane, knowing that he might draw attention in Chang's mirrors if he started jockeying between lanes. In another two minutes he got to the major intersection of Sepulveda and Ventura Boulevard. He could see the lights of Fortune Fine Foods & Liquor a block farther down Sepulveda at the next intersection. He buzzed Chu.

'I'm at the light at Ventura and don't see him. He might already be there. I'm going to park and go in. You stay out and look for the car. Buzz me when you see either him or the car.'

As soon as the light turned green Bosch pinned the accelerator and jumped into the intersection, nearly broadsiding a red-light runner. He cruised up the next block and took a right into the market's parking lot. He didn't see Chang's car or any parking spaces. He pulled through the lot into the alley and parked behind a trash bin with a NO PARKING sticker on it. He jumped out and trotted back to the market's front door.

Just as Bosch was going through the automatic door marked ENTER he saw Chang coming out of the door marked EXIT. Bosch instinctively raised his hand and brushed it through his hair, blocking his face with his arm, and kept going.

He walked between the two checkout counters. Two women, different from the day before, stood at the cash registers waiting for customers.

'Where's Mr Li?' Bosch asked without stopping.

'In his office at the back,' said one of the women.

Bosch called Chu. 'He just walked out the front door. Stay with him. I'll check on Li.'

'Got it.'

When Bosch got to Li's office, the door was closed. He felt adrenaline burst inside him as he pushed the door open without knocking and found Li and another Asian man sitting at the two desks. They were in a conversation that abruptly stopped when the door opened. Li jumped up and Bosch saw immediately that he was physically unharmed.

'Detective!' Li exclaimed. 'I was just about to call you! He was here! That man you showed me was here!'

'I know. I was following him. What happened?'

Li hesitated for a moment to gather his words.

'Sit down and calm down,' Bosch said. 'Then tell me. Who are you?' Bosch pointed at the man seated at the other desk.

'This is Eugene Lam, my assistant manager.'

The man stood up and offered his hand to Bosch.

Bosch shook his hand. 'You were both here when Chang came in?' he asked. 'The man in the photograph I showed you.'

'Yes, Eugene and I were both here. He just walked into the office.'

'What did he want?'

'He said I had to pay the Triad now. He said my father was gone and I had to pay now. He said he would come back in one week and I had to pay.'

'Did he say what would happen if you didn't pay?'

'He didn't have to.'

Bosch nodded. Li was right. The threat was implicit. Bosch was excited. Chang was attempting to extort Li and that could lead to an arrest that could ultimately lead to a murder charge.

Harry turned to Lam. 'And you witnessed this?'

Lam was clearly hesitant but then nodded. Bosch thought that maybe he was reluctant to be involved.

'You did or you didn't, Eugene? You just told me you were here.'

Lam nodded again before responding. 'Yes, I saw the man, but . . . I don't speak Chinese. I understand a little bit, but not that much.'

Bosch turned to Li. 'He spoke to you in Chinese?'

Li nodded. 'Yes. Are you going to arrest this man? Will I have to appear in court?' He was clearly scared of the possibility.

'Look, if he killed your father, that's what we want him for. And I am sure you will do what you need to do to help us put your father's killer away.'

Li nodded but Bosch could still see hesitation. Considering what had happened to his father, Robert clearly didn't want to cross Chang or the Triad.

'I need to make a quick call to my partner,' Bosch said. 'I'm going to step out and make it, then I'll be back in here.'

Bosch left the office and closed the door. He called Chu. 'You got him?'

'Yes, he's heading back to the freeway. What happened?'

'He told Li he had to start making the payments his father had been making. To the Triad.'

'Holy shit! We've got our case!'

'Don't get too excited. A case of extortion maybe—and that's only if the kid cooperates. But we're getting closer. Which way is he headed?'

'He's in the right lane for the southbound one-oh-one. It looks like he's heading back the way he came. He's in a hurry. He's tailgating the guy in front of him but it's not doing him any good.'

'OK. I'm going to talk to these guys a little longer and then I'll clear out. Call me when Chang stops somewhere.'

'"These guys"? Who else besides Robert Li?'

'His assistant manager, Eugene Lam. He was in the office when Chang came in. Though Chang was speaking Chinese and Lam only knows English. He won't be a good witness.'

'OK, Harry,' Chu said. 'We're on the freeway now.'

'Stay with him and I'll call you as soon as I get clear,' Bosch said.

Bosch closed the phone and went back into the office.

'Do you have video surveillance in the store?' he asked.

'Yes,' Li said. 'Same system we have in the south-end store. Only we have more cameras in this location.'

Bosch looked up at the ceiling and the upper walls. 'There is no camera in here, right?'

'No, Detective,' Li said. 'Not in the office.'

'Well, I'm going to need the disc so we can prove Chang came here.'

Li nodded hesitantly and Bosch watched as he pulled out the disc.

Li's reluctance seemed to grow with Bosch's more detailed questioning about what had happened with Chang. Harry began to believe that the murder victim's son would eventually refuse to cooperate with a prosecution. Still, Chang's attempted extortion could be used in other ways. It could provide probable cause. And with PC, Bosch could arrest Chang and search his belongings for evidence, whether Li cooperated or not.

As he walked out of the store's automatic door, Bosch called Chu again.

'We're all the way back to his apartment,' Chu said. 'No stops. He pulled the curtains closed. I think he might be in for the night.'

'OK. I'm heading that way.'

Bosch closed the phone. He was excited. The case had new life.

CHANG DIDN'T COME OUT of his apartment until nine on Friday morning, and when he did, he was carrying something that immediately put Bosch on high alert.

A large suitcase.

Bosch phoned Chu. They had split the overnight surveillance into four-hour shifts, each man taking a sleeping stint in his car. Chu was on the four-to-eight sleep shift but Bosch hadn't heard from him yet.

'You awake? Chang's making a move.'

Chu still had sleep in his voice. 'Yeah, what move? You were supposed to call me at eight.'

'He put a suitcase in his car. He's running. I think he was tipped off.'

'To us? Harry, who would tip him?'

'I don't know,' Bosch said. 'But you put our business out all over Monterey Park so who knows who could've tipped off this guy. All I know right now is that it looks like he's splitting town.'

'All over Monterey Park? Are you just making this shit up?' Chu's voice carried the requisite outrage of the accused.

Bosch followed Chang's Mustang north out of the parking lot, staying a block back. 'You told me the other night that the third guy you showed Chang's photo to over there made the ID. OK, so that's three guys and they all have partners and they all have roll calls and they all talk.'

'Well, maybe this wouldn't have happened if we hadn't told Tao and Herrera to back off like we didn't trust them.'

Bosch checked his mirror for Chu. He was trying not to let his anger distract him from the tail. They couldn't lose Chang now.

'Move up. We're heading to the ten. After he gets on I want you to switch off with me.'

'Got it.'

Chu's voice still held anger. Bosch didn't care. If Chang had been tipped off about the investigation, then Harry would find who had made the call and he would burn them to the ground, even if it were Chu.

Chang got on the westbound 10 freeway and soon Chu passed Bosch to take the lead. Bosch moved over a lane, dropped back and made a call to Lieutenant Gandle.

'Harry, what's up?'

'We've got problems. The first one is that our guy put a suitcase in his trunk this morning and is on the ten heading towards the airport.'

'Shit, what else?'

'It looks to me like he was tipped off, maybe told to get out of town.'

'Or maybe he was told all along to split after he clipped Li. Don't go off the deep end on that, Harry. Not until you know something for sure.'

It annoyed Bosch that his own lieutenant wasn't backing him, but he let it go for now and concentrated on the choices that involved Chang.

'Do we take Chang down?' he asked.

'You sure he's flying? How big's the suitcase?'

'Big. The kind you pack when you're not coming back.'

Gandle sighed as he put another decision to be made on his plate. 'OK, let me talk to some people and I'll get back to you.'

Bosch assumed that would be Captain Dodds. 'There is some good news, Lieutenant,' he said.

'Holy shit, imagine that,' Gandle exclaimed. 'What good news?'

'Last night we tailed Chang to the other store. The one our victim's son runs in the Valley. He extorted him, told the kid he had to start paying now that his old man was gone.'

'What, this is great! Why didn't you tell me this?'

'I just did.'

'That gives us probable cause to arrest.'

'To arrest but probably not prosecute. The kid is a reluctant witness. He would have to come in to make the case and I don't know if he'll hold up. And either way, it's not a murder charge. That's what we want.'

'Well, at the very least, we could stop this guy from getting on a plane.'

Bosch nodded as the beginning of a plan started to form. 'It's Friday. If we hold on to him and book him late in the day, he wouldn't get a hearing till Monday afternoon. That would give us at least seventy-two hours to pull a case together.'

'With the extortion being the fall-back position.'

'That's right.'

Bosch was getting another call beeping in his ear. He asked Gandle to get back to him as soon as he had run the scenario by the powers that be, and then took the other call without looking at the screen.

'Harry? This is Teri Sopp.'

'Oh, hi, Teri. What's up?'

'I just wanted you to know I convinced them to use the casing you gave me yesterday in the testing programme for electrostatic enhancement. We'll see if we can raise a print off it.'

'You're my hero! Is there any way it can be done on Monday morning?'

'Monday? I don't think we'll get to the actual application un—'

'The reason is, we may have our suspect in jail before the end of the day. We think he's trying to leave the country and we might need to arrest him. That will give us till Monday to make the case, Teri. I hate to ask another favour, but we're going to need everything we can get.'

There was a hesitation before she responded. 'I'll see what we can do. In the meantime, if you arrest him, bring me down a print card so I can make the comparison as soon as I have something on this end. *If* I have something.'

'You got it, Teri. Thanks a million.'

Bosch closed his phone and searched the freeway in front of him. He saw neither Chu's car—a red Mazda Miata—or Chang's Mustang. He hit Chu on speed dial. 'Chu, where are you?'

'South four-oh-five. He's going to the airport. What's happening?'

'Gandle's making the call on whether we take Chang down or not.'

'We can't let him go.'

'That's what I say. We'll see what they say.'

Bosch hung up and worked his way through traffic until he had caught up. Switching off lead two more times, they followed Chang to the LAX exit at Century Boulevard. It was now clear that Chang was leaving the city and they were going to have to stop him. He called Gandle.

'Harry, whadaya got?'

'He's on Century Boulevard four blocks from LAX.'

'I haven't been able to talk to anybody yet.'

'I say we take him down. We book him for murder and worst-case scenario is on Monday we file on him for extortion. He'll get bail but the judge will slap no travel on it, especially after him trying to leave today.'

'Your call, Harry, and I'll back you.'

Meaning it would still be Bosch who had made the wrong call if by Monday everything fell apart and Chang waltzed out of jail a free man.

'Thanks, Lieutenant. I'll let you know.'

Moments after Bosch closed his phone Chang turned right into a long-term parking lot that provided a shuttle service to all of the airport terminals.

As expected, Chu called. 'This is it. What do we do?'

'We take him. We wait till he parks and he has that suitcase out of the trunk. We take him down at the shuttle station.'

'Roger that.'

They hung up. Bosch was in the lead and so he entered the parking lot directly behind Chang, taking a ticket out of an automatic feeder. The arm rose and he followed Chang down the main parkway. When Chang turned right Bosch kept going, parked in the first space he saw, and then doubled back on foot to where Chang and Chu had turned. He saw Chang one lane over, struggling to pull his big suitcase out of the Mustang's trunk.

Apparently realising he would look suspicious without luggage in a long-term lot, Chu started walking towards the shuttle stop carrying a brief-case and a raincoat like a man on a business trip.

Chang locked his car and lugged the heavy suitcase to the shuttle stop. Chu was already standing there. Using the parked vehicles as cover, Bosch cut behind a minivan and came out two cars away. This would give Chang little time to recognise that the approaching man should have luggage if he was in the long-term lot.

'Bo-Jing Chang,' Bosch said loudly on approach.

The suspect jerked his body round to look at Bosch. Up close, Chang looked strong and wide, formidable. Bosch saw his muscles tense.

'You're under arrest. Please place your hands behind your back.'

Chang's fight-or-flight response never had a chance to kick in. Chu stepped behind him and clipped one cuff to his right wrist while grabbing hold of the left wrist. Chang struggled for a moment, but Chu expertly cuffed the other wrist and the arrest was complete.

'What is this?' Chang protested. 'What I do?' He had a strong accent despite his many years in LA.

'We're going to talk about all of that, Mr Chang. Just as soon as we get you back to the Police Administration Building.'

'I have flight.'

'Not today.'

Bosch showed him his badge and ID, and then introduced Chu, making sure to mention that Chu was from the Asian Gang Unit. Bosch wanted to get that percolating in Chang's head.

Bosch's next move was to call for a patrol unit to transfer Chang down-town, and a tow truck to take his car to the downtown police garage. Bosch was in no hurry at this point: the longer it took to transport Chang down-town, the closer they were to 2 p.m., the cut-off time in felony arraignment court. If they delayed Chang getting into court, he could be secured as a guest of the city jail over the weekend.

After about five minutes of standing in silence while Chang sat on a bench in the shuttle stop's shelter, Bosch turned and gestured to the suitcase and spoke to Chang conversationally, as if the answer didn't matter.

'That thing looks like it weighs a ton,' he said. 'Where were you going?'

Chang knew the drill. He said nothing. There was no such thing as small talk when you were under arrest. He stared straight forward and did not acknowledge Bosch's question in any way.

Bosch looked down the long row of parked cars and saw a patrol car make the turn towards them. He waved.

He felt his phone vibrate twice and pulled it out to check the message. The screen said he had received a video from his daughter.

He would have to check it later. It was very late in Hong Kong and he knew she was probably in bed and expecting a response, but he had work to do. He put the phone away as the patrol car stopped in front of them.

'I'm going to ride in with him,' he said to Chu. 'In case he decides to say something.'

'Maybe I should ride with him instead.'

Bosch looked at Chu. It was one of those moments. Harry knew it would be better for Chu to make the ride with Chang because he had the best shot of establishing a rapport with Chang and convincing him to talk. But it would mean Bosch ceding some control of his case. It would also mean he was showing trust in Chu, just an hour after pointing the finger of blame at him.

'OK,' Bosch finally said. 'You ride with him.'

Chu nodded, seeming to understand the significance of Bosch's decision.

'You want me to drive your car in?' Bosch said. 'I don't mind leaving mine here.'

'No, it's OK, Harry. I'll leave mine and come and get it later. You wouldn't want to hear what I've got on the stereo anyway.'

Bosch smiled. 'OK, then, I'll take mine.'

Bosch told the two patrol officers to put Chang in the back of the patrol car and then turned to Chu.

'I'm going to put Ferras to work on search warrants for Chang's property. Any admission from him will help with the probable cause. So talk to him about where he was going and why. Make it conversational. I don't want to have to advise him. Let's stretch everything out.'

'Got it. I know what to do.'

'OK, I'm going to wait here for the tow truck so you'll get there way ahead of me. Put him in a room and let him stew. Good luck.'

Chu slipped into the back of the patrol car and closed the door. Bosch slapped his palm twice on the roof and watched the cruiser pull away.

IT WAS ALMOST NOON by the time Bosch got back to the squad room. He found Ignacio Ferras in place in his cubicle, working on his computer.

'Where are we at?' he asked.

'I'm almost done with the search-warrant app.'

'OK, you got a judge waiting on this?'

'Yeah, I called Judge Champagne's clerk. I'm in right after lunch.'

It sounded like Ferras had things moving. Bosch was impressed.

'Sounds good. Where's Chu?'

'Last I knew he was in the video room watching the guy.'

Before joining Chu, Bosch stepped into his cubicle and dropped his keys on his desk. He saw that Chu had left Chang's heavy suitcase here and had bagged the suspect's other possessions and left them all on the desk.

Bosch read Chang's airline boarding pass, which he had apparently printed at home, and saw that he had an Alaska Airlines ticket for a flight to Seattle. This made Harry pause because he was expecting to learn that Chang had been headed to China. Flying to Seattle didn't exactly sell an allegation of attempting to flee the country.

He put the plastic evidence bag back down and picked up the bag containing the phone. It would have been easy for him to open the phone quickly and scan the call log for the numbers of Chang's associates. But Bosch decided to play by the rules. He would wait for Judge Champagne's approval. Opening a phone was treated the same as opening the trunk of a car on a traffic stop. You had to do it correctly or whatever you found might be taken out of the case by the courts.

The phone on his desk buzzed. The caller ID display said XXXXX, meaning it was a call transferred over from Parker Center. He picked up.

'This is Bosch.'

There was no one there.

'Hello. This is Detective Bosch. Can I help you?'

'Bosch . . . you can help yourself.' The voice was distinctly Asian.

'Who is this?'

'You do yourself the favour and you back off, Bosch. Chang is not alone. We are many. You back the fuck off. If not, there will be consequences.'

'Listen to me, you—'

The caller had hung up. Bosch dropped the phone into its cradle and stared at the empty ID screen. He knew that someone calling to threaten him would not be so stupid as to use a traceable number. Instead of worrying about that, he concentrated on the timing of the call and its content. Somehow, Chang's Triad associates knew already that he had been picked up. They also knew Bosch by name.

Once again dark thoughts entered Bosch's brain. Unless Chang was meeting a fellow traveller at LAX or was being watched all the time, the evidence once more pointed to a leak inside the investigation.

He walked back to the video room, a small electronics room between the RHD's two interview rooms where suspects could be observed.

Bosch opened the door and found both Chu and Gandle in the room watching Chang on the monitor. Bosch's entrance made it crowded.

'Anything?' Bosch asked.

'Not a word so far,' Gandle said. 'He wouldn't talk in any language. He hasn't even asked for a lawyer. At least that would be something.'

'I looked at his plane ticket,' Bosch said. 'Seattle doesn't help us, either.'

'No, I think it does, actually,' Chu said.

'How?'

'I figured he was going to fly to Seattle and go across the border to Vancouver. I have a contact in the Mounties and he was able to check passenger lists for me. Chang's booked on a flight tonight from Vancouver to Hong Kong. Cathay Pacific Airlines. It clearly shows he tried to leave quickly and deceptively.'

Bosch nodded. 'Nice work, Chu.'

'Thanks.'

'Did you tell this to Ignacio? Chang's attempt to smoke his trail will help with the probable cause for the search warrant.'

'He knows. He put it in.'

'Good.'

Bosch looked at the monitor. Chang was sitting at a table with his wrists now handcuffed in front of him to an iron ring bolted through the centre of the table. His massive, rounded shoulders looked ready to burst the seams of his shirt. He was staring dead-eyed at the wall directly across from him.

Bosch looked at Chu. 'We're going to need to filibuster this. Are you up for it?'

'What's that mean?'

'I want you to go in there and ask him questions. Doesn't matter if he doesn't answer them. We can say we gave him the opportunity to tell us what happened and when he didn't we formally arrested and advised him. Can you do that?'

Chu reluctantly nodded. 'OK, I'll try.'

'Good. Doesn't matter what you ask him. Just give us another hour. After that we'll take him down to latents and print him. I don't want him in a cell till two at the earliest.'

'Got it.'

Chu left the room and Gandle started out after him but Bosch tapped him on the shoulder and signalled him to stay. Bosch waited until the door was closed before speaking.

'I just got a phone call. A threat. Somebody told me to back off the case.'

'You try to trace the call? You think it's serious?'

'A trace would be a waste of time. And as far as the threat goes, let them come. I'll be waiting. But the point is, how did they know that we picked up Chang? Within two hours one of his Triad pals calls up and tells me to back off. We've got a leak, Lieutenant. Somebody's talking to—'

'Whoah, whoah, whoah, we don't know that. There could be explanations. He had a cellphone. Maybe he was supposed to check in from the airport. Could be anything.'

Bosch shook his head. His instincts told him otherwise. There was a leak somewhere. Gandle opened the door. He didn't like this conversation and wanted to get out of the room. But he looked back at Bosch before leaving.

'You better be careful with this,' he said. 'Until you have something like this nailed down, you be very careful.'

Gandle closed the door behind him, leaving Bosch alone. He turned to the video screen and saw Chu in the interview room speaking to Chang. Chang remained mute and motionless. He showed no recognition in his eyes or body language that he even heard Chu's questions.

Bosch went back out to the squad room, feeling upset about the phone threat and Gandle's seeming lack of concern about the leak that spawned it.

Ferras's cubicle was empty now and Bosch assumed he had left with the search-warrant application for his appointment with the judge.

Everything was riding on the search warrant. They had Chang on the attempted extortion of Robert Li—if Li agreed to file a complaint and testify—but weren't even close on the murder. He sat down at his desk and pushed the heels of his palms into his eyes. Everything about the case was on hold until the judge signed. All he could do was wait, or maybe relieve Chu and take a turn at the filibuster.

Then he remembered the video message he had got earlier from his daughter.

He pulled out his phone and opened it. On the last day of his daughter's most recent visit to LA they had gone to the phone store and she had selected his and her cells, choosing a model that would allow them to communicate on multiple levels. He didn't use it much for email but he knew how to play the videos she liked to send. He often played them over.

Bo-Jing Chang temporarily faded away. Concern about the leak receded. Bosch had a smile of anticipation on his face when he pushed the button and opened her latest video message.

BOSCH STEPPED into the interview room and left the door open. Chu was in midquestion but stopped and looked up at the intrusion.

'Dave, why don't you take a break?' Bosch said. 'I can take over for a little while here.'

'Oh . . . uh, sure, Harry.'

He stood up and Bosch moved to the side so he could leave the room.

Bosch waited a moment until he was sure Chu was gone, then moved swiftly behind Chang and grabbed him round the neck with his arms. His rage grew uncontrolled. He locked his arms tightly in the chokehold long outlawed by the department. He felt Chang tense as he realised his air intake had been cut.

'OK, motherfucker, the camera's off and we're in a soundproof room. Where is she? I will kill you right here if—'

Chang reared up from his seat, pulling the anchor bolt of the cuff ring right through the top of the table. He smashed Bosch back against the wall behind them and together they fell to the floor. Chang fought like an animal, using his feet against one of the anchored legs of the table as leverage and he repeatedly smashed Bosch back into the corner of the room.

'*Where is she?*' Bosch yelled.

Chang was making grunting sounds but showing no sign of losing power. His wrists were cuffed together but he was still able to swing his arms together back over his head like a club. He was going for Bosch's face at the same time as he was using his body to crush him into the corner.

Realising the chokehold wasn't going to work, Bosch let go and caught Chang's wrist on one of his backward swings. He shifted his weight and turned the blow aside. Chang's shoulders turned with the shift in momentum and Bosch was able to get on top of him on the floor. Bosch raised his hands and brought down a hammer blow on the back of Chang's neck.

'I said where is—'

'*Harry!*' The voice came from behind him. It was Chu.

'*Hey!*' Chu yelled into the squad room. '*Help!*'

The distraction allowed Chang to rise up and get his knees under his body. He then pushed up and Bosch was thrown into the wall and then down to the floor. Chu jumped on Chang and was trying to wrestle him to the ground. There were running steps and soon men were piling onto Chang, pinning him to the floor. Bosch rolled away.

For a moment everyone was silent and the room filled with the sounds of all of the men gasping for breath. Gandle then appeared in the doorway.

'What the hell happened?'

'I don't know,' Chu said. 'I came back to get my jacket and all hell was breaking loose.'

All eyes in the room turned to Bosch.

'They've got my daughter,' he said.

FIVE

Bosch stood in Gandle's office. Not still. He couldn't stand still. Not with the terror growing inside his chest. He paced in front of the desk.

'What's this about, Harry?'

Bosch pulled out his phone and pushed the play command on the video program. Then he handed the phone to Gandle, who watched the video.

'Oh, Jesus . . . Oh, Je—Harry, how do you know this is real?'

'What are you talking about? It's real. *They have her and that guy knows who and where!*' Bosch pointed in the direction of the interview room. He was pacing more quickly now, like a caged tiger. 'I need to make him tell—'

'You're not going anywhere near him,' Gandle said without looking up. 'Harry, where is she? Hong Kong?'

'Yes, Hong Kong, and that's where he was going. It's where the Triad he's in is based. On top of that I told you they said there'd be consequences if—'

'Nobody says anything on the video. How do you know it's Chang's people?'

'They don't have to say anything! The video says it all!'

'OK, OK, let's think this through. They have her and what's the message? What are you supposed to do?'

'Let Chang go.'

'What do you mean, let him just walk out of here?'

'I don't know. Yeah, kick the case somehow. That's what they want, for him to walk. Look, I can't just stand here. I have to—'

'We have to get this to forensics. That's the first thing. Have you called your ex to see what she knows?'

Bosch realised that in his immediate panic upon seeing the video, he had not called Eleanor Wish. 'You're right. Give me that.'

'Harry, it's got to go to forens—'

Bosch leaned across the desk and grabbed the phone out of Gandle's hand. He switched over to the phone program and hit a speed dial for Eleanor Wish. He checked his watch while he waited for the call to go through. It was after 4 a.m. on Saturday in Hong Kong. He didn't understand why he hadn't heard from Eleanor if their daughter was missing.

'Harry?' The voice was alert. She had not been dragged from sleep.

'Eleanor, what's going on? Where's Madeline?'

He walked out of Gandle's office and headed towards his cubicle.

'I don't know. She hasn't called me and doesn't answer my calls. How do you know what's going on?'

'I don't but I got a . . . a message from her. Tell me what you know.'

'What did her message say?'

'It didn't say anything. It was a video. Just tell me what's going on there.'

'She didn't come home from the mall after school. It was Friday so I usually let her go with her friends. She usually checks in about six and asks for more time, but this time she didn't. Then when she didn't come home I called and she wouldn't answer. I left her a bunch of messages and I got really angry. You know her, she probably got angry back and she didn't come home. I've called her friends and they all claim not to know where she is.'

'Eleanor, it's after four in the morning there. Did you call the police?'

'Harry . . .'

'What?'

'She did this once before.'

Bosch dropped heavily into the seat at his desk and huddled down, holding the phone tight against his ear. 'What are you talking about?'

'She stayed with a friend all night to teach me a lesson,' Eleanor said.

'I called the police then and it was all very embarrassing because they found her at her friend's. I'm sorry I didn't tell you. But she and I have been having problems. She's at that age, you know? She talks about wanting to live in LA with you. She—'

Bosch cut her off. 'Listen, Eleanor, I understand all of that but this is different. Something's happened.'

'What do you mean?' Panic flooded her voice.

He was reluctant to tell her about the video but felt he now had to. She needed to know. He described the thirty seconds of video, leaving nothing out. Eleanor made a high-pitched keening sound that only a mother could make for a lost daughter.

'Oh my God, oh my God.'

'I know, but we're going to get her back, Eleanor. I—'

'What do they want, money?'

'No . . .' Bosch tried to speak calmly, hoping it would be contagious over the phone when the impact of his words came through. 'I think it's a message to me, Eleanor. They're not asking for money. They're just telling me that they have her.'

'You? Why? What do they—Harry, what did you do?' She said the last question in a tone of accusation. Bosch feared it was a question he might be impaled on for the rest of his life.

'I'm on a case involving a Chinese Triad. I think—'

'*They took her to get to you? How did they even know about her?*'

'I don't know yet, Eleanor. I'm working on it. We have a suspect—'

Again she cut him off, this time with another wail. It was the sound of every parent's worst nightmare come to life. In that moment Bosch realised what he was going to do. He lowered his voice further when he spoke.

'Eleanor, listen to me. I need you to pull yourself together. You need to start making calls. I'm coming over. I'll be there before dawn on Sunday morning. In the meantime, you have to get to her friends. You have to find out who she was with at the mall and where she went. Anything you can find out about what happened. Do you hear me, Eleanor?'

'I'm hanging up and calling the police.'

'*No!*'

Bosch looked around and saw that his outburst had drawn attention from across the squad room. He slid farther down into his seat and crouched over his desk so no one could see him.

'What? Harry, we have to—'

'Listen to me first and then do what you think you need to do. I don't think you should call the police. Not yet. If the people who have her find out, we might never get her back. We can't take the chance.'

She didn't respond. Bosch could hear her crying.

'Eleanor? Listen! Do you want to get her back or not? Get your shit together. You were an FBI agent! You can do this. I need you to work it like an agent until I get there. I'm going to have the video analysed. In the video she kicked at the camera and it moved. I saw a window. They might be able to work with it. I will come directly to you when I land. You have all of that?'

There was a long moment before Eleanor responded. When she did, her voice was calm. She had got the message. 'I have it, Harry. I still think we have to call the Hong Kong Police.'

'If that's what you think, then fine. Do you know anybody there?'

'No, but they have a Triad bureau. They've come into the casino.'

Almost twenty years removed from her time as an agent, Eleanor was a professional card player. For at least six years she had been living in Hong Kong and working for the Cleopatra Casino in nearby Macau. All the high rollers from the mainland wanted to play against the *gweipo*—the white woman. She was a draw. She played with house money, got a cut of the winnings and no part of the losses. It was a comfortable life. She and Maddie lived in a high-rise in Happy Valley and the casino sent a helicopter to pick her up on the roof when it was time to go to work.

Comfortable until now.

'Talk to your people at the casino,' Bosch said. 'If there is someone you are told you can trust, then make the call. I need to hang up and get moving here. You'll hear from me before I fly.'

She answered as if in a daze. 'OK, Harry.'

'And Eleanor?'

'What?'

'See if you can get me a gun. I can't take my own over.'

'They put you in prison for guns over here.'

'I know that, but you know people from the casino. Get me a gun.'

'I'll try.'

Bosch hesitated before hanging up. He wished he could reach out and touch her, somehow try to calm her fears.

'Try to stay calm, Eleanor. For Maddie. We can do this.'

'We're going to get her back, right, Harry?'

Bosch nodded to himself before answering. 'That's right. We're going to get her back.'

THE DIGITAL IMAGE UNIT was one of the subgroups of the Scientific Investigation Division and was still located at the old police headquarters at Parker Center. Bosch traversed the two blocks between the old and new buildings like a man running late for a plane. He badged his way past the front desk and took the elevator up to the third floor.

SID was in the process of being readied for the move to the PAB. At least a dozen cardboard boxes were stacked on one side of the first room of the two-room suite. There were no pictures or maps on the walls and a lot of the shelves were empty. He found one tech at work in the rear lab.

Barbara Starkey was a veteran who had jumped around among specialities in SID over nearly four decades in the department. As such she had seen first-hand the explosive growth of technology in crime detection. As she liked to tell the rookie techs, when she started in forensics, DNA were just three letters in the alphabet. Now she was an expert in almost all areas of forensics.

Starkey looked up from a twin-screen computer workstation.

'Harry Bosch! The man with the plan.'

Bosch had no time for banter. He approached and got right to the point. 'Barb, I need your help.'

Noting the urgency in his voice, Starkey frowned. 'What's up, darling?'

Bosch held his phone up. 'I've got a video on my phone. I need to blow it up and slow it down to see if I can identify the location. It's an abduction.'

Gesturing towards her screen, Starkey said, 'I'm right in the middle—'

'My daughter's on it, Barbara. I need your help now.'

This time Starkey didn't hesitate. 'OK, can you email the video to me?'

'I don't know. I've never tried.'

Starkey walked him through it and he sent Starkey an email with the video as an attachment. Starkey opened her email and downloaded the video. Soon she had it playing on the left screen. Harry looked at the images of his daughter and tried hard to stay focused.

'I'm so sorry, Harry,' Starkey said.

'I know. Let's not talk about it.'

On the screen, Maddie Bosch, thirteen years old, sat tied to a chair. A gag made of bright-red cloth cut tightly across her mouth. She wore her school uniform, a blue plaid skirt and white blouse with the school crest above the left breast. She looked at the camera—presumably her own cellphone camera—with eyes that tore Bosch's heart out. Desperate and scared were only the first words of description that went through his mind.

There was no sound, or rather no one said anything at first on the video. For fifteen seconds the camera held on her. She was simply on display for him. Then the person behind the camera reached into the frame and pulled the gag temporarily loose from Maddie's mouth.

'*Dad!*'

The gag was immediately replaced, muffling what was yelled after that single word and leaving Bosch unable to interpret it.

The hand then dropped down in an attempt to fondle one of the girl's breasts. She reacted violently, shifting sideways in her bindings and kicking her left leg up at the outstretched arm. The video frame momentarily swung out of control and then was brought back to Maddie. For the last five seconds of video the camera just held on her. The screen then went black.

Starkey didn't respond at first. Keeping any nonprofessional response out of her face, she put both her hands on an editing deck attached to the computer's keyboard.

'Harry, I'm going to go through this frame by frame but it's going to take some time,' she said. 'I'll call you the moment I find anything. Trust me, Harry. I know she's your daughter.'

Bosch nodded. He knew he had to let her work without breathing down her neck. It would bring the best results.

'OK. Can we just take a look at the kick and then I'll leave you to it? When she kicked at him there was a flash of light. Like a window.'

Starkey rolled the video back to the moment Maddie had kicked at her captor. In real time the video at that point had been a blur of sudden movement followed by a quick correction back to the girl. But now in stop-action of frame-by-frame playback, Bosch saw that the camera had momentarily swept left across a room to a window, and then back.

'You're good, Harry,' Starkey said. 'We may have something here.'

Bosch bent down to look over her shoulder and get closer. Starkey backed up the video and rolled it slowly forward again.

The room appeared to be a low-rent hotel room with a single bed and a table and lamp directly behind the chair Maddie was tied to. The wall over the bed was pockmarked with holes left by nails used to hold up wall hangings. The pictures had possibly been removed to make the location harder to identify.

Starkey backed the video up to the window and then froze it there. It was a vertical window with a single pane that had been cranked open in full outward extension and in the glass was a reflection of an urban cityscape.

'Where do you think this is, Harry?'

'Hong Kong. She lives there with her mother. Can you make that part bigger?' Bosch asked.

Using the mouse, Starkey outlined the window and then moved a copy of that part of the video over to the second screen. She increased its size and then went through some focusing manoeuvres.

'We don't have the pixels, Harry, so if I run a program that sort of fills in what we don't have, we can kind of sharpen it. Maybe you'll recognise something in the reflection.'

The first thing Bosch noted was that the location of the room was up high. The reflection showed a channel down a city street from at least ten storeys up, he judged. He could see the sides of buildings lining the street and the edge of a large billboard or building sign with the English letters N-O. There was also a collage of street-level signs with Chinese characters.

Beyond this Bosch could see tall buildings in the distance. He recognised one by the two white spires on the roof. The twin radio antennas were braced by a crossbar and the configuration always reminded Bosch of American football goalposts. Outlining the buildings was a mountain ridge line broken only by a structure that had a bowl shape supported by two thick columns.

'Is this helping, Harry?'

'Yeah, yeah, definitely. This has to be Kowloon. The reflection goes across the harbour to Central and then the mountain peak behind it. This building with the goalposts is the Bank of China. Very famous part of the skyline. And that is Victoria Peak behind it. To reflect all of this I'm pretty sure you'd have to be across the harbour in Kowloon. Can you print this?' He pointed to the second screen with the isolated view of the window.

'Sure thing. There's one thing that's sort of weird, though.'

'What's that?'

'You see in the foreground this partial reflection of the sign?' She used the cursor to put a box around the two letters N and O that were part of a larger sign and word in English. 'You have to remember, this is a reflection. It's like a mirror, so everything is in reverse. But these letters aren't backwards. So that means—'

'The sign is backwards?'

She was right. It was strange but not something he had the time to dwell on at the moment. It was time to get moving. He wanted to call Eleanor and tell her he thought their daughter was being held in Kowloon. Maybe it would connect with something at her end. It was a start at least.

'Can I get that copy?'

'I'm already printing it. It takes a couple minutes because it's a high-res printer.'

'Got it.' Bosch stared at the image on the screen, looking for any other details that would help.

'Kowloon?' Starkey asked. 'Sounds sort of ominous.'

'My daughter told me it means Nine Dragons.'

'See, I told you. Who would name their neighbourhood Nine Dragons unless they wanted to scare people away?'

'It comes from a legend. During one of the old dynasties the emperor was supposedly just a boy who got chased by the Mongols into the area that is now Hong Kong. He saw the eight mountain peaks that surrounded it and wanted to call the place Eight Dragons. But one of the men who guarded him reminded him that the emperor was a dragon, too. So they called it Nine Dragons. Kowloon.'

'Your daughter told you this?'

'Yeah. She learned it in school.'

Silence followed. Bosch could hear the printer working somewhere behind him. Starkey got up and pulled the print-out of the window reflection out of the printer. She handed it to Bosch.

'Thanks, Barbara.'

'I'm not done, Harry. Like I said, I'm going to look at every frame of that video and if there's something else that will help, I'll find it.'

Bosch just nodded and looked down at the print-out in his hand.

'You'll find her, Harry. I know you will.'

'Yeah, me too.'

BOSCH CALLED HIS EX-WIFE while on the way back to the PAB.

She answered the call with an urgent question. 'Harry, anything?'

'Not a lot but we're working on it. I am pretty sure the video I was sent was shot in Kowloon. Does that mean anything to you?'

'No. Kowloon? Why there?'

'I have no idea. But we may be able to find the place. I'll take the first flight out tonight. Have you called anybody? What have you got?'

'*I don't have anything!*' she yelled. 'My daughter is somewhere out there and I don't have anything! The police don't even believe me!'

'What are you talking about? You called them?'

'Yes, I called them. They put my name into the computer and got a hit. The police have a file on me. And they knew about the time before. When I thought she was kidnapped and she'd run to her friends. So they didn't believe me. They think she ran away again and her friends are lying to me. They said wait a day and call back if she doesn't show up.'

'Did you tell them about the video?'

'I told them but they didn't care. They said if there is no ransom demand, then it was probably staged by her and her friends to get attention. They don't believe me!'

She started crying in frustration and fear but Bosch considered the police reaction and thought it could work in their favour.

'Eleanor, listen to me, I think this is good. I told you before, I don't want the police. The people who have her will see the police coming a mile away. But they won't see me.'

'This isn't LA, Harry. You don't know your way round like you do there.'

'I'll find my way and you'll help me.'

There was a long silence before she responded. 'Harry, you have to promise me you'll get her back.'

'I will, Eleanor,' he responded without hesitation. 'I promise you.'

He walked into the main lobby, holding his jacket open so the badge on his belt could be seen at the fancy new reception counter.

'I've gotta go now, but did you find out about that other thing yet?'

'You mean the gun?' Eleanor asked.

'Yeah, that.'

'Harry, it's not even dawn here. I'll get on that when I am not calling people in their beds.'

'Right, OK. Let's call each other if we get something.'

'Goodbye, Harry.'

Bosch closed his phone and caught the next elevator up to RHD.

There was no sign of Ferras or Chu. Bosch pulled an address book out of a drawer and opened it at a page where he listed airlines that flew LAX to Hong Kong. All the flights would leave between 11 p.m. and 1 a.m. and they would land early on Sunday morning. Between the fourteen-plus hour flight and fifteen-hour time difference, all of Saturday would evaporate during the journey.

Bosch first called Cathay Pacific and was able to book a window seat on the first flight out. It would land at 5.25 on Sunday morning.

'Harry?'

Bosch swivelled in his seat and saw Gandle standing in the entrance to his cubicle. He signalled him to stand by and finished the call, writing down the record-locator code for his ticket. He then hung up.

'Lieutenant, where is everybody?'

'Ferras is still at the courthouse and Chu's booking Chang.'

'How'd Ferras do?'

'I don't know. He hasn't called in. The question is, how are you doing? Did forensics look at the video?'

'Barbara Starkey is working on it right now. She already got this.'

Bosch pulled the print-out of the window from his coat pocket and unfolded it. He explained to Gandle what he thought it meant.

'It sounded like you were booking a flight. When do you go?'

'Tonight. I lose a whole day but I gain it coming back. I get there early Sunday. I have all of Sunday to find her. I then fly back on Monday morning and get here on Monday morning. We go to the DA and file on Chang. It will work, Lieutenant.'

'Look, Harry, don't worry about the case. Just get over there and find her. We'll worry about the case.'

'Right.'

'What about the police? Your ex call them in?'

'She tried. They're not interested. They think she's a runaway and we should wait to see if she turns up. And that's fine with me because I don't want the police involved. Not yet.'

'Look, they must have entire units dedicated to the Triads. Your ex probably called some dipshit on a desk. You need to bring in some expertise.'

'Boss, I'm sure they have their experts. But the Triads have flourished for more than two hundred years. You don't do that without having lines into the police department. If it was one of your daughters, would you call in a bunch of people you can't trust or would you handle it yourself?' Bosch knew Gandle had two daughters. One was back east studying at Hopkins and he worried about her all the time.

'I hear you, Harry.'

'I just want Sunday. If I can't find her, I'll go to the police on Monday morning. I'll do whatever is necessary but I want Sunday to find her myself.'

'Well, if things don't work out on Sunday, you call me. You know, another time, another crime. We can always get Chang later.' Lieutenant Gandle, father of two daughters, was telling Bosch that he was willing to let Chang walk if it would get Harry's own daughter safely home.

'You're a good man, Lieutenant.'

'And, of course, I didn't just say any of that.'

'It's not going to come to that, but I appreciate what you didn't just say. Besides, the sad truth is, we may have to kick this guy loose on Monday anyway. Unless we come up with something over the weekend or on the searches.'

Gandle nodded and told Bosch what he always told him, to keep him in the loop, and then headed back to his office.

Bosch put the print-out on his desk and took a magnifying glass out of a drawer and began a study of every square inch of the image, looking for anything that might help. He was ten minutes into it and finding nothing new when his cell rang. It was Ferras.

'Harry, I got it. We got approval to search the phone, suitcase and car.'

'Ignacio, you're a hell of a writer. Still pitching a perfect game.'

It was true. So far, in the three years they had been partnered, Ferras had yet to write a search-warrant application that had been turned down. He might be intimidated by the streets but he wasn't cowed by the courthouse.

'Thanks, Har. I'm coming back now.'

'Why don't you divert over to the garage and handle that? I've got the phone and the suitcase right here. I'll dive in now. Chu is booking Chang.'

'Will do,' Ferras said.

'Good,' Bosch said. 'Call me if you strike gold.'

Bosch closed the phone. He didn't see the need to tell Ferras about his daughter's plight yet. Ferras had three young kids of his own and a reminder of how vulnerable he really was wouldn't be helpful at a time when Bosch was counting on his best work.

IT TOOK BOSCH less than five minutes to determine that Bo-Jing Chang's cellphone would be of little use to the investigation. The call log contained a listing of only two recent calls, both to toll-free numbers, and one incoming call. All three were placed or received that morning. There was no record beyond that. The phone's history had been wiped clean.

Bosch knew a full forensic analysis of the phone could possibly result in the wiped data being rebuilt, but for immediate purposes the phone was a bust. He called the 800 numbers and learned they belonged to Hertz rent-a-car and Cathay Pacific Airlines. Chang had probably been checking on his itinerary and his plan to drive from Seattle to Vancouver to catch the plane to Hong Kong. Bosch also checked the number from the incoming call in the reverse directory and learned it had come from Tsing Motors, Chang's employer. While it was unknown what the call was about, the number certainly added no new evidence or information to the case.

Bosch had counted on the phone not only adding to the case against Chang but possibly providing a clue to his daughter's location. The disappointment hit him hard and he knew he had to keep his mind moving in order to avoid dwelling on it. He shoved the phone back into the evidence bag and hoisted Chan's big suitcase onto his desk. He found a small padlock securing the zipper closed. He took out his picks and opened the lock in less than thirty seconds. He unzipped the bag and opened it across his desk.

Chang's suitcase was partitioned equally into halves. He started on the left side, removing and examining every item of clothing piece by piece.

It looked like Chang had thrown all his possessions into the suitcase. The clothes were bundled tightly together rather than folded as if for use on a trip. At the centre of one bundle he found a watch, in another an antique baby rattle. At the centre of the last bundle he opened was a small bamboo frame containing a faded photo of a woman. Chang's mother, Bosch presumed.

Chang was not coming back, Bosch concluded after searching only half of the suitcase.

In the right side there were more clothing bundles and shoes, plus a smaller zippered bag for toiletries. Bosch went through the bundles first, finding nothing unusual in the clothing. The first bundle was wrapped around a small jade statue of a Buddha. The second bundle was wrapped around a sheathed knife.

The weapon was a showpiece with a blade that was only five inches long and a handle made of carved bone. The carving was a depiction of a one-sided battle in which men with knives and arrows and axes slaughtered unarmed men who appeared to be praying. Bosch assumed this was the massacre of the Shaolin monks that Chu had told him was the origin of the Triads. Although it was possibly proof of Chang's membership in the Brave Knife Triad, it wasn't evidence of any crime. Bosch kept searching.

Soon he had emptied the suitcase. He felt the lining with his hands to make sure there was nothing hidden beneath and came up empty.

The last thing he looked at were the two pairs of shoes Chang had packed. First, he zeroed in on a pair of work boots he had seen Chang wearing the day before. They were old and worn but the laces were new and the leather had been oiled on repeated occasions. Bosch pulled the laces out so he could pull the tongue back all the way to look inside. Using a pair of scissors, he prised up the cushioning in the instep to see if it hid any sort of secret compartment in the heel. There was nothing in the first boot but in the second he found a business card that had been slipped between two layers of cushioning.

Bosch felt a kick of adrenaline as he put the boot aside to look at the card. He had finally found something.

It was a two-sided card. Chinese on one side and English on the other. Bosch, of course, studied the English side.

Jimmy Fong
Fleet Manager
Causeway Taxi Service

There was an address in Causeway Bay and two phone numbers. Bosch wondered what he had—if he had anything at all. Causeway Bay was not far from the shopping mall from which his daughter was mostly likely abducted. He flipped the card over and studied the Chinese side. It appeared that the card said the same thing on both sides.

Bosch put the card in an evidence envelope so that Chu could take a look at it and moved on to the other pairs of shoes. In another twenty minutes he was finished and had found nothing else. Disappointed, he put all the belongings back in the suitcase.

He called his partner. He was anxious to know if the search of Chang's car had gone better than the search of his phone and suitcase.

'We're only about halfway through,' Ferras said. 'Nothing so far.'

Bosch felt his hopes beginning to ebb away. Chang was going to come up clean. And that meant he was going to walk the following Monday.

'Did you get anything out of the phone?' Ferras asked.

'No, nothing. It was wiped. There wasn't much in the suitcase, either.'

'Well, we haven't even got inside the car yet. They started with the trunk. We'll check the door panels and the air filter, too.'

'Good. Let me know.'

Bosch closed the phone and then immediately called Chu.

'You still at booking?'

'No, man, I cleared booking half an hour ago. I'm in the courthouse waiting to see Judge Champagne and get the PCD signed.'

After booking a suspect for murder it was required that a judge sign a Probable Cause Detention document, which laid out the evidence that led to the suspect's incarceration. Getting a PCD signed was usually routine but nonetheless Chu had made a good move going back to the judge who had signed the search warrant.

'What's going on with your daughter, Harry?'

'She's still missing.'

'I'm sorry. What can I do?'

'We got the search warrant,' Bosch said. 'There was nothing on the phone but there was a business card hidden in one of his shoes. It's got English on one side and Chinese on the other. I know you don't read Chinese, but if I faxed it over to the AGU, could you have someone there take a look?'

'Yeah, Harry, but do it now. That place is probably clearing out.'

Bosch looked at his watch. It was four thirty on a Friday afternoon. Squad rooms across the city were turning into ghost towns.

'I'll do it now. Call over there and tell them it's coming.'

He closed the phone and left the cubicle for the copy office on the other side of the squad room.

Four thirty. In six hours Bosch had to be at the airport. He knew that once he was on the plane his investigation would go on hold for the next fourteen-plus hours. He knew that he couldn't get on that plane with nothing. One way or another he had to make a break.

After he had faxed a copy of the card over to the Asian Gang Unit he went back to his cubicle. He had left his phone on his desk and he saw that he had missed a call from his ex-wife. He called her back.

'You find something?' he asked.

'I've had very long conversations with two of Maddie's friends. This time they were talking. They told me about two kids Maddie had been hanging out with recently, a girl called He'—she said the girl's name with a heavy Chinese accent on it. It sounded like *He-yuh*—'and her brother, who are not from the school. They met them at the mall but they're not even from Happy Valley.'

'Do they know where they come from?'

'No, but they knew they weren't local. They said Maddie seemed to really get tight with He and that brought her brother into the picture. This is all in the past month or so. Since she came back from her visit with you, in fact. Both girls said she had put some distance between her and them.'

'What's the brother's name?'

'All I got was Quick. He said his name was Quick but, like his sister, He, they never got a last name.'

'That's not a lot of help. Anything else?'

'Well, they said that Quick was sort of rough trade. They thought he was at least seventeen. He had a car. He has tattoos and bracelets and he smokes. I guess . . . well, I guess they were sort of attracted to the element of danger.'

'They or Madeline?'

'Maddie mostly.'

'Did they think she might have gone with him on Friday after school?'

'They wouldn't say so but, yes, I think that's what they were trying to say. The mall opens in a couple of hours,' Eleanor continued. 'I plan to be there with photos of Maddie.'

'That's a good idea. There might be a video. If Quick was a problem in the past, mall security might know him.'

'I guess.' She paused. 'You know, you haven't really told me what you think is going on. I'm not stupid. I've worked out what you're doing. You're trying not to upset me with the facts but I think I need to know the facts now, Harry.'

Bosch knew that she was right. If he wanted her best effort, then she had to know all that he knew.

'All right. I'm working on the murder of a Chinese man who owned a liquor store. He was killed on the same day that he made a regular weekly payment to the Triad. That put us on to Bo-Jing Chang, the Triad bagman. The trouble is, we've got no evidence connecting him to the murder. Then today we had to take Chang down because he was about to flee the country. We have the weekend to get enough evidence to support the charge. He won't talk and I've just been through his suitcase and phone, and we're still working on the car. So far nothing. We don't have enough for a search warrant for his home.'

'And how does this connect to our daughter?'

'Eleanor, I'm dealing with people in the LAPD I don't know. Somebody got the word to Chang directly or to a Triad that we were on to him and that's why he tried to bolt. They could have just as easily backgrounded me and zeroed in on Madeline as a way to get to me. I got a call. Somebody told me there would be consequences if I didn't back off Chang. I never dreamed that the consequences would be . . .'

'Maddie,' Eleanor said, finishing the thought.

A long silence followed and Bosch guessed that his ex-wife was trying to control her emotions, hating Bosch but at the same time having to rely on him to save their daughter.

'Harry?'

'What?'

'If we get her back, you may never see her again. I just need to tell you that.' Her voice was clipped but very obviously filled with dark rage.

Bosch paused. He knew she was entitled to her anger and everything else. Anger might make her sharper in her efforts.

'There is no *if*,' he finally said. 'I'm going to get her back.'

He waited for her to respond but got only silence.

'OK, Eleanor. I'll call you when I know something.'

After closing the phone, Bosch turned to his desktop computer and printed a copy of Chang's booking photo to take with him to Hong Kong.

After that Chu called back and said he had got the PCD signed and was leaving the courthouse. He said he had spoken to an officer at the AGU who had taken Bosch's fax and could confirm that both sides of the business card said the same thing. The card came from the manager of a taxi fleet based in Causeway Bay. Bosch was still bothered by the card being secreted in Chang's shoe and by it being from a business located so close to where his daughter had last been seen by her friends. Bosch had never been a believer in coincidence. He wasn't going to start now.

Bosch thanked Chu and hung up, just as Lieutenant Gandle stopped by his cubicle on the way out.

'Harry, I feel like I'm leaving you in the lurch. What can I do for you?'

'There's nothing that can be done that is not already being done.'

He updated Gandle on the searches and the lack of solid findings so far.

He also reported that there was nothing new on his daughter's whereabouts. Gandle's face turned sour. 'We need a break,' he said.

'We're working on it.'

'OK, you have my numbers. Call me anytime, day or night, if you need anything. I'll do whatever I can.'

'Thanks, Boss.'

Gandle awkwardly put his hand out and Bosch shook it. It was probably the first time since they had met three years earlier that they had shaken. Gandle left then and Bosch surveyed the squad room. He was the only one left.

He turned and looked at the suitcase. He knew he had to lug it down to evidence lockup. The phone had to be booked into evidence, too. After that he would leave as well. But not for a leisurely weekend with the family. Bosch was on a mission. And he would stop at nothing to see it through. Even under Eleanor's threat. Even if it meant that saving his daughter might mean he'd never see her again.

HIS PLAN was to go home before heading to the airport to pick up his passport and lock up his gun. He would not be allowed to carry the weapon into a foreign country without state department approval—a process that would take days if not weeks. He didn't plan to pack any clothes because he didn't see himself having time to change clothes in Hong Kong. His mission would begin the moment he stepped off the plane.

As he got into his car his phone started to vibrate. The call was from Barbara Starkey, the video tech.

'Barbara. You should've gone home about three hours ago.'

'Yeah, well, I told you I would look at this thing.'

'Thank you, Barbara. It means a lot. What did you find?'

'A couple of things. First of all, I have a print-out here that is a little sharper, if you want it.'

Bosch was disappointed. It sounded like there wasn't much more than what he already had. 'Anything else?' he asked. 'I'm on my way to the airport.'

'Yes, I have a couple of other visual and audio identifiers that might help you,' Starkey said.

Bosch paid full attention now. 'What are they?'

'Well, one I think might be a train or a subway. Another is a snippet of conversation. And the last one I think is a silent helicopter.'

'What do you mean, *silent*?'

'I mean literally silent. I have a flash reflection in the window of a helicopter going by, but I don't have any real audio track to go with it.'

Bosch didn't respond at first. He knew what she was talking about. The whisper jet helicopters that the rich and powerful used to move around Hong Kong. He had seen them. Commuting by helicopter wasn't uncommon but he knew only a few buildings in each district were allowed to operate landing pads on their roofs. One reason his ex-wife chose the building where she lived was because of the helicopter pad on the roof, which meant she could get to the casino in Macau in twenty minutes door-to-door.

'Barbara, I'll be there in five minutes,' he said.

He headed over to Parker Center. He parked in the garage and entered through the back door. When he walked into the mostly abandoned lab it had actually been seven minutes since he had closed the phone.

'You're late,' Starkey said.

'Sorry, thanks for waiting.'

'I'm just giving you a hard time. I know you're on the run so let's just look at this thing.'

She pointed to one of her screens where there was a frozen image of the window from the phone video. Starkey put her hands on the dials.

'OK,' she said. 'Keep your eyes up here at the top of the glass reflection.'

She turned one dial slowly, reversing the tape. In the murky glass reflection Bosch saw what he had not seen before. Just as the aim of the camera started its swing back until it was focused on his daughter, a small helicopter moved across the top of the reflection like a ghost. It was a good find and Bosch was excited.

'The thing is, Harry, to be in that window that chopper has to be flying pretty low.'

'So either it just took off or it was landing.'

'I think it was ascending. It appears to rise slightly as it crosses the reflection. Now when I look for an audio track . . .' She switched to the other screen where there was an audio graph showing different isolated streams of audio she had taken from the video. '. . . and take out as much of the competing sound as I can, I get this.'

She played a track with almost a flat-line graph and all Bosch could hear was distant traffic noise that was chopped into waves.

'That's rotor wash,' she said. 'You don't hear the helicopter itself but it's disrupting the ambient noise. It's like a stealth chopper or something.'

Bosch nodded. He now knew his daughter was held in a building near one of the few rooftop helicopter pads in Kowloon.

'That help?' Starkey asked.

'You better believe it.'

'Good. I also have this.'

She played another track and it contained a low hissing sound. It began, grew louder and then dissipated.

'What is it? Water?'

Starkey shook her head. 'I had to work at this. It's air. Escaping air. I would say you are talking about an entrance to an underground subway station or maybe a vent through which displaced air is channelled up and out when a train comes into the station. Your location is up high. Maybe fifteen storeys, judging by the reflection. So this audio is hard to pinpoint. Could be ground level to this building or a block away. Hard to tell.'

'It still helps.'

'And the last thing is this.'

She played the first part of the video when the camera was holding on Bosch's daughter and just showing her. She brought up the sound and filtered out competing audio tracks. Bosch heard a muffled line of dialogue.

'What is that?' he asked.

'I think it might be outside the room. I haven't been able to clean it up any better. Listen again to the end of it.'

She played it again. Bosch stared at his daughter's scared eyes while concentrating on the audio. It was a male voice that was too muffled to be understood and then ended abruptly in midsentence.

'Somebody cut him off?'

'Or maybe an elevator door closed and that cut him off.'

Bosch nodded. The elevator seemed like a more likely explanation because there had been no stress in the tone of the voice before the cut-off.

Starkey pointed at the screen. 'So when you find the building, this room will be close to the elevator.'

Bosch stared at his daughter's eyes for one last and long moment.

'Thank you, Barbara.' He stood behind her and gave her shoulders a squeeze.

'Good luck, Harry. Go get your daughter.'

'That's the plan.'

SIX

Bosch got only fitful sleep on the flight over the Pacific. By moving too fast to think during the day, he had kept himself ahead of the fear and guilt, the brutal recriminations. He was able to put it all aside because the pursuit was more important than the baggage he was carrying. But on Cathay Pacific flight 883 he could run no more. As the jet hurtled through the black towards the place where Madeline was somewhere hidden, he spent the long hours sitting in darkness, fists balled tightly and eyes staring blankly.

The head winds over the Pacific were weaker than anticipated and the plane landed early at the airport on Lantau Island at 4.55 a.m. When the jet's door opened he moved quickly and, carrying only a small backpack, he soon took over the lead of all the passengers heading towards customs and immigration.

At the customs checkpoint an inspector flipped through his passport and then checked a computer screen Bosch couldn't see.

'You have business in Hong Kong, Mr Bosch?' the inspector asked.

'No,' Bosch said. 'My daughter lives here and I come to visit her pretty often.'

He eyed the backpack slung over Bosch's shoulder. 'You checked in your bags?'

'No, I just have this. It's a quick trip.'

The inspector nodded and directed Bosch to step through a metal detector. Then he was cleared and heading into the baggage terminal. He spotted a money-exchange window that was open despite the early hour. He stepped up, pulled a cash envelope out of his backpack and told the woman behind the glass he wanted to change 5,000 US dollars into Hong Kong dollars. It was Bosch's earthquake money, cash he kept hidden in the gun locker in his bedroom. He had learned a valuable lesson back in 1994 when an earthquake rocked LA. Cash is king. Don't leave home without it. Now the money he kept hidden for just such a crisis would hopefully help him overcome another.

After getting his money he headed to the exit doors. The first surprise of the day came when he saw Eleanor Wish waiting for him in the main hall of the airport. She was standing next to a man in a suit who had the feet-splayed posture of a bodyguard. Eleanor made a small gesture with her hand in case Harry hadn't noticed her. He saw the mixture of pain and hope on her face and had to drop his eyes to the floor as he approached.

'Eleanor. I didn't—'

She grabbed him in a quick and awkward embrace that abruptly ended his sentence. He understood that she was telling him that blame and recriminations were for later. There were more important things now.

She gestured to the man in the suit. 'This is Sun Yee.'

Bosch wasn't sure whether his first name was Sun or Yee, so he just nodded and the man nodded back. Harry guessed he was in his late forties. Eleanor's age. He was short but powerfully built. His chest and arms pressed the contours of the silk suit jacket to its limit. He wore sunglasses although it was still well before dawn.

'He's driving us?' Bosch asked.

'He's helping us,' Eleanor corrected. 'He works in security at the casino.'

That was one mystery solved. 'Does Sun Yee speak English?'

'Yes, I do, Mr Bosch,' Sun Yee said.

Bosch studied him for a moment and then looked at Eleanor and saw in her face a familiar resolve. It was a look he had seen many times when they had been together. Sun Yee was part of the package.

'Then call me Harry,' he said.

Sun Yee bowed slightly.

Bosch knew that if circumstances dictated it, he could make his way alone through the city. But for now he was willing to go with Eleanor's plan.

They started walking towards the glass doors and Bosch let Sun Yee take a lead so he could talk privately with his ex-wife. Despite the strain playing clearly on her face, she was just as beautiful as ever to him. She had her hair tied back in a no-nonsense manner, accentuating the determined set of her jaw. No matter what the circumstances, he could never look at her without thinking about the could-have-beens.

'Tell me what's happening, Eleanor,' he said. 'What's new at this end?'

'I spent four hours at the mall yesterday. They have surveillance video that shows her with the brother and sister I told you about. Quick and He. It's all from a distance. They're not identifiable on it—except for Mad. I'd be able to pick her out anywhere.'

'Does it show the grab?'

'There was no grab. They were hanging out together. Then Quick lit up a cigarette and somebody complained. Security moved in and kicked him out. Madeline walked out with them. Voluntarily. They never came back in.'

Bosch could see it. It could have all been a plan to lure her out. Quick lit up, knowing all along that he would be ejected from the mall, and Madeline would go out with him. 'What time was it when they walked out?'

'Six fifteen.'

Bosch did the maths. That was Friday. His daughter had walked off the mall videotape almost thirty-six hours ago.

'When's it get dark here? What time?'

'Usually around eight. Why?'

'The video that was sent to me was shot in daylight. So less than two hours after she walked out of the mall with them she was in Kowloon and they made the video.'

'I want to see the video, Harry.'

'I'll show you in the car. Did you get my message? Did you find out about helicopter pads in Kowloon?'

Nodding, Eleanor said, 'I called the head of client transportation at the casino. He told me that in Kowloon there are seven rooftop helicopter pads. I have a list.'

'Good. Did you tell him why you wanted the list?'

'No, Harry. Give me some credit.'

Bosch looked at her and then moved his eyes to Sun Yee, who had now opened up a lead of several paces on them. Eleanor got the message.

'Sun Yee's different. He knows what's going on. I brought him in because I can trust him. He's been my security at the casino for three years.'

Bosch nodded. His ex-wife was a valuable commodity to the Cleopatra Resort and Casino in Macau. They paid for her apartment and the helicopter that brought her to and from work at the private tables where she played against the casino's wealthiest clients. Security—in the form of Sun Yee—was part of that package.

'Yeah, well, too bad he wasn't watching over Maddie, too.'

Eleanor abruptly stopped and turned towards Bosch. Unaware, Sun Yee kept going. Eleanor got in Harry's face.

'Look, you want to get into this right now? Because I can if you want. We can talk about Sun Yee and we can also talk about you and how your work put my daughter in this . . . this . . .' She never finished. Instead, she grabbed Bosch by the jacket and started shaking him angrily until she was hugging him and starting to cry.

Bosch put his hand on her back. '*Our* daughter, Eleanor,' he said. 'Our daughter, and we're going to get her back.'

Sun Yee noticed they were not with him and stopped. He looked back at Bosch, his eyes hidden behind the dark glasses. Harry raised a hand to signal him to hold for a moment and keep his distance.

Eleanor finally stepped back and wiped her nose with the back of her hand.

'You need to keep it together, Eleanor. I'm going to need you.'

'*Stop* saying that, OK? I will keep it together. Where do we start?'

'Did you get the MTR map I asked for?' The MTR was Hong Kong's subway system.

'Yes, I've got it. It's in the car.'

'What about the card from Causeway Taxis? Did you check it out?'

'We didn't have to. Sun Yee already knew about it. Most of the taxi companies are known to hire Triad people. Triad people need legitimate jobs to avoid suspicion. Most get taxi licences and work a few shifts here and there as a front. Your suspect was probably going to see the fleet manager about a job.'

'Did you go to the address? Did you talk to the fleet manager?'

'No. I didn't want to make a move like that without asking you. But you were in the air and I couldn't ask. Besides, this is a guy who was probably going to give Chang a job. That's all. He wouldn't be involved in an abduction. And even if he was involved, he wasn't going to talk about it.'

Bosch thought Eleanor was probably right, but the fleet manager would be someone to come back to if other efforts to locate his daughter didn't pan out. 'OK,' he said. 'What about the gun?'

'If you're sure,' she said hesitantly, 'Sun Yee knows where you can get one. In Wan Chai.'

Bosch nodded. Of course that would be the place to get a gun. Wan Chai was where the underside of Hong Kong came to the surface. He had not been there since coming from Vietnam on leave forty years before. But he knew that some things and places never changed.

'OK, let's get to the car. We're losing time.'

They stepped through the automatic doors and Bosch was greeted by the warm, wet air. He felt the humidity start to cling to him.

'Where are we going first?' Eleanor asked. 'Wan Chai?'

'No, the Peak. We'll start there.'

IT WAS KNOWN AS Victoria Peak during colonial times. Now it was just the Peak, a mountaintop that rose behind the Hong Kong skyline and offered stunning vistas across the central district and the harbour to Kowloon. It was a popular destination with tourists all year round and Bosch had been there several times with his daughter, often eating lunch in the observatory's restaurant or the shopping galleria built behind it.

Bosch and his ex-wife and her security man made it to the top before dawn broke over the city. They left Sun Yee's black Mercedes in the lot by the galleria and walked down the path that edged the side of the mountain. Bosch had his backpack over his shoulder. The air was heavy with humidity and already his shirt was sticking to his back.

'What exactly are we doing?' Eleanor asked.

The question was the first she had spoken in a long time. On the drive in from the airport Bosch had set up the video and handed her his phone. She watched it and then silently handed the phone back. It was a terrible silence that lasted until they were on the path.

Bosch unzipped the backpack and handed Eleanor the photo print from the video. He then handed her a flashlight from the bag as well.

'That's a freeze-frame from the video. When Maddie kicks at the guy and the camera moves, it caught the window.'

Eleanor studied the print while they walked. Sun Yee walked several paces behind them.

Bosch continued to explain his plan. 'You have to remember that everything in the window is reflected backwards. But you see the goalposts on top of the Bank of China building? Well, between those posts you can see the pagoda down here. I think it's called the Lion Pagoda. I've been up here with Maddie.'

'So have I. It's called the Lion Pavilion. Are you sure it's on here?'

'Yeah, you need the magnifying glass. Wait till we get up here.'

The path curved and Bosch saw the pagoda-style structure ahead. It was in a prominent position offering one of the better views of the Peak. Bosch stepped through the arched entrance and out to the viewing pavilion. The giant city spread out below him. There were a billion lights out there in the receding darkness and he knew one of them belonged to his daughter. He was going to find it.

Eleanor stood next to him and held the print-out under the beam of the flashlight. Sun Yee took a bodyguard's position behind them.

'I don't understand,' she said. 'You think you can reverse this and pin-point where she was?'

'That's right.'

'Harry . . .'

'There are other markers. I just want to narrow it down.'

Bosch pulled his binoculars from the backpack. They were powerful magnifiers he used on surveillance assignments. He raised them to his eyes.

It was still too dark. Bosch lowered the binoculars. He would have to wait.

'What other markers, Harry?'

Bosch pointed out the markers Barbara Starkey had told him about, par-ticularly the portion of the backwards sign with the letters O and N. He also told her about the audio track from a nearby subway.

'You add it all up and I think we can get close,' he said. 'If I can get close, I'll find her.'

'Well, I can tell you right now you are looking for the Canon sign.'

'You mean Canon cameras? Where?'

She pointed in the distance towards Kowloon. Bosch looked through the binoculars again.

'I see it all the time when they fly me in and out over the harbour. There is a Canon sign on the Kowloon side. It's just the word Canon standing free on top of a building. It rotates. If you were behind it in Kowloon when it rotated towards the harbour, you would see it backwards. Then in the reflec-tion it would be corrected. That has to be it.'

'Yeah, but where? I don't see it anywhere.'

'It's normally lit up but they probably turn it off a couple hours before dawn to save energy. We'll be able to see it in about fifteen minutes.'

Bosch reluctantly lowered the binoculars and for the next ten minutes watched the light creep over the mountains and into the basin.

The dawn came up pink and grey. The harbour was already busy as workboats and ferries crisscrossed paths in what looked like some kind of natural choreography. Bosch saw a low-lying mist clinging to the towers in Central and across the harbour in Kowloon. He smelled smoke.

'It smells like LA after the riots,' he said. 'Like the city's on fire.'

'It is in a way,' Eleanor said. 'We're halfway through Yue Laan.'

'Yeah, what's that?'

'The hungry ghost festival. It began last week. It's set to the Chinese cal-endar. It is said that on the fourteenth day of the seventh lunar month the gates of hell open and all the evil ghosts stalk the world. Believers burn offerings to appease their ancestors and ward off the evil spirits.'

'What kind of offerings?'

'Mostly paper money and papier-mâché facsimiles of things like houses and cars. Things the spirits supposedly need on the other side.'

Bosch gazed down on the city and realised what he had taken as morning mist was actually smoke from the fires, hanging in the air like the ghosts themselves. 'Looks like there's a lot of believers out there.'

'Yes, there are.'

Bosch raised the binoculars again. Sunlight was finally hitting the buildings along the harbourside. He panned back and forth, always keeping the goalposts on top of the Bank of China in his field of vision. Finally, he found the Canon sign sitting atop a glass- and aluminium-skinned building that was throwing sharp reflections of light in all directions. He estimated the building was twelve floors high.

'I see the sign,' he said, without looking away.

'Let me see,' Eleanor said.

Bosch handed over the binoculars and she quickly zeroed in on the Canon sign. 'Got it,' she said. 'The Peninsula Hotel is across the street and within two blocks of it. It's one of the helicopter-pad locations.'

Bosch followed her line of sight across the harbour. It took him a moment to find the sign. It was now catching the sun full on. He was beginning to feel the adrenaline kicking in.

He saw a wide road cutting north into Kowloon next to the building with the sign on top. 'What road is that?' he asked.

Eleanor kept her eyes on the binoculars. 'It's Nathan Road,' she said. 'Goes from the harbour up into the New Territories.'

Bosch turned back to look out towards Nathan Road and Kowloon.

'Nine Dragons,' he whispered to himself.

'What?' Eleanor asked.

'I said, that's where she is.'

THEY GOT BACK into Sun Yee's Mercedes and headed down the mountain towards Wan Chai. Along the way Bosch realised that one route down would take them by the apartment building where Eleanor and his daughter lived.

'Eleanor, let's go by your place first. I forgot to tell you to bring Madeline's passport. Yours, too.'

'Why?'

'Because this won't be over when we get her back. I want both of you away from here until it is.'

Eleanor turned to Sun Yee and spoke in Chinese. Sun Yee immediately pulled to the side of the road and stopped. She turned round to face Bosch.

'We'll stop for the passports,' she said evenly. 'But if we need to disappear, don't think for a minute we will be going with you.'

Bosch nodded. It was enough for him that she was willing to do it.

'Maybe you should pack a couple of bags and put them in the trunk, too.'

She turned back round without responding. Sun Yee looked over at her and spoke in Chinese. She nodded and Sun Yee started down the mountain again. Bosch knew that she was going to do what he'd asked.

Fifteen minutes later Sun Yee stopped in front of the twin towers known by locals as the Chopsticks. And Eleanor, having said not a single word in those fifteen minutes, extended an olive branch to the back seat.

'You want to come up? You can make a coffee while I pack the bags. You look like you could use it.'

'Coffee would be good but we don't have—'

'It's instant coffee.'

'OK, then.'

Sun Yee stayed with the car and they went up. The Chopsticks were actually two interlinked towers that rose seventy-three storeys from the midslope of the mountain above Happy Valley. It was the tallest residential building in all of Hong Kong and as such stuck out like two chopsticks protruding from a pile of rice. Eleanor and Madeline had moved here shortly after arriving from Las Vegas six years earlier.

Bosch gripped the handrail in the elevator as they went up. He didn't like the idea that just below the floor was an open shaft that went straight down forty-four floors. The door opened on a small foyer and Eleanor used a key to go in the first door on the right.

'Coffee's in the cabinet over the sink. I won't take long.'

'Good. You want a cup?'

'No, I'm good. I had some at the airport.'

They entered the apartment and Eleanor split off to go to her bedroom while Bosch found the kitchen and went to work on the coffee. Sipping the hot mixture, he took in the stunning view of Hong Kong and its harbour. Bosch had been in the apartment only a few times and never tired of seeing this. Most times when he came to visit, he met his daughter at her school after classes.

A huge white cruise ship was making its way through the harbour towards the open sea. Bosch watched it for a moment and then noticed the Canon sign sitting atop the building in Kowloon. It was a reminder of his mission. He turned towards the hallway and found Eleanor in their daughter's room, crying as she put clothes into a backpack.

'I don't know what to take,' she said. 'I don't know how long we'll be away or what she'll need. I don't even know if we'll ever see her again.'

Her shoulders trembled as she let the tears fall. Bosch put a hand on her left shoulder but she immediately shrugged it off. She would take no comfort from him. She roughly zipped the backpack closed and left the room with it. Bosch was left to look about the room by himself.

Keepsakes from trips to LA and other places were on every horizontal surface. On a small desk there was an open laptop computer, its screen dark. Posters from movies and music groups covered the walls. Numerous stuffed animals from earlier years were crowded against the pillows on the bed. Bosch couldn't help but feel like he was somehow invading his daughter's privacy by being in the room uninvited by her.

'You ready?'

Bosch turned. Eleanor was in the doorway.

'I'm ready.'

Bosch grabbed a pillow and a folded blanket off the bed. Eleanor saw what he was doing.

'She might be tired and want to sleep,' Bosch explained.

They left the apartment and in the elevator Bosch held the blanket and pillow under one arm and one of the backpacks in the other.

'Can I ask you something?' he said.

'What?'

He acted like he was studying the pattern of ponies on the blanket he was holding. 'How far can you trust Sun Yee? I'm not sure we should be with him after we get the gun.'

Eleanor answered without hesitation. 'I told you, you don't have to worry about him. I trust him completely. Maddie does, too. He's staying with us.'

'How does Maddie even—' Bosch stopped. He suddenly understood what she was saying. Sun Yee was the man Madeline had told him about.

He and Eleanor were together.

'You get it now?' she asked.

'Yeah, I get it,' he said. 'But are you sure Madeline trusts him?'

'Yes, I'm sure. If she told you otherwise, then she was just trying to get your sympathy. Yes, her life has been . . . disrupted a bit by my relationship with Sun Yee. But he has shown her nothing but kindness and respect. She'll get over it. That is, once we get her back.'

Sun Yee had the car waiting in the drop-off circle at the front of the building. Harry and Eleanor put the backpacks in the trunk but Bosch took the pillow and blanket with him into the back seat. Sun Yee pulled out and they went the rest of the way into Happy Valley and then over to Wan Chai.

Bosch tried to put the conversation from the elevator out of his mind. It wasn't important at the moment because it wouldn't help him get Maddie back. But it was hard to compartmentalise his feelings. His daughter had told him back in LA that Eleanor was in a relationship. But being hit with the reality of it here in Hong Kong was difficult. He was riding with a woman he still loved and her new man. It was hard to take.

Sitting behind Eleanor, he looked over the seat at Sun Yee and studied the man's stoic demeanour. He was no hired gun here. He had more of a stake than that. Bosch realised that could make him an asset.

As if sensing the eyes on him, Sun Yee turned and looked at Bosch. Even with the blackout shades guarding his eyes, Bosch could tell Sun Yee had read the situation and knew there were no secrets any longer.

Bosch nodded. It wasn't any sort of approval he was giving. It was just the silent message that he now understood they were all in this together.

WAN CHAI was the part of Hong Kong that never slept. The place where anything could happen and anything could be had for the right price. Anything. Bosch knew that if he wanted a laser sight to go with the gun they were going to pick up, he could get it. If he wanted a shooter to go with the set-up, he could probably get that, too. And this didn't even begin to address the other things like drugs and women that would be available to him in the strip bars and music clubs along Lockhart Road.

It was eight thirty and full daylight as they cruised down Lockhart. Many of the clubs were still active, shutters closed against the light but neon burning brightly up above in the smoky air. Men in rumpled suits, their steps slowed by a night of alcohol or drugs, were moving slowly on the wet pavement. Double-parked outside the rows of red taxis, the occasional Rolls-Royce or Mercedes idled, waiting for the money to run out inside and the journey home finally to begin.

In front of almost every establishment was an ash can for burning offerings to the hungry ghosts. Many were alive with flames. Bosch saw a woman in a silk robe with a red dragon on the back standing outside a club called the Red Dragon. She was showering what looked like real Hong Kong dollars into the flames leaping from the can in front of her club. She was hedging her bets with the ghosts, Bosch thought. She was going with the real thing.

In another two blocks the clubs got smaller and seedier. The neon signage in Chinese and English was more garish and usually accompanied by posters containing photographs of the beautiful women supposedly waiting inside. Sun Yee double-parked near an intersection and released his seat belt. Bosch did the same.

Sun Yee turned back to look at him. 'You don't go,' he told Bosch.

Bosch looked at him. 'You sure? I have money.'

'No money,' Sun Yee said. 'You wait here.'

He got out. Bosch stayed in the car. 'What's going on?'

'Sun Yee's calling on a friend for the gun. It's not a transaction involving money.'

'Is Sun Yee in a Triad?'

'No. He wouldn't have got the job in the casino. And I wouldn't be with him.'

Bosch wasn't so sure about the casino job being off limits to a Triad man. Sometimes the best way to know your enemy is to hire your enemy.

'*Was* he in a Triad?'

'I don't know. I doubt it. They don't let you just quit.'

'But he's getting the gun from a Triad guy, right?'

'Look, Harry, we are getting the gun you told me you had to have. Do you want it or not?'

'Yes, I want it.'

'Then we are doing what needs to be done to get it. And Sun Yee is risking his job and freedom doing it, I might add. Gun laws are harsh here.'

'I understand. No more questions. Just thank you for helping me.'

In the silence that followed Bosch could hear muffled but pulsing music coming from one of the shuttered clubs. Through the windshield he saw

Sun Yee approach three men in suits who were standing outside a club called the Yellow Door. Sun Yee spoke briefly with the men and then nonchalantly opened his suit jacket so they could see he was not armed. One of the men did a quick but competent pat-down and Sun Yee was then allowed to enter through the signature yellow door.

They waited for nearly ten minutes. During that time Eleanor said almost nothing. Bosch knew she was fearful of their daughter's situation and angry with his questions, but he needed to know more than he knew.

Then Bosch saw Sun Yee step back through the yellow door. But instead of heading back to the car he crossed the street and went into a noodle shop.

'Now what, he's getting food?' Bosch asked.

'I doubt it,' Eleanor said. 'He was probably sent over there.'

Bosch nodded. Precautions. Another five minutes went by and when Sun Yee emerged from the noodle shop he was carrying a Styrofoam to-go carton that was secured with two rubber bands. He carried it flat, as if to avoid dishevelling the plate of noodles within. He got back to the car and got in. Without a word he handed the carton over the seat to Bosch.

Holding the carton low, Bosch pulled off the rubber bands and opened it as Sun Yee pulled the Mercedes away from the kerb. The carton contained a medium-sized pistol made of blue steel. There was nothing else. No back-up magazine or extra ammunition. Just the gun and whatever was in it.

Bosch dropped the carton to the floor of the car and held the pistol in his left hand. The five-point star stamped into the grip told Bosch the weapon was a Black Star pistol manufactured by the government of China for the military. He had seen them on occasion in LA, and a fair number were obviously smuggled into Hong Kong.

Bosch held the pistol down between his knees and ejected the magazine. It was double-stacked with fifteen 9mm Parabellum rounds. He thumbed them out and put them into a cup holder in the armrest. He then ejected a sixteenth round from the chamber and put it in the cup holder with the others. He had sixteen rounds and that was it.

Bosch looked down the sight to focus his aim. He peered into the chamber, looking for any sign of rust, and then checked the gun's action and trigger several times. The weapon seemed to be functioning properly.

'Happy?' Eleanor asked from the front seat.

Bosch looked up from the weapon and saw that they were on the down ramp to the Cross Harbour Tunnel. It would take them directly to Kowloon.

'Not quite. I don't like carrying a gun I've never fired. For all I know, the pin could have been filed and I'll be drawing dead when I need it.'

'Well, there's nothing we can do about that. You just have to trust Sun Yee.'

The Sunday-morning traffic was light in the two-lane tunnel. Bosch waited until they passed the low point in the middle and had started up the incline towards the Kowloon side. He quickly wrapped his daughter's blanket around the gun and his left hand. He then pulled the pillow over and turned to look out of the rear window. There were no cars in sight behind them.

'Whose car is this anyway?' he asked.

'It belongs to the casino,' Eleanor said. 'I borrowed it. Why?'

Bosch lowered the window. He held the pillow up, pressed the muzzle into the padding, and fired twice. The bullets snapped off the tunnel's walls.

Even with the wadding around the gun the two reports echoed loudly in the car. The car swerved slightly as Sun Yee looked into the back seat.

Eleanor yelled, '*What the hell did you do?*'

Bosch dropped the pillow to the floor and raised the window. The weapon had fired easily and without a jam. He was down to fourteen bullets and was good to go.

'I had to make sure it worked,' he said.

'*Are you crazy?* You could get us arrested before we do anything!'

'If you keep your voice down and Sun Yee stays in his lane, we'll be fine.'

Bosch leaned forward and tucked the weapon into his waistband at the small of his back. They would be in Kowloon soon.

It was time.

SEVEN

Nathan Road was a wide, four-lane boulevard lined with high-rise buildings as far as Bosch could see. It was a crowded mix of commercial and residential buildings, ranging from dowdy mid-century constructions to the slick glass and steel structures of recent prosperity. The clutter of video screens and signs was an intense riot of colour and motion.

When the Canon sign was directly overhead, Bosch asked Sun Yee to stop.

Sun Yee pulled to the kerb and Bosch jumped out. He'd taken the photo print from his backpack and had it ready. Sun Yee then pulled away to find a parking space, leaving Eleanor and Bosch on the sidewalk.

'OK,' Bosch said. 'We start from here.' He was looking at the bottom edge of the sign's letters. It was rotating slowly. He looked back down and referred to the photo. 'I think we have to go at least another block farther in from the harbour.'

'Let's wait for Sun Yee.'

'Call him and tell him where we're going.' Bosch started off.

Eleanor had no choice but to follow. 'All right, all right.'

She pulled out her phone and started to make the call. As he walked, Bosch kept his eyes high on the buildings, looking for air-conditioning units. It was now midmorning. The streets were crowded with people and Bosch had to pay attention to avoid collisions. Smoke was in the air and the smell of fire. The hungry ghosts were close. The streetscape was replete with neon, mirrored glass and giant plasma screens broadcasting silent jerking images.

They walked another two blocks and then Bosch saw and heard another piece of the puzzle drop into place. Across the street was an entrance to the Metropolitan Transportation Railway. A glass enclosure leading to the escalators down to the underground subway.

'Wait,' Bosch said, stopping. 'The MTR. You could hear it on the video.'

As if on cue, the growing whoosh of escaping air rose as a train came into the underground station. It sounded like a wave. Bosch looked down at the photo in his hand and then up at the buildings surrounding him.

'Let's cross.'

They hurried across the street on a flashing pedestrian signal. More people were coming up out of the station than were going down. Kowloon was getting more and more crowded. The air was thick with humidity.

Bosch turned round and looked up. They were in an area of older construction. It was almost like having walked through first class to economy on a plane. The buildings on this block were shorter and in poorer condition than those in the blocks closer to the harbour. Harry noticed many open windows and many individual air-conditioning boxes hanging from windows. He could feel the reservoir of adrenaline inside open up.

'OK, this is it. She's in one of these buildings.'

He started moving down the block to get away from the crowding and loud conversations surrounding the MTR entrance. Halfway down the block, he stopped and referred to the photo again. He knew he was close but it was beginning to dawn on him that the final part of his search was impossible. He had travelled nearly eight thousand miles to find his daughter and he was about as helpless as the ragtag women begging for coins from the pavement.

'Let me see the photo,' Eleanor said.

Bosch handed it to her. 'All these buildings look the same.'

'Let me just look.'

She took her time and Bosch watched her regress two decades to the time she was an FBI agent. Her eyes narrowed and she analysed the photo as an agent, not as the mother of a missing girl.

'OK,' she said. 'There's got to be something here.'

Just then Sun Yee came up, his face flushed from the exertion of trying to track a moving target. Eleanor said nothing to him but slightly moved her arm to share the photo with him. They had reached a point in their relationship where words weren't necessary.

Bosch turned and looked down the corridor of Nathan Road. Whether it was a conscious move or not, he didn't want to see what he no longer had. From behind he heard Eleanor say, 'Wait a minute. There's a pattern here.'

Bosch turned back. 'What do you mean?' he said.

'We can do this, Harry. There's a pattern that will lead us right to her.'

Bosch felt a shiver run down his spine. He moved in close to Eleanor so he could see the photo. 'Show me,' he said, urgency fuelling each word.

Eleanor pointed to the photo and ran her fingernail along a line of air conditioners reflected in the window. 'In the building we are looking for, not every window has an air-conditioning unit. Some, like this room, have open windows. So there is a pattern. We have only part of it here because we don't know where this room is in relation to the building.'

'It's probably in the centre. The audio analysis picked up muffled voices cut off by the elevator. The elevator is probably centrally located.'

'That helps. We know because of the subway that we're close. OK, so let's say windows are dashes and AC boxes are dots. In this reflection we see a pattern for the floor she is on. You start with the room she is in—a dash—and then you go dot, dot, dash, dot, dash.' She tapped her nail on each part of the pattern on the photo. 'So that's our pattern. Looking up at the building, we'd be looking for it going left to right.'

She turned and looked up at the wall of buildings that ran the entire length of the street. 'Should we split up the buildings?'

'OK,' he said. 'Which one should I take?'

Pointing, she said, 'You take that one, I'll take this one and, Sun Yee, you check that one. If you get done, you leapfrog to the next building. We go till we find it. We know from the photo they're up high. I don't think the first eight floors matter.'

She was right, Bosch realised. It would make the search faster than he had anticipated. He stepped away and went to work on the building he was assigned, his eyes scanning back and forth floor by floor. Eleanor and Sun Yee separated and did the same.

THIRTY MINUTES LATER Bosch was halfway through scanning his third building when Eleanor called out.

'I've got it!'

Bosch headed back to her. She had her hand raised and was counting up the floors of the building across the street. Sun Yee soon joined them.

'Fourteenth floor.'

Bosch counted the floors, his eyes rising with his hopes. He got to the fourteenth level and identified the pattern. 'That's it.' He zeroed in on the window that would have been the one that caught the reflection in the video. It was closed now.

'This is Chungking Mansions,' Eleanor said, recognition in her voice.

'You know it?' Bosch asked.

'I've never been here but everybody knows about Chungking Mansions. It's the cheapest place in the city to stay and it's the first stop for every Third and Fourth World immigrant who comes here. Every couple of months you read about somebody being arrested or shot or stabbed and this is their address. It's like a postmodern Casablanca—all in one building.'

'Let's go.'

Bosch started across the street in the middle of the block, wading into slow-moving traffic, forcing taxis to stop and hoot their horns.

'Harry, what are you doing?' Eleanor yelled after him.

Bosch didn't answer. He made it across to the other side and went into Chungking Mansions.

It was like stepping onto another planet. The first thing that hit him was the smell. Intense odours of spices and fried food invaded his nostrils as his eyes became accustomed to the dimly lit Third World farmers' market that spread before him in narrow aisles and warrens. Six-foot-wide shop stalls offered everything from watches and cellphones to newspapers and foods. There was an edgy, gritty feel to the place that left Bosch casually checking his wake every few steps to see who was behind him.

He moved to the centre, where he came to an elevator alcove. There was a line fifteen people deep waiting for two elevators, except that one elevator was open, dark inside and obviously out of commission. There were two security guards at the front of the line checking to make sure everybody going up had a room key or was with somebody who had a key.

Bosch stood wondering how he was going to get to the fourteenth floor when Eleanor and Sun Yee caught him up. Eleanor grabbed him by the arm. 'Harry, enough with the one-man army! Don't run off like that.'

Bosch looked at her. It wasn't anger he saw in her eyes. It was fear. She wanted to be sure she wasn't without him when she faced whatever there was to face on the fourteenth floor.

'I just want to keep moving,' Bosch said.

'Then move with us, not away from us. Are we going up?'

'We need a key to go up.'

'Then we have to rent a room.'

'Where do we do that?'

Eleanor looked at Sun Yee. He nodded and led them to a row of counters with signs in multiple languages.

'You rent the room here,' Sun Yee said. 'There is more than one hotel.'

Bosch realised that what Sun Yee was saying was that there were multiple hotels within the building, all of them competing for the business of the cut-rate traveller.

'Ask which one has the fourteenth floor,' he said.

'There won't be a fourteenth floor.'

Bosch realised he was right. 'Fifteenth, Sun Yee. Which one has the fifteenth floor?'

Sun Yee went down the line asking about the fifteenth floor until he stopped at the third counter and waved Eleanor and Bosch over. 'Here.'

The man behind the counter looked like he had been there for forty years. His bell-shaped body seemed form-fitted to the stool he sat on. He was smoking a cigarette attached to a four-inch holder made of carved bone. He didn't like getting smoke in his eyes.

'Do you speak English?' Bosch asked.

'Yes, I have English,' the man said tiredly.

'Good. We want a room on the four—the fifteenth floor.'

'All of you? One room?'

'Yes, one room.'

'No, you can't one room. Only two persons.'

Bosch realised that he meant the maximum occupancy of each room was two people. 'Then give me two rooms on fifteen.'

The deskman slid a clipboard across the counter.

Bosch quickly scribbled his name and address on the registration form and slid the board back.

'ID, passport,' the deskman said.

Bosch pulled out his passport; the man checked it and handed it back.

'How much?' Bosch asked.

'How long you stay?'

'Ten minutes.'

The deskman moved his eyes over all three of them as he considered what Bosch's answer meant.

'Come on,' Bosch said impatiently. 'How much?' He reached into his pocket for his cash.

'Two room, one thousand-five hundred Hong Kong dollars.'

Sun Yee stepped forward and put his hand down over Bosch's money. 'No, too much.'

He started speaking quickly and authoritatively to the deskman, refusing to let him take advantage of Bosch. But Harry didn't care. He peeled fifteen hundreds off his roll and threw them on the desk.

'Keys,' he demanded.

The deskman disengaged from Sun Yee and swivelled round to the double row of cubbyholes behind him. He selected two keys from the slots but when Bosch put out his hand, the deskman withheld the keys.

'Key deposit one thousand.'

Bosch realised he should never have flashed his roll. He quickly pulled it again, this time holding it below the counter, and peeled off two more bills. He slapped them down on the counter. When the deskman finally offered the keys, Harry grabbed them and started back to the elevator.

The line for the elevators was now more than thirty people deep. The longest few minutes of Bosch's life were spent waiting to go up. Eleanor tried to calm his growing impatience by engaging in conversation.

'When we get up there, what's the plan?'

Bosch shook his head. 'No plan. We play it like it lays.'

'That's it? What are we going to do, just knock on doors?'

Bosch held up the photo of the reflection again. 'No. We know from this that our window is the seventh down on the side that fronts Nathan Road. When we get up there, we hit the seventh room from the end.'

'Hit?'

'I'm not knocking, Eleanor.'

Finally, it was their turn. The security guard checked Bosch's key and passed him and Eleanor towards the elevator door, but then put his arm out behind them and stopped Sun Yee. The elevator was at capacity.

'Harry, wait,' Eleanor said. 'Let's take the next one.'

Bosch pushed into the elevator. 'You wait if you want. I'm not.'

Eleanor hesitated for a moment and then stepped into the elevator. She called out something in Chinese to Sun Yee as the door closed.

The elevator moved slowly. It stank of body odour and fish. Bosch breathed through his mouth to try to avoid it. He realised he was also a contributor to the problem. The last time he'd showered was on Friday morning in LA. To him, that seemed like a lifetime ago.

Finally, the door opened on fifteen. By then the only passengers left were Bosch, Eleanor and two men who had pushed sixteen. Glancing at the two men, Harry stepped out of the elevator, his left hand behind his hip and ready to go for the gun the moment it was necessary. Eleanor came out behind him.

The elevator alcove was in the centre of an 'H' floor design. Bosch moved towards the hallway to the right because he knew this would be the side of the building fronting Nathan Road.

He immediately started counting doors and moved to the seventh door, room 1514. He felt his heart hit a higher gear as a charge went through him. This was it. This was what he was here for.

He leaned forward, putting his ear to the door's crack. He listened intently but heard no sounds from within the room.

'Anything?' Eleanor whispered.

Bosch shook his head. He put his hand on the knob and tried to turn it.

He didn't expect the door to be unlocked but he wanted a feel for the hardware and how solid it might be.

The doorknob was old and loose. Bosch dropped to one knee and looked closely at it. It would be a simple pick but there could be a bolt lock or a security chain inside. He pulled his badge wallet out. Before going through airport security he had slid his two best picks behind the badge, knowing that the two thin metal strips behind it would likely be mistaken for part of the badge on the X-ray. His plan had worked and now he removed the picks and quietly manoeuvred them into the doorknob lock.

It took him less than a minute to turn the lock. He held the knob without pushing the door open.

'Ready?' he whispered.

Eleanor nodded. Bosch then reached back under his jacket and pulled out the gun. He thumbed off the safety catch and looked at Eleanor. In unison, they mouthed the words *one, two, three* and he pushed the door open.

There was no security chain in place. The door moved all the way open and Bosch quickly entered the room. Eleanor came in right behind him.

The room was empty.

BOSCH STEPPED THROUGH the room to the tiny bathroom. He slapped the dirty plastic shower curtain back from a small, tiled showering space but it was empty. He walked back into the room and looked at Eleanor.

'She's gone.'

'Are you sure this is even the room?' she asked.

Bosch was. He had already looked at the pattern of cracks and nail holes on the wall over the bed. He took the folded photo print out of his jacket and handed it to her. 'This is the room.'

He put the gun back under his jacket and in the waistband of his trousers. He tried to keep the searing sense of futility and dread from engulfing him.

'There's got to be some sign that she was here,' Eleanor said, dropping down to look under the bed.

'Eleanor, she's not under the bed. She's gone and we need to keep moving. Call Sun Yee and tell him not to come up. Tell him to get the car.'

'No, this can't be. She can't be gone. We . . .'

Bosch came round the bed and leaned down behind her. He put his arms round her and pulled her up to standing.

'Come on, Eleanor, we have to go. We're going to find her.'

He ushered her towards the door, but she broke free and headed to the bathroom. She had to see it empty for herself.

'Eleanor, please.'

She disappeared into the room and Bosch heard her pull the shower curtain back. But then she didn't return.

'Harry!'

Bosch quickly crossed the room and entered the bathroom. Eleanor was lifting the wastebasket. At the bottom of the basket was a small wad of toilet paper with blood on it.

Eleanor retrieved it with two fingers and held it up. The blood had made a stain smaller than a dime. Harry knew that she was assuming that they were looking at their daughter's blood.

'We don't know what this means yet, Eleanor.'

His counsel was ignored. Her body language suggested a breakdown was coming. 'They drugged her,' she said. 'They put a needle in her arm.'

'We don't know that yet. Let's go downstairs and talk to the guy. We'll find out who rented the room on Friday.'

She didn't move. She stared at the blood and tissue like it was a red and white flower.

Bosch always carried sealable evidence bags in his coat pockets. He pulled one out and Eleanor put the wad in it. He put it into his pocket.

'OK, let's go.'

They finally left the room. Bosch had one arm round Eleanor's back and was looking at her face as they entered the hall. He half expected her to break free and run back to the room. But then he saw some sort of recognition flare in her eyes as she focused down the hall.

'Harry?'

Bosch turned, expecting it to be Sun Yee. But it wasn't. Two men were approaching from the end of the hall. Bosch realised that they were the men who had been the last passengers in the elevator going up. The moment they saw Harry and Eleanor, their hands went inside their jackets. Bosch saw one man close his grip and instinctively knew he was pulling a gun.

Bosch brought his right arm up to the centre of Eleanor's back and shoved her across the hall towards the elevator. At the same time he brought his left hand up behind his back and grabbed his gun. One of the men yelled something Bosch didn't understand and raised his weapon.

Bosch pulled his own gun and brought it round on aim. He opened fire at the same moment that shots were fired by one of the men down the hall. Bosch fired repeatedly, and continued after he saw both men go down.

Holding his aim, he moved forward on them. One was lying over the other's legs. One was dead; the other was barely alive and breathing shallowly, but at the same time he was still trying to pull his gun from the waistband of his trousers. Bosch saw that the hammer spur had got snagged in the waistband.

Bosch reached down and roughly pulled the gun loose. The man's hand dropped to the floor. Bosch slid the gun out of his reach.

'Where is she?' Bosch said. 'Where is she?'

The man made a grunting sound and blood dripped from his mouth down the side of his face. Bosch knew he would be dead in another minute.

Bosch heard a door open down the hallway and then quickly close. Most people in a place like this wouldn't want to get involved. Still, he knew it wouldn't be long before the police stormed the hotel on the report of a shooting. He turned back to the dying man.

'Where is she?' he repeated. 'Where's my—'

He saw that the man was dead.

'Shit!' Bosch got up and turned to Eleanor. 'They had to have—'

She was on the floor. Bosch rushed to her and dropped down to the floor. 'Eleanor!'

He was too late. Her eyes were open and as blank as the man's in the hallway.

'No, no, please, no. *Eleanor!*' He couldn't see any wound but she wasn't breathing. He shook her by the shoulders and got no response. He put one hand behind her head and opened her mouth with the other. He leaned forward to blow air into her lungs. But then he felt the wound. He pulled his hand out of her hair and it was covered in blood. He turned her head and saw the wound in the hairline behind her left ear. He realised she had probably been hit as he had pushed her into the alcove. He had pushed her into the shot.

'Eleanor,' he said quietly.

Bosch leaned forward and put his face down on her chest between her breasts. He smelled her familiar fragrance. He heard a loud, awful groan and realised it had come from himself.

For thirty seconds he didn't move. He just held her. Then he heard the elevator open and out stepped Sun Yee. His eyes went to Eleanor on the floor.

'Eleanor!' He rushed to her side.

'She's gone,' Bosch said. 'I'm sorry.'

'Who did this?'

Bosch started to get up. He spoke in a monotone. 'Over there. Two men fired on us.'

Sun Yee looked into the hallway and saw the two men on the ground. Bosch saw the confusion and horror on his face.

Bosch stepped back into the hall and picked up the gun he had pulled from the man's waistband. Tucking it into his own trousers, he went back to where Sun Yee was kneeling next to Eleanor's body, her hand in his.

'Sun Yee, I'm sorry. They took us by surprise.'

He waited a moment. Sun Yee said nothing and didn't move.

'We have to go,' Bosch said. 'I'm sure the police are on their way.'

He put his hand on Sun Yee's shoulder and pulled him back. Bosch knelt next to Eleanor and picked up her right arm. He wrapped her hand round the gun he had got from Sun Yee. He fired a shot into the wall, then carefully placed her arm back down on the floor, her hand still holding the gun.

'What are you doing?' Sun Yee demanded.

'Gunshot residue. Is the gun clean, or will it be traced back to whoever gave it to you?'

'It's clean.'

'Then let's go. We have to take the stairs. There's nothing we can do for Eleanor now.'

Sun Yee bowed his head for a moment and then slowly stood up.

They moved down the hall but Sun Yee suddenly stopped to examine the two men on the floor.

'Come on,' Bosch prompted. 'We have to go.'

Sun Yee finally followed. They hit the stairwell door and started down.

'They're not Triad,' Sun Yee said.

Bosch was two steps ahead. He stopped and looked back up at him.

'What? How do you know?'

'They're not Chinese. Indonesian, Vietnamese—I think Vietnamese.'

Bosch started down again and picked up the pace. As he moved he thought about this piece of information and couldn't see how it fitted with what was already known. When he got to the bottom, he opened the exit door a crack to get his bearings. He saw that the door opened on to a pedestrian alley that ran between Chungking Mansions and the building next door. Bosch could hear traffic and sirens close by.

The door was suddenly pushed closed. Bosch turned and Sun Yee had one hand flat on the door. He pointed angrily at Harry with the other.

'You! You get her killed!'

'I know. I know, Sun Yee. My case brought all of this—'

'No, they not Triad! *I told you.*'

Bosch stared at him for a moment, not comprehending.

'You show your money and they rob.'

Bosch now understood. He was saying that the two men lying dead with Eleanor had merely been robbers after Bosch's money. But there was something wrong. It didn't work. Harry shook his head.

'They were in front of us in the elevator line. They didn't see my money.'

'They were told.'

Bosch considered this and his thoughts came to the deskman. He already wanted to pay that man a visit. The scenario Sun Yee had spun made the need more immediate.

'Sun Yee, we need to get out of here. The police are going to close all the exits once they get up there and see what they have. Drive the car round to the front. I'm going back inside but I'll be at the front in five minutes.'

'What will you do?'

'You don't want to know.'

BOSCH WALKED OUT of the alley onto Nathan Road and immediately saw the crowd of onlookers gathered to watch the police response to the call inside Chungking Mansions. Police and fire rescue vehicles were arriving, causing traffic snarls and confusion. Bosch pushed his way through the crowd and got to the aisle where the hotel desks were. He saw that the diversion had worked in his favour. The aisle was empty.

When he got to the desk where he had rented the two rooms, he saw that the man on the stool was there with his back turned, shoving paperwork into a briefcase. It looked like he was getting ready to leave.

Bosch jumped over the counter and smashed into the man, knocking him to the floor. Bosch jumped on top of him and hit him twice in the face with his fist.

'No, please!' the man managed to spit out between punches.

Bosch quickly glanced back to make sure it was still clear. He then pulled the gun from behind him and pressed the muzzle into the man's chin.

'You got her killed, you motherfucker! And I'm going to kill you.'

'No, please! Sir, please!'

'You told them, didn't you? You told them I had money.'

'No, I have not.'

'Don't lie to me or I'll kill you right now. You told them!'

The man lifted his head off the floor. 'OK, listen, listen, please. I said nobody to get hurt. You understand? I said nobody to—'

Bosch pulled the gun back and brought it down hard on the man's nose. His head snapped back. Bosch pushed the barrel into his neck.

'I don't care what you said. They killed her! Do you understand that?'

The man was dazed and bleeding. 'I am very sorry, sir. Please don't—'

'OK, this is what you're going to do. You want to live, then you tell me who rented room fifteen-fourteen on Friday. Fifteen-fourteen. Right now.'

'OK, I tell you. I show you.'

Bosch pulled his weight back off him. The man was bleeding from the mouth and nose. Bosch quickly reached up and pulled the security fence down to the counter, indicating the desk was closed.

The man reached into his briefcase and pulled out a stack of room registration forms. Bosch saw his own on top. He reached over and grabbed it, and crumpled it into his coat pocket, all the while keeping his aim on the man.

'Friday, room fifteen-fourteen. Find it.'

The man put the forms on the back counter and started going through them. Bosch knew he was taking too much time. The police would come at any moment. If they caught him with a gun, he'd go to prison no matter what.

Looking at the gun as he placed it down prompted the realisation that he had left Eleanor lying dead and alone up there. It put a spear through Bosch's chest. He closed his eyes to try to push the thought away.

'Here it is.'

Bosch opened his eyes. The man was turning to him from the rear counter. Bosch heard a distinct metal snap. He saw the man's right arm start to swing round and knew there was a knife before he saw it. He moved forward and into the man, raising his left forearm to block the knife and driving his right fist towards his attacker's throat.

The knife tore through the sleeve of Bosch's jacket and he felt the blade slice into his forearm. But his punch to the throat sent the man backwards and he fell on the overturned stool. Bosch dropped on him again, grabbing his knife hand by the wrist and smashing it back repeatedly against the floor until the weapon clattered loose on the concrete.

Holding the man down by the throat, Bosch thought again about Eleanor lying dead up on fifteen. Her life and everything taken from her before she could even say a word. Before she could see her daughter safe.

Bosch raised his left fist and struck the man viciously in the ribs, again and again, until the man lapsed into unconsciousness.

Bosch was winded. He picked up the switchblade, folded it closed and dropped it into his pocket. Then he got up and shoved the fallen registration forms into the counterman's briefcase and closed it. He leaned over the counter to look out through the security fence. It was still clear in the aisle, though he could now hear announcements made through a megaphone coming from the elevator alcove. He knew that police procedure would be to shut the place down and secure it.

He raised the security gate two feet and then grabbed the gun and put it into his rear waistband. After checking to make sure he had left no blood on the counter, he climbed over with the briefcase and walked away.

As he moved, Bosch held his arm up to check the wound through the rip in his coat sleeve. It looked superficial but it was a bleeder. He pulled his coat sleeve up to bunch it around the wound and absorb the blood.

At the elevator alcove the police were herding everybody out to the street for questioning about what they might have heard or seen. Bosch knew he couldn't go through that process. He made a U-turn and headed down an aisle towards the other side of the building. He got to an intersection of aisles and caught a glimpse to his left of two men hurrying away from the police activity.

Bosch followed, realising he wasn't the only one in the building who wouldn't want to be questioned by the police.

The two men disappeared into a narrow passageway between two of the now-shuttered shops. Bosch followed them to a staircase down into a basement where there were rows of storage cages for the shopkeepers above. He saw the men heading towards a glowing red Chinese symbol over a door and knew it had to be an exit. The men pushed through and an alarm sounded. They slammed the door behind them.

Bosch ran towards the door and pushed through. He found himself in the same pedestrian alley he had been in earlier. He quickly walked out to Nathan Road and looked for Sun Yee and the Mercedes.

Headlights flashed from half a block away and Bosch saw the car waiting in front of the clot of police vehicles parked haphazardly in front of the entrance of Chungking Mansions. Sun Yee cruised up to him and Bosch got in the front.

'You took long time,' Sun Yee said.

'Yeah, let's get out of here.'

Sun Yee glanced at the briefcase with Bosch's bleeding knuckles wrapped around the handle. He said nothing and accelerated away from Chungking Mansions.

Bosch turned to look back at the building where they had left Eleanor. Somehow, Bosch had always thought they would grow old together. Their divorce didn't matter. Other lovers didn't matter. It had always been in the back of his mind that in the long run they would be together. Now all of that was gone and it was because of the choices he had made. He wasn't sure how he was going to live with it.

He leaned forward and put his head in his hands.

'Sun Yee, I'm sorry . . . I loved her, too.'

Sun Yee didn't respond for a long time and when he spoke, he brought Bosch out of the downward spiral and back into focus.

'We must find your daughter now. For Eleanor we will do this.'

Bosch straightened up and nodded. He then leaned forward and pulled the briefcase onto his lap. 'Pull over when you can. You have to look at this stuff.'

Sun Yee put several blocks between them and Chungking Mansions before pulling to a stop. They were across the street from a ramshackle market.

Bosch opened the briefcase and handed the unruly stack of hotel registration forms to Sun Yee. Most had been filled out in Chinese.

'What do I look for?' Sun Yee asked.

'Date and room number. Friday was the 11th. We want that and room fifteen-fourteen. It's got to be in that stack.'

Sun Yee started reading. Bosch looked out of the window at the market. Through the open entry points he saw rows of stalls, old men and women selling their wares under a flimsy roof of plywood and tenting. On a folding table near the entrance were papier-mâché items for sale to be burned. Bosch saw a row of tigers and wondered why a dead ancestor would need a tiger.

'Here,' Sun Yee said. He held a registration form.

'What's it say?'

'Tuen Mun. It is in the New Territories. This man lives there.'

'What's his name?'

'Peng Qingcai.'

Qingcai, Bosch thought. An easy jump to an Americanised name to use with girls at the mall might be Quick. Maybe Peng Qingcai was the boy Madeline had left the mall with on Friday.

'Can you find it?'

'Yes, I know this place.'

'Good. Let's go.'

Once they were on their way, Bosch shrugged off his jacket and rolled up his shirtsleeve to take a better look at the knife wound on his arm. Blood was finally clotting in the wound.

Sun Yee looked over at it quickly and then back at the road. 'Who did this to you?'

'The man behind the counter. He saw my money and set us up. I was so stupid.'

'It was a mistake.'

Sun Yee had certainly backed off his angry accusation in the stairwell. But Bosch wasn't backing off his own assessment. He had got Eleanor killed. 'Yeah, but I wasn't the one who paid for it,' he said.

Bosch pulled the switchblade out of the jacket pocket and reached to the back seat for the blanket. He cut a long strip off the blanket and wrapped it round the wound to keep blood from running down his arm. He pulled his jacket back on. Luckily it was black and the bloodstains weren't readily noticeable.

'Tell me about Tuen Mun,' he said.

'Very crowded,' Sun Yee said. 'Only Chinese. Heavy-duty Triad. It is not a good place for your daughter to be.'

Bosch didn't think it would be. But he saw one thing positive about it. Hiding a white girl might be hard to do without notice. If Madeline was being held in Tuen Mun, he would find her.

They would find her.

EIGHT

The vast geographic zone surrounding the Kowloon peninsula that was known as the New Territories had been added by lease to Hong Kong more than a century ago as a buffer against outside invasion of the British colony. When the lease was up and Hong Kong was transferred back to the People's Republic of China in 1997, the New Territories remained part of the Special Administrative Region, or SAR, which allowed Hong Kong to continue to function as one of the world's centres of capitalism and culture, a unique place in the world where East meets West. The NT was populated with the poorest and most uneducated citizens of the SAR. Crime was high and money scarce. The lure of the Triads was strong.

'Many pirates were here when I grew up,' Sun Yee said.

It was the first either he or Bosch had spoken in more than twenty minutes of driving as each man had lapsed into private thoughts. They were just entering Tuen Mun on a freeway. Bosch saw row after row of tall residential structures that were plainly government-built public housing estates. This was no gleaming skyline. It was drab and depressing, a fishing village turned into a massive vertical housing complex.

'What do you mean by that? You're from Tuen Mun?'

'I grew up here, yes. Until I was the age of twenty-two.'

'Were you in a Triad, Sun Yee?'

Sun Yee didn't answer. He acted like he was too busy engaging the turn signal and checking the mirrors as they exited the freeway.

'I don't care, you know,' Bosch said. 'I care about only one thing.'

Sun Yee nodded. 'I know.'

Bosch was wondering if Sun Yee was trying to tell him something by mentioning the pirates. 'Who were these pirates?' he asked.

'Smugglers. They came up the river from the South China Sea. They controlled the river.'

'What did they smuggle?'

'Everything. They brought in guns and drugs. People.'

'And what did they take out?'

It was a long moment before Sun Yee answered.

'Electronics. American DVDs. Children sometimes. Girls and boys.'

'And where do they go?'

'This depends on what they want them for. Some of it is sex. Some is organs. Many mainlanders buy boys because they have no sons.'

Bosch thought of the wad of toilet paper with the bloodstain on it. Eleanor had jumped to the conclusion that they had injected Madeline to sedate her. He now realised that they could have extracted blood rather than injected it, for blood typing.

Everything changed. His daughter's abductors may not simply be holding her until Bosch kicked Chang loose in Los Angeles. They might be preparing to move her or sell her into a netherworld of dark choices from which she would never return. He tried to push the possibilities out of the way.

'We have time,' he said, knowing full well he was talking to himself and not Sun Yee. 'Nothing's happened to her yet. They wouldn't do anything until they heard from LA.'

Bosch turned to look at Sun Yee and he nodded in agreement.

'We will find her,' he said. He pointed through the windshield at a government apartment tower so tall that Bosch had to lean down beneath the visor to see its roofline. 'We are here,' he said.

The building had open walkways along the front of every floor. Laundry hung over the walkway railings at intervals on almost every floor, turning the drab façade into a colourful mosaic that differentiated it from the duplicate buildings on either side of it. A sign in multiple languages over the tunnel-like entrance at the centre announced incongruously that the place was called Miami Beach Garden Estates.

'The address is on the sixth floor,' Sun Yee said after double-checking the Chungking Mansions registration form.

'Park it and we'll go up.'

Sun Yee nodded and drove past the building. At the next intersection he made a U-turn and drove back, pulling to the kerb in front of a playground that was surrounded by a ten-foot fence and crowded inside with children and their mothers. Bosch knew he had parked there as a safeguard against having the car stolen or vandalised while they left it alone.

They got out and walked towards the entrance to the building.

The passageway led to a bank of elevators where two women holding the hands of small children waited. A security guard sat behind a tiny counter but never looked up from his newspaper.

Bosch and Sun Yee followed the women onto the elevator. One of the women inserted a key in the control board and then pushed two buttons. Before she pulled out the key Sun Yee quickly reached over and hit the 6 button.

The first stop was on six. Sun Yee and Bosch moved down the walkway to the third door on the left side of the building. Bosch noticed that against the railing in front of the door of the next apartment down was a small altar with an ash can that was still smoking following a sacrifice to the hungry ghosts. The odour of burnt plastic was in the air.

Bosch took a position to the right of the door where Sun Yee had stopped. He swung his arm back underneath his coat and gripped the handgun.

Sun Yee looked at him and Bosch nodded that he was ready. Sun Yee knocked on the door and they waited.

No one answered.

He knocked again. This time louder.

No one answered.

Sun Yee stepped back from the door. 'What do you wish to do?'

Bosch looked down at the smoking ash can thirty feet away. 'Let's ask them next door if they've seen this guy around.'

Sun Yee led the way and knocked on the next door. This time it was opened. A small woman of about sixty peeked out. Sun Yee smiled and spoke to her in Chinese. Soon the woman relaxed and stood aside so they could enter.

As Bosch stepped over the threshold Sun Yee whispered to him, 'Five hundred Hong Kong dollars. I promised her.'

'No problem.'

It was a small two-room apartment. The first room served as the kitchen, dining room and living room. It was sparsely furnished and smelled of hot cooking oil. Bosch peeled five hundred-dollar bills off his roll and put them under a dish of salt that was on the kitchen table.

Sun Yee continued his conversation in Chinese. Bosch nodded and smiled and acted like he knew what was being said. Three minutes went by and then Sun Yee broke off the interview so he could summarise for Bosch.

'She is Fengyi Mai. She lives here alone. She said she has not seen Peng Qingcai since yesterday morning. He lives next door with his mother and his younger sister, He. She has not seen them either. But she heard them yesterday afternoon. Through the wall.'

Bosch thought about all of this for a few moments, before asking, 'She's sure it was yesterday that she saw him? What was he doing?'

While Bosch waited for the translation he watched the woman closely. Though she had maintained good eye contact with Sun Yee during the earlier questions, she began looking away while answering the latest questions.

'She is sure,' Sun Yee said. 'She heard a sound outside her door yesterday morning and when she opened it, Peng was there burning an offering. He was using her altar.'

Bosch nodded but he was sure the woman was lying about something.

'What did he burn?'

Sun Yee asked the woman. She looked down as she gave her answer.

'She said he burned paper money.'

Bosch stood up and went to the door. Outside he turned the ash can over on the walkway. Smoking black ash spread across the walkway. Fengyi Mai had obviously burned a sacrifice within the past hour or so. He grabbed an incense stick from the altar and used it to poke through the hot debris. For the most part it was all ash. Bosch pushed it around some more and soon uncovered a piece of melted plastic, charred black and shapeless.

He went back inside the apartment.

'Ask her when she last used the altar and what it was she burned.'

Sun Yee translated the answer. 'She used it this morning. She also burned paper money.'

'Ask her why she's lying.'

Sun Yee hesitated.

'Ask her.'

Sun Yee asked the question and the woman denied lying.

Bosch walked over to the table, picked up the bills and put them back in his pocket. 'Tell her we pay nothing for lies, but that I'll pay two thousand for the truth.'

The woman protested after hearing Sun Yee's translation but then Sun Yee's demeanour changed and he angrily barked at her and the woman clearly got scared. She put her hands together as if to beg his forgiveness and then walked into another room.

'What did you tell her?' Bosch asked.

'I told her she must tell the truth or she would lose her apartment.'

Bosch raised his eyebrows. Sun Yee had certainly kicked it up a notch.

'She believes I am police officer and you are my supervisor,' he added.

'How'd she get that idea?' Bosch asked.

Before Sun Yee could answer, the woman came back carrying a small cardboard box. She went directly to Bosch and handed it to him. Harry opened it and found the remains of a melted and burnt cellphone.

While the woman gave Sun Yee an explanation, Bosch pulled out his own cellphone and compared it to the burnt phone. Despite the damage, it was clear the phone the woman had retrieved from her ash can was a match.

'She said Peng was burning that,' Sun Yee said. 'It made a very foul smell that would be displeasing to the ghosts so she removed it.'

'It's my daughter's.'

'Are you sure?'

'I bought it for her. I'm sure.'

Bosch opened his own phone and scrolled through his photos until he found one of his daughter. 'Show her this. See if she's seen her with Peng.'

Sun Yee showed the phone to the woman and asked the question. The woman shook her head. Bosch didn't need the translation. He stood up and pulled out his money. He put 2,000 Hong Kong dollars on the table—less than $300 American—and headed to the door.

'Let's go,' he said.

THEY KNOCKED ON Peng's door again but got no answer. Bosch knelt down to untie and retie his shoe. He studied the lock as he did so.

'What do we do?' Sun Yee asked after Bosch stood back up.

'I have picks. I can open the door.'

Bosch could see reluctance cloud Sun Yee's face, even with the sunglasses.

'We watch first,' Sun Yee said. 'Peng could come back. He could lead us to Madeline.'

Bosch looked at his watch. It was half past noon. 'I don't think we have time. We have to keep moving if we are going to find her.'

Sun Yee turned and looked directly at Bosch. 'One hour. We watch. If we come back to open the door, you don't take the gun.'

Bosch nodded. He understood. Getting caught breaking and entering was one thing. Getting caught breaking and entering with a gun was about ten years of something else.

'OK, one hour.'

They returned to the car and Sun Yee said he wanted to move it to a less noticeable spot. He drove up the street and parked by a retainer wall that surrounded the trash bins for the building across the street. They still had a view of the door of Peng's apartment.

'I think we're wasting our time,' Bosch said. 'They're not coming back.'

'One hour, Harry. Please.'

Bosch noted it was the first time Sun Yee had called him by his name. It didn't placate him. He pulled the box out of his jacket pocket. He opened it up and looked at the phone.

'You watch the place,' he said. 'I'm going to work on this.'

The plastic hinges on the phone had melted and it broke in two when he applied too much pressure. The LCD screen was cracked and partially melted. Bosch put that part aside and concentrated on the other half. The battery compartment cover was melted, making it difficult to remove the battery. He used one of his picks to prise it out. Beneath it was the cradle for the phone's memory card.

It was empty.

'Shit!' Bosch threw the phone into the foot well. Another dead end.

He looked at his watch. It had been only twenty minutes since he had agreed to give Sun Yee the hour. But all of Bosch's instincts told him he had to get into that apartment. His daughter could be in there.

'Sorry, Sun Yee,' he said. 'You can wait here, but I can't. I'm going in.'

He leaned forward and pulled the gun out of his waistband. He wanted to leave it outside the Mercedes in case they were caught in the apartment and the police connected them with the car. He wrapped the gun in his daughter's blanket, opened the door and got out. He walked through an opening in the containment wall and put the bundle on top of one of the overfull trash bins. He would easily be able to retrieve it when he got back.

When he stepped out of the containment area, he found Sun Yee out of the car and waiting.

'OK,' Sun Yee said. 'We go.'

They started back to Peng's building.

'Let me ask you something, Sun Yee. Do you ever take those shades off?'

Sun Yee's answer came without explanation. 'No.'

Once again the security guard in the lobby never looked up. The building was big enough that there was always somebody waiting for an elevator with a key. In five minutes they were back in front of Peng's door. While

Sun Yee stood at the railing as a lookout, Bosch worked the lock.

'OK,' he said, when he got it open.

Sun Yee followed Bosch into the apartment.

Before he had even closed the door Bosch knew they would find death in the apartment. There was no overpowering odour, no blood on the walls, but after attending more than 500 murder scenes as a cop, he had developed what he considered a sense for blood. The fact that it could be his own daughter's made the recognition dreadful.

He held up his hand to stop Sun Yee from entering further. 'Don't touch anything and follow in my steps if you can.'

The apartment layout was the same as the unit next door. A two-room dwelling, this one shared by a mother with her two teenage children. There was no sign of any disturbance in the first room. There was a sofa that had a pillow and sheet haphazardly tossed on it and Bosch assumed the boy slept here while the sister and mother took the bedroom.

Bosch moved across the room and into the bedroom. A curtain was drawn across the window and the room was dark. With his elbow Bosch pushed up the wall switch and the light came on. The bed was unmade but empty. There was no sign of struggle or disturbance or death. Bosch looked to his right. There was a door that he guessed led to a bathroom.

He always carried latex gloves. He pulled a pair out of his pocket and put a glove on his left hand. He opened the door.

The small bathroom was awash in dried blood, splashed over the sink, the toilet and the tiled floor. There were spatter and drip lines on the back wall and the dirty white plastic shower curtain with flowers on it.

It would have been impossible to step into the room without stepping on one of the blood trails. But Bosch didn't worry about it. He had to get to the shower curtain. He had to know.

He quickly moved across the room and yanked the plastic back.

The shower stall was tiny, no bigger than an old phone booth. But some-one had managed to pile three bodies on top of each other in there.

Bosch held his breath as he leaned in to try to identify the victims. They were fully clothed. The boy, who was the biggest, was on top. He was face down atop a woman of about forty—his mother—who was sitting slouched against a wall. Both of their throats had been savagely cut from ear to ear.

Behind and partially underneath the mother—as if hiding—was the body of a young girl. Her long dark hair was covering her face.

'Ah God,' Bosch called out. 'Sun Yee!'

Soon he heard Sun Yee behind him and the sharp intake of breath.

'There's a girl on the bottom and I can't tell if it's Maddie,' he said. 'Put these on.'

He pulled another pair of gloves from his pocket and handed them to Sun Yee, who quickly snapped them on. Together they gently moved the two bodies until they could see the face of the girl beneath. She, too, had been slashed across the throat. Her eyes were open and looked fearfully at death. It tore Bosch's heart to see that look, but it wasn't his daughter's face.

'It's not her,' he said. 'It's gotta be her friend. He.'

Harry turned away from the carnage and went out to the bedroom. He sat down on the bed and exhaled loudly. 'What happened here?' he asked in a whisper.

He heard Sun Lee putting the bodies back as they had found them. Sun Yee stepped out of the bathroom and adopted his bodyguard stance. He said nothing. Harry noticed that there was blood on his gloved hands.

'Could another Triad have taken her from him? Then killed them all to cover the tracks?'

Sun Yee shook his head. 'That would have started a war. But the boy is not Triad.'

'What? How do you know that?'

'There is only one Triad in Tuen Mun. Golden Triangle. I looked and he did not have the mark.'

'What mark?'

Sun Yee hesitated for a moment, reached up to his mouth and pulled down his lower lip. On the soft inside skin there was a blurred black-ink tattoo of two Chinese characters. Bosch assumed they meant Golden Triangle.

'So you are in the Triad?'

Sun Yee released his lip and shook his head. 'No more. It has been more than twenty years.'

'I thought you can't just quit a Triad. If you leave, you leave in a box.'

'I made a sacrifice and the council allowed me to leave. I also had to leave Tuen Mun. This is how I went to Macau.'

'What kind of sacrifice?'

Sun Yee looked even more reluctant than when he'd shown Bosch the tattoo. But slowly he reached up to his face again, this time removing his sunglasses. For a moment Bosch noticed nothing wrong, but then he realised that Sun Yee's left eye was a prosthetic. He had a glass eye. There was a slightly noticeable scar hooking down from the outside corner.

'You had to give up an eye to quit the Triad?'

'I do not regret my decision.' He put his sunglasses back on.

Between Sun Yee's revelations and the horror scene in the bathroom, Bosch was beginning to feel like he was in some sort of medieval painting. He reminded himself that his daughter was still alive and out there.

He stood up. 'OK, I don't know what happened here, but we have to stay on the trail. There's got to be something in this apartment that will tell us where Maddie is. We've got to find it and we're running out of time.'

For the next twenty minutes the men searched the apartment. They found nothing useful until they got to the kitchen and Bosch noticed that like the apartment next door, there was a dish of salt on the table. Only here the salt was piled higher. Someone had built the granules into a mound. Bosch ran his fingers through the pile and found a small square of black plastic that he recognised as the memory card from a cellphone.

'Got something.'

Sun Yee turned from a kitchen drawer he had been looking through.

Bosch held up the memory card. 'It was in the salt.' He was sure it was the card missing from his daugher's phone. He wanted to go to work on it right away but decided that extending their stay in the apartment was not the smart move. 'Let's get out of here,' he said.

Bosch moved to the window and looked through the curtain down to the street before giving the all-clear sign. Sun Yee opened the door and they quickly exited. Bosch glanced behind him as he stepped away from the door and saw that the old woman next door was on the walkway, kneeling in front of her altar. Bosch did a double take when he saw that she was using a candle to burn one of the real hundred-dollar bills he had given her.

Bosch turned and moved down the walkway in the opposite direction. He knew he was in a world beyond his understanding. He only had to understand his mission to find his daughter. Nothing else mattered.

BOSCH RETRIEVED THE GUN and as soon as he was back in the car he took out his phone, an exact duplicate of his daughter's. He removed the battery and memory card and slid the card from his daughter's phone into the cradle. He replaced the battery, closed the compartment and waited for the phone to boot up. When the phone was ready, he quickly went to the call records. There were none. The page was blank.

'There's nothing on here. No record of any calls,' he said to Sun Yee as they headed away from the building. He went to the email file and again found the screen empty. 'Nothing transferred with the card,' he said, agitation growing in his voice.

'This is common,' Sun Yee said calmly. 'Only permanent files go on the memory card. Look to see if there are any videos or photos.'

Using the little ball roller in the middle of his phone's keyboard, Bosch went to the video icon and selected it. The video file was empty. He clicked on the photo icon and here he found a list of stored JPEG photos.

'I've got photos.'

One by one he started opening the photos, but none seemed recent. They were photos of Madeline's friends and from school trips but did not appear to be in any way related to her abduction.

'Nothing,' he reported to Sun Yee.

He kept trying, moving across the screen and clicking on icon after icon in the hope of finding a hidden message. Finally, he found Madeline's phone book.

'Her phone book's on here.'

He opened the file and saw the list of contacts. He didn't know all of her friends and didn't know which names might be out of place. He clicked on the listing for *Dad* and got a screen that had his own cell and home numbers but nothing that shouldn't be there.

He went back to the list and moved on, finally finding what he thought he might be looking for when he got to the Ts. There was a listing for Tuen Mun that contained only a phone number.

Sun Yee pulled into a long, thin park that ran along the river and under one of the bridges. 'We go here until we know where we are going.'

Bosch held the phone out to him. 'This is the only number not listed under a name.'

'Why would she have this number?'

'That's the point. She wouldn't. We have to assume her phone was taken away from her. Peng was probably using it during the abduction to set up the deal. He probably saved this number to the card. Either because he was using it a lot or he wanted to leave a trail if something happened. This is why he hid the card in the salt. So somebody would find it.'

Sun Yee took the phone and studied the screen. 'This is a cell number.'

'How do you know?'

'It begins with a nine. This is a cell designation in Hong Kong.'

'OK, what do we do? It might belong to the guy who has my daughter.'

Sun Yee stared out at the river, trying to come up with an answer.

'We could text him,' he said. 'Maybe he will respond to us.'

'Yeah, try to deke him. Maybe we get a location from him.'

'What is "deke"?'

'Fake him out. Decoy him. We act like we know and set up a meet. He gives us his location.'

Sun Yee pondered this while continuing to watch the river. A barge was slowly making its way south towards the sea.

'He may recognise that number and know it is a deke,' Sun Yee finally said. 'We should use my phone. The message should be sent in traditional Chinese. To help make it real.'

'Right. Good idea.'

Sun Yee pulled his cellphone out and asked for the number Bosch had found. He opened up a text field but then hesitated. 'What do I say?'

'Well, we need to put some urgency into it. Make it seem like he has to respond, and then has to meet.'

They talked about it for a few minutes and finally came up with a text that was simple and direct. Sun Yee translated and sent it. In Chinese, the message said: *We have a problem with the girl. Where can we meet?*

'OK, we wait,' Bosch said.

Bosch checked his watch. It was 2 p.m. He had been on the ground in Hong Kong for nine hours and not only was he no closer to his daughter but he had also lost Eleanor Wish for ever. He glanced over at the phone in Sun Yee's hand, hoping for a quick return to the message.

It didn't come.

Minutes of silence went by as slowly as the boats on the river. Bosch tried to concentrate his thoughts on Peng Qingcai and the chain of events that had led to the abduction of his daughter.

'This all comes back to me, Sun Yee. I made the mistake that allowed all of this to happen.'

'Harry, there is no reason to—'

'No, wait. Just hear me out. You need to know all of this because you might see something I don't.'

Sun Yee said nothing and Bosch continued.

'It's all starts with me. I was working a case with a Triad suspect in LA. I couldn't get any answers so I asked my daughter to translate the Chinese markings on a tattoo. I sent her a photo. I told her it was a Triad case and she couldn't show the tattoo or talk about it with anybody. But that was my mistake. Telling that to a thirteen-year-old was like announcing it to the world—her world. She'd been hanging out with Peng and his sister. They were from the other side of the tracks. She probably wanted to impress them. She told them about the case and that's where this all started.'

He looked over at Sun Yee but couldn't read his face.

'What tracks?' he asked.

'It's just an expression. They weren't from Happy Valley, that's all that means. And like you said, Peng wasn't a part of any Triad in Tuen Mun but maybe he knew people, maybe he wanted to get in. Maybe he thought this might be his ticket in. He told someone what he had heard. They put it together with LA and told him to grab the girl and send me the video. But from there, something happened. Something changed. Maybe Peng offered her to the Triad up here and they took her. Only they still didn't take him. Instead, they killed him and his family.'

Sun Yee shook his head slightly. 'But why would they kill his family?'

'Look at the timing, Sun Yee. The lady next door heard the voices through the wall in the late afternoon, right? By then I was on the plane and they somehow knew it. They couldn't risk that I would find Peng or his sister or mother. So they eliminated the threat.'

Sun Yee incisively zeroed in on something Bosch had left out. 'How did they know you were coming on the plane?'

Bosch nodded. 'Good question. I think they knew because from the start there has been a leak in the investigation back in LA. Somebody tipped the suspect that we were onto him and that made him try to split. That was why we had to arrest him before we were ready and why they grabbed Maddie.'

'You don't know who?'

'Not for sure. But when I get back, I'll find out. And I'll—'

Sun Yee's hand vibrated. He had received a text. Bosch leaned over to look as Sun Yee read. The message, in Chinese, was short.

'What's it say?'

'Wrong number.'

'Shit. He didn't accept the deke.'

'What now?'

'Send another message. Tell him we meet or we go to the police.'

'Too dangerous. He might decide just to get rid of her.'

'Not if he has a buyer lined up. He might hurry up the deal and that's the chance we take, but he won't get rid of her.'

'We don't know if this is the right person.'

Bosch shook his head. He knew Sun Yee was right. Shooting messages into the dark was too risky.

'Sun Yee, do you have anybody in casino security who could run this number down and get us a name and billing address?'

Sun Yee considered the question, then shook his head. 'No, this is not possible. There will be an investigation because of Eleanor . . .'

Bosch understood. Sun Yee had to do what he could to limit the blow-back on his company. Bosch started thinking of an alternate plan. David Chu back in LA might have sources that could run down the name and address. He might also be the leak in the investigation. But it could be anyone in his unit or another police department they were working with.

'OK, I think I might know someone.'

Bosch replaced his own card in his phone and when it had rebooted he made the call to Chu, checking his watch. It was almost midnight in Los Angeles.

Chu answered after one ring. 'Detective Chu.'

'David, it's Bosch. Sorry to call so late.'

'Not late at all. I'm still working.'

Bosch was surprised. 'On the Li case? What's happening?'

'Yes, I spent a good part of the evening with Robert Li. I am trying to convince him to cooperate with a prosecution of Chang for extortion.'

'Is he going to?'

'So far no. Have you found your daughter?'

'Not yet. But I have a line on her. That's where I need your help. Can you run down a Hong Kong cell number for me?'

There was a pause before Chu answered. 'Harry, the police there are much more capable of this than I am.'

'I know, but I'm not working with the police on this. I can't risk the potential for a leak. I'm close. I've tracked her all day and it's down to this number. I think it belongs to the man who has her. Can you help me?'

Chu didn't respond for a long moment.

'If I help you, my source on this will be within the Hong Kong Police, you know that, right?'

'You don't have to tell them the reason you need the information.'

'But if things blow up over there, it could come back to me.'

Bosch began to lose his patience but tried to keep it out of his voice.

'Look, there isn't a lot of time. Our understanding is that she is being sold. Most likely today. Maybe right now. I need this information, Dave. Can you get it for me or not?'

This time there was no hesitation.

'Give me the number.'

CHU SAID he would need at least an hour. Bosch hated the idea of giving up so much time when every minute could be the minute his daughter changed to the next set of hands, but he had no choice. He closed the phone call by telling Chu not to share his request with anyone inside the department.

The minutes went by very slowly and felt very costly. Bosch reviewed his moves, going back to the moments he examined the body of John Li. He came to realise fully that his relentless pursuit of the killer had put others in jeopardy. His daughter. His ex-wife. A whole family in Tuen Mun. The burden of guilt he would now carry was so heavy he was not sure he was up to it.

For the first time he put *if* into the equation of his life. If he got his daughter back, he would find a way to redeem himself. *If* he never saw her again, there could be no redemption.

All things would end.

These realisations made him physically shudder and he turned and opened the car door. 'I'm going to take a walk.'

He stepped out and closed the door before Sun Yee could ask him a question. There was a path that went along the river and he started walking it, his head down, his mind on dark thoughts.

Soon he became aware of a horn honking behind him and he glanced back. He saw Sun Yee standing outside the car, excitedly waving him back. Bosch started trotting back.

Sun Yee dropped back into the car and Bosch jumped in beside him.

'What?'

'Another message. A text.'

'What's it say?'

'It says, "What problem? Who is this?"'

Bosch nodded. The sender was still feigning ignorance. He didn't know what this was about, yet he had sent this text unbidden and this told Bosch that they were closing in on something.

'How do we respond?' Sun Yee asked.

Bosch didn't answer immediately. He was thinking.

'OK, send him back a text. Say no text because it's not safe. Say you want to meet in person.'

'That's it? They ask what the problem is. I don't answer?'

'No. The longer we keep this going, the more time we give Maddie.'

Sun Yee nodded. He typed in the message Bosch suggested and sent it. 'Now we wait again,' he said.

Bosch didn't need the reminder. But something told him the wait would not be long. The deke was working and they had someone on the other end of the text on the hook. He had no sooner come to this conclusion than another text came in on Sun Yee's phone.

'He wants to meet,' Sun Yee said, looking at the screen. 'Five o'clock at Geo.'

'What's that?'

'A restaurant at the Gold Coast, an hour's drive from here. Very famous. It will be very crowded on a Sunday afternoon.'

Bosch had to consider that the person they were dealing with was playing them, sending them an hour out of the way. Before committing to the meeting he first needed to check on what Chu had come up with. As Sun Yee started the car, Bosch called Chu's number again.

'Detective Chu.'

'It's Bosch. It's been an hour.'

'Not quite but I'm still waiting. I made the call and haven't heard back.'

'Did you talk to somebody?'

'Uh, no, I left a message. I guess because it's so late he might not be—'

'It's not late, Chu! It's late there, not here. Did you make the call or not?'

'Harry, please, I made the call. I just got mixed up. It's late here, it's Sunday over there. Maybe because it's *Sunday* he isn't as tied to his phone as he normally is. I will call you as soon as I have something.'

'Yeah, well, it might be too late by then.'

Bosch closed the phone. He was sorry he had trusted Chu.

'Nothing,' he said to Sun Yee.

NINE

They got to the Gold Coast in forty-five minutes. It was a resort on the western edge of the New Territories that catered for travellers from mainland China as well as Hong Kong. A tall gleaming hotel rose above Castle Peak Bay and open-air restaurants crowded the promenade that edged the harbour.

The Geo was wisely chosen by the text contact. It was sandwiched between two similar open-air restaurants and all three were heavily crowded. An arts and crafts show on the promenade doubled the number of people in the area and the places from which an observer could hide from view.

Sun Yee dropped Bosch at the entrance to the Gold Coast and drove on. As he walked through the hotel, Bosch stopped in the gift shop and bought sunglasses and a baseball-style hat with the hotel's golden emblem on it. He also bought a map and a throwaway camera.

By ten to five, Bosch had made his way to a restaurant called Yellow Flower, which was next to and afforded a full view of the Geo. The plan they had hatched was simple. They wanted to identify the owner of the phone number in his daughter's contact list and follow him when he left the Geo.

As he waited to be seated, Bosch surveyed the three crowded restaurants. Several large parties, whole families joined together for a Sunday-afternoon meal, were easy for him to discount because he didn't expect their man to be in a party. Even so, he quickly realised how daunting the task of spotting the contact would be.

He was led to a bad table in a corner that they passed off on singles but which had a view of all three restaurants. He checked his watch again and then spread the map out on the table. He made one more survey of the restaurants but did not see any likely candidates for the contact. No one like him, sitting by himself wearing sunglasses or any other sort of disguise. He began to think that the contact had got wise to their charade and had deked them instead.

He checked his watch just as the second hand swept towards the twelve and it would be five o'clock. Sun Yee's first text would go out at five, saying he was caught in traffic and would be late.

Bosch looked out across the restaurants, hoping to see a quick movement, somebody glancing at a text on their phone.

'Hello, sir. Just one?' A waitress had come up to his table.

Bosch answered without looking at her, his eyes moving from person to person at the tables in Geo. 'Can you bring me a cup of coffee for now? Black.'

'OK, sir.'

He could feel her presence move away. Bosch spent another minute with his eyes on the crowd. He expanded the search to include Yellow Flower and the third restaurant, called Big Sur. He saw a woman talking on a cellphone but nobody else using a phone.

Bosch's own phone buzzed in his pocket. He pulled it out and answered, knowing it would be Sun Yee.

'He answered the first text. He said, "I am waiting." That's all.'

'I didn't see anyone,' Bosch said. 'Where are you?'

'At the bar at the back of Big Sur. I didn't see anyone.'

'OK, ready for the next one?'

'Ready.'

Bosch opened the menu and studied it while keeping his right hand on the table so he could see his watch. Sun Yee would send the next text at 5.05.

The waitress brought his coffee and asked Bosch to order. The hint was clear. Order or move on. They needed to turn the table.

'OK, just bring me some rice with shrimp.' He handed her the menu so she would go away.

The waitress left him and he resumed his watch on the restaurants. Still he picked up nothing that fitted. The woman he had noticed before took another call. She was sitting at a table with a little boy.

Bosch's phone vibrated on the table.

'Got another response,' Sun Yee said. 'If I'm not there in five minutes, the meeting is off.'

'And you didn't see anybody?'

'Nothing. I'll send the next one at five ten.'

'OK.'

Bosch closed the phone. They had designed the third text as the one that would finally draw the contact out. The message would say that Sun Yee was cancelling the meeting because he had spotted a tail and believed it was the police. He would urge the contact to leave Geo immediately.

The waitress came and put down a bowl of rice. The shrimp on top were whole, their distended eyes cooked white. He pushed the bowl away.

His phone buzzed.

'Harry, it's Chu.'

Bosch checked his watch. It was time for the last text. 'I gotta call you back.'

He closed the phone and once more looked out across the tables of the three restaurants, hoping for the needle-in-the-haystack moment that would reveal the contact. Somebody reading a text, maybe typing a response.

Nothing came. The futility of the plan began to open a hollow in his chest. His eyes moved to the table where the woman and boy had sat and he saw that they were gone. He swept the restaurant and saw them leaving. The woman was moving fast, dragging the boy by the hand.

Bosch opened his phone and punched in a call to Sun Yee.

'The woman and the boy coming your way. I think it might be her.'

'She got the text?'

'No, I think she was sent to make the contact. The texts went off site. We have to follow the woman. Where's the car?'

'Out front.'

Bosch stood up, put three hundred-dollar bills down on the table and headed towards the exit.

SUN YEE was already in the car waiting at the front of Yellow Flower. Bosch ducked into the car and Sun Yee immediately pulled away into the traffic.

'They are in the white Mercedes a block and a half ahead.'

'Is she driving?' Bosch asked.

'No, she and the boy got into a waiting car. A man was driving.'

'OK, you got them? I need to make a call.'

'I have them.'

As Sun Yee followed the white Mercedes, Bosch called Chu back.

'It's Bosch.'

'OK, I got some information through HKPD. But they were asking me a lot of questions, Harry.'

'Give me the information first.' Bosch pulled out a notebook and pen.

'OK, the phone number you gave me is registered to a company. Northstar Seafood and Shipping. Northstar is one word. It's located in Tuen Mun, up in the New—'

'I know. You have the exact address?'

Chu gave him an address on Hoi Wah Road and Bosch repeated it out loud. Sun Yee nodded his head. He knew where it was.

'OK, anything else?' Bosch asked.

'Yes. Northstar is under suspicion, Harry.'

'What's that mean? Suspicion of what?'

'I couldn't get anything specific. Just of illegal shipping and trade practices. Like I said, just questions about why I was tracing the number.'

'What did you tell them?'

'That it was a blind trace. The number was found on a piece of paper in a homicide investigation. I said I didn't know the connection.'

'That's good. Is there any name associated with this phone number?'

'Not directly, no. But the man who owns Northstar is Dennis Ho. He is forty-five years old and that's all I could get without making it seem like I was working something specific. Does it help?'

'It helps. Thanks.'

Bosch ended the call and then updated Sun Yee on what he knew.

'Have you heard of Dennis Ho?' he asked.

Sun Yee shook his head. 'Never.'

Bosch knew they had to make a major decision.

'We don't know if this woman has anything to do with this,' he said, pointing ahead at the white Mercedes. 'We could just be spinning our wheels here. I say we break off this and go direct to Northstar.'

'We don't need to decide yet. We are already heading towards the waterfront. They may be going there.'

Bosch nodded. Both angles of investigation were still in play.

FOR THE NEXT HALF-HOUR they edged the coastline on Castle Peak Road, always keeping the Mercedes in sight. They drove without speaking. They had reached a point where they knew time was short and there was nothing else to say. Either the Mercedes or Northstar would lead them to Maddie Bosch or it was likely they would never see her again.

As the vertical build-up of housing estates in Central Tuen Mun appeared ahead, Bosch saw the turn signal on the Mercedes engage.

'They're turning left,' he warned.

'That's a problem,' Sun Yee said. 'The industrial waterfront is ahead. They are turning towards residential neighbourhoods.'

They were both silent for a moment, hoping a plan would materialise.

'Which way?' Sun Yee finally asked.

Bosch felt a tearing inside. His choice here could mean his daughter's life. Instinctively he came to the same conclusion he had reached after the call from Chu.

'Let her go,' he finally said. 'We go to Northstar.'

Sun Yee kept going straight and they passed the white Mercedes as it took the left. Bosch glanced out of the window at the car as it slowed down. The man driving glanced at him but only for a second.

'Shit,' Bosch said. 'He looked at me. The driver. I think they knew we were following them. I think we had it right—she's part of this.'

'Then this is good. If they knew we were following, then turning away from the waterfront could be an effort to lead us away from Northstar.'

'Let's hope you're right.'

Soon they entered an area filled with ramshackle warehouses and packing plants lined along the wharfs and piers. River barges and medium-sized seafaring boats were docked, sometimes two and three abreast. Several fishing boats were moored out in the harbour. All of it seemed abandoned for the day. No work on Sunday.

The traffic thinned and Bosch began to worry that the casino's slick black Mercedes would be too noticeable as they approached Northstar. Sun Yee must have been thinking the same thing. He pulled into a parking lot.

'We are very close,' he said. 'I think we leave the car here.'

'I agree,' Bosch said.

They got out and walked the rest of the way in, scanning in all directions for lookouts.

Northstar Seafood and Shipping was located on wharf seven. A large green warehouse with Chinese and English printing on its side fronted the dockside and a pier extended out into the bay beyond it. Four seventy-five-foot net boats with black hulls and green pilothouses were tied up on either side of the pier. Docked at the end was a bigger boat with a large crane jutting skywards.

From his viewpoint at the corner of a warehouse on wharf six, Bosch could see no activity on the docks and boats. He was beginning to think he had made a terrible mistake in not keeping the tail on the white Mercedes. Then Sun Yee tapped his shoulder and pointed down the pier.

Bosch followed his aim to the crane. The steel arm extended from a platform that sat atop a rail system fifteen feet over the deck of the boat, which was obviously designed to go out to sea and relieve smaller net boats of their catch so that they could continue to harvest. The crane was controlled from a small booth on the upper platform, and in the tinted windows of the booth Bosch could see a man silhouetted by the sun beyond the boat.

Bosch pulled himself back round the corner with Sun Yee. 'Bingo,' he said, his voice tightening with the sudden blast of adrenaline.

Bosch was now convinced that his daughter was on that boat. But getting to the boat without the lookout spotting them seemed impossible. They could wait for him to come down for a break, but there was no telling when that would be. Waiting defied the urgency growing in Bosch's chest.

He checked his watch. It was almost six. It would be at least two hours before total darkness. They could wait and then make a move. But two hours could be too long. The text messages had put his daughter's abductors on the alert. They could be about to make some sort of move with her.

As if to drive this possibility home, the deep throb of a marine engine suddenly sounded from the wharf. Bosch stole a glimpse round the corner and saw exhaust rising from the stern of the last boat on the wharf. And now he saw movement behind the windows of the pilothouse.

He ducked back. 'They started the boat,' he reported.

'How many did you see?' Sun Yee asked.

'At least one inside the pilothouse and one up on the crane. We need to do something. Now.'

He was tempted to move round the corner and go down the wharf shooting. He had a fully loaded .45 and liked his chances. He'd seen worse in the tunnels in Vietnam. Eight bullets, eight dragons. And then there would be him. Bosch would be the ninth dragon, as unstoppable as a bullet.

'What's the plan?' Sun Yee asked.

'I go in and I get her. If I don't make it, I'll make sure none of them do either. Then you go in and get her and put her on a plane out of here. You've got her passport in your trunk. That's the plan.'

Sun Yee shook his head. 'They will be armed. This plan is not good.'

'You got a better idea? We can't wait for dark. That boat's about to go.'

Bosch moved to the edge and took another look. Nothing had changed. The boat was rumbling on idle but still tied to the end of the pier. It was almost as if they were waiting for something. Or someone.

Bosch ducked back and calmed himself. He considered everything around him. Maybe there was something other than a suicide run at this.

He looked at Sun Yee. 'We need a boat. With a small boat we could create a distraction on the other side. Enough for somebody to go down the pier without being seen.'

Sun Yee nodded. 'Yes, a boat could work. You want me to get one?'

'Yeah. I'm going down the pier to get my daughter,' Bosch said.

Sun Yee reached into his pocket and pulled out the car keys. 'Take the keys. When you have your daughter, drive away. Don't worry about me.'

Bosch shook his head. 'We'll get someplace nearby but safe and then I'll call you. We'll wait for you.'

Sun Yee nodded. 'Good luck, Harry.'

'And good luck to you,' Bosch said.

After Sun Yee left, Bosch kept his back against the front wall of the warehouse and prepared to wait. He had no idea how Sun Yee would commandeer a boat but he trusted that somehow he would.

He turned to look round the corner of the warehouse and make another check of activities on the Northstar boat when he saw the white Mercedes approaching from the south.

Bosch slid down the wall to make himself less noticeable. Nets hung out to dry from the rigging of two boats between him and the approaching car also gave him camouflage. He watched as the car turned onto wharf seven and then headed down the pier towards the crane boat.

Bosch did some quick computing and concluded that the man behind the wheel was the man whose phone number was on his daughter's phone. He had sent the woman and child—probably his wife and son—inside Geo as decoys who would help him identify the person who had been texting him. Spooked by Sun Yee's last message, he had dropped them off at some safe spot, and then driven to wharf seven where Bosch's daughter was being held.

It was a lot to string together considering the few known facts he had, but Bosch believed he was on target and that something was about to happen that wasn't part of the original plan. He was hurrying things up or—worse—getting rid of the merchandise.

The Mercedes stopped in front of the crane boat. The driver jumped out and quickly moved across a gangway onto the boat. He yelled something to the man in the booth, but did not break stride as he headed to the pilothouse.

For a moment, there was no further movement. Then Bosch saw the man step out of the crane booth and start climbing down from the platform. After reaching the deck he followed the Mercedes man into the pilothouse.

Bosch knew that this was his chance to move down the pier unseen. He pulled out his phone and called Sun Yee. The phone rang eight times and then went to message.

'Sun Yee, where are you? The Mercedes man is here and they left the boat unguarded. Get back here and be ready to drive. I'm going in.'

Bosch pocketed the phone and stood up. He checked the crane boat one last time, then bolted down the pier holding the gun in a two-handed grip, up and ready.

STACKS OF EMPTY CRATES on the pier afforded Bosch partial cover but the last twenty yards to the gangway of the crane boat were wide open and exposed. He picked up speed and quickly covered the distance, ducking at the last moment behind the Mercedes idling next to the gangway, noting the distinctive sound and smell of the diesel engine. He peeked over the line of the trunk and saw no reaction to his moves coming from the boat. He jumped from cover and moved quickly across the gangway to the pilothouse. He pressed himself against the wall next to the door.

Harry slowed his breathing and listened. He heard nothing over the sound of the throbbing engines other than the wind through the rigging of the boats on the pier. He turned to look in through a small square window in the door. He saw no one inside. He quietly opened the door and entered.

The room was the operation centre of the boat. Besides the wheel, Bosch saw glowing dials and screens. Against the back wall were bunks with a curtain that could be pulled to for privacy.

On the floor on the forward left was an open hatch with a ladder leading down into the hull. Bosch crouched next to the opening. He heard men's voices below, at least three of them. The language spoken was Chinese. He did not hear his daughter's voice, but he knew she was down there, too.

Bosch moved to the boat's control centre and zeroed in on two side-by-side switches with red lights above them. He turned one switch off and immediately heard the hum of the engines decrease by half. He had killed an engine.

He waited five seconds and turned the other switch, killing the second engine. He then moved to the rear corner of the room, pulled the curtain closed halfway and waited. He knew he would be in a blind spot for anyone coming up the ladder from the hull. He returned his gun to his belt and took the switchblade out of his coat pocket.

Soon he heard running steps from below. This told him the meeting of the men below was in the forward section of the hull. He counted only one set of approaching steps. That would make it easier.

A man began to rise through the hatch, his back to the bunks. Without looking round he moved quickly to the controls, and looked for a reason for the engine stall. He found nothing wrong and went through procedures to restart the engines. Bosch quietly crawled out of the bunk and the moment the second engine trundled to life, he put the point of the switchblade against the man's spine.

Grabbing him by the collar, Bosch whispered, 'Where's the girl?'

The man said something in Chinese.

'Tell me where the girl is.'

The man shook his head.

Bosch roughly yanked him out through the door and bent him over the side. The water was twelve feet below.

'Can you swim, asshole? Where's the girl?'

'No . . . speak,' the man managed to say. 'No speak.'

Keeping the man down over the rail, Bosch looked around for Sun Yee—his translator—but didn't see him.

Where the hell was he?

The momentary distraction allowed the man to make a move. He swung an elbow backwards into Bosch's ribs. It knocked Bosch back into the side wall of the pilothouse. The man spun round and raised his hands to attack. Bosch prepared to cover himself, but the man's foot came up first, kicking Bosch's wrist and knocking the knife into the air.

The man quickly waded in with both fists, striking with short, powerful impacts to the midsection. Bosch felt the air explode out of his lungs just as another kick came up and hit him below the chin.

Bosch went down. He tried to shake off the impact but his eyesight started to close into tunnel vision. His attacker calmly stepped away and Bosch heard the switchblade scrape on the deck as he picked it up. Struggling for consciousness, Bosch reached behind his back for the gun.

'Can you swim, asshole?' said the man in clear English.

Bosch pulled the gun from behind his back and fired twice. The first shot only ticked the man's shoulder, but the second caught him in the chest. He went down with a look of surprise on his face.

Harry slowly pulled himself up onto his hands and knees. He knew he had to move quickly. The gunshots would have been heard by the men in the boat.

Just as he got to his feet a riot of gunfire erupted from the direction of the bow. Bullets zinged over his head and ricocheted around. Bosch ducked behind the pilothouse. He came up and found a line of sight through the windows of the structure. He saw a man advancing with pistols in each hand. Behind him was the open bow hatch through which he had climbed.

Bosch knew he had only six rounds left. He needed to go on the offensive and take the gunman out quickly and efficiently.

He looked around and saw a row of rubber docking bumpers secured along the rear gunwale. He put the gun into his belt loop and then grabbed one of the bumpers out of its receptacle. He edged back to the rear window of the pilothouse and looked through the structure again. The gunman had chosen the port side of the pilothouse and was preparing to move to the stern. Bosch stepped back and hurled the bumper over the top of the pilothouse. While it was still in the air he started moving down the starboard side, pulling his gun out as he moved.

He got to the front of the pilothouse just as the gunman was ducking away from the flying bumper. Bosch opened fire, hitting the man repeatedly until he went down on the deck without getting off a single shot.

Bosch moved in and made sure the man was dead. He then threw his empty .45 over the side and picked up the dead man's weapons—two more Black Star semiautomatics.

Bosch knew at least one more man was below in the hold with his daughter. He stuck the two guns in his belt and took the ladder down like a fireman, locking his feet around the vertical bars and sliding into the hull. At the bottom he dropped and rolled, pulling out his weapons.

Bosch's eyes adjusted to the dim light and he saw that he was in an empty bunk room that opened on a central passageway. The only light came from the overhead hatch down in the bow. Between Harry and that point were six compartment hatches—three on each side of the passageway. The last hatch on the left was wide open. Sticking one of the guns back in his belt, he started to move, the remaining gun up and ready.

He moved down the passageway checking the compartments, finding each empty but obviously not used recently to haul fish. Steel-walled and windowless, each chamber had a ground layer of detritus of cereal and other food boxes and empty water containers. Fishing nets refashioned as hammocks hung on hooks bolted to the walls. There was a putrid smell that had nothing to do with the catch the vessel once hauled. This boat carried human cargo.

The last stop in the passageway was the open hatch. Bosch crouched low and moved into the compartment in one fluid stride.

It too was empty.

But it was different. There was no trash here. A battery-powered light hung from a wire attached to a hook on the ceiling. There was an upturned shipping crate stacked with unopened cereal boxes, packs of noodles and gallon jugs of water. Bosch looked for any indication that his daughter had been kept in the room, but there was no sign of her.

Bosch heard the hinges on the hatch behind him screech loudly. He turned just as the hatch banged shut. He watched the seal on the upper-right corner turn into the locked position and immediately saw that the internal handles of the four-point locking system had been removed. He was being locked in. He waited for the next lock to turn, and the moment the bolt started to rotate Bosch fired both guns into the door. He heard someone call out as if surprised or hurt. He then heard a banging sound out in the hallway as a body hit the floor.

Bosch moved to the hatch and tried to turn back the bolt with his hand. It was too small for his fingers to find purchase. In desperation, he stepped back and threw his shoulder into the door, hoping to snap the rusting lock assembly. But it didn't budge.

He was locked in.

He moved back close to the hatch and tilted his head to listen. There was only the sound of the engines running now. He banged the heel of one of the guns loudly on the metal hatch.

'Maddie?' he called out. 'Maddie, are you here?'

No response. He banged again on the hatch, this time even louder.

'Give me a sign, baby. If you're here, make some noise!'

Again there was no response. Bosch pulled out his phone and opened it to call Sun Yee. But he saw he had no signal.

Harry leaned his sweating forehead against the hatch in defeat. He opened his collar another button and slid down the rusting metal until he was sitting with his knees up on the floor. He was trapped in a place as claustrophobic as the tunnels he had once inhabited in Vietnam, and his daughter wasn't even on the boat. The battery on the overhead light was dying and soon he would be left in darkness. Defeat and despair overtook him. He had failed his daughter and he had failed himself.

BOSCH SUDDENLY LOOKED UP from his contemplation of failure. He had heard something. Above the drone of the engines, he'd heard a banging sound.

He jumped up. He heard another banging sound and knew somebody was checking the compartments in the same way he had.

He pounded on the hatch with the heels of both guns. He yelled above the clanging echo of steel on steel.

'*Sun Yee? Hey! Down here!*'

There was no response, but then the bolt of the upper-right seal turned. The door was being unlocked. Bosch stepped back and waited. The bottom-left seal was turned next and then the hatch door slowly began to open. Bosch raised the guns, unsure if he had anything left to fire.

In the dim light of the passage he saw Sun Yee's face.

'*Where the fuck you been?*'

'I was looking for a boat and—'

'I called you. I told you to come back.'

Bosch moved forward into the passageway. The Mercedes man was lying face down on the floor a few feet from the hatch. Hoping to find him still alive, Harry turned him over, rolling him into the slop of his own blood.

He was dead.

'Harry, where is Madeline?' Sun Yee asked.

'I don't know. Everybody's dead and I don't know!'

Unless . . . One final plan began to work into Bosch's brain. One final chance. The white Mercedes. Gleaming and new. The car would have all the extras, including a navigation system, and the first address in its stored data would be the Mercedes man's home. They would go there. They would go to the home of the Mercedes man and Bosch would find his daughter.

Harry studied the body in front of him. He presumed he was looking at Dennis Ho, the man behind Northstar. He patted the dead man's pockets, looking for car keys, but he found none and just as quickly as his plan had formed Bosch began to feel it disappear.

'His keys! We need his keys or we—'

He suddenly stopped. He realised he had missed something. When he had made his run on the pier and ducked for cover behind the white Mercedes, he had heard and smelled the car's diesel engine. The car had been left running.

At the time it meant little to Bosch because he was sure his daughter was on the boat. Now he knew different. There was only one reason why Dennis Ho would have left his car running. He intended to come back to it. Not *with* the girl, because she was not on the boat. But to *get* the girl once the storage compartment in the hull was ready and it was safe to transfer her.

Bosch charged up the ladder and out of the pilothouse. He crossed the gangway and ran to the driver's door of the white Mercedes and flung it open. He checked the back seat and found it empty. He then looked for a button that would open the trunk.

Finding none, he turned the car off and grabbed the keys. Moving to the back of the car, he pushed the trunk button on the ignition key.

The trunk lid lifted automatically. There, lying on a blanket inside, was his daughter. She was blindfolded and gagged. Her arms were pinned to her body with several wrappings of duct tape. Her ankles were taped together as well.

Bosch cried out at the sight of her. 'Maddie! It's me, baby! It's Dad!' He went to work quickly on the blindfold and the gag. 'You're safe now, Maddie. You're safe!'

As the gag came loose the girl let out a shriek that pierced her father's heart and would stay with him always. It was at once an exorcism of fear, a cry for help and the sound of relief and even joy.

'Daddy!'

She started to cry as Bosch lifted her out of the trunk. Sun Yee was suddenly there and helping.

'It's going to be OK now,' Bosch said. 'It will all be OK.'

Bosch used the teeth of one of the keys to start cutting through the tape. He noticed that Madeline was still wearing her school uniform. The moment her arms and hands were free she grabbed Bosch round the neck and squeezed with all her life.

'I knew you would come,' she said between gasping sobs.

Bosch didn't know if he had ever heard words that meant more to him. He held her just as tightly in his own arms.

'Are you hurt, Maddie? If they hurt you, we need to get you to—'

'No, I'm not hurt.'

He pushed back from her and put his hands on her shoulders as he studied her eyes. 'You sure? You can tell me.'

'I'm sure, Dad. I'm fine.'

'OK. Then we need to go to the airport.' He turned to Sun Yee. 'Can you get us to the airport?'

'No problem.'

Bosch put his arm round his daughter and they started to follow Sun Yee. It wasn't until they got to the car that she asked the question he'd been dreading.

'Dad?'

'What, Maddie?'

'Where's Mom?'

BOSCH DIDN'T ANSWER her question directly. He simply told his daughter that her mother could not be with them at the moment but had packed a bag for her, and that they needed to leave Hong Kong.

The explanation seemingly bought Harry some time to consider how and when he would give the answer that would alter the rest of his daughter's life. When they got to the black Mercedes, he put her in the back seat before going to the trunk to grab the backpack. He didn't want her to see the bag Eleanor had packed for herself.

He got in the front passenger seat and handed the backpack to her. He then checked his watch and gave Sun Yee a nod.

'Let's go.'

Sun Yee started driving, proceeding out of the waterfront area at a brisk but not attention-getting pace.

After a few minutes of silence, Bosch turned and glanced at his daughter. She was staring out through the window. There were tears on her cheeks.

'Maddie, you all right?'

Without looking away from the window, she said, 'She's dead, isn't she?'

'What?'

Bosch knew exactly who and what she was talking about but was trying to stretch time, to put off for as long as possible the inevitable.

'I'm not stupid, you know. You're here. Sun Yee's here. She should be here. She would be here but something's happened to her.'

Bosch felt an invisible punch hit him square in the chest. Madeline was hugging the backpack in front of her and still looking out of the window.

'Maddie, I'm sorry. I wanted to tell you but this wasn't the right time.'

'When is the right time?'

Bosch nodded. 'You're right. Never.'

He reached across the seat and put his hand on her knee but she immediately pushed it away. It was the first sign of the blame that he would always carry.

'I'm so sorry. I don't know what I can say. Your mother wanted only one thing, Maddie. To get you home safe. She didn't care about anything else, including herself.'

Madeline put her hands over her eyes. 'It's all my fault.'

Bosch shook his head even though she wasn't looking at him. 'Maddie, no. Listen to me. Don't ever say that. Don't even think that. It's not your fault. It's my fault. Everything here is my fault.'

She didn't respond. She hugged the backpack closer and kept her eyes on the roadside as it passed by in a blur.

AN HOUR LATER they were at the drop-off kerb at the airport. Bosch helped his daughter out of the Mercedes and then turned to Sun Yee. They had said little in the car. But now it was time to say goodbye and Bosch knew his daughter could not have been rescued without Sun Yee's help.

'Sun Yee, thank you for saving my daughter.'

'You saved her. Nothing could stop you, Harry Bosch.'

'What will you do? The police will come to you about Eleanor, if not everything else.'

'I will handle these things and make no mention of you. This is my promise. No matter what is said to you, know this to be the truth.'

Bosch nodded. 'Good luck,' he said.

'Good luck to you, too.'

Bosch shook his hand and then stepped back. After another awkward pause, Madeline stepped forward and hugged Sun Yee. Bosch saw the look on his face and knew that no matter their differences, Sun Yee had found some sort of resolution in Madeline's rescue.

'I am so sorry,' Madeline said.

Sun Yee stepped back and broke the embrace. 'You go on now,' he said. 'You have a happy life.'

They left him standing there and headed into the terminal.

BOSCH FOUND the first-class window at Cathay Pacific and bought two tickets on the 11.40 p.m. flight to Los Angeles, having to use two credit cards to cover the cost. He didn't care. He knew that first-class passengers were accorded special status that moved them quickly through security checks and first onto planes, even if they were a dishevelled man with blood on his jacket and a thirteen-year-old girl with tears on her cheeks. Bosch also understood that his daughter had been left traumatised by events and, while he couldn't begin to know how to care for her in this regard, he instinctively felt that any added comfort couldn't hurt.

As expected, they breezed through security. Now they had three hours to kill.

'You hungry, Mads?'

'Not really.'

'When did you last eat something?'

She had to think. 'I had a piece of pizza at the mall on Friday. Before . . .'

'OK, we've got to eat, then.'

They took an escalator up to an area where there were a variety of restaurants overlooking the duty-free shopping mecca. Bosch chose a sit-down restaurant in the centre of the concourse that had good views of the shopping level. His daughter ordered chicken fingers and Bosch ordered a steak and French fries.

'So am I going to live in LA with you now?'

Bosch nodded. It seemed like the first time she had said more than two words since they had said goodbye to Sun Yee. 'I think so.'

He studied her face for a reaction. It remained unchanged—blank stare over cheeks streaked with dried tears and sadness.

'I want you to,' Bosch said. 'And last time you were over you said you wanted to stay.'

'But not like this.'

'I know.'

'Will I ever go back to get my things and say goodbye to my friends?'

Bosch thought for a moment before responding. 'I don't think so,' he finally said. 'I might be able to get your things sent. But you're probably going to have to email your friends, I guess.'

'At least I'll be able to say goodbye.'

Bosch nodded and was silent, noting the obvious reference to her lost mother. She soon spoke again, jumping the conversation to a new place.

Her mind was like a balloon caught in the wind, touching down here and there on unpredictable currents.

'Are we, like, wanted by the police here?'

Bosch looked around to see if anyone had heard the question.

'I don't know,' he said quietly. 'We could be. I could be. But I don't want to find out here. It will be better to deal with all of this from LA.'

Then she asked a question that hit Bosch between the numbers. 'Dad, did you kill those men that had me? I heard a lot of shooting.'

Bosch thought about how he should answer—as a cop, as a father—but didn't take too long. 'Let's just say that they got what they deserved. And that whatever happened was brought on by their own actions. OK?'

'OK.'

When the food came they stopped talking and ate ravenously. Bosch had chosen the table so that he had a good view of the security gate. He had no idea if he was even on any police radar yet but he had cut a deadly path across Hong Kong and had to remain alert to it catching up with him.

'Are you going to finish your French fries?' Maddie asked.

Bosch turned his plate so she could reach the fries. 'Have some.'

When she reached across the table, her sleeve pulled back and Bosch saw the bandage in the crook of her elbow. He thought of the bloodstained tissue Eleanor had found in the room at Chungking Mansions.

Bosch pointed at her arm. 'Maddie, how did you get that?'

She put her other hand over the wound as if that could stop all consideration of it. 'Please, Dad, I don't want to talk about it. Not now.'

'OK, sweetheart, we'll talk about it when you want.'

After the meal they headed down to the shopping area. Bosch bought a complete set of new clothes in a men's store and a pair of jogging shoes and arm sweatbands in a sports shop. Maddie declined the offer of new clothes.

After the shopping, they headed to the first-class lounge and signed up to use the shower facilities. Bosch showered quickly because he didn't want to be separated from his daughter for long. Before getting dressed he checked the wound on his arm. It was clotted and beginning to scab over. He used the armbands he had just bought as a double-bandage over the wound.

Once he was dressed he bundled his old clothes and shoes together and buried them under the paper towels and other debris in the trash can.

Feeling somewhat refreshed and ready for the long flight ahead, he stepped out and looked around for his daughter. He didn't see her anywhere in the lounge and went back to wait for her near the entrance to the women's shower room. After fifteen minutes and no sign of Madeline, he started getting worried. He went and asked the woman behind the counter to send an employee into the shower room to check on his daughter.

The woman said she would do it herself. Bosch followed and then waited when she went in. He heard the shower running when the door was opened. He then heard voices and soon the woman stepped out.

'She's in the shower and she said everything is fine. She said she was still going to be a while.'

'OK, thanks.'

The woman went back to her position and Bosch checked his watch. The boarding of their flight would not start for at least half an hour. He went back to the lounge. He couldn't imagine where Madeline's thoughts were. He knew she needed help and that he was completely unequipped to provide it. His governing thought was simply to get her back to Los Angeles and to go from there.

Just as the flight was announced, Madeline came down the hallway. She had changed her clothes and her hair was slicked back and wet. Somehow, she was cold.

'Are you all right?' Bosch asked.

'I just wanted a long, hot shower.'

'I understand. They called our flight. We need to go.'

They left the lounge and made their way to the gate. Bosch saw no more than the usual gathering of security. Their tickets were taken, their passports checked, and they were allowed to board.

A flight attendant informed them that they were the only ones flying first class and that they could pick their seats. It felt like they had the plane to themselves. Bosch wasn't planning on taking his eyes off his daughter until they were in Los Angeles.

As the loading of the plane neared completion, the pilot came on the speaker and announced that they would spend thirteen hours in the air. That meant they would land in Los Angeles at 9.30 on Sunday night, two hours before they had taken off in Hong Kong.

Bosch did the maths and reckoned that it would add up to a thirty-nine-hour day before it was over. The longest day of his life.

Eventually, the big plane was cleared for takeoff and it trundled down the runway, picked up speed and climbed into the dark sky. Bosch breathed a little easier as he looked out of the window and saw the lights of Hong Kong disappear below the clouds. He hoped never to be back again.

His daughter reached across the space between their seats and grabbed his hand. He looked over and held her eyes. She had started to cry again. Bosch squeezed her hand.

'It's going to be all right, Maddie.'

She nodded and held on.

TEN

It was almost midnight by the time they got to the house on Woodrow Wilson Drive. Bosch carried the backpack into the guest room and his daughter followed.

'Now that you'll be living here full-time, we can fix up this room any way you want,' Bosch said. 'I know you had a lot of posters and stuff back in Hong Kong. You can do whatever you want here.' There were two cardboard boxes stacked in the corner that contained old case files Bosch had copied. 'I'll get these out of here,' he said.

After moving them into his bedroom Bosch sat down on the bed and looked at his daughter. She was still standing in the middle of the room. The look on her face cut Bosch deeply. He could see the reality of the situation hitting her. It didn't matter that she had repeatedly voiced a desire to live in LA. She was now here permanently and grasping it was a daunting task.

'Maddie, I just want to tell you something,' he said. 'I've only had to be your father for two or three weeks a year. That was easy. This is going to be hard. I am going to make mistakes and I'm going to need you to be patient with me while I learn. But I promise to do the best I can.'

'OK.'

'Now, what can I get you? Are you hungry? Tired? What?'

'No, I'm fine. I guess I shouldn't have slept so much on the plane.'

'Doesn't matter. Sleep is always good. It heals.'

She nodded and looked awkwardly around the room. It was a basic guest room. A bed, chest of drawers and a table with a lamp.

'Tomorrow we'll get you a TV to put in here. And also a computer and a desk. We'll need to go shopping for a lot of things.'

'I think I need a new cellphone. Quick took mine.'

'Yeah, we'll get you a new phone, too. I have your memory card from the old one, so you won't lose your contacts.'

She looked over at him and he realised he had made a mistake.

'You have the card? Did you get it from Quick? Was He there?'

Bosch held his hands up in a calming gesture and shook his head. 'I never met Quick or his sister, He. I found your phone but it was broken. All I got was the memory card.'

'She tried to save me. She found out what Quick was going to do and tried to stop it. But he kicked her out of the car.'

Bosch waited for her to say more but that was it. He wanted to ask her many questions about the brother and sister and everything else but his role as father overtook his role as cop. Now wasn't the right time. He had to get her calmed and settled. There would be time later to be a cop.

He studied her face and she seemed to be drained of emotion. She still looked tired, even after all the sleep on the plane.

'Everything's going to be OK, Maddie. I promise.'

She nodded. 'Um, do you think I can just be alone for a little while?'

'Sure you can. It's your room. I think I should make some calls, anyway.' He got up and headed to the door. 'You tell me if you need anything, right?'

'Yes, Dad. Thanks.'

He closed the door and went out to the living room. He pulled his phone and called David Chu.

'It's Bosch. Sorry to call so late.'

'No problem. How is it going over there?'

'I'm back in LA.'

'You're back? What about your daughter?'

'She's safe. What's the status on Chang?'

There was a hesitation before Chu answered. 'Well, he walks in the morning. We don't have anything to file on him.'

'What about the extortion?'

'I took a last run at Li and Lam today. They won't file a formal complaint. They're too scared. Li said somebody already threatened him.'

Bosch thought about the threatening call he had received on Friday. He assumed it was the same caller. 'So Chang walks away scot-free in the morning and heads to the airport,' he said. 'He gets on a plane and we never see him again.' Bosch shook his head, his rage boiling over. 'Goddamn those motherfuckers.'

Bosch realised his daughter might be able to hear him. He opened one of the living-room sliders and stepped out onto the rear deck.

'They were going to sell my kid,' he said. 'For her organs.'

'God,' Chu said. 'I thought they were just trying to intimidate you.'

'Yeah, well, they took her blood and she must've matched somebody with a lot of money because the plan changed.'

'Is she back here with you, Harry?'

'I told you, she's safe.'

Bosch knew that Chu would read his indirect answer as a lack of trust, but what was new? He couldn't help it after the day he'd had.

Bosch ended the call and stood against the railing looking out at the night. It was almost midnight on a Sunday and yet the freeway down below was packed. There was certainly something safe about being home, but he couldn't help thinking about what had been lost and left behind. It was like the hungry ghosts had followed him across the Pacific. Could the forces that grabbed Maddie in Hong Kong find her here? It seemed unlikely, but he couldn't risk leaving her alone. The problem was that he wasn't plugged into the neighbourhood, never socialised with people on his street. He didn't know who would be safe and any different from a complete stranger chosen from the child-sitter ads in the phone book. It was beginning to dawn on him that he had no business raising his own daughter.

'Dad? Are you all right?'

He turned. His daughter stood in the open doorway.

'Sure, baby. Why?'

She stepped out onto the deck and stood next to him at the rail. 'It sounded like you were mad when you were on the phone.'

'It's about a case. It's not going well. Listen, I don't want you left alone. Maybe in the morning we should take a look at the school down at the bottom of the hill. I could take you down there and you could check it out. Maybe sit in a class or two. How would that be? I know the assistant principal and I trust her. She'll take care of you.'

His daughter hooked a strand of hair behind her ear and stared out at the view for a few moments before answering.

'I guess that would be OK.'

'OK, good, then we'll do that. I'll call in the morning and set it up.'

'Dad?'

'What, baby?'

'I heard what you said on the phone. About them selling me for my organs. Is that true?'

'I don't know, darling. I don't know what their exact plan was.'

'Quick took my blood. He said he was going to send it to you. You know, so you could run DNA and know that I was really kidnapped.'

'Yeah, well, he betrayed you and he got what he deserved.'

She immediately turned towards him and Bosch realised he had slipped up.

'What do you mean? What happened to him?'

Bosch didn't want to go down the slippery slope of lying to his daughter. He also knew that his daughter obviously had feelings for Quick's sister, if not for Quick himself. She probably still didn't understand the depth of his betrayal.

'He's dead.'

Her breath caught in her throat and she brought her hands to her mouth. 'Did you . . . ?'

'No, Maddie, I didn't do it. I found him dead at the same time I found your phone. I guess you somehow liked him, so I'm sorry. But he betrayed you, baby.' Bosch turned from the railing. 'Let's go in now.'

'What about Quick's sister, He?'

Bosch stopped and looked back at her. 'I don't know about He.'

He moved to the door and went inside. There, he had lied to her for the first time. It was to save her from some grief, but it didn't matter. He could already feel that he was beginning to slide down the slope.

His phone buzzed in his pocket. He saw that it was Lieutenant Gandle.

'I hear you're back. You got your daughter?'

'Yeah, I was going to call you. She's safe. She's going to live with me.'

'What happened back there? Anything I need to worry about?'

Bosch wasn't sure what to tell him. He decided to put it off.

'I'm hoping there's no blowback. But you never know.'

'I'll let you know what I hear. Are you coming in?'

'Uh, I need to take a couple of days to get my daughter settled and in school and stuff. I want to get her some counselling.'

'Are you OK, Harry?'

'I'm fine.'

'I guess Chu told you about Chang getting kicked. I'm sorry. There's nothing we could do.'

'Yeah, Chu told me.'

SUE BAMBROUGH, the assistant principal of the school, had agreed to allow Madeline to attend eighth-grade classes and see if she liked the school. When Bosch checked in at the office to pick her up, Bambrough asked him to sit down and then proceeded to tell him that his daughter was still in class and assimilating quite well.

Bosch already knew Bambrough. A couple of years earlier a neighbour who had a child attending the school asked him to speak to the kid's class about police work and crime. Bambrough was a bright, hands-on administrator who had interviewed Bosch at length before allowing him to address any students. She had taken a hard line on the quality of police work in the city but her arguments were well thought out and articulated. Bosch respected her.

'Class ends in ten minutes,' Bambrough said. 'I'll take you to her then. There is something I would like to talk to you about first, Harry.'

Bosch sat down in front of her desk. 'What is it?'

'Well, your daughter's quite a storyteller. She was overheard during the midmorning break telling other students that she just moved here from Hong Kong because her mother was murdered and she got kidnapped. My concern is that she's self-aggrandising in order to—'

'It's true. All of it.'

'What do you mean?'

'She was abducted and her mother was killed trying to rescue her.'

'Oh dear God! When did this happen?'

Bosch regretted not telling Bambrough the whole story when they had talked that morning. He had simply told her that his daughter was going to be living with him and wanted to check the school out.

'Over the weekend,' he answered. 'We arrived last night.'

Bambrough looked like she had taken a punch. 'Over the weekend? Are you telling me the truth?'

'Of course I am. She's been through a lot. I know it might be too soon to put her in school, but . . . I'll take her home now and if she wants to come back, I'll let you know.'

'Well, what about counselling? What about a physical examination?'

'I'm working on all of that.'

'Don't be afraid to get her help. Children like to talk about things. It's just that sometimes it's not to their parents. I have found that children have an innate ability to know what they need in order to heal themselves and survive. Without her mother and with you being new at full-time parenting, Madeline may need an outside party to talk to.'

Bosch nodded at the end of the lecture. 'She'll get whatever she needs. What would I need to do if she wants to go to school here?'

'Just call me. You're in the district and we have the space. There will be some minor paperwork for enrolment and we'll have to get her records from Hong Kong. You'll need her birth certificate and that's about it.'

Bosch realised that his daughter's birth certificate was probably back in the apartment in Hong Kong. 'I don't have her birth certificate. I'll have to apply for one. But I have her passport,' he offered.

'Well, we can make do with that until you get the birth certificate. I think the important thing now is to take care of your daughter psychologically. You need to get her talking to a counsellor.'

'Don't worry, I will.'

A chime sounded the change of classes and Bambrough stood up. They left the office and walked down a main hallway. The campus was long and narrow because it was built on the hillside. Bosch saw Bambrough still trying to absorb the idea of what Madeline had just been through and survived.

'She's a strong kid,' he offered.

'She'll have to be after an experience like that.'

Children were crowding the hallway as they changed classes. Bambrough saw Bosch's daughter before he did.

'Madeline,' she called.

Bosch waved. Maddie had been walking with two girls, seeming already somehow to be making friends. She said goodbye to them and rushed over.

'Hi, Dad.'

'Hey, how'd you like it?'

'It was fun, I guess.'

Her voice was reserved and Bosch didn't know if that was because the assistant principal was standing right there with them. He decided to save her from the small talk.

'Well, are you ready, Mad? We're going to go shopping today, remember?'

'Sure, I'm ready.'

Bosch looked at Bambrough. 'Thank you for doing this and I'll be in touch.'

His daughter chimed in with her own thanks and they left the school. Once they got in the car, Bosch started up the hill to their house.

'So, what did you really think, Mad?'

'Uh, it was OK. It's just not the same, you know?'

'Yeah, I know. We can look at some private schools. There's a few nearby.'

'I think that school will be fine,' she said after some thought.

'You sure?'

'I think so. Can I start tomorrow?'

Bosch looked over at her and then back at the curving road. 'That's sort of fast, isn't it? You just got here last night.'

'I know, but what am I supposed to do? Sit and cry all day?'

'No, but I thought if we took things kind of slow, it might—'

'I don't want to fall behind. School started last week.'

Bosch thought for a few moments about what Bambrough had said about kids knowing what they need to heal. He decided to trust his daughter's instincts.

'OK, if you feel it's right. I'll call Mrs Bambrough back and tell her you want to enrol.'

As Bosch pulled into the carport next to the house his phone buzzed.

It was Ignacio Ferras. 'Harry, I hear you're back and your daughter's safe.'

He sure was late getting the news. Bosch unlocked the kitchen door and held it open for his daughter.

'Yeah, we're good. What are you working on?'

'Oh, just a few things. Writing up some summaries on John Li.'

'What for? That one's over. We blew it.'

'I know, but I need to file the search-warrant returns with the court. That's sort of why I'm calling. You bugged out Friday without leaving any notes on what you found on the searches of the phone and the suitcase.'

'Yeah, well, I didn't find anything. That's one reason why we didn't have a case to file, remember?'

Bosch threw his keys on the dining-room table and watched his daughter go down the hall to her room. He felt a growing annoyance with Ferras. At one point he had embraced the idea of mentoring the young detective, but he was now finally accepting the reality that Ferras would never recover from being wounded in the line of battle. Physically, yes. Mentally, no. He would never be the full package again. He would be a paper pusher.

'So put down zero returns?' Ferras asked.

Bosch momentarily thought of the business card from the taxi service in Hong Kong. It had been a dead end and wasn't worth putting into the search-warrant return. 'Yeah, zero returns. There was nothing.'

'And nothing on the phone.'

Bosch suddenly realised something. 'Nothing *on* the phone, but did you guys go to the company for the records?'

Chang may have wiped all call records off his phone but he wouldn't have been able to touch the records kept by his cellular service carrier.

There was a pause before Ferras answered. 'No, I thought—you had the phone, Harry. I thought you contacted the phone company.'

'I didn't because I was heading to Hong Kong.'

All phone companies had protocols for receiving and accepting search warrants. It was a simple thing to do but it had fallen through the cracks. Now Chang had been kicked loose and it was probably too late.

'Goddamnit,' Bosch said. 'You should've been on that, Ignacio.'

'Me? That's bullshit, man. You had the phone. You're going to blame me for this?'

'I'm blaming us both. Yeah, I could've done it, but you *should*'ve made sure it was done. But you didn't because you left early and you let it slide. You've been letting the whole job slide, partner.'

There, he had said it.

'And you are full of shit, partner. You mean because I'm not like you, losing my family to the job and then *risking* my family to the job, that I'm letting it slide? You don't know what you're talking about.'

Bosch was stunned silent by the verbal shot. Ferras had hit him right in the spot. Finally, he shook it off and came back.

'Ignacio,' he said calmly, 'I don't know when I will be back into the squad room this week, but when I get in there, we're gonna talk.'

'Fine. I'll be here.'

'Of course you will. You're always in the squad room. I'll see you then.'

Bosch closed the phone before Ferras could protest. Bosch was sure

Gandle would back him when he asked for a new partner. He went back into the kitchen to grab a beer and take the edge off the conversation. He opened the refrigerator but stopped. He was going to be driving his daughter around the Valley shopping in the afternoon.

He closed the refrigerator and walked down the hallway. The door to his daughter's room was closed. 'Maddie, you ready to go?'

'I'm changing. I'll be out in a minute.'

It had been a clipped, don't-bother-me tone. Bosch wasn't sure what to make of it. The plan was to go to the phone store first and then to get clothing and furniture and a new computer. He was going to get his daughter whatever she wanted and she knew it. Yet she was being short with him and he wasn't sure why. One day on the job as a full-time father and he already felt like he was lost at sea.

THE NEXT MORNING Bosch and his daughter set to work assembling some of the purchases of the day before. First in line was the computer desk and chair they had bought at the IKEA store in Burbank.

Harry had moved the coffee table out of the way and spread the parts of the desk out on the floor of the living room. He and Madeline sat cross-legged on the floor, trying to understand the assembly instructions.

'It looks like you start by attaching the side panels to the desk top,' Madeline said.

'You sure? I thought that just meant you have one each of those parts.'

'No, because there are two side panels and they're marked one. I think it means step one.'

Bosch's phone rang and he slowly climbed to his feet, his knees aching after being rescued from his crossed-leg position. He made it over to the dining-room table to grab the phone before the caller hung up.

'Harry, it's Dr Hinojos. How are you?'

'Plugging away, Doc. Thanks for the call back.' Bosch stepped out onto the deck, closing the door behind him.

'I'm sorry I didn't get back until today,' Hinojos said. 'Mondays are always brutal here. What's up?'

Hinojos ran the department's Behavioral Science Section, the unit that offered psychiatric services to the rank and file. Bosch had known her almost fifteen years, since she had been assigned to evaluate him after he'd had a physical altercation with a supervisor at Hollywood Division.

Bosch kept his voice low. 'I wanted to ask if you would do me a favour.'

'Depends on what it is.'

'I want you to talk to my daughter.'

'Your daughter. Harry, you know that we see police officers only here, not their families. I can give you a referral to a child practitioner.'

'I don't want a child shrink. That's where the favour comes in. I want her to talk to you. You know me, I know you. Like that.'

'But, Harry, it doesn't work like that here.'

'She got abducted last weekend. And her mother got killed trying to get her back. The kid's got baggage, Doc.'

'Oh my gosh, Harry!'

'Yeah, not good. She needs to talk to somebody besides me. I want it to be you, Doctor.'

Another pause and again Bosch let it play out. There wasn't much sense in pushing it with Hinojos. Bosch knew that from first-hand experience.

'Well, I have some time today,' Hinojos said. 'Could she meet me at one?'

'No problem. Should I bring her there, or will that be a problem?'

'I think it will be fine. I won't record it as an official session.'

Bosch got a call-waiting beep in his ear. He pulled the phone away from his ear to check the caller ID. It was Lieutenant Gandle.

'OK, Doc,' Bosch replied. 'Thank you for this.'

'It will be good to see you, too. Maybe you and I should have a conversation. I know your ex-wife still meant a lot to you.'

'Let's take care of my daughter first. Then we can worry about me. I'll drop her with you and then get out of the way.'

He hung up and checked to see if Gandle had left a message. There was none. He headed back inside and saw that his daughter had already assembled the main structure of the desk.

'Wow, girl, you know what you're doing.'

'It's pretty easy.'

He had just got back down on the floor when the land line started to ring from the kitchen. He got up and hustled to get it.

'Bosch, what are you doing?' It was Lieutenant Gandle.

'I told you I was taking a few days.'

'I need you to come in. There are two guys from the Hong Kong Police Department sitting in Captain Dodds's office and they want to talk to you.

You didn't tell me that your ex-wife is dead, Harry. You didn't tell me about all the dead bodies they say you left in your wake over there.'

Bosch paused as he considered his options.

'Tell them I'll see them at one thirty,' he finally said.

Gandle's response was sharp. 'One thirty? What do you need three hours for? Get down here now.'

'I can't, Lieutenant. I'll see them at one thirty.'

Bosch hung the phone up and then pulled his cell from his pocket. He had known that the Hong Kong cops would eventually come and he already had a plan for what to do.

The first call he made was to Sun Yee. He knew it was late in Hong Kong but he couldn't wait. The phone rang eight times and then went to message.

'It's Bosch. Call me when you get this.'

Next Bosch scrolled through his contact list and found a number he had not used in at least a year. This time he got an immediate answer.

'Mickey Haller.'

'It's Bosch.'

'Harry? I didn't think I'd—'

'I think I need a lawyer.'

ELEVEN

Gandle came charging out of his office the moment he saw Bosch enter the squad room. 'Bosch, I told you to get in here forthwith. Why—'

He stopped when he saw who had entered behind Bosch. Mickey Haller was a well-known defence attorney.

'Lieutenant,' Bosch said, 'Mr Haller is here to advise me and help me convince the men from Hong Kong that I committed no crimes in their city. Now, do you want to introduce me to them or should I do it myself?'

Gandle hesitated, and then led them to the conference room off Captain Dodds's office. Waiting there were the two men from Hong Kong. They stood up upon Bosch's arrival and handed him business cards. Alfred Lo and Clifford Wu, both from HKPD's Triad Bureau.

Bosch introduced Haller and handed the cards to him.

'Why don't we sit down and hash this thing out?' Haller said.

Everyone, including Gandle, took seats around the conference table.

Haller spoke first. 'Let me start things off here by saying that my client, Detective Bosch, is not waiving any of his constitutionally guaranteed rights at this time. We are on American soil here and that means he doesn't have to speak to you gentlemen. However, he is also a detective and he knows what you two men are up against on a daily basis. Against my advice he is willing to talk to you. So the way we will work this is that you can ask him questions and he'll try to answer them if I think he should. We hope to end this conversation with you two fellows leaving with a greater understanding of the events of this past weekend in Hong Kong. But one thing is certain and that is that you will not be leaving with Detective Bosch. His cooperation in this matter ends when this meeting ends.'

Haller punctuated his opening salvo with a smile.

Before coming into the PAB, Bosch had met with him for nearly an hour. After they were finished they took Maddie to her meeting with Dr Hinojos and then drove over to the PAB.

Being a detective, Bosch was walking a thin line. He wanted his colleagues from across the Pacific to know what had happened, but he wasn't going to put himself, his daughter or Sun Yee in jeopardy. He believed that all his actions in Hong Kong were justified. He had told Haller he had been in kill-or-be-killed situations initiated by others. And that included his encounter with the deskman at Chungking Mansions.

Lo took out a pen and notebook and Wu asked the first question, revealing that he was the lead man. 'First, we would ask, why did you go to Hong Kong on such short trip?'

Bosch shrugged like the answer was obvious. 'To get my daughter and bring her back here.'

'On Saturday morning your former wife she report the daughter missing to police,' Wu said.

'On Saturday morning I was thirty-five thousand feet over the Pacific. I can't speak for what my ex-wife was doing then.'

'We believe your daughter was taken by someone named Peng Qingcai. Do you know him?'

'Never met him.'

'Peng is dead,' Lo said.

Bosch nodded. 'That doesn't make me unhappy.'

'Mr Peng's neighbour, Mrs Fengyi Mai, she recall speaking with you at her home on Sunday,' Wu said. 'You and Mr Sun Yee.'

'Yes, we knocked on her door. She wasn't much help. She didn't know where Peng was.'

'Did you go to Peng's apartment?'

'We knocked on the door but nobody answered. After a while we left.'

'You acknowledge that you were with Mr Sun Yee?' he asked.

'Sure. I was with him.'

'How do you know this man?'

'Through my ex-wife. They met me at the airport on Sunday morning and informed me that they were looking for my daughter because the police department there did not believe she had been abducted.' Bosch studied the two men for a moment before continuing. 'You see, your police department dropped the ball. And if I'm dragged into this, I'll call every newspaper in Hong Kong—doesn't matter what language—and tell them my story.'

The plan was to use the threat of international embarrassment to the HKPD to make the detectives move cautiously.

'Are you aware,' Wu said, 'that your ex-wife, Eleanor Wish, died of gunshot wound to the head in Chungking Mansions, Kowloon?'

'Yes, I am aware of that.'

'Were you present when this happened?'

Bosch looked at Haller and the attorney nodded.

'I was there. I saw it happen.'

'Can you tell us?'

'We were looking for our daughter. We didn't find her. We were in the hallway about to leave and two men started to fire at us. Eleanor was hit and she . . . got killed. And the two men were hit, too. It was self-defence.'

Wu leaned forward. 'Who shot these men?'

Haller leaned forward. 'I don't think I'm going to allow Detective Bosch to get into who-shot-who theories,' he said. 'I am sure your fine police department's forensic unit has already determined the answer to that question.'

Wu moved on. 'Was Sun Yee on the fifteenth floor?'

'Not at that time.'

'Can you give us more detail?'

'About the shooting? No. But I can tell you that we found tissue with blood on it in the room where they had held my daughter.'

Bosch studied them to see if they reacted to this information. They showed nothing.

There was a file on the table in front of the men from Hong Kong. Wu opened it and took out a document. He slid it across to Bosch.

'This is statement from Sun Yee. Please read and acknowledge for accuracy.'

Haller leaned in next to Bosch and they read the two-page document. Bosch immediately recognised it as their investigative theory disguised as a statement from Sun Yee. About half of it was correct, the rest assumption.

Harry knew they were either trying to bluff him into telling what really happened or they had arrested Sun Yee and forced him to sign his name to the story they preferred, namely that Bosch had been responsible for a bloody rampage across Hong Kong.

But Bosch remembered what Sun Yee had said to him at the airport. *I will handle these things and make no mention of you. This is my promise.*

'Gentlemen,' Haller said, completing his read of the document first. 'This document is—'

'Bullshit,' Bosch finished. He slid the document back across the table.

'No, no,' Wu said quickly. 'This is real. This is signed by Mr Sun Yee.'

'Maybe you held a gun to his head. Is that how you do it over there?'

'Detective Bosch!' Wu exclaimed. 'You will come to Hong Kong and answer these charges. You have killed many people. You have used firearms. You placed your daughter above all Chinese citizens and—'

'They were blood-typing her!' Bosch said angrily. 'They took her blood. You know when they do that? When they're trying to match organs.'

He paused and watched the growing discomfort on Wu's face. Haller's strategy had been right. Rather than focus on defending Bosch's actions as self-defence, make it clear to the men from Hong Kong what would be brought to the international media stage should they pursue any sort of case against Bosch. Now was the time to move in for the kill.

'Gentlemen, you can hang on to your signed statement there,' Haller said, a smile playing on his face. 'Let me summarise the facts that are supported by the actual evidence. A thirteen-year-old American girl was abducted in your city. Her mother dutifully called the police to report this crime. The police declined to investigate the crime and then—'

'The girl had run away before,' Lo interjected. 'There was no reas—'

Haller held up a finger to cut him off. 'Does not matter,' he said, now a tone of contained outrage in his voice and the smile gone. 'Your department was told an American girl was missing and chose, *for whatever reason*, to ignore the report. This forced the girl's mother to look for her daughter herself. And the first thing she did was to call in the girl's father from Los Angeles.'

Haller gestured to Bosch. 'Detective Bosch arrived and together with his ex-wife and a friend of the family, Mr Sun Yee, they began the search that the Hong Kong Police had determined they would not be involved in. On their own, what they found was evidence that they were going to sell her for her organs!'

His outrage was growing and Bosch believed it was not an act. For a few moments Haller let it float over the table like a thundercloud before continuing. 'Now, as you gentlemen know, people got killed. Suffice it to say that left alone in Hong Kong without any help from the police, this mother and father trying to find their daughter encountered some very bad people and there were kill-or-be-killed situations. There was *provocation*!'

Bosch saw the two Hong Kong detectives physically lean back as Haller shouted the last word.

The lawyer continued in a calm voice. 'Whatever happened occurred because your department failed this young American girl and this family. And if you are now going to sit back and analyse what actions Detective Bosch took because your department failed to act properly—if you are looking for a scapegoat to take back with you to Hong Kong—then you won't find one here. We won't be cooperating. However, I do have someone here you *will* be able to talk to about all of this. We can start with him.'

Haller pulled a business card out of his shirt pocket and slid it across the table to them. Wu picked it up and studied it. Haller had shown it to Bosch earlier. It was the business card of a reporter from the *Los Angeles Times*.

'Jock Meekeevoy,' Lo read. 'He has information about this?'

'That's Jack McEvoy. He has no information now. But he would be very interested in a story like this.'

This was all part of the plan. Haller bluffing. The truth was that McEvoy had been laid off by the *Times* six months earlier. Haller had dug the old card out of a stack of business cards he kept.

'It will make a great story,' Haller said calmly. 'Thirteen-year-old American girl kidnapped in China for her organs and the police do nothing.

Her parents are forced into action and the mother is killed trying to save her daughter. From there it will go international for sure. Every paper, every news channel in the world will want a part of this story.'

Haller now opened his own file that he had carried into the meeting. It contained news stories he had printed following an Internet search. He slid a set of print-outs across the table to Wu and Lo.

'What you have there is a package of news articles I will be providing to Mr McEvoy and any other journalist who makes an enquiry. These articles document the recent growth of the black market in human organs in China. The waiting list in China is said to be the longest in the world. Doesn't help that a few years back and under pressure from the rest of the world, the Chinese government banned the harvesting of organs from executed prisoners. That only heightened the demand for organs on the black market. I am sure you will be able to see where Mr McEvoy will be going with his story. It's up to you now to decide if that is what you want to happen.'

Wu turned so he could whisper in rapid-fire Chinese directly into Lo's ear. He then straightened himself. 'We would like to make private telephone call before continuing the interview,' he said.

Gandle stood up. 'You can use my office.' He led them out.

'You think they're going to go away?' Bosch asked Haller when they were alone.

'I think they're already gone,' Haller said. 'I think this thing just ended. What happens in Hong Kong stays in Hong Kong.'

WHILE THEY WAITED for the Hong Kong detectives to return, Bosch decided to check his desk for interoffice envelopes and other messages. There were no envelopes, but he saw a blinking red light on his phone. He had a message.

Bosch sat down and typed his code into the phone. He had five messages. The first four were routine calls about other cases. He made a few notes on a desk pad and erased the messages.

The fifth message was from Teri Sopp in latent prints. It had been left at 9.15 that morning.

'Harry, we did the electrostatic enhancement test on the casing you gave me. We pulled a print off it and everybody here's pretty excited. We got a match on the Department of Justice computer, too. So call me as soon as you get this.'

He called latents and asked for Teri Sopp. He waited ten seconds, his excitement growing. Chang might have been kicked loose and may already be back in Hong Kong for all Bosch knew, but if his fingerprint was on the casing of one of the bullets that killed John Li, then that was a game changer. They could charge him and seek an extradition warrant.

'This is Teri.'

'It's Harry Bosch. I just got your message.'

'I was wondering where you were. We got a match on your casing.'

'That's wonderful. Bo-Jing Chang?'

'I'm in the lab. Let me go to my desk. It was a Chinese name but not the one on the print card you gave me. Let me put you on hold.'

She was gone and Bosch felt a fissure suddenly form in his assumptions of the case.

'Harry, are you coming?'

He looked up and out of the cubicle. Gandle had escorted the two Hong Kong detectives back to the conference room and was signalling him to come back as well. Bosch pointed to the phone and shook his head. Not satisfied, Gandle came over to Bosch's cubicle.

'Look, they are folding on this,' he said urgently. 'You need to get in there and finish it off.'

'My lawyer can handle it. I just got a call that changes—'

'Harry?'

It was Sopp back on the line. Bosch covered the mouthpiece.

'I have to take this,' he said to Gandle. Then, dropping his hand and speaking into the phone, he said, 'Teri, give me the name.'

Gandle shook his head and went back towards the conference room.

'OK, it's Henry Lau, L-A-U. DOB is September the 9th, 1982.'

'What's he in the computer for?'

'He was pulled over two years ago in Venice.'

'That's all he's got? What about an address?'

'The address on his licence is eighteen Quarterdeck, Venice. Unit eleven.'

Bosch copied the information into his pocket notebook.

'OK, and this print you pulled, it's solid, right?'

'No doubt, Harry. It came up glowing like Christmas. This technology is amazing. It's going to change things.'

'Thanks for this, Teri. We're going to move on it right now.'

Bosch hung up. He first looked over the cubicle wall at the conference room. He could see Haller gesturing towards the two men from Hong Kong.

Bosch checked his partner's cubicle but Ferras was still at lunch. He made a decision and picked up the phone again.

David Chu was in the AGU office and took Bosch's call. Harry updated him on the latest piece of information to come out of latent prints and told him to run Henry Lau's name through the Triad files. In the meantime, Bosch said, he was heading over to pick Chu up.

'Where are we going?' Chu asked.

'To find this guy.'

Bosch hung up and headed to the conference room. When he opened the door, Gandle put his it's-about-time look on his face.

'Harry, these men still have questions for you,' Gandle said.

'I'm sorry but they'll have to wait. We've caught a break on the Li case and I need to move on it. Now.'

Gandle got up and started towards the door.

'Harry, I think I can handle this,' Haller said from his seat.

Bosch thanked him and followed Gandle out of the door.

'What happened?' Gandle asked.

CHU WAS WAITING at the front of the AGU building, holding a briefcase, when Bosch pulled up. He hopped in and Bosch took off.

'We're starting in Venice?' Chu asked.

'That's right. What did you find on Henry Lau?'

'Nothing.'

Bosch looked over at him. 'Nothing?'

'As far as we know, he's clean. I could not find his name anywhere in our intelligence files. I also talked to some people and made some calls. Nothing. By the way, I did print out his DL photo.'

He opened his briefcase and pulled out the colour print-out of Lau's driver's-licence photo. Bosch stole quick glances at it as he drove. The freeways were congested downtown. Lau had a fresh face and a stylish cut to his hair. It was hard to connect the face with the cold-blooded murder of a liquor-store owner. The address in Venice didn't fit well either.

'I ran a check with the ATF. Henry Lau is the registered owner of a 9mm Glock Model Nineteen. Not only did he load it, he owns it. He bought it six years ago, the day after he turned twenty-one.'

To Bosch that meant they were getting warm. Lau owned the right gun and his purchase of the weapon as soon as he was of legal age made him a traveller in the world Bosch knew. His connection to John Li and Bo-Jing Chang would become apparent once they had him in custody.

They connected to the 10 and as they headed west towards the Pacific Bosch's phone buzzed. 'Harry, it's Dr Hinojos. We're waiting for you.'

Bosch had forgotten. For more than thirty years he had simply moved with an investigation without having to think about anybody else.

'Oh, Doctor! I'm so sorry. I–I'm on my way to pick up a suspect. I had to—is there any way you can stay with Maddie a little longer? Are you free?'

'Well, this is . . . I suppose she could stay here. I am just doing admin work the rest of the day. Are you sure this is what you want to do?'

'Look, I know this is bad. But this case is the reason she's here. I have to ride it out. I'm going to grab this guy if he's home and come back downtown. I'll call you, then I'll come get her.'

'OK, Harry. I could use the extra time with her. You and I are also going to need to find time to talk. About Maddie and then about you.'

'OK, we will. Is she there? Can I speak to her?'

'Hold on.'

After a few moments Maddie got on the line. 'Dad?'

With one word she imparted all of the messages: surprise, disappointment, disbelief, terrible letdown.

'I know, baby. I'm sorry. Something's come up and I need to go with it. Go with Dr Hinojos and I will be there as fast as I can.'

'All right.'

'OK, Mad. I love you.' He closed the phone and put it away. 'I don't want to talk about it,' he said before Chu could ask a question.

'OK,' Chu said.

The traffic opened up and they made it into Venice in less than half an hour. Along the way Bosch took another call, this time from Haller. He told Harry that the Hong Kong Police would bother him no further.

'They'll be in touch about your ex-wife's body, but that's it. They're dropping any inquiry into your part in this.'

'Thank you, Mickey.'

'All in a day's work. You be safe now, Harry.'

Bosch closed the phone and concentrated on finding Henry Lau.

Venice was a bohemian community with uptown prices. The building where Lau resided was a condominium complex in one of the newer glass and stucco structures that were slowly crowding out the little weekend bungalows that had once lined the beach. Bosch parked in an alley off the next street and they walked back.

They entered through a glass door and stood in a small vestibule with an inner security door and a button panel for calling up to individual units. Lau lived in unit eleven. Bosch started pushing the buttons for the other units. They waited and finally a woman answered one of the calls.

'Yes?'

'Los Angeles Police, ma'am,' Bosch said. 'Can we speak with you?'

'Can you hold your badges to the camera, please?' the woman said.

Bosch had not realised there was a camera and looked around.

'Here.' Chu pointed to a small aperture at the top of the panel. They held up their badges and soon the inner door buzzed. Bosch pulled it open.

The door led to a common area that was open to the sky. There was a small lap pool in the centre and the building's twelve town homes all had entrances here. Number eleven was on the west side.

Bosch approached the door to number eleven, knocked on it and got no answer. The door to number twelve opened and a woman stood there.

'I thought you said you wanted to speak to me,' she said.

'We're actually looking for Mr Lau,' Chu said. 'Do you know where he is?'

'He might be at work. But I think he was shooting at night this week.'

'Shooting what?' Bosch asked.

'He's a screenwriter and he's working on a movie.'

Just then the door to number eleven cracked open. A bleary-eyed man peered out. Bosch recognised him from the photo Chu had printed.

'Henry Lau?' Bosch said. 'LAPD. We need to ask you some questions.'

TWELVE

Henry Lau had a spacious home with a deck that had a view of the Pacific across Venice Beach. He invited Bosch and Chu in and asked them to sit down in the living room. Chu sat down but Bosch remained standing. He wasn't getting the vibe he was expecting. Lau seemed to take their knocking on his door as routine and expected. Harry hadn't counted on that.

Lau was wearing blue jeans, sneakers and a T-shirt with a silk-screened image of a long-haired man wearing sunglasses and a caption that said, 'The Dude Abides'. If he had been sleeping, he had slept in his clothes.

'The Dude!' Chu said cheerfully. 'I loved that movie, man.'

'Loved?' Lau asked. 'You shouldn't really talk about film in the past tense. It lives on, man.'

Bosch had no idea which movie they were talking about. He pointed Lau to a square, black leather chair with armrests a foot wide.

'Have a seat, Mr Lau, and we'll try not to take up too much of your time.'

Lau was small and catlike. He sat down and brought his legs up onto the chair.

'Is this about the shooting on the beach?' he asked.

Bosch glanced at Chu and then back at Lau. 'What shooting is that?'

'The one a couple of weeks back. But I guess that's not why you're here if you don't even know when it was.'

'That's correct, Mr Lau. We are investigating a shooting but not that one. Do you know a man named Bo-Jing Chang?'

'Bo-Jing Chang? No, I don't know that name.'

He looked genuinely surprised by the name. Bosch signalled Chu and he pulled Chang's booking photo out of his briefcase. He showed it to Lau.

After studying it Lau shook his head. 'No, don't know him. What shooting are we talking about here?'

'Let us ask the questions for now,' Bosch said. 'Then we'll get to yours. Your neighbour said you're a screenwriter?'

'Yes.'

'You write anything I might have seen?'

'Nope. I've never had anything that actually got made until right now.'

'Well, then, who pays for this nice pad on the beach?'

'I pay for it. I get paid to write. I just haven't had anything hit the screen yet. It takes time, you know?'

Bosch moved behind Lau and the young man had to turn in his comfortable seat to track him. Bosch wanted to keep Lau off guard.

'Where did you grow up, Henry?' he asked.

'San Francisco. Came down here to go to school and stayed.'

'You a Giants or Dodgers man?'

'Giants, baby.'

'That's too bad. When was the last time you were in South LA?'

The question came from left field and Lau had to think before answering. 'I don't know, five or six years at least. Been a while, though. I wish you could tell me what this is about because then I might be able to help you.'

'So if somebody said they saw you there last week, they'd be lying?'

Lau smirked like they were playing a game. 'Either that or they were just mistaken. You know what they say? That we all look alike.'

Lau smiled brightly and looked to Chu for confirmation. Chu held his ground and just returned a dead-eyed stare.

'What about Monterey Park?' Bosch asked.

'Uh, I went out there a couple times for dinner, but it's really not worth the drive.'

'So you don't know anyone in Monterey Park?'

'No, not really.'

Bosch had been circling, asking general questions and locking Lau in. It was time to circle closer now.

'Where's your gun, Mr Lau?'

Lau put his feet down on the floor. He looked at Chu and then back at Bosch.

'This is about my gun?'

'Six years ago you bought and registered a Glock Model Nineteen. Can you tell us where it is?'

'OK, I get it. Let me guess. Mr Asshole in unit eight saw me holding it out there on the deck after the beach shooting and he made a complaint?'

'No, Henry, we haven't spoken to Mr Asshole. Are you saying that you had the gun with you after the shooting on the beach?'

'That's right. I heard shots out there and a scream. I was on my own property and am entitled to protect myself.'

Bosch nodded to Chu. Chu opened the slider and stepped out onto the deck to make a call about the beach shooting.

'Look, if somebody said I fired it, they are full of shit,' Lau said.

Bosch looked at him for a long moment. He felt like there was something missing, a piece of the conversation he didn't know about yet.

'Can you show us your gun, Henry?'

'Sure, I'll go get it. It's in the locked box in a drawer next to my bed.'

He sprung up from the chair and headed towards the stairs.

'Henry,' Bosch said, 'hold it there. We're going to go with you.'

Lau looked back from the stairs. 'Suit yourself.'

Bosch turned to the deck. Chu was coming back through the door. They followed Lau up the stairs and then down a hallway to the master bedroom, a grand room with ten-foot windows looking out over the beach.

'I called Pacific Division,' Chu said to Bosch. 'The shooting was on the night of the 1st. They have two suspects in custody on it.'

Bosch flipped back through the calendar in his mind. It was the Tuesday one week before the killing of John Li.

Lau sat down on the unmade bed next to a two-drawer side table. He opened the bottom drawer and pulled out a steel box.

'Hold it right there,' Bosch said.

Lau put the box on the bed and stood up, his hands up.

'Hey, I wasn't going to do anything, man. You asked to see it.'

'Why don't you let my partner open the box,' Bosch said, pulling a pair of latex gloves from his coat pocket and handing them to Chu.

'Suit yourself. The key is on a little hook on the back side of the table.'

'Why'd you buy the gun, Henry?'

'Because I was living in a complete shit hole at the time and the gangs were all over the place. But it's funny. I paid a million dollars for this place and they're still right out there on the beach, shooting the place up.'

Chu reached behind the table and found the key. He then used it to open the box. A black felt gun bag sat on some folded papers. There was a passport and a box of bullets as well. Chu carefully lifted the bag out and opened it, producing a black steel semiautomatic pistol. He examined it.

'One box of Cor Bon 9mm bullets, one Glock Model Nineteen. I think this is it, Harry.'

Lau took a step towards the door but Bosch immediately put his hand on his chest to stop him and then backed him against the wall.

'Look,' Lau said, 'I don't know what this is about but you people are freaking me out here. What the hell is going on?'

Bosch kept his hand on his chest. 'Just tell me about the gun, Henry. You had it the night of the 1st. Has it been out of your possession at any time since then?'

'No, I . . . Right there is where I keep it.'

'Where were you last Tuesday, three o'clock in the afternoon?'

'Um, last week I was here. I think I was here working. No, wait! Wait! Last Tuesday I was at Paramount all day. We had a read-through of the script with the cast. I was over there all afternoon.'

'And there will be people who will vouch for you?'

'At least a dozen. Matthew McConaughey will vouch for me. He was there. He's playing the lead.'

Bosch assumed McConaughey was a movie star but he had never heard of him. He made a jump then, hitting Lau with a question designed to keep him off-balance. It was amazing what fell out of people's pockets when they were being knocked back and forth by seemingly unrelated questions.

'Are you associated with a Triad, Henry?'

Lau burst out laughing. 'What? What are you—Look, I'm out of here.'

He slapped Bosch's hand away and pushed off the wall in the direction of the door again. It was a move Harry was ready for. He grabbed Lau by the arm and spun him round. He clipped his ankle with a kick and threw him face down on the bed. He then moved in, kneeling on his back while he cuffed him.

'This is crazy!' Lau yelled. 'You can't do this!'

'Calm down, Henry, just calm down,' Bosch said. 'We're going to go downtown and straighten all of this out.'

'But I've got a movie! I have to be on the set in three hours!'

'Fuck the movies, Henry. This is real life and we're going downtown.'

Chu led the way, carrying the metal box containing the Glock. Bosch followed, keeping Lau in front of him and one hand on the chain between the cuffs. But when they got to the top of the stairs Bosch stopped.

'Wait a minute. Back up here.' Something had caught Bosch's eye.

He walked Lau backwards until they got to a framed diploma from the University of Southern California. Lau had graduated with a liberal arts degree in 2004.

'You went to USC?' Bosch asked.

'Yeah, the film school. Why?'

Both the school and graduation year matched the diploma Bosch had seen at Fortune Fine Foods & Liquor. Bosch knew that several thousand kids graduated every year from USC, many of them of Chinese descent. But he had never trusted in coincidences.

'Did you know a guy at USC named Robert Li—spelled L-I?'

Lau nodded. 'Yeah, I knew him. He was my room-mate.'

Bosch felt things suddenly begin to crash together with an undeniable force.

'What about Eugene Lam? Did you know him?'

Lau nodded again.

'I lived with him, too. Like I told you, in a shit hole down in gangland.'

Bosch knew that USC was an oasis of fine education surrounded by neighbourhoods where personal protection would be an issue.

'And those guys knew you bought the gun for protection down there?'

'We went together. They helped me pick it out. Why are you—'

'Do you see them any more? Do you stay in touch?'

'I'm still in touch with Rob and Huge. I saw them both last Wednesday. We play poker almost every week.'

Bosch glanced over at Chu. The case had just broken wide open.

He put a hand on Lau's shoulder and turned him towards the stairs. 'Let's go back to the living room and talk, Henry. I think there is a lot you can tell us.'

THEY PUT EUGENE LAM in an interview room and let him cook. In RHD, they called it seasoning the roast. You let the suspect marinate in time. It always made him more tender. Chang had been the exception to this rule. He had held up like a rock. Innocence gave you that resolve.

It was Thursday, two days after the case had come together. They had used the time to work on evidence-gathering and preparing a strategy. Bosch had also enrolled his daughter in school. She had started classes that morning.

They had waited for Eugene Lam in the alley behind Fortune Fine Foods & Liquor. They believed Lam was the shooter but also the weaker of the two suspects. They would bring him in first, then Robert Li.

An hour later, Bosch entered the room carrying a cardboard box containing the case evidence and sat down across the table from Lam. The suspect looked up with scared eyes. They always did after a period of isolation. What was just an hour on the outside was an eternity inside.

Bosch put the box down on the table. 'Eugene, I'm here to explain the facts of life to you,' he said. 'So listen closely. The fact of the matter is that you are going to prison. No doubt about that. But what you are going to decide in the next few minutes is how long you go for. It can be until you are a very old man or you can leave yourself a chance at getting your freedom back one day. You're a very young man, Eugene. I hope you make the right choice.'

He paused and waited but Lam shook his head in a show of bravado.

'I told you people, I want a lawyer. I know my rights. You can't ask me any questions once I ask for a lawyer.'

Bosch nodded in agreement. 'Yeah, you're right about that, Eugene. You're absolutely right. But, see, that's why I'm not asking you anything here. I'm just telling you that you have a choice to make. Silence is certainly a choice. But it you choose silence, you'll never see the outside world again.'

Lam shook his head and looked down. 'Please leave me alone.'

'Maybe it would help you if I gave you a clearer picture of where you're at here. You see, I am perfectly willing to show you my whole hand because you know what? It's a royal flush. You play poker, right? You know that's the hand that can't be beat. And that's what I've got here.'

Bosch paused. He could see curiosity in Lam's eyes. He couldn't help but wonder what they had on him.

'We know you did the dirty work on this thing, Eugene. You went into that store and you shot Mr Li dead in cold blood. But we're pretty sure it wasn't your idea. It was Robert who sent you in there to kill his father. And he's the one we want. I've got a district attorney ready to make you a deal—fifteen to life if you give us Robert. You'll do the fifteen for sure, but after that you convince a parole board you were just a victim in this and you walk free . . .'

Lam quietly said, 'I want a lawyer.'

Bosch responded with resignation in his voice. 'OK, man, that's your choice. We'll get you a lawyer.'

He looked up at the ceiling where the camera was located and raised an imaginary phone to his ear.

He then looked back at Lam. 'All right, they're making the call. If you don't mind, while we're waiting here I'm going to tell you a few things. You can share them with your lawyer when he gets here.'

'Whatever,' Lam said. 'I don't care as long as I get the attorney.'

'OK, then let's start with the crime scene. You know, there were a few things about it that bothered me from the beginning. One is that Mr Li had the gun right there under the counter and never got the chance to pull it. Another was that there were no head wounds. No shot to the face.'

'Very interesting,' Lam said sarcastically.

'And you know what all of that told me? That said that Li probably knew his killer and hadn't felt threatened. And that this was purely a piece of business. This wasn't revenge, and it wasn't personal. This was business.'

Bosch reached down into the box for the plastic evidence bag that held the bullet casing taken from Li's throat. He tossed it on the table.

'You remember looking for that? Wondering what happened to that casing? Well, there it is. There's the mistake that brought it all down on you.'

He paused while Lam stared at the casing, fear lodging in his eyes.

'You never leave a soldier behind. Isn't that the shooter's rule? But you did, man. You left that soldier behind and it brought us right to your door. There was a fingerprint on the casing, Eugene. We raised it with something called electrostatic enhancement. And the print we got led us to your old room-mate, Henry Lau. Yeah, Henry was very cooperative. He told us the last time he fired and then reloaded his gun was at a range eight months ago. His fingerprint was sitting on that shell all that time.'

Harry reached down to the box and removed Henry Lau's gun, still in its black felt bag. He took it out of the bag and put it on the table.

'We had Henry's weapon checked out by ballistics yesterday and sure enough, it's our murder weapon all right. This is the gun that killed John Li at Fortune Liquors on September the 8th. The problem was that Henry Lau has a solid alibi for the time of the shooting. He was in a room with thirteen other people. And on top of that, he told us he hadn't given his gun out to anybody to borrow.'

Bosch leaned back and scratched his chin with his hand, as if he was still trying to figure out how the gun ended up being used to kill John Li.

'Damn, this was a big problem, Eugene. But then we got lucky.'

He paused for effect and then brought down the hammer.

'You see, whoever used Henry's gun to kill John Li cleaned it up and reloaded it so Henry wouldn't ever know his gun had been borrowed. It was a pretty good plan, but he made one mistake.' Bosch leaned forward across the table and looked at Lam eye to eye. 'One of the bullets in the magazine had a nice readable thumbprint on it. Your thumbprint, Eugene. We matched it to the print they took when you traded in your New York driver's licence for a California DL.'

Lam's eyes slowly dropped away from Bosch's and down to the table.

Bosch picked up the gun and the bag with the casing in it and put them back in the box. He grabbed the box with both hands and stood up.

'So that's where we're at, Eugene. You think about all of that while you're waiting for your lawyer.'

Bosch moved slowly towards the door. He hoped Lam would tell him to stop and come back, that he wanted to make the deal. But the suspect said nothing. Harry put the box under one arm, opened the door and walked out.

BOSCH CARRIED the evidence box back to his cubicle and dropped it heavily on his desk. He looked over at his partner's cubicle to make sure it was still empty. Ferras had been left behind in the Valley to keep an eyeball on Robert Li. If he figured out that Lam was in police custody and possibly talking, he might make a move.

Soon Chu and Gandle, who had been watching Bosch with Lam in the AV room, came to the cubicle.

'I told you it was a weak play,' Gandle said. 'He had to have been wearing gloves when he reloaded the gun. He knew you were playing him.'

'Yeah, well,' Bosch said. 'I thought it was the best we had.'

'I agree,' Chu said, showing his support for Bosch.

'We're still going to have to kick him loose,' Gandle said. 'We know he had the opportunity to take the gun but we have no proof that he actually did. You can't go to court with just that.'

'Is that what Cook said? Where is he anyway?'

As if to answer for himself, Abner Cook, the deputy DA who had come over to observe in the AV room, called Bosch's name from across the squad room.

'Get back here! He's calling for you.'

Bosch got up and walked back to the interview room.

'What is it?' he said. 'We called your lawyer and he's on the way.'

'What about the deal? Is it still good?'

'For the moment. The DA's about to leave.'

'Bring him in. I want the deal.'

'What are you giving us, Eugene? I'll bring in the DA when I know what's on the table.'

Lam nodded. 'I'll give you Robert Li . . . and his sister. The whole thing was their plan. The old man was stubborn and wouldn't change. They needed to close that store and open another in the Valley. One that made money. But he said no. He always said no and finally Rob couldn't take it any more.'

Bosch slid back into his seat, trying to hide his surprise about Mia's involvement. 'And the sister was part of this?'

'She was the one who planned it. Except . . .'

'Except what?'

'She wanted me to show up early and hit them both. The mother and father. But Robert told me no. He didn't want his mother hurt.'

'Whose idea was it to make it look like a Triad hit?'

'That was her idea and then Robert sort of planned it. They knew the police would go for it.'

Bosch hardly knew Mia but he knew enough about her story to feel sad about the whole thing. He glanced up at the overhead camera, hoping his stare would send the message to Gandle that he needed to put somebody on locating Mia Li so the arrest teams could move in simultaneously.

Bosch brought his eyes back to Lam. He was staring dejectedly at the table.

'What about you, Eugene? Why'd you get involved in this?'

Lam shook his head. Bosch could read the regret in his face. 'I don't know. Robert said he was going to lay me off because his father's store was losing too much money. He told me I could save my job . . . and that when they opened the second store in the Valley it would be mine to run.'

It was no more pitiful an answer than any other Bosch had heard over the years. There were no surprises left when it came to motivations for murder.

'What about Henry Lau? Did he give you the gun or did you take it without him knowing?'

'We took it—I took it. We were playing poker one night at his place and I said I had to go to the bathroom. I went into the bedroom and got it. I knew where he kept the key to the box. I took it and then I put it back afterwards— the next time we played. We didn't think he'd ever know.'

That seemed entirely plausible to Bosch. He would be able to question Lam in more detail later, but he had one last aspect to cover before bringing Cook in.

'What about Hong Kong?' he asked.

Lam looked confused by the question. 'Hong Kong? What about it?'

'Which one of you had the connection over there?'

Lam shook his head in bewilderment. It seemed real to Bosch.

'I don't know what you mean. I have no connection there and as far as I know, neither do Robert or Mia. Hong Kong wasn't mentioned.'

Now Bosch was confused. Something didn't connect here.

'What about the Triad Mr Li was paying off?'

'We knew about them and Robert knew when they came to collect every week. That's how he planned it. I waited and when I saw Chang leave the store I went in. Robert told me to take the disc out of the machine but to leave the other discs there. He knew one had Chang on it and the police would see it as a clue.'

A nice bit of manipulation on Robert's part, Bosch thought. And he had gone for it just as planned.

'What did you two tell Chang when he came to the store the other night?'

Lam looked down. He seemed embarrassed. 'Robert told him that the police had shown us his photo and told us that he had committed the murder. He told him the police were looking for him and would arrest him. We thought that would make him run, and it would look like he had done the crime.'

Bosch stared at Lam as the ramification of the statement slowly sank in. He had been totally manipulated every step of the way.

'Who called me?' he asked. 'Who told me to back off the case?'

Lam slowly nodded. 'That was me,' he said. 'Robert wrote a script for me and I made that call from a payphone downtown. I'm sorry, Detective Bosch. I didn't want to scare you but I had to do what Robert told me to do.'

Bosch nodded. He was sorry too, but not for the same reasons.

AN HOUR LATER Bosch and Cook emerged from the interview room with a full confession and agreement of cooperation from Eugene Lam. Cook said he would be filing charges immediately against the young killer as well as Robert and Mia Li.

Bosch gathered with Chu, Gandle and four other detectives in the conference room to discuss the arrest procedures. Ferras was still in his car watching Fortune Fine Foods & Liquor from across the street but Gandle reported that a detective sent to the Li home in the Wilshire District had come back to say that there appeared to be no one at home.

'Do we wait for Mia to show up, or do we take Robert down now before he starts wondering about Lam?' Gandle asked.

'I think we've got to move,' Bosch said. 'He already has to be wondering where Lam is. If he starts getting suspicious, he might run.'

Gandle looked around the room for objections. There were none.

'OK, then, let's mount up,' he said. 'We take down Robert in the store and then we go and find Mia. I want these people booked before the end of the day. Tell Ferras we're on the way. I'll ride up with you and Chu.'

Everybody stood up and filed out of the conference room. Bosch and Gandle lagged behind. Harry pulled out his phone and hit a speed-dial button for Ferras.

'You know, I still don't get it. Who took your daughter?' Gandle said. 'Lam claims he doesn't know anything about it. And at this point he has no reason to lie. Do you still think it was Chang's people, even though we now know he was clear on the killing?'

Ferras answered the call before Bosch could respond to Gandle.

'It's me,' Bosch said. 'Where's Li?' He held a finger up to Gandle, holding him while he took the call.

'He's in the store,' Ferras said. 'You know, we need to talk, Harry.'

Bosch could tell by the tension in his partner's voice that it wasn't Robert Li who Ferras wanted to talk about. Sitting there in his car alone all morning, something was festering in his brain.

'We'll talk later. Right now we have to move. We turned Lam. He gave us everything. Robert *and* his sister. She's part of this. Is she in the store?'

'Not that I saw. She dropped the mother off about an hour ago.'

Tired of waiting, Gandle headed off towards his office and Bosch was left thinking that he was safe for the time being from having to answer the lieutenant's question. Now he just had to deal with Ferras.

'OK, sit tight,' he said. 'Let me know if anything changes.'

'You know what, Harry? You didn't give me a chance, man.'

There was a whining tone in his voice that set Bosch on edge.

'What chance? What are you talking about?'

'I'm talking about you telling the lieutenant you wanted a new partner. He's trying to move me to autos, you know.'

'Ignacio, it's been two years. Two years of chances. But now's not the time to talk about this. We'll do it later, OK? In the meantime, just sit tight. We're on our way.'

'No, you sit tight, Harry.'

Bosch paused for a moment. 'What's that supposed to mean?'

'It means I'll handle Li.'

'Ignacio, listen to me. You're by yourself. You don't go in that store until you have an arrest team with you. You understand?'

'I don't need a team and I don't need you, Harry.'

Ferras disconnected. Bosch hit redial as he started moving towards the lieutenant's office. Ferras didn't pick up. When Bosch entered Gandle's office the lieutenant was donning his Kevlar vest.

'We've got to move,' Bosch said. 'Ferras is going off the map.'

AFTER RETURNING from the funeral, Bosch took off his tie and grabbed a beer out of the refrigerator. He went out on the deck, sat back on the lounge chair and closed his eyes. He thought about putting on some music, maybe a little Art Pepper to bounce him out of the blues.

But he found himself unable to move. He just kept his eyes closed and tried to forget as much as he could about the two weeks that had just passed. The beer would help, if only on a temporary basis. It had been the last one in the refrigerator and he had vowed that it would be the last one for him as well. Now he had his daughter to raise.

As if thoughts of her conjured her presence, he heard the sliding door open. 'Hey, Mads.'

'Dad.'

In only the one word her voice sounded different, troubled. He opened his eyes and squinted in the afternoon sunlight. She had already changed out of her dress and was wearing blue jeans and a shirt that had come from the bag her mother had packed for her. Bosch had noticed she wore more of the few things her mother had put into the backpack in Hong Kong than all of the clothes they had shopped for together.

'What's up, baby?'

'I wanted to talk to you.'

'OK.'

'I'm really sorry about your partner.'

'Me too. He made a bad mistake and he paid for it. But I don't know, it just doesn't seem like the punishment fitted the crime, you know?'

Bosch's mind momentarily shifted to the ghastly scene he'd encountered inside the manager's office of Fortune Fine Foods & Liquor. Ferras face down on the floor, shot four times in the back. Robert Li collapsed in the corner, shaking and moaning, staring at his sister's body near the door, the fifth bullet self-administered to the temple and the gun fallen by her side. Mrs Li, the matriarch of this family of killers and victims, standing stoically in the doorway and not shedding a tear.

Ignacio had not seen Mia coming. She had dropped her mother off at the store, but something made her come back. It was speculated in the squad room that she had spotted Ferras on his surveillance and knew that the police were about to close in. She drove home, retrieved the gun that her murdered father had kept below the counter, and then went to the Valley store. It would remain a mystery what her plan was. Perhaps she was looking for Lam or her mother. Or maybe she was just waiting for the police. But she returned to the store and came in through the employee entrance in the back at approximately the same time that Ferras entered through the front door to arrest Robert single-handedly. She watched Ferras enter her brother's office and then came up behind him.

Bosch pushed the vision and the thoughts away. He sat up and looked at his daughter. He saw the burden in her eyes and he knew what was coming.

'Dad, I made a bad mistake, too. Only I'm not the one who paid for it.'

'What do you mean, sweetheart?'

'When I was talking to Dr Hinojos she said I have to unburden. I have to say what's bothering me.'

Tears started to flow now. Bosch sat sideways on the lounge chair and took his daughter by the hand and guided her to a seat right next to him. He put his arm across her shoulders.

'You can tell me anything, Madeline.'

She closed her eyes and held a hand over them. 'I got Mom killed,' she said. 'I got her killed and it should've been me.'

'Wait a minute, wait a minute. You're not respons—'

'No, wait, listen to me. I did it, Dad, and I need to go to jail.'

Bosch pulled her into a crushing hug and kissed the top of her head. 'You listen to me, Mads. I know what happened but it doesn't make you responsible for what other people did. I don't want you thinking that.'

She pulled back and looked at him. 'You know? *You know* what I did?'

'You trusted the wrong person . . . and the rest, all the rest, is on him.'

She shook her head. 'No, no. The whole thing was my idea. I knew you would come and I thought maybe you'd make her let me go back with you.'

'I know.'

'How do you know?' she demanded.

Bosch shrugged. 'It doesn't matter,' he said. 'What matters is that you couldn't have known that Peng would take your plan and make it his.'

She bowed her head. 'Doesn't matter. I killed my mother.'

'Madeline, no. If anybody is responsible it's me. It was a robbery and it happened because I was stupid, because I showed my money in a place

I should never have shown it. OK? I made the mistake, not you.'

She could not be calmed or consoled. 'You wouldn't even have been there if we hadn't sent that video. I did that! I knew you would be on the next plane! I was going to escape before you landed. You would get there and everything would be all right, but you would tell Mom it wasn't safe for me there and you'd take me back.'

Bosch just nodded. He had put roughly the same scenario together a few days before, when he realised Bo-Jing Chang had nothing to do with the murder of John Li.

'But now Mom is *dead*! And they're *dead*! And it's all *my* fault!'

Bosch grabbed her by the shoulders and turned her towards him.

'How much of this did you tell Dr Hinojos?'

'None. I wanted to tell you first. You have to take me to jail now.'

Bosch pulled her into another hug and held her head against his chest.

'No, baby, you're staying here with me.' He gently caressed her hair and spoke calmly. 'We all make mistakes. Everybody. Sometimes, like my partner, you make a mistake and can't make up for it. You don't get the chance. But sometimes you do. We can make up for our mistakes here. Both of us.'

Her tears had slowed. He heard her sniffle. He thought maybe that this was why she had come to him. For a way out.

'We can maybe do some good and make up for the things we did wrong.'

'How?' she said in a small voice.

'I'll show you the way, baby. I'll show you and you'll see that we can make up for this.'

Bosch hugged his daughter tightly and wished he never had to let her go.

an author in **hong kong**

For nearly twenty years the Harry Bosch novels have had as their starting point the sun-drenched, edgy boulevards of downtown Los Angeles. But in *Nine Dragons*, author Michael Connelly (pictured left) takes his veteran LAPD detective to Hong Kong, where, in the course of one long, violent day, he moves relentlessly through the city tracking down clues that he hopes will lead him to his missing daughter.

The search leads Bosch at one point to Chungking Mansions. Any visitor to Hong Kong can take the ferry across the harbour to Kowloon and find this building at 36-44 Nathan Road. While Connelly was doing his research for *Nine Dragons* he kept returning to the mansions, which he describes in a recent interview as 'a whole world in one building, a home from home for many of the third- and fourth-world countries'. Connelly says he felt a palpable sense of intrigue and danger whenever he entered the place, a feeling that anything might happen there.

It is the most extraordinary building. It has seventeen storeys and consists of five blocks, A, B, C, D and E. The labyrinthine lower floors house a world bazaar of money-changers, mobile-phone salesmen, import-export businesses, ethnic food stalls and sari shops. On the upper floors there are a number of hotels and guesthouses all under the same roof, with about 4,000 people living in the 1,980 rooms at any one time.

Chungking Mansions opened its doors in 1961 and became home to many Chinese residents. Since then, because the rooms there are among the cheapest in the city, it has turned into a legendary haunt for backpackers and an infamous refuge for illegal immigrants, petty criminals and drug traffickers. With this in mind, it's probably never going to lose the dangerous character with which it is imbued in *Nine Dragons*, even though the property's owners have spent millions of Hong Kong dollars improving security and upgrading fire safety in recent years.

Fire precautions, much needed in Chungking Mansions, are not on local minds when it comes to the late-summer Hungry Ghosts Festival (Yue Laan), which is in full swing when Michael Connelly's hero arrives in Hong Kong. As Bosch looks out over the dawning city, he confuses the wisps of smoke rising from the streets with early-morning mist. But the smoke is a feature of Yue Laan, a month-long period when Chinese people set up altars and burn offerings of incense, paper money and papier-maché models of material goods that they hope will buy favour with and comfort their ancestors—the Hungry Ghosts— on the other side.

During the festival, which reaches its climax on the fifteenth day of the seventh month in the Chinese lunar calendar, offerings of fresh foods and roasted meats are displayed by day outside homes and offices, and, at night-time, colourful lanterns guide the 'lonely spirits', those that have no living ancestors, to the festivities. Operas and puppet shows are performed on makeshift stages to entertain the Hungry Ghosts and distract them from wreaking havoc. Floating lanterns in the shape of water lilies lead them back to Hell at the end of the month. The festival is believed to be such an inauspicious time that people avoid getting married, moving home or changing career while it is in progress.

Everyone you ask has a different story about the origins of Yue Laan. One popular version centres on Mu-lien, a Buddhist monk blessed with 'divine sight', who saw his mother suffering as a hungry ghost in Hell. All the food he offered turned to flame as it touched her lips. He asked Buddha for guidance, and Buddha told him that his mother's sins were so grievous that they could only be expiated by the communal prayers and chanting of monks, and the offering up of food and other essentials to the spirits of the dead. Mu-lien did as he was instructed and finally his mother's spirit was able to ascend to Heaven. And so the tradition of sacrificial offerings began.

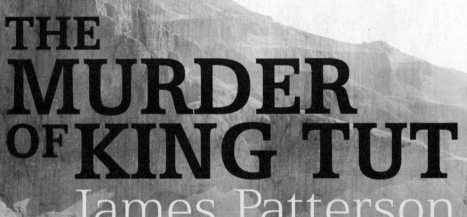

THE
MURDER
OF KING TUT

James Patterson
and Martin Dugard

Everyone knows about Tutankhamen, the
boy king of ancient Egypt who died young.
Everyone has heard of the many theories
relating to his untimely end.
But author James Patterson believes there
is much more to Tut's story than meets the
eye, and that the possibilities are as
astounding as fiction.

PROLOGUE

Valley of the Kings, 1900

It was New Year's Eve when a sombre, good-looking explorer named Howard Carter, speaking fluent Arabic, gave the order to begin digging.

Carter stood in a claustrophobic chamber more than 300 feet underground. The air was dank, but he craved a cigarette. He was addicted to the damn things. Sweat rings stained the armpits of his white shirt and dust coated his work boots. The sandal-clad Egyptian workers at his side began to shovel for all they were worth.

It had been almost two years since Carter had been thrown from his horse far out in the desert. That lucky fall had changed his life.

He had landed hard on the stony soil but was amazed to find himself peering at a deep cleft in the ground. It appeared to be the hidden entrance to an ancient burial chamber.

Working quickly and in secret, the twenty-six-year-old Egyptologist obtained the proper government permissions, then hired a crew to begin digging.

Now he expected to become famous at a very young age—and filthy rich.

Early Egyptian rulers had been buried inside elaborate stone pyramids, but centuries of ransacking by tomb robbers inspired later pharaohs to conceal their burial sites by carving them into the ground. Once a pharaoh died, was mummified, then sealed inside such a tomb with all his worldly possessions, great pains were taken to hide its location.

But that didn't help. Tomb robbers seemed to find every one.

Carter, a square-shouldered man who favoured bow ties, linen trousers and homburg hats, thought this tomb might be the exception. The limestone chips that had been dumped into the tunnels and shaft by some long-ago builder— a simple yet ingenious method to keep out bandits—appeared untouched.

Carter and his workers had spent months removing the shards. With each load that was hauled away, he became more and more certain that there was a great undisturbed burial chamber hidden deep within the ground. If he was right, the tomb would be filled with priceless treasures, as well as a pharaoh's mummy. Howard Carter would be rich beyond his wildest dreams, and his dreams were indeed spectacular.

'The men have now gone down a ninety-seven-metre vertical drop,' Carter had written to Lady Amherst, his long-time patron, 'and still no end.' Indeed, when widened, the narrow opening that he had stumbled upon revealed a network of tunnels leading farther underground.

At one point, a tunnel branched off into a chamber that contained a larger-than-life statue of an Egyptian pharaoh. But that tunnel had dead-ended into a vertical shaft filled with rock and debris.

As the months passed, the workers forged on, digging ever deeper, so deep in fact that the men had to be lowered down by rope each day. Carter's hopes soared. He even took the unusual step of contacting Britain's consul general in Cairo to prepare him for the glorious moment when a 'virgin' tomb would be opened.

Now he stood at the bottom of the shaft. Before him was a doorway sealed with plaster and stamped with the mark of a pharaoh—*the entrance to a burial chamber.*

Carter ordered his workers to knock it down.

The shaft was suddenly choked with noise and a storm of dust as the men demolished the ancient door. Carter hacked into his handkerchief as he struggled to see through the haze.

His heart raced as he finally held his lantern into the burial chamber. The workers standing behind him peered excitedly over his shoulder.

There was nothing there.

The treasure, and the pharaoh's mummy, had already been stolen.

By somebody else.

Palm Beach, Florida, present day

'This is James Patterson calling. Is Michael around? I have a mystery story to tell him.'

As most people would expect, I love a good mystery, and I thought

I might have unearthed a real cracker to write about, which was why I had put in a call to Michael Pietsch, my editor at Little, Brown. Michael is also the publisher.

As I waited for Michael to come on the line, I looked around my first-floor office. Am I completely mad? I wondered.

The last thing I needed right now was another writing project. I already had a new Alex Cross novel on the go, and a Women's Murder Club brewing, plus a Maximum Ride to finish. In fact, there were *twenty-four* manuscripts—none of them yet completed—laid out on the expansive desk surface that occupies most of my office. I could read some of the titles: *Swimsuit, Witch & Wizard, Daniel X, Women's Murder Club 9, Worst Case* . . .

'I *am* completely crazy, aren't I?' I said as Pietsch came on the line. Michael is a calm and calming presence, very smart, and a wonderful father who knows how to handle children—like me—most of the time. Over the years we have become a good fit and have turned out more than a dozen number-one best sellers together.

'Of course you're crazy, but why the phone call?' he asked. 'Why aren't you writing?'

'I have an idea.'

'Only one?'

'I really like this one, Michael. Let me talk at you for a minute. Since you seem to know everything about everything, you are probably aware that a collection of King Tut memorabilia is touring the world. People are lining up everywhere; the exhibit is usually sold out weeks in advance. I actually visited a Tut exhibit years ago at the Met in New York, and then recently in Fort Lauderdale. I've seen first-hand how Tut's story blows people's minds—men, women and children, rich and poor.

'There's something about Tut that brings ancient Egypt to life for most of us. It's not just the incredible treasures he was buried with, or the art, or the near-miraculous discovery of the burial chamber by Howard Carter. It's all of that, of course, but there's something magical here, something iconic. Tut's name was scrubbed from Egyptian history books for thousands of years, and now Tut is probably the most famous pharaoh of them all. And yet nobody knows that much about him.

'Michael, I want to do a book about Tut. Three parts: present day, as I learn—*hopefully*—more and more about the Boy King; then the amazing discovery of the tomb and treasures by Carter, who is probably worth a book on his own; and a third part about Tut himself.

'So what do you think? Are you going to try to stop me? Just this once, will you save me from myself?'

Michael's infectious laughter travelled across the phone lines.

'Well, Jim, like just about everyone else, I'm fascinated by ancient Egypt, the pyramids, the Valley of the Kings, Tut, Nefertiti, the Rameses boys. So I have to tell you, I like the idea very much.'

Now it was my turn to smile and to laugh in relief.

'I'm really glad. So let me tell you what I thought would close the deal— though, obviously, I don't need it. Michael, I have a hunch that Tut was murdered. And I hope, at least on paper, to prove it.'

Michael laughed again. 'You had me at "King Tut",' he quipped.

PART ONE

CHAPTER 1

Valley of the Kings, 1492 BC

'This is far enough! Stop right here.'

More than 500 prisoners of war halted their march towards Thebes in a great field situated two miles from the city. A contingent of the palace guard watched over them in the sweltering midday sun. Not that it was necessary. The emaciated prisoners' feet were bound with leather cord that was just long enough for them to frog-march; they could not run.

Ineni, the well-regarded royal architect, watched over the sad scene. He knew these men well. They had just spent five years in a remote valley excavating a new burial place for Tuthmosis I.

By day they had endured withering summer heat and surprisingly frigid blasts of desert cold that sometimes strafed the valley. At night they had slept under a sky shot through with stars.

It had been more than 1,000 years since Cheops had built his great pyramid up the Nile in Giza. As grand and awe-inspiring as they were, pyramids turned out to be beacons of temptation for every local thief and tomb robber. There wasn't a single one that hadn't been looted. Not one.

But Ineni believed he had the solution to the pyramid problem. Using the slave labour provided by these prisoners, he had carved a *secret* burial chamber for Tuthmosis I. Not merely a makeshift cave, the tomb contained several tunnels, hallways and half a dozen rooms. The pharaoh's stone sarcophagus would reside precisely in the centre, in the largest, most luxurious room.

True, Ineni thought, brushing a bead of sweat from his eyebrow, such an underground tomb was hardly as grand as a soaring pyramid. But in many ways it was better. The walls were smooth to the touch and painted with vivid scenes from the pharaoh's life—both the one he had just lived and the glorious one yet to come.

Most important, the pharaoh would be undisturbed. Hopefully, for all eternity.

Ineni liked the design so much that he was already working on a similar tomb for himself. 'I superintended the excavations of the cliff tomb of His Majesty,' Ineni would write on the walls of his own burial chamber. 'Alone, no one seeing, no one hearing.'

Of course, he hadn't been totally alone. The prisoners had done their part. He had got to know them, Hittites and Nubians. He'd heard about their wives and children. Some of the prisoners had become his friends.

After the tomb for Tuthmosis I was sealed and the entry concealed with stone, he had marched the men away from the area—a place that one day would simply be known as the Valley of the Kings, because so many other pharaohs would choose Ineni's architectural contrivance as a means of hiding their final resting places.

Ineni scanned the faces of the prisoners. They knew the location of the pharaoh's secret tomb, and that was unacceptable. The architect turned away from the men, then signalled to the guards.

'Do what must be done. Be merciful. Do it quickly. These are good men.'

And so the bloody slaughter of the prisoners began. Their screams rose to the heavens, and Ineni hoped that the many gods of Egypt approved of his difficult but necessary decision.

Thebes, 1357 BC

Amenhotep the Magnificent knocked back a stiff gulp of red wine as he shuffled into the sunlit throne room.

Once upon a time the pharaoh had been lean and muscular, a warrior feared throughout the known world. Now he was 'prosperous', which was a polite way of saying that his great belly preceded him wherever he went.

'You'll get fat from all that wine,' cooed Tiye, his queen and favourite wife—possibly because she had a sense of humour that matched his own.

'Too late.' Amenhotep slurred his words noticeably. 'At least a dozen years too late.'

Just back from a morning of sailing, Tiye had entered from the main hall without fanfare, her sandalled feet quietly slapping the tiled floor. The queen had full lips, a pleasingly ample bosom, and wore a white linen dress with vertical blue stripes that was cinched at her narrow waist.

They both knew why she'd come to see him today.

'Pharaoh,' she said, standing over him, 'we must talk. This one time you must listen to a woman, my love. You *must*.'

Amenhotep pretended to ignore his queen. He thought about swabbing a little opium on his abscessed teeth, just to take the edge off, and then maybe having a nap before dinner. No. First a visit to the lovely Resi over at the harem for a midafternoon romp, then sleep. Amenhotep got a happy feeling just thinking about her.

Up in Memphis, the northern capital of his kingdom, the bureaucrats would be pestering him with crop reports and tax estimates. Nothing but meetings all day long. Yes, Egypt needed officials like that; the country would be a lawless backwater without the legion of clerks. But after three decades in power, Amenhotep needed a break.

Which is why he loved Thebes much more than Memphis.

Thebes, just a week's journey up the Nile from Memphis, was so different from the northern capital, it might as well have been in a separate country. In Thebes a pharaoh could bask in the desert sun, drink wine whenever he wanted, and make love to his entire harem—a dozen beauties, each selected by him—without a single bureaucratic interruption. In Thebes a pharaoh had time to think, to dream. In Thebes the pharaoh answered to no one—except his wife.

Amenhotep looked up at Tiye. 'I am a fat old pharaoh who is no longer fit to rule this kingdom. Is that what you're about to say? Tell me.'

Tiye bit her tongue. In many ways, she loved this fat old man, this *deity*. But now Amenhotep was dying. Decisions had to be made before it was too late—for Egypt, and for its queen.

'All right,' he said with a sigh. 'Let's talk. I'm dying. What of it?'

'The future of Egypt is at stake. You know that. You need to take action.'

'I will never share power with that *accident*,' shouted the pharaoh.

Amenhotep had rallied somewhat from his drunken state. Now the palace walls shook with his angry protestations. He and Tiye were alone, but everyone from the bodyguards at the door to the servant girls polishing the great tiled hallway were privy to their battle. Soon these commoners would be gossiping to their friends and families, and the details of the royal argument would spread throughout Thebes.

'You are speaking about a *child* created in a moment of passion. Perhaps the pharaoh would like to describe what was accidental about that.'

'I do not regret the act of making love, only the result of our lovemaking. He will not reign as co-regent. I couldn't bear it. He is a snivelling whelp.'

Tiye sneered. 'We both know that he will succeed you one day.'

'You hope so, don't you? Does my queen not admit that she has selfish reasons for wanting that boy elevated to co-regent?'

'The queen admits nothing of the kind. The queen wants what's best for Egypt. Surely you wish your son to step into power—armed with your many years of hard-earned wisdom?'

You will lose everything if someone else succeeds me, thought the cynical Amenhotep. *So don't tell me what's best for Egypt. Have you braved thirst and burning deserts to wage war on the Hittites? Have you smelled the cedar forests of Byblos? You wear the gold and lapis lazuli that come as tribute from lands I conquered, but you know nothing of the world outside Thebes.*

'His arms hang to his knees, and his face is as long as a horse's,' Amenhotep declared. 'He hasn't enough muscle to wield a sword. To be pharaoh is to be god in the flesh. That boy is a freak.'

'He was born to lead our people. He can drive a chariot as well as any man,' said Tiye. 'He is well-read and smart.'

The pharaoh snorted. The mere sight of his son—also named Amenhotep—at the reins of a chariot was hilarious. It was a wonder the imbecile hadn't been trampled to death already. 'Steering through a grain field is one thing. Charging into battle is quite another,' he said.

Suddenly, Amenhotep felt woozy. The opium had gone to work, but the pain was still unbearable. What he needed was more wine.

Amenhotep ignored his goblet and raised the full pitcher to his lips. The ruby liquid spilled along his face, then trickled down his thick neck and under his collar onto the copper skin of his belly. It came to rest on the white kilt around his waist, leaving a stain that looked like blood. The pharaoh tumbled backwards into his pillows. This was an act of retreat, and they both knew it.

Tiye stood over him to close the deal, as the sun's fiery rays taunted the crocodiles and cobras painted on the tiled floor. 'This must be done, Pharaoh. And soon.'

'They have almost finished decorating my burial chamber,' the pharaoh muttered. He reached for a plate of bread flavoured with honey and dates, unaware that the grains of sand in every bite were the source of his pain. Year after year, the desert grit in the bread wore away the enamel on his teeth, inviting the decay and infection that would soon take his life.

Tiye handed him another goblet filled with wine, then remained still as Amenhotep chased the bread with a long gulp. She was as serene as the Sphinx as she waited for her husband to bend to her strong will.

'Tuthmosis would have been a great pharaoh,' he said mournfully.

'That son now wanders the afterworld,' Tiye replied.

Amenhotep nodded sadly. Their oldest boy, his beloved, his favourite, was dead. Soon he would join him. Egypt would need a new pharaoh. The only way to control the selection was to do it himself.

'Bring the accident to me,' Amenhotep roared. 'Of course he will be pharaoh. But shame on me for leaving Egypt to him. Shame on both of us.'

Didlington Hall, near Swaffham, England, 1887

'Howard, is that you? What do you think you're doing in here?' asked Lord Amherst, swinging open the library doors. 'These artefacts are *irreplaceable*. I've told you that before. You are a stubborn boy.'

Thirteen-year-old Howard Carter quickly turned his head towards His Lordship. He was caught! He had been warned repeatedly about this room. He was definitely a stubborn boy.

It was the middle of the day. Young Carter was supposed to be helping his father, who was painting a new commission for His Lordship. In a moment of boredom, the boy had slipped away to the most forbidden and imposing room at Didlington Hall: the library.

He couldn't help himself. The room was utterly fascinating, its silence augmented by the startling, massive stone statues situated about the room, imported straight from the sands of Egypt. To gaze at them allowed

Carter to see into the history of the known world. These pieces truly *were* irreplaceable.

Fortunately, Lord Amherst was a nice man with five daughters; Carter was the closest thing to a son he'd ever had. He recognised the slender, strong-jawed young man's innate, sometimes fierce curiosity and saw in him something of himself. He and young Carter both wanted—no, that would be too soft a description—*demanded* answers about what had come before them. They were obsessed with the ancient past.

So rather than kicking Carter out of the library, Lord Amherst proceeded to walk him through the wood-panelled room, patiently explaining the significance of the more notable books. There was a priceless collection of Bibles, many printed centuries earlier. There was a section devoted to incunabula, books printed shortly after the invention of the printing press. There were books with fancy bindings, first editions by famous authors and so forth.

And then there was the *Egyptian* collection.

In addition to owning tome after tome detailing the known history of ancient Egypt, Lord Amherst had rather obsessively decorated the library with Egyptian relics. The taller statues were bigger than a man and loomed like sentinels among the overstuffed wing-back chairs and oil reading lamps. There were dozens of smaller statues too, and rare texts printed on papyrus that had been sealed behind glass so that human hands like Howard's couldn't damage them. Amherst had bought the collection from a German priest two decades earlier and had added to it every year since.

'Not only is it the largest collection of Egyptology in all of Great Britain,' he told Carter, 'it is the joy of my life.'

'And mine as well,' Carter chimed in.

The tour concluded with a history-changing announcement: Lord Amherst was hereby offering the young man unlimited access to his collection. Never mind that something as simple as bumping into a statue could cause thousands of pounds' worth of damage—Amherst had seen the passion in Carter's eyes as he told him of the mysteries of Egyptian culture, with its strange alphabet and belief in the afterworld and the amazing burial chambers.

Amherst encouraged Carter to immerse himself in Egyptology. And that was precisely what Howard Carter did—until the day he died.

Didlington Hall, 1891

It was late May, almost June. Howard Carter, now seventeen, strode up the Watteau Walk towards the white columns marking the south entrance of Didlington Hall.

There was a fragrance of fresh grass in the air but a weariness in his step. He had spent the day as he spent most days, sketching household pets. It was a living—not a good living, and certainly not an exciting living, but he had no other skills and little formal education.

Though he had grown accustomed to being treated as family by the Amhersts, the fact of the matter was that while he was able to put on airs alongside the best of the nobility and was always welcome to spend hours in Lord Amherst's library, he was doomed to a life of very modest income and minimal prestige.

Carter stepped into the cool entrance hall. The great expanse was lined with expensive paintings and other works of art, some of which dated back to the eleventh century.

A butler showed Carter to the library. Lady Amherst was there, as was her youngest daughter, twenty-five-year-old Alicia. They greeted Carter warmly and introduced him to an affable stranger who clearly had a flirtatious relationship with Alicia.

The stranger was a bony young man in his early twenties named Perky Newberry. His face and hands were deeply tanned from hours outdoors, and his face was half covered with a prominent moustache. Carter soon learned that Newberry was an Egyptologist who was pursuing Alicia's heart and Lady Amherst's pocketbook. He was fresh from a November–April stint along the Nile, surveying ruins at a place called Beni Hasan.

Lady Amherst, who had always loved Carter, was obviously keen on having the two of them meet. Carter sat and listened eagerly as Newberry told incredible stories about life on the Nile. He spoke of working in the tombs from first light all the way through to the evening meal, then devoting the greater part of the night to study and discussion. Newberry's tone was intense, and he had a deep passion for his work. Carter liked him instantly.

On behalf of the British Museum, Newberry's expedition had undertaken to create a visual record of the drawings and colourful hieroglyphics inside the pharaohs' tombs before they faded away completely—something that often happened when ancient drawings were exposed to air and the presence of human beings. The task was enormous. There were some 12,000 square feet of wall drawings to sketch.

And while the job had gone well at first, the relationship between Newberry and his sketch artist had soured. Now, as he was raising money to fund another season in Egypt, Newberry was also searching for a new sketch artist. The job required someone with significant knowledge of Egypt and a talent for drawing and painting.

That person, it soon became obvious, was Howard Carter.

Alexandria, 1891
Only the hugely irritating fact that he was seasick prevented Carter from bursting with excitement. My God, he was in Alexandria, Egypt. He steadied himself against the roll of the steamship as he scanned the docks for Perky Newberry.

Carter had just reached the ancient port founded by Alexander the Great, the man responsible for ending the great Egyptian empires. Some said the city was the gateway to Africa; others called it the crossroads of the world. For the seventeen-year-old Carter, Alexandria was simply the place where his life would begin.

But first he had to find Perky Newberry.

It was Newberry who had rescued Carter from the tedium of drawing family pets and had sent him to train at the British Museum so he would be prepared for his role as a sketch artist. Perky had gone ahead of Carter to Egypt and should now have been waiting for him onshore.

Somewhere. *But where?*

Carter was slender, with a lantern jaw and a whisper of the bushy moustache he would wear for the next four decades. The air was hot like the mouth of a blast furnace, and he could feel the searing heat of the deck burning through the soles of his shoes. He was dressed for October in England, not October in Egypt. He would eagerly have traded his suit and tie for the dock workers' simple white robes. None of them seemed bothered by the heat.

Carter squinted into the pale sunshine, scanning the distant dock for a sign of Newberry. But there was no Englishman among the mélange of half-dressed Moors, Turks, Nubians and Egyptians. No sign of Newberry's straw hat.

Where the hell are you, Perky?

Carter studied the skyline and spotted Pompey's priapic pillar jutting above Alexandria like some ancient Roman practical joke. He double-checked that he had everything he needed to go ashore. His list was short: sketchbook, notebook, suitcase.

The ship's anchors splashed into the Great Harbour like a shotgun blast. Immediately, a locust-like plague of dock workers clambered up over the side. Carter barely avoided being knocked over as he made his way to the gangplank being lowered off the edge of the ship. He scuttled down into a waiting boat, and a local man rowed him ashore.

Carter paid the man and stepped up onto the stone dock. And there stood Perky Newberry, resplendent in his straw boater, smiling broadly.

'Where were you?' Carter dared to complain to his boss and employer. 'I'm always prompt and efficient myself.'

Perky Newberry just laughed. 'Well, you'd better be, with that attitude of yours. Welcome to Egypt, Carter.'

Howard Carter's Egyptian adventure was about to begin. Though he didn't realise it then, a boy had come to find the Boy King.

Beni Hasan, 1891

Carter woke up inside a tomb. He was eager to begin working, though it was totally dark, and the small room smelled like, well, death warmed up.

The floor of the burial place was carved stone covered in a fine layer of sand. Bats clung to the ceiling, the rustle of their wings making a sound like what Carter would one day call 'strange spirits of the ancient dead'.

Newberry lay nearby. Like Carter, he had spent the night in the tomb, for they had arrived after nightfall and had nowhere else to sleep.

If this was to be Howard Carter's first day as an Egyptologist—and it was—it couldn't have got off to a more atmospheric start.

From Alexandria, Carter and Newberry had taken the train to Cairo, where they spent a week with Flinders Petrie, whom Lord Amherst had called 'the master' of Egyptian excavation because of his years of experience in the tombs.

Those days spent in the Egyptian metropolis had been exciting, but soon it was time to move on. From Cairo, Carter and Newberry chugged south. The tracks hugged the Nile, but while the scenery on the train ride from Alexandria had been lush and green through the river delta, just outside Cairo it had turned barren and desolate. A thin strip of greenery sprouted along either side of the Nile, thanks to its annual habit of overflowing its banks, but otherwise the sensation of being surrounded by desert was powerful indeed.

After 200 miles, the men disembarked at Abu Qirqas station, where they hired donkeys—one each for themselves, and one each for their luggage. Carter had no problem handling his animals, thanks to his many years spent living in the country.

The fertile black loam of the riverside path soon turned dry and rocky. The sun was setting, and Carter and Newberry knew that it would be a race just to get to the tombs before dark.

They lost.

The trail became increasingly narrow and rugged as it climbed an escarpment. But eventually they reached the tombs, which provided acceptable shelter from the wind and night-time cold. Their remote location allowed the two men simply to step through the ancient stone doorway and stretch out for the night.

Now Carter shuffled outside to see for himself what the Egyptian desert looked like at dawn. He wasn't disappointed.

'The view was breathtaking,' he later wrote. 'The Nile Valley glowing softly in the sunlight, stretching far into the distance, the edges of the tawny desert contrasting amiably with the fertile plain.'

He was in a land that couldn't have been more different from the verdant pastures of Swaffham.

But Howard Carter felt as if he had finally come home.

CHAPTER 2

Thebes, 1347 BC

The mad roar of the crowd penetrated the temple's thick stone walls, shaking them to their foundations. It was bedlam on the streets of Thebes—deafening noise mingled with the spectacle of men and women frantically making love in back alleys, oblivious to the stench of stale urine, desert dust and whisky vomit.

Such was the Sed festival in Thebes, a time when all of Egypt celebrated the immortality of the pharaoh. But the partying was happening on the other side of these sacred walls.

Inside the temple at Karnak, Queen Nefertiti was oblivious to the noise of the masses. A slender, shaven-headed package of genius and raw sexuality, she had the knack of making men go weak in the knees by her mere presence. (Her name means 'a beautiful woman has come'.) Nefertiti was also known for her poise, but at the moment she was seized by an urge to slap someone hard across the face. Whether it should be her anxious wimp of a husband or the silly sculptor with the peasant beard who was taking hours to draw a simple sketch, she couldn't decide.

So Nefertiti settled onto her throne and tried to see her husband through the eyes of the sculptor. Amenhotep IV was in his early twenties and at the height of his power and virility. Yet he had hideous buckteeth and long spidery hands. *And those ears! Could they possibly get any bigger?*

Yet she loved him in her way. All his life, her husband had been a freak. But he was her freak, and that freak happened to be the pharaoh, which made her queen.

And what a queen she was turning out to be—performing sacred rituals once reserved just for pharaohs; frequently wearing the Nubian wig that only men had worn prior; even driving her own chariot with the skill of a man.

Much of this was possible because Egypt had always treated women better than other ancient civilisations had. Women could conduct business, own property, represent themselves in legal disputes and become doctors. Women had even become pharaoh, and queens with the strength of Nefertiti could control their much weaker husbands.

'You look divine,' purred Nefertiti now.

'I *am* divine,' laughed Amenhotep IV. It was their little joke.

'Is it so difficult to show me as I am?' he finally barked at the artist. He was a new pharaoh and still didn't understand that raising his voice showed weakness. His father, Amenhotep the Magnificent, had died from a painful infection of the mouth. Amenhotep IV had briefly served alongside his father as co-regent.

Nefertiti saw that he looked all too human on this, the day Egypt was supposed to bask in his strength as pharaoh.

This was a problem: the pharaoh needed to prove his immortality by galloping a chariot through the teeming masses outside. Even under the best of conditions, it was a bold and reckless ride that could easily end in a crash, which would be a disaster for the young pharaoh.

As palace insiders were all too aware, Amenhotep IV was very poor at the reins of a chariot. This ritual race could become a suicide run for him.

Yet if by some miracle he pulled it off, his claim to Egypt's throne would be secure. No longer would his masculinity be questioned. With one death-defying ride, Amenhotep IV would demonstrate his power in a most public way. Egypt would know that he was their one true pharaoh.

But if anything went wrong—if Amenhotep IV got thrown or dropped the reins and crashed into the crowd; if a wheel somehow broke off, and the chariot spun out of control—it would be obvious that the strange-looking man claiming to be the pharaoh was no god. And if a pharaoh was not divine, the temple high priests would find another to take his place.

Somehow they would kill him. And possibly his queen as well.

'How are you?' Nefertiti asked. 'I have nothing but confidence in you, sire.'

'You lie—so beautifully,' the pharaoh replied.

'How much longer?' Nefertiti whirled and shouted at the sculptor.

'At least thirty minutes.' The little man crumpled a sheet of papyrus to start afresh.

'You have ten.'

'But, Queen—'

'Not a second more.'

'I'll do my best,' the sculptor replied.

Nefertiti pursed her lips in a thin crocodile smile—and made a mental note to have the so-called artist killed once the statue was complete.

THE PRIESTS, PREENING AND PRATTLING, filed into the temple room when the sculptor finally left. They were as haughty as the queen's famed cats. Nefertiti despised their power and how they used religion to make themselves rich.

'Where to next?' Amenhotep IV said to the aged high priest, Ptahmose, slipping back into his ceremonial Sed cloak.

'The temple of Wepwawet awaits, sire. We must apply holy ointment to the standard.'

'I do not honour that god,' Amenhotep proclaimed. 'Wepwawet is nothing to me.'

The priests shuddered at this heresy. Even Nefertiti was shocked, though her religious belief was much the same as her husband's. Egypt was a land of several gods, and all were to be worshipped according to law.

Before Nefertiti could say something diplomatic, Amenhotep grabbed her hand and yanked her down the smooth stone corridor towards the street. 'I know what I'm doing!' he told her as the raucous crowd grew so loud the pair could hear nothing else.

The royal couple entered the reviewing stand through the back and stood where they could observe the assembled masses without being seen themselves.

Nefertiti was awed at the sight of the crowd. 'They are here for you,' she told her husband. 'They love you, as I do.'

Rich and poor, scribe, surgeon and farmer, had come from all over Egypt. They had cheered with delight when their pharaoh oversaw the morning's cattle census. An even larger group gasped in wonder as he donned the Sed cloak at noon. But that was six hours ago.

Now the crowd numbered in the tens of thousands. Too much sun and too much ale had turned their enthusiasm into restlessness. Artisans, shopkeepers, even slaves were chanting as one, demanding to see their pharaoh make the dangerous chariot run.

How could he possibly fail—if he was divine?

Nefertiti glanced at her husband, expecting to see him trembling in fear. Instead, Amenhotep wore a look of serenity. 'When I am done with this, I will have put my mark on all of Egypt,' he told her. 'No longer will I allow those pompous buffoons in the temple—'

'You speak that way about the priests?' Nefertiti whispered. She had little respect for the priests but knew better than to talk like this. What was happening to her husband? Was he saying all this because he knew he was about to die?

'That's right. You heard me. No longer will they have any say in how I rule my kingdom. Starting tomorrow, Amun, Re-Harakhty and all their other pitiful gods will be banished.'

'You speak heresy,' Nefertiti said. She felt faint. Had Amenhotep gone mad? Was it his terror speaking now?

'We will worship Aten—and Aten alone.' Aten was the sun god.

'Do the priests know? Any of them? Does Ptahmose know?'

Her husband's cunning smile answered her question.

'They will be furious!' she said. 'They will come after you. *And me as well.*'

'That won't matter. Do you want to know why?'

Actually, she didn't. In his current state, Amenhotep IV was likely to say something utterly crazy. He didn't disappoint.

'I'm building a new city for us.'

'I don't understand, Pharaoh,' said Nefertiti. 'What new city? Where would it be? Why haven't you told me before?'

'It will lie halfway between here and Memphis,' he continued. 'It will be the greatest city in the world. I will never leave there. Not even to wage war or collect tribute. Thebes and Memphis can return to the desert for all I care.'

The crowd was loudly chanting the pharaoh's name, but Nefertiti wasn't ready to let him go. She clung to her husband and said nothing more. But he pulled away and began walking up to the reviewing stand—without so much as a kiss or a goodbye.

'Oh!' he said, turning round to her. 'I have saved the best for last. Tomorrow I will change my name to honour our god's greatness. No one will ever again confuse me with my father.'

'What will I call you?' the queen asked, her mind reeling and her knees weak.

'Akhenaten.'

And then, to deafening applause, the pharaoh strode to his chariot and began his ride to immortality.

AN EVEN GREATER ROAR echoed through Thebes as the pharaoh's horses picked up speed.

High atop the reviewing stand, Nefertiti watched . . . *Akhenaten* . . . and tried to appear calm.

Meanwhile, two deep-set eyes leered at her. They belonged to her husband's royal scribe, a powerfully built man in his late thirties named Aye.

The populace was mesmerised by the horse-faced pharaoh galloping his favourite chariot, but Aye couldn't have cared less. He was tantalised by the nervous young queen. She slipped her index finger into her mouth to bite her painted nail before remembering that thousands might witness her insecurity.

The royal scribe licked his lips. He could have almost any woman in Egypt, but she was the one he wanted. Aye studied her graceful neck and the rest of her, down to the gentle sway of her hips. She was much smarter than the pharaoh, who was a freak undeserving of her. Having served under his father, Aye knew how a pharaoh should look and behave—and Amenhotep was no such man.

But if not Amenhotep, then who should reign? Aye wondered.

He answered his own question: *me.*

Nefertiti suddenly turned his way. She caught him staring but pretended not to notice. She never seemed to notice him.

Aye smiled and glanced down to the street. Miraculously, the pharaoh had survived the first leg of his journey and was now making the turn for home.

Just then a wheel flew off, bouncing wildly into the crowd and nearly beheading a spectator. Screams rent the air. Terrified onlookers fled, certain that the chariot would plough into them and kill dozens of innocents.

The pharaoh was thrown forward out of the basket onto the flank of the horse in front of him. He somehow managed to hold on to the reins but he dangled face down over the side of the animal. The frightened team galloped faster and faster, dragging the chariot, hoofs perilously close to the pharaoh's face.

Aye turned towards Nefertiti, whose hands now covered her mouth. Even as the future of Egypt hung on what happened in the next few seconds, Aye couldn't take his eyes off her. She was extraordinary in every way, truly a queen, possibly the most impressive person in all of Egypt.

Then the crowd exploded with a roar so loud that the ground beneath the reviewing stand shook.

Aye flicked his eyes back towards the street and saw that the pharaoh had somehow righted himself and pulled himself up onto the back of the horse. He now sat astride the white charger, fully in control as the team galloped on. Down came Nefertiti's hands. Away went the look of horror. She was a woman renewed, glowing with pride and love.

As the pharaoh halted the horses at the base of the reviewing stand, the crowd screamed in adulation. He looked up at Nefertiti, his eyes relieved and confident. He dismounted and walked slowly down the centre of the boulevard, basking in the divine certainty that he was both ruler and god.

And then Nefertiti placed her lips to Aye's ear. He could smell her perfume and feel the heat of her skin. More than ever, he lusted for this beautiful woman.

'Starting tomorrow, Aye,' she told him, 'Egypt will be changed for ever. Mark my words. And, Aye?'

'Yes, my queen?'

'If I ever see you looking at me that way again, I will feed your heart to the crocodiles.'

Amarna, 1345 BC

Only in the ancient world was such a thing possible—such a miracle in architecture. In just two years, the city of Amarna was complete. Aye had been in charge of the site, and now he sent word to the pharaoh. He figured he had three weeks, maybe four, until Akhenaten and his host of minions arrived.

But he had underestimated his king's desire to flee Thebes.

A week after his message was received, Aye was sipping ale on the terrace of the new royal palace. He was bored and lonely. His wife was still in Thebes. Even worse, so were his harem girls.

He gazed out at the Nile, marvelling at the view. It truly was a gorgeous afternoon. The sky was a clear blue, and the heat tolerable if he stayed in the shade.

Then the royal vizier saw a sight so shocking that he nearly dropped his ceramic mug.

Cruising up the Nile was an armada of ships. Dozens. No, make that hundreds of vessels. Their great triangular sails were visible from miles away. Aye could see thousands of citizens from Thebes lining the decks, ready to start their new lives in Amarna.

And on the prow of the largest barge, to see first-hand all that he'd created, stood Akhenaten. The stunning Nefertiti and their three coquettish daughters were at his side.

Akhenaten raised the royal standard in triumph, but Aye was focusing on Nefertiti and those three girls.

No boys. Just girls.

'I'll kill him,' Aye said in a flash of inspiration. Of course. It was the perfect solution.

Magnificent as she was, Nefertiti had not yet borne the pharaoh an heir. And with no male heir, there was no clear succession. If the pharaoh died—suddenly—there was no one to stop Aye from declaring himself pharaoh.

No one but Nefertiti, the queen bee.

'I'll deal with her when the time comes,' Aye mumbled, already planning his crime. But he couldn't afford to make a mistake. To kill the pharaoh and go undetected would require a perfect murder. He would have to be patient, choosing just the right moment and the right means of execution.

Aye pursed his lips. If nothing else, he was patient. The plan had been revealed to him in an instant, every detail and twist, but it would take some time to execute.

'Someday *I* will be the pharaoh,' he said boldly.

Amarna, 1892

This was amazing—*Amarna!*

Howard Carter carefully studied the lie of the land to make sure he had found just the right spot. What he wanted was a place with a view that was also close to the tombs. He had already examined the sand for drainage lines so that he wouldn't be swept away by a torrential downpour or the Nile when it overflowed its banks.

Now, at last, he settled on a spot. *This was it.*

Turning his head slowly in either direction to survey the horizon, he nodded to his small army of construction workers, who sprang into action— or at least moved as quickly as their somewhat relaxed approach to life and labour allowed.

Imagine—he was building a home here, a simple structure made of mud bricks like the ancient Egyptians used. For the first time in his life, Howard Carter was putting down roots, albeit shallow ones.

He would be labouring in Amarna, former home to Akhenaten and Nefertiti. The once-grand, now-ruined city was located at a broad bend in the Nile, on a low plateau fronted by a stunning array of cliffs. There was a shortage of housing in the newly rediscovered city, hence Carter's need to build his own. And this would be his home until he built something finer in Medinet Habu, miles from the valley, later on.

It was January, the peak of the dig season. Carter had left Beni Hasan— and Perky Newberry—for Amarna, thanks once again to the patronage of Lord Amherst. He would work there under veteran Flinders Petrie, making elaborate drawings of discoveries large and small.

Immediately on Carter's arrival, Petrie had made it known that they would travel by foot at all times. Petrie, a frugal man, didn't feel a need to purchase donkeys when walking was just as quick and far less expensive.

In addition, Carter received word that he was no longer just a sketch artist. Petrie had seen dozens of book-educated Englishmen come into the field, certain that their knowledge had prepared them to be excavators, and most had failed miserably.

Now, owing to a shortage of excavators and an intuitive belief that the cocksure young Carter could be trained more easily than someone older and less ambitious, Petrie informed Carter that excavation was being added to his daily list of chores.

Surprisingly, the results thus far had been less than stellar. 'Carter's interest is entirely in painting and natural history,' Petrie had written in his journal on January 9, less than a week after Carter's arrival. 'He is of no use to me as an excavator.'

An early review of the man who would make the most famous discovery ever in the Valley of the Kings.

Amarna, 1345 BC

The fierce and bellicose General Horemheb could not believe what he was hearing from this silly, useless pharaoh.

'We will not be waging war on our neighbours,' Akhenaten decreed, slouching in his throne.

The general should not have been cowed by the words of the pharaoh, but the intensity with which Akhenaten stared into his eyes was unsettling. Some men took power from privilege. Others took it from their position. And still others took it from their physical prowess. The pharaoh pretended he possessed all three. This gave him a surety that Horemheb found disconcerting to say the least.

So while Horemheb longed to topple the pharaoh's misguided government with some great military takeover, he found himself listening to this most incredible statement delivered by a freakish weakling, and there was nothing he could do about it.

'But, Pharaoh, if I may, we depend on war for many things: our wealth, our security, our status. This will mean the ruin of us. Your father—'

'I don't want to hear about my father. My father is in his tomb. His ways and his gods are things of the past. Just as dead as he is.'

'But, sire, we are the most powerful nation in all directions. Certainly we must protect that.'

Things have changed for the worse since the move to Amarna, Horemheb wanted to shout. *The country is going soft. The king never even leaves the palace. The great cities of Memphis and Thebes are in decline. We, as an Egyptian people, are in rapid decline.*

But he said none of these things. Instead, Horemheb listened to the pharaoh drone on in his stupid, idealistic way.

'And we will. We will worship Aten, who will protect our borders. But I see no need to wage war. What is so wrong with being a peaceful nation?'

'I believe in peace through strength, sire. We know this works from long experience.'

'I would expect to hear nothing less from you, General. That is your job.'

'And what is strength if it is not wielded? May I ask you that?'

The pharaoh smiled in a most condescending manner. 'General, when was the last time you spent a day just dreaming?'

Horemheb's jaw nearly dropped off his head. 'I beg your pardon?'

'You heard me. Do you ever write poetry? Do you ever lose yourself in thought? Have you ever completed a painting?'

'I am a warrior, sire. I am not trained to sit and think; I am trained to do.'

'Then do *this*.'

Akhenaten closed his eyes as if to meditate.

Horemheb waited until he could wait no longer. 'Sire, what is it you would like me to do?'

'Relax. Take your mind off war. Egypt no longer needs conflict, for we are protected by the great sun god, who will provide for all our needs.'

And lead us to ruin, Horemheb thought angrily.

'You are dismissed,' said the pharaoh with a gentle wave of his hand. 'Go and write a poem.'

Amarna, 1341 BC

'Tut. My poor Tut. What shall become of you?'

Nefertiti held her newborn son in her arms and feared for his life. Technically, the child was not her own, for he did not spring from her loins. But that idiot husband of hers with the wandering eye was the father, so the child might as well be the son of the queen.

The birth mother's name was Kiya, and the pharaoh had given the pretty young harlot the title Greatly Beloved Wife, which placed her above even Nefertiti in his esteem.

Kiya was—had been—a Mitannian princess named Tadukhepa, sent to Egypt by her father as a peace treaty between the two nations. For three long years Nefertiti had endured the woman's presence, watching her repeatedly take the queen's place in the pharaoh's bed. The man whom Nefertiti once loved had become a stranger to her, devoted to his beloved Aten and his child bride.

The pharaoh had begun telling people that he himself was Aten, that he and the god were one and the same. It was Nefertiti who had the nerve to correct him, and for that he had cast her from his bed.

I am still the mother of his children, she reminded herself.

Yes, but all girls. This one, the son, will be the next pharaoh. When the pharaoh dies, the empire will fall to this child, this baby. And what will become of me?

What does it matter? There will be nothing left of the great Egyptian nation by the time my husband dies. That fool has seen to that.

The people of Egypt were starving and reverting to their nomadic ways, forsaking their farms and cities for a difficult existence on the move, all thanks to Akhenaten's neglect or perhaps his insanity. The priests of Thebes wanted to kill him for usurping their gods with his own—and for asserting himself as a god.

And the royal vizier pretended to be a faithful servant, but once he got tired of Akhenaten's preening, he too would want to stab the pharaoh in the back.

And what of Horemheb?

Surely the general went to sleep each night and dreamed only of a military takeover.

So what stopped them? Could it be that they actually believed the pharaoh was a god? What fools men are. Or what liars.

The baby started to cry. Poor Tut.

Nefertiti was about to whisper to the child, telling him that at that very moment his mother was being placed inside her tomb. She had died giving birth, and Tut would never feel the comfort of her arms or suckle her bosom.

But the time for such talk was past.

'Be still, my son,' Nefertiti said. 'I am your mother now, and I will raise you to be the pharaoh your father should have been. You will be king. I promise you.'

CHAPTER 3

Deir el-Bahri, 1894

The blazing sun was beating down on Howard Carter's neck. It was Ramadan, the Muslim holy month, which meant that dig season was over, since the men fasted during the day. This made them too weak to dig in the hot sun.

Now Carter, working alone, alternately photographed and sketched the northwest chamber of a newly excavated temple near Luxor. He was nineteen years old.

It was Carter's second season excavating the structure dedicated to Hatshepsut, a female pharaoh nearly as famous as Nefertiti. It was a rocky location, situated at the base of a cliff, two miles from the Nile. Daytime temperatures often soared above 110 degrees Fahrenheit, and there was no shade.

Still, Carter worked from dawn to dusk, in the fashion he had learned from Petrie, mainly because he so loved what he did. This was his life. There was nothing else for him.

His boss now was a Frenchman named Edouard Naville. The prolific excavator had long believed that a vast temple complex lay beneath the soil at Deir el-Bahri, and the results of several seasons' work were proving he might be correct. Grand columns and towering walls now rose from the ground, unearthed after centuries of landslides and storms had covered them.

Naville had been pleased with Carter's growing professionalism but was also concerned that the young Englishman was too slow when it came to sketching and photographing. The same methodical bent that Petrie had once encouraged was now seen as a serious flaw.

But this cloud had a silver lining. Naville had requested a second artist to help Carter. The man hired for the task was none other than Carter's thirty-year-old brother, Vernet. The two had worked side by side through the early months of 1894, producing a series of dazzling sketches that were soon to be reproduced in book form. When Naville closed the site for Ramadan, he asked the Carter brothers to continue working. But the strapping Vernet fell prey to the heat and deprivation. He was forced to return to England, leaving his brother to finish Naville's job alone.

Carter had enjoyed the time with Vernet, but he never once contemplated returning home with his brother. The life of an Egyptologist had its perils to be sure. It wasn't everyone's idea of the ideal job. But for Howard Carter, it was paradise.

And, one day, he hoped to be a modern-day king—in the Valley of the Kings. He dreamed of making the greatest tomb discovery of them all, even though he had no idea what it might be.

Deir el-Bahri, 1899

There was no shade to be had in the valley of Deir el-Bahri, not so much as a dancing speck. So as Carter set up his easel on top of the ruins of an ancient and quite spectacular mortuary temple, the clock was ticking.

The rising March sun was just now lining the horizon. Within an hour, the heat of the day would get uncomfortable, and beads of sweat would drench Carter's hatband. Within two hours, his brushstrokes would dry almost as soon as he applied the watercolours. And within three hours, the lead of his pencil would become too soft to sketch even a single line.

So he worked quickly, drawing the exterior of the temple, making sure that its massive proportions were in scale with the equally massive cliff rising like a great wall behind it.

Carter had acquired a reputation as a very good artist—indeed, his subjects ranged from the animals in the Cairo zoo to intricate tomb interiors. But he had been in Egypt for eight years now. It was impossible for him to paint a watercolour like the one on which he now laboured without mentally filling in the history behind it.

The temple before him had belonged to Queen Hatshepsut. It had taken fifteen years to build. The building looked more like a palace than a tomb and was peculiar for being so ostentatious. At the time of its construction, back in the fifteenth century BC, pharaohs were trying to conceal their burial places, not flaunt them for tomb robbers.

But just as this was no ordinary temple, Hatshepsut had been no ordinary pharaoh. After her husband (who was also her half-brother) died, she had broken centuries of tradition and ruled as the first female pharaoh. Her reign had been prosperous, as were those of her children and her children's children.

Carter knew that Hatshepsut had once been deeply in love, for she was a queen before she was a pharaoh. He knew also of her father, Tuthmosis I, the first pharaoh to be buried in what came to be known as the Valley of the Kings rather than in a pyramid.

The pyramids, so obvious and tempting, had been easy to plunder, which meant the pharaohs were deprived of their possessions during their journeys into the afterworld. Carving a tomb in a desolate valley seemed the best way to discourage thieves.

Sadly, the architect Ineni had been wrong about that.

Carter dabbed more paint on the paper—quickly. The sun was low on the horizon and directly in his eyes. He averted his gaze to reduce the risk of ophthalmia, bleeding of the eyes that came from looking too long at the sun. The disease was common among Egyptologists and could easily end a career.

A few hundred yards off, tourists and their Egyptian guides were dismounting mules and making their way to the temple.

Little did they know that one of the world's most promising Egyptologists was in their midst. Carter had worked his way up from being a poorly paid junior draughtsman and was now learning the methods of the great excavators.

The key to becoming an excavator, Carter knew all too well, was luck. But after that came money, a great deal of money. He needed to find a wealthy benefactor to cover his costs. He had seen such patrons in Luxor, hanging out at the Winter Palace Hotel or enjoying the Nile nightlife aboard lavish yachts.

Carter didn't know how to mingle comfortably in that society—or any society, really—but it was time that he learned.

How hard could it be to fool a bunch of fools?

Valley of the Kings, January 1900

'Gentlemen are invited to take off their coats,' Carter advised the tour group as they approached the tomb. 'It will get rather warm inside. Ladies, I'm afraid you'll have to settle for removing your hats.'

His work ethic and passion for Egyptology had already lifted the ambitious twenty-five-year-old Carter from the obscurity of his early days to the relative power of his new position as chief inspector for the Antiquities Service in Upper Egypt.

Carter had beaten Perky Newberry to the job, and now he oversaw all excavation in the region.

Many within the British Egyptology community found this distasteful, even ridiculous. They objected to Carter's lack of book knowledge, his lack of a university degree, and, perhaps most of all, his lack of table manners. To them, Carter was not one of the world's foremost Egyptologists, just its most infamous and crude.

Even Gaston Maspero, Carter's new boss, admitted that his charge was obstinate.

But Carter also had supporters and admirers, many of them female. Lady Amherst still welcomed Carter to Didlington Hall whenever he returned to England. He was something of a hero to her family for his ongoing series of adventures in the Egyptian desert.

Carter was certainly someone to reckon with, even if he didn't know which fork to use for his salad. He was now museum curator for the entire Valley of the Kings. The area was an isolated jumble of hills, cliffs and dry riverbed located three miles west of the Nile, just below the 'horn', the highest point in the Theban hills.

Nobody knew exactly how many Egyptian rulers were interred beneath the sunbaked earth. And there was a good chance no one would ever know. Time and weather, crumbling rock and blowing sand had completely changed the valley floor and enhanced its natural camouflage.

Actually to stumble upon a tomb was to find the proverbial needle in a haystack, which is why any discovery was so precious and why everyone, from tourist to tomb raider, was eager to see inside each burial chamber.

Since Italian circus strong man-cum-Egyptologist Giovanni Belzoni had performed the first serious excavation of the area in 1815, the tombs of more than two dozen pharaohs had been found within its craggy, soaring walls. Belzoni had stopped excavating in the valley after thirteen years because he believed there was nothing left to find. The discovery of tomb after tomb since then proved he'd been wrong.

In exchange for a 'concession'—permission to dig in the valley—excavators agreed to split all treasure fifty-fifty with the Egyptian government. Sometimes the discovery process was as simple as clearing away a few scattered rocks. At other times finding a tomb required scraping away mountains of hard-packed sand and stone, clear down to the bedrock.

The allure was treasure first, history second.

CARTER COULD NOT AFFORD to purchase a concession.

Nonetheless, just a few weeks into his new position, he was busily making the valley his own. In addition to setting up a donkey corral that could accommodate 100 animals, he had begun installing heavy metal gates on all the tomb entrances—to keep out the troublesome robbers and squatters who prowled the valley at night. He was also introducing electric lighting to make the tombs more inviting to the European tourists who visited the valley during the day.

And for reasons that had nothing to do with his job and everything to do with his own future success, Carter had begun to woo wealthy foreign tourists, hoping they might be convinced to fund a concession for him.

The American businessman Theodore Davis was just such a tourist.

Davis was a small, hugely opinionated man with a dense white moustache spanning ear to ear. A regular visitor to Luxor (the site of ancient Thebes), he had begun to display an obsessive interest in Egyptology.

Now Carter stood with Davis and his group at the entrance to the tomb of Amenhotep II, a spectacular and yet dangerous place to be leading novices, especially rich, influential ones who might break a leg or suffer heat stroke.

The tomb had been carved into a high cliff, and they had all climbed a long, shaky ladder to the opening, with Carter leading the way. These tourists were hardly dressed for tomb exploration, the men wearing hard shoes and ties, and the women floppy hats and long dresses. Carter gave them each a candle and issued sharp instructions not to lag behind. He led them down a narrow, low-ceilinged corridor, which descended steeply into the side of the cliff.

'Pay careful attention to each and every step, please,' Carter advised as the earth suddenly disappeared: the tomb builders had excavated a well thirty feet deep and ten feet wide to dissuade—or trap and mangle—the uninvited. Carter had laid boards across the chasm, and one by one the party made its way safely to the other side. In truth, he was playing up the danger a bit to pique the interest of these potential investors.

The tunnel plunged deeper into the earth, revealing an ancient stairwell that had given way, and forced the group to scramble over a pile of loose stones. Paintings lined the walls here, ancient murals in subtle shades of maroon and yellow.

At the site of another crumbled stairway, the tourists had to pick their way, hand over hand, up the rocky pile, then squeeze through a narrow opening to continue the journey. By now most were sweating and breathing hard. The close air made some of them sick. More than one finger and forearm had been burned by dripping wax as the sightseers struggled to manage their candles.

Yet they gamely pressed on, following Carter, quite literally, into the bowels of the earth.

The corridor turned a corner, and suddenly the group was inside a great rectangular chamber, and this room made the difficult trip worth every step.

The ceiling was painted with blue and yellow stars. And there, in the middle of the room, was a stone sarcophagus—with the mummy still inside.

'Notice the band of hieroglyphics around the top of the sarcophagus,' said Carter in a hoarse whisper. 'That is the mummy's curse, and that's the *only* thing that has protected it from being stolen.'

As the group gaped in awe, Carter had to suppress a smile. What incredible idiots they were! The hieroglyphics said nothing of the sort. He was lying through his teeth, hoping that his fabrication might incite Davis to purchase a concession.

To Carter's delight, it did just that.

Valley of the Kings, 1902

Forty-three. As Howard Carter stood at the top of the Theban horn, looking straight down into the Valley of the Kings, that was the number on his mind.

It had rained the night before, a violent colossus of a storm that had literally formed rivers and caused landslides along the hills.

The upper layer of soil had been washed away, making it the perfect place for Carter to be strolling at that very moment. With his eyes fixed on the ground and the number forty-three rattling around his head, he was scanning the freshly scrubbed earth for a telltale fissure or cleft that might yield a new tomb entrance.

Once again his heart was pounding. Carter still felt an indescribable power in the Valley of the Kings and believed that the area had a life of its own. He found it alternately spiritual and playful, a mischievous wasteland that continually taunted Egyptologists who believed there was nothing left to discover. Time and again, great explorers had declared that they'd found all there was to find. And then the valley would reveal another tomb or another cache of mummies, and the frantic spending and digging would resume.

Carter had carefully studied the detailed records of every Egyptologist since Napoleon and his men came through here at the turn of the nineteenth century. He had also studied the pharaohs' line of succession, comparing their names with the list of mummies that had already been found. Simple cross-referencing told him that several pharaohs were still somewhere below him in the valley floor, just waiting to be discovered.

So now he gazed out over the valley, wondering about the mysterious forty-three.

Forty-three was not a person's name. Tomb discoveries were numbered sequentially, and in the previous three years an astounding ten new tombs had been located by the Frenchman Victor Loret. But after finding KV 42 in 1900 and allowing Carter to help him do the major portion of the excavation, Loret had quit the valley.

KV 43 was still out there, waiting for someone to find it.

Carter suspected, sadly, that he would not be that man. The cost of hiring several hundred diggers for a season was more than £5,000 sterling. Add to that astonishing sum the cost of a yearly concession, lodgings, food, donkeys, shovels, picks and wheelbarrows, and it was obvious that Egyptology was the calling of the rich. What chance did Carter, the son of a simple portrait artist, have of finding a great pharaoh's tomb? But still he could dream. And he was *here* rather than in dreary old England.

Carter stared out at the folds and tucks of the valley, as if merely by looking long enough he would spot some obscure sign of a tomb. Finally, he settled down onto the ground, sitting crosslegged on the only smooth patch of yellow dirt for 100 yards in any direction. He opened the cover of his sketchbook. Holding his pencil lightly to the page, he drew a simple outline of the valley floor and the low flat mountains to the west. His challenge, as always, was somehow to capture the peace and grandeur that permeated that place. But for all Carter's genius as an artist, pencil lines on a piece of white paper could never fully convey the wonders of this magical spot.

There was great history here, if only he could find some of it himself, if only he could find KV 43.

Valley of the Kings, February 1, 1903

Carter blinked rapidly several times as he stumbled out into the pale morning light in this place that he loved. A loyal Egyptian worker immediately handed him water and a cigarette.

As Carter took a greedy swallow, another local man slipped a long, double-breasted overcoat round Carter's shoulders. This might have given the young Englishman an air of casual elegance were it not for the fact that onlookers swore he looked like a ghost.

He was, in truth, thoroughly exhausted, having spent most of the night sleeping outside on the hard ground.

At 4 a.m. he left a pair of men to stand guard, then went inside to prepare for the great unveiling—draping electric lights, placing beams over the deep wells, hanging rope ladders and handrails, and constructing wooden walkways so that his eighteen guests wouldn't destroy fragile archaeological items.

Howard Carter had finally found his tomb.

Tuthmosis IV was the eighth monarch of Egypt's Eighteenth Dynasty. He reigned from 1401 to 1391 BC and was the father of Amenhotep the Magnificent and the grandfather of Akhenaten. His body was sealed inside a stupendous tomb in the southeast corner of the Valley of the Kings. Elaborate pains had obviously been taken to hide the burial site, including a location several hundred yards away from any other dead pharaoh. Tuthmosis IV had deliberately chosen the most desolate, distant spot possible. Nevertheless, many years after his death, tomb robbers found him.

On January 17, 1903, so did Howard Carter.

Tuthmosis IV was KV 43.

This was the first great find of Carter's career.

He'd had to wait two weeks for his patron, Theodore Davis, to return from a boat trip upriver to Aswan. Now Carter would lead yet another tour, only this time it would be to a tomb that he had discovered.

Davis had purchased an exclusive valley concession in 1902 and immediately hired Carter to lead the excavation. That first season had been inconclusive, with Carter discovering only the tomb of a minor noble and a box containing two leather loincloths.

For the 1903 season, Carter chose to excavate a small, forgotten valley within the Valley of the Kings. In days his men had uncovered a tomb entrance, complete with small vessels embedded in the rock, which the Egyptians believed held magical powers.

He led the large group into that opening now.

The path descended quickly. By this time Carter was working mostly on adrenaline, proud of his discovery even as he delivered a clipped monologue about the tomb's contents: the war chariot, the sarcophagus, the mass of beautiful debris strewn about the burial chamber—no doubt by the tomb robbers.

The air was rank, and Carter would have to bring in fans and run lines of air from the outside as the excavation continued. But for now it was good enough. As he escorted the satisfied group back up the steep passage to the main entrance, Carter's workday was done. He felt a little like a god himself.

Tea and a lunch awaited, served on white tablecloths. The group, clearly awed by what they had just seen, celebrated Carter and Davis as they dined.

Carter deflected the praise onto his egomaniacal boss, who was beginning to see himself not just as a benefactor but as an Egyptologist in his own right. There were plenty of accolades to go round, and everyone proclaimed what a successful dig season this was going to be.

'All praise goes to Mr Davis!' said Howard Carter, believing not a word of it.

All praise goes to me, and perhaps to Tuthmosis IV, he thought.

Valley of the Kings, February 12, 1904

Carter could barely breathe, and poor Perky Newberry was about to pass out from the bad air, but their goal was within reach, and they soldiered onwards into the most recently discovered burial chamber.

The subtext of this great moment was that Howard Carter had done it again. It was almost unbelievable, but just a few weeks after finding the tomb of Tuthmosis IV, he'd unearthed another tomb on the same side of the valley. Inside was a mummy in a coffin.

The dead man's identity was unknown thus far, but Carter had made an amazing find. Not long before, he had come across evidence of Hatshepsut's burial place. The female pharaoh's temple on the other side of the mountain was perfectly aligned with this latest tomb. To Carter's way of thinking, it was possible, even likely, that a tunnel connected them.

'I do not hope for an untouched tomb,' he had written to Edouard Naville, alluding to every Egyptologist's prayer of finding a virgin burial chamber. 'Rainwater will be a great enemy, but hope for the best.'

Carter was certainly right about the rainwater. The storms that wiped the hillsides clean of debris had sent chunks of rock and sand into tomb openings, where they had hardened like cement. Since mid-October his workmen had swung pickaxes in the tomb corridors, clearing out the compacted earth.

Bits of pottery and other funerary debris had been found in the dirt, keeping Carter's hopes alive that the elusive mummy of Hatshepsut might be buried here. Finding it could be the highlight of his career and make Howard Carter famous around the world.

Finally, after four months, the workers had reached the burial chamber. Perky Newberry and Carter pulled down the mud-and-stone blocking that formed the chamber's doorway. Then both men entered.

A wave of dank, noxious air washed over them as the hole widened. Several steps inside, Newberry couldn't take it any more.

He pleaded with Carter to follow, then staggered back towards the light. But Carter pushed onwards. *How could he not?* He had worked thirteen long, hard years for this day, this discovery.

The heat and dank air conspired against him. Every stitch of his clothing was drenched in sweat, and he gasped for each breath.

The tomb, as he had predicted, was not untouched. Inside was an *empty* sarcophagus, a Canopic jar and broken vases bearing the names of Hatshepsut and her father.

They were items of historical interest, nothing more.

And *more* is what he wanted.

Howard Carter would no longer be satisfied with simply locating tombs. Now he wanted tombs of significance, untouched throughout history, and he especially wanted the great treasures buried with every pharaoh.

Carter 'emerged from the tomb,' wrote a friend of Theodore Davis's, 'a horrid object, dripping and wet, with a black dust over his face and hands—he was very sick, too, and had to lie down for some time.'

But the very next day, Carter was back at work, searching for that elusive virgin tomb that would make him a household name.

Maybe it would be Hatshepsut.

Or perhaps another pharaoh of even greater importance.

The treasure hunt continued and, in truth, it became Howard Carter's whole life.

Amarna, 1335 BC

Nefertiti wept as she had never wept before.

'Aye!' she finally yelled. 'Bring me Aye. I need him right this minute. Now!'

The royal scribe came running into the pharaoh's bedroom. Nefertiti was slumped at the foot of the bed, her supple frame hidden in an elaborate robe. The pharaoh lay on his back, unclothed, covered only by a scrap of bed sheet Nefertiti had laid across his lower body.

'He's dead,' Nefertiti said before Aye could utter a word.

Their eyes locked, and in that brief exchange, in the fire of Nefertiti's eyes, the power in the royal palace shifted inexorably in the new widow's favour. She was no longer the wife of the pharaoh but ruler of all of Egypt. She was divine. And Aye was still just the scribe—that is, if she allowed him to live.

Aye cleared his throat. 'What happened?'

'What do you think happened, Scribe? Isn't it obvious to you? I could barely get him off me.'

Aye had a clear mental picture of the queen straining to shove her dead mate off her after his final collapse.

'I'll see to his burial, Majesty,' he said. 'I will do everything.'

'And send out the messengers,' Nefertiti commanded, her lower lip quivering. 'Send them to Memphis and to Thebes. Announce to one and all that the great pharaoh is dead.'

'Majesty, do you think that wise? I mean, until we know who will succeed Akhenaten?' The royal scribe looked at her insolently. To be sure, Aye was a powerful man in the kingdom, and he baulked at taking orders from any woman.

Nefertiti glared at him. 'Have you forgotten that my husband fathered a child out of wedlock?' Her voice dripped with sarcasm. She had also given Akhenaten an heir since arriving in Amarna, but the child had died. 'When the time comes, and he has grown into a man, I will place my husband's son on the throne, but for now *I am the pharaoh*, Aye. Make no mistake about that.' She paused and looked at Akhenaten once more. 'Now, leave me with my husband. Go. Do your duties.'

Aye lowered his eyes and spun on his heels, then charged from the sun-filled room.

He would do as he was told—for now anyway.

NEFERTITI GAZED DOWN at her husband. Then she sat on the bed beside him, gently running her hand across his shaved head. She traced a lone finger down to his chest, then she stroked his face, memorising every detail.

These would be their last moments together, and she wanted to remember him as the powerful man he had once been, not the weak and whimsical pharaoh he had become. Nefertiti shuddered to think what would soon happen to this body she had known so well.

She placed her index finger atop the bridge of his nose. The royal mummifiers would start here, slipping a long wire up the nostrils into that marvellous and eccentric brain. They would spin the wire until the brain's gelatinous tissue broke down and revealed itself as grey snot running out of the nose. They would then turn the body over, positioning the head at the edge of an alabaster table to let the brain pour into a bucket glazed with gold.

Nefertiti now placed her hand low on her husband's groin, anticipating the spot where they would slice him open, shove a hand up inside, and yank out the internal organs.

She smiled as she placed her hand at the top of his sternum, the spot where she had laid her head so many times and felt the beating of his heart. At least they would leave his heart intact. Like her people, she believed the heart was the source of all knowledge and wisdom. Akhenaten would need its greatness to cast the spells that would reanimate his corpse.

Seventy days, she thought. That was how long it took to finalise the mummification process.

Seventy days to dry out the body in the desert heat so that it didn't decompose before reaching the afterworld.

Seventy days until they placed her husband in his tomb six and a half miles from where she now sat.

Let the other pharaohs entomb themselves in the Valley of the Kings— Akhenaten had chosen a spot just outside his beloved Amarna, a glorious valley all his own, bathed in sunlight so that he might delight in the wondrous majesty of Aten for evermore.

'I will join you there someday,' said Nefertiti, leaning down and kissing the lips that had travelled up and down every inch of her body.

She gazed down at him one last time and then left the room. Her husband was dead. Their son had predeceased him, and of his remaining children, just one was a boy.

It was now her duty to rule alongside the child until he became a man. She beckoned her lady in waiting.

'Yes, Queen?'

'Bring me Tutankhamen.'

PART TWO

CHAPTER 4

Palm Beach, Florida, present day

One of the most fascinating pieces discovered in the tomb of King Tut was an armless mannequin. Presumably, it was used for draping his clothes. Tut's face was painted on the mannequin. The face is a boy's, and it seems gentle and kind and knowing.

As I do on many mornings, I was walking round Donald Trump's golf paradise in West Palm, my favourite course anywhere. But my mind was on Tut. What an incredible mystery this was turning out to be. I was becoming nearly as obsessed as Howard Carter must have been.

With all due respect, Dr Cross and Lindsay Boxer, I'll return to your crime scenes after I've finished with Tut.

This was a completely different writing process for me, primarily because of all the research involved. I had been fortunate to hook up with Marty Dugard, a talented and generous writer and researcher who had already travelled to London, then to the Valley of the Kings, to help me make the story as authentic as possible and, more important, to gather details that might solve the murder mystery.

The story had so much potential—much more than most detective novels. After all, it was about kings and queens, buried treasure, an explorer who reminded me of a pissed-off Indiana Jones, and the murder of a teenage boy and probably his sweetheart.

As soon as I got back to the office, I found a thick folder assembled by my indefatigable assistant, Mary Jordan. The evidence that this *was* a murder story was starting to mount.

A press release on March 8, 2005, had announced the results of a full-body CT scan of Tut's mummy by Egyptian authorities. This was the study that prompted Zahi Hawass—secretary-general of the Supreme Council of Antiquities—to announce that Tut had died from an infection resulting from a broken leg. The particular infection, in his opinion, was probably caused by gangrene.

It seemed like a safe bet for the secretary-general, until I read a little further:

'The broken left femur shows no signs of calcification or haematoma', both of which would have begun developing immediately after the accident.

In fact, part of the expert team reviewing the results of the CT scan refused to agree that the broken leg was the cause of death. They believed the leg was accidentally broken *after* the tomb was discovered, when someone had tried to move the body. But in a 2007 interview, Hawass again stated that Tut had died from a broken leg.

The next bit of evidence I discovered was even more curious: X-rays had previously shown a thickening of the skull consistent with a calcified membrane, which can occur when a blood clot forms around an area of high trauma. This is known as a chronic subdural haematoma. However, the CT scan showed no evidence of a blow to the head. Maybe the Egyptian investigating committee was spending too much time trying to justify the broken-leg theory and not enough on the wound at the base of Tut's skull.

The earlier X-rays were the product of R. G. Harrison, a British anatomist who had done extensive work on Tut back in the 1960s and 1970s. Not only had Harrison X-rayed the skeleton, but he had taken the rather extreme measure of separating the skull from the other bones and X-raying it individually. Based on his findings, Harrison suspected foul play.

This made sense to me. A subdural haematoma could develop if somebody whacked you very hard on the skull and you survived the blow, only to die some weeks later. In the meantime, the bruise from the blow would become a blood clot, and that blood clot—the chronic subdural haematoma—would calcify.

All of which made me wonder why anyone would say that Tut had died from a leg fracture. An opposing position seemed more likely, and that got me excited. Based on the results of the 2005 report, combined with the 1969 and 1978 X-rays, it appeared that Tut's leg had not been broken during his lifetime, and that he had suffered a blunt-force trauma to the back of the skull.

So if Tut had been murdered, possibly clubbed to death, who did it?

Valley of the Kings, 1907
Oh, how the mighty had fallen!

Howard Carter stood outside the Winter Palace Hotel with a clutch of watercolours under one arm. His jacket was threadbare, with unsightly patches at the sleeves. The shoes on his feet weren't much better, the leather unpolished and worn.

He set up his easel near the marble steps leading up to the hotel lobby, praying that some fool tourist might take a shine to one of his paintings. The sale would net him much-needed money for whisky and cigarettes, and perhaps even a civilised lunch inside the hotel.

Howard Carter might have been impoverished, but he still had standards.

His problems had begun when he was transferred away from the valley by the Antiquities Service. His new posting, near Cairo, meant that Davis had to find a new executive Egyptologist. Even worse, the ancient tombs at Saqqara proved to be an administrative nightmare for Carter.

When he had allowed his Egyptian tomb guards—quite justifiably—to use force against a drunken mob of French tourists, it became an international incident. After nine months of increasing shame and disgrace, Carter had been forced to resign.

Truth be told, he desperately wanted to get back to the valley. He still hoped to find Hatshepsut's mummy—and maybe even the ever-elusive virgin tomb.

That tomb, if recent events in the valley were any indication, might belong to a long-forgotten pharaoh named Tutankhamen. King Tut had somehow slipped through the cracks of history—or been purposefully edited from it.

His name was *nowhere* to be found among the many shrines and temples where the succession of pharaohs had been chiselled in stone. In 1837, the British Egyptologist Sir John Gardner Wilkinson had noticed the name on a statue. But other than that single mention, Tutankhamen was virtually unknown.

Ironically, it was the American Theodore Davis—the man Carter had originally persuaded to finance a valley concession—who had stumbled upon interesting new evidence about Tutankhamen.

THE INCREDIBLE STORY, as Carter heard it, began with Theodore Davis and his new chief executive Egyptologist, Edward Ayrton, taking a midday break from the stifling heat.

Davis and Ayrton 'owned' the Valley of the Kings, in a manner of speaking. Davis still held exclusive rights to dig there and, with Carter exiled, the Petrie-trained Ayrton was now Davis's top man.

The season had been solid so far, with the tomb of the pharaoh Siptah discovered on December 18. Now, the January sun having driven them to find a sliver of shade in the valley's southwest corner, the two men took a moment to plan their next excavation.

Ayrton smoked quietly as the eccentric Davis stared off into space—or so it appeared.

'My attention was attracted to a large rock tilted to one side,' Davis later recalled, 'and for some mysterious reason I felt interested in it.'

The two men trekked back out into the sunlight. The rail-thin Ayrton had been hired by Davis just a few months earlier but was already used to the man's impulsive behaviour. If Davis wanted to have a look at the rock, then they would have a look at the rock.

Ayrton appraised the boulder from several angles. Then, noticing something peculiar, he dropped to his knees and began moving the loose soil away from the base.

There, buried for ages, was a spectacular find!

'Being carefully examined and dug about with my assistant, Mr Ayrton, with his hands, the beautiful blue cup was found,' Davis later wrote.

The cup was of a glazed material known as faience and, with the exception of a few nicks, was intact. The ancient Egyptians had used such cups at funerals. This one was stamped with the name of a pharaoh— *Tutankhamen*.

The cup seemed to imply that this Tutankhamen—*whoever he was*—had been buried nearby in the Valley of the Kings.

With the 'beautiful blue cup' clutched firmly in his hand, Davis added the name of this mysterious new pharaoh to his list of tombs to be found. And Davis was sure he would be the one to do it.

Howard Carter, making his living selling watercolours to tourists, could do nothing about this new development. He merely stored the information away.

Tutankhamen was out there somewhere just waiting to be found by somebody.

Amarna, 1335 BC

The morning sun, so benevolent and omniscient, blessed Nefertiti as she awaited Tut's arrival in her private quarters. Akhenaten had been dead for only a few hours. She had already selected a group of 'mourners', women who would openly grieve at her husband's funeral, beating their exposed breasts and tearing out their hair.

The time had come for the queen and her boy to have a grown-up talk about his future and, indeed, the future of all of Egypt.

Nefertiti loved the six-year-old Tutankhamen: his trusting brown eyes, his passion for board games, even his endless questions about why the royal family never travelled to cities like Thebes and Memphis. In fact, Nefertiti adored everything about Tut except for one niggling detail: he wasn't her son by birth.

As a very bright and practical woman of the times, Nefertiti understood that a pharaoh might have needs that could not be fulfilled by just one woman. But it had infuriated her when Akhenaten had married and impregnated Kiya. The great god Aten had been just and wise when he had taken Kiya's life as she gave birth to Tut. And Nefertiti made sure that there would never again be a second wife around the royal court.

She had tended to her husband's every fantasy, and when she couldn't, Nefertiti directed his affections towards the harem girls, for it was common knowledge that no pharaoh, not even one as outlandish as Akhenaten, would marry a common whore.

So it was that Nefertiti began to raise Tutankhamen as her own.

The boy never knew his real mother, and though he had been told of her life and tragic death, he was still too young fully to comprehend being conceived in the womb of one woman and reared by the loving hands of another.

'Did you want to see me, Mother?' He was so innocent—and yet so full of life. Nefertiti was overcome with warmth as she gazed upon the boy. She did love him, deeply, but not everyone in the court did. For some, he was already a hated rival.

'Yes, Tut. Come. Sit next to me. Sit close to your mother.'

Tut walked across the tiled floor in his bare feet and plopped onto the divan next to Nefertiti.

'I heard about the pharaoh,' he said softly. 'I'm sorry.'

She placed a hand underneath his chin and lifted it until his eyes met hers. 'Your father hadn't been feeling well for a long time,' she told him. 'Tut, there's something else we need to talk about. I need you to pay attention to what I have to tell you now.'

'Yes, Mother?'

'You are just a boy and have not yet been trained in the ways of the pharaoh. But you must know that this is your destiny.'

The boy stopped her. 'I don't understand.'

'You will be pharaoh one day, Tut.'

'I don't want to be pharaoh. I don't! Why can't you be pharaoh, Mother?'

'It is not considered best for a woman to rule Egypt, Tut. But because I am of royal blood, I will find a way to rule for as long as it takes you to learn to be a great pharaoh.'

'How long will that be, Mother?'

'A dozen years, maybe fewer, because you're so bright, Tut. There is no hurry. The important thing is that you learn to be wise and strong and full of compassion for the people of Egypt, as your father was. He was a good man, always a good man.'

'Smenkare would have made a good pharaoh,' said Tut. 'And he was your son. This day must make you sad.'

The boy was smart, which was probably why she loved him as she did.

'Smenkare is dead, Tut.' She neglected to add that she had never loved her own son as much as she loved Tut. She had tried, but there was no light in Smenkare's eyes, and she felt no connection between them. Someone like that should never rule Egypt.

'No, Tut. It must be you.'

Tut simply nodded. 'So what do I do next? Help me, Mother.'

'See how we're sitting here, right next to each other?'

'Yes. Of course I do.'

'This is how we will rule Egypt at first. Side by side, the two of us. For now I will make the decisions, because you are too young. But as you become a man, you will fill a bigger space and have the knowledge to make good decisions.'

'Then I will rule as pharaoh?'

'Yes, Tut. And I know that you will do great things. You will be a pharaoh people will always remember.'

Amarna, 1334 BC

That was the plan for the boy who would be king, though it didn't turn out that way. Not even close. Once again death would intrude—perhaps even murder.

'To be pharaoh, you must become a man,' the military instructor informed Tut. 'Someday, you will be as big and strong as I. Once you are through with your training, no man will stand in your way.'

Studying the instructor's bulging biceps and massive chest, Tut had a hard time believing that could ever be true, but he listened closely to every word.

They stood in a great green field on the west side of the Nile. It was February, and the mild sun kissed the earth.

Tut was a skinny child whose slightly cleft palate gave him a mild lisp but who otherwise bore the flawless beauty of his mother. His arms were thin, and his sandal-clad feet supported legs that weren't much bigger around.

'Are you ready, sire?' asked the instructor.

Tut tried to speak, but in his nervousness only a sigh escaped his lips.

The instructor concealed a smile. 'Let's talk about the types of bows we will be using in our archery practice, then.'

The list was too long for Tut to remember right away—though the instructor made it clear that the pharaoh would be proficient in each of them, along with shield and mace, sword fighting, spear throwing, chariot riding, horse riding, hand-to-hand combat, daggers, boomerangs, clubs and battle-axes. For today's lesson there was a double-composite angular bow, a composite angular bow, bow staves and short self bows. That was *all* he had to master.

The bows were made of birch that was wrapped in sinew and bark for durability. Gold leaf and ivory decorations adorned their curved shafts. The instructor's great bow was taller than Tut, while Tut's bow was only big enough to reach just above his knee when he stood it on the ground.

The instructor placed the bow in Tut's little hands. 'Now listen to me. You will want these with you in the afterworld. On the day you are buried, all your bows will be buried with you. So learn to use them well, Highness. The rules of combat you are about to learn will stand you in good stead . . . for ever.'

Tut notched an arrow in the bow and pulled back the string. His shot hit the target cleanly on the first try, though it wasn't far from the boy.

'Very good, sire. You are a natural.'

Amarna, 1333 BC

'You're late. I won't tolerate this, Tutankhamen. There's no excuse for such conduct.'

Tut raced into the royal classroom at the prince's school with mud from the Nile still coating the soles of his feet, his favourite hunting bow in his hand. He had been out in the reeds again, shooting ducks, and had realised too late that it was time for class.

He had had no chance to clean up, and now, pharaoh-in-training or not, he would face the instructor's wrath.

'Instructor, I—'

'Quiet. Not a word from you. Sit down and practise your hieroglyphics.'

The teacher was a thin, dyspeptic young man who didn't walk about the room so much as he flitted like a nervous bird. Tut liked to mimic him for the amusement of his sister, but now she was too busy giggling at Tut's misfortune for him to attempt a joke.

The standard punishment for tardiness was to write the twenty-five characters of the hieroglyphic alphabet on a piece of papyrus 100 times. The task often took two hours, which the instructor knew was absolute torture for Tut.

He was eight now, and his latest passion was chariot lessons. Two hours spent writing meant two hours fewer spent at the reins, speeding across the open desert.

Much as his father would have hated it, Tut longed for the day when he would lead the warriors of Egypt into battle. He pictured himself in a chariot, two mighty steeds galloping before him, an army of thousands responding to his every command.

'Well done, Pharaoh,' whispered his sister Ankhesenpaaten. She was a few years older than him, and she was a beautiful girl, even better-looking than Tut.

'Someday,' the teacher announced, 'when you reign over Egypt as the one true pharaoh, you can have me killed for my insolence, but until then this is my classroom and you will do as you are told—and that includes arriving on time. *Am I understood, Tutankhamen?*'

A furious, red-faced Tut nodded his head and placed a fresh reed in his mouth, making sure not to make eye contact with his sister. Tut chewed the end of the reed, feeling the fibres break apart until they formed a loose and supple paintbrush.

Then he dipped his new writing implement into a bowl of water and touched it to a block of solid ink. He began to draw on a piece of papyrus, his hand effortlessly forming the falcons, owls, feet and myriad other images that made up the hieroglyphic alphabet.

But soon the afternoon heat and the quiet of the classroom had his mind wandering. He loved the outdoors, and to be stuck inside on such a beautiful day wounded his spirit.

Tut longed to be swimming in the Nile, ever mindful of the crocodiles that lurked there. Or maybe taking Ankhesenpaaten for a chariot ride—he adored her. Or perhaps simply standing on a mountaintop, gazing out at the purplish rocks of a distant hill, revelling in the fantastic notion that all of this land, as far as the eye could see, would one day be his.

This was not merely a boy's daydream—it was for real.

AS HE DREW HIS CHARACTERS, Tut kept an eye on his strict instructor, the bane of his youth. The last thing he needed was another unjust punishment on top of the others he'd accrued. Nefertiti had been very clear in her warnings about Tut's studies. If he failed a subject or even fell behind, he would lose the right to go out beyond the palace walls. Tut could think of no more horrendous penalty.

Then, to Tut's amazement and joy, the same warm afternoon sunlight that had sent his mind wandering now cast a spell over the instructor. Tut watched eagerly as the man rested in his chair and his eyelids began to close. The instructor's head then lolled back and his mouth opened slightly, until, ever so softly, he began to snore.

Ankhesenpaaten put one hand over her mouth to keep from giggling. Tut gently placed his brush on an ivory palette and tapped her on the shoulder while jerking a thumb towards the door.

'No,' Ankhesenpaaten mouthed. 'We can't do that, Tut. We *mustn't*.'

Tut insisted, standing quietly and taking hold of her arm. With a quick glance at the instructor, whose soft snore was deepening into something louder, she stood, too.

Together, the royal boy and girl tiptoed towards the door and the freedom of the river world. To be safe, Tut grabbed his hunting bow on the way out.

Suddenly, Aye's hulking torso blocked their path. 'Where do you think you're going?' the royal scribe boomed, making Ankhesenpaaten jump in fear.

The instructor jerked awake and leaped to his feet.

Aye gripped Tut and Ankhesenpaaten tightly by the arms and dragged them back into the room, digging his fingernails into Tut's bicep. 'Let go of me,' Tut cried, but Aye only squeezed harder. 'I will be pharaoh one day, and you will be gone from the palace. I promise it, Scribe. You too, Teacher!'

Then Tut wrenched his arm free and ran, and he didn't stop running until he stood on the banks of the Nile. What was even better was that Ankhesenpaaten had run with him—every step of the way.

'WHAT DO YOU THINK they'll do to us if they ever catch us?' asked a smiling Tut, crouching down below the reeds so they wouldn't be seen by Aye or their other nemesis, the teacher.

Ankhesenpaaten was usually the practical one. Her impulsive decision to escape along with Tut had perhaps been the greatest surprise he had known since the day their father died.

But it was a nice sort of surprise, the kind that made him feel less alone in the world. It felt really good to have a comrade in arms—a friend—if only to share the inevitable punishment that would follow this outrageous adventure.

Tut looked into his sister's eyes and smiled. Technically, she was his half-sister, thanks to his father's union with the ill-fated Kiya, and though she and Tut were the fruit of the same father, it more often felt as if they were best friends than brother and sister.

She was like him, and she wasn't. It was hard to explain. Except that he loved her dearly. He so dearly loved his Ankhe.

'They're not going to beat us,' Tut announced, answering his own question.

'Why do you say "*they*"?' she asked. 'It's Mother who will determine our punishment.'

'That's not exactly the way it works,' Tut said patiently. 'Aye and the instructor are men. They think they have power over Mother.'

As part of the process of learning to become pharaoh, Nefertiti had taken great pains to include Tut in important meetings with her advisers. Even a boy could see that Aye coveted the great power that Nefertiti possessed. The royal vizier often cast angry glares at Tut, as if the boy had somehow offended him just by being there.

Aye frightened Tut, and as Tut remained in the reeds thinking about him, he gently rubbed the marks Aye's thick nails had left on his upper arm.

'You need to watch out for Aye,' Tut told his sister. 'I don't trust him. Neither should you. I think he wants to marry Mother and become pharaoh.'

Ankhesenpaaten smiled at this.

'He can't do that, Tut. You're the pharaoh.'

'Not if he marries the queen. Marriage into royal blood would allow Aye to take the throne.'

Tut paused to let that sink in, tilting his head to watch a duck extend its wings as it glided in for a landing.

'I don't like that,' Ankhesenpaaten said softly, 'and I don't like Aye. Not a bit. He's angry, and he's rude to Mother. And General Horemheb is a sneaky one. Keep an eye on him also.'

'I will be wary of them all,' said Tut. Then he did something he really hadn't expected to do. He leaned in close and kissed Ankhe. And perhaps even more surprising, she didn't protest.

Then, confident that they had avoided capture, the two children rose from their hiding place and sprinted towards the river, laughing. They were less afraid of the crocodiles lurking there than of the powerful men crawling about the palace.

CHAPTER 5

Thebes, 1908

Howard Carter had been summoned.

His old friend and Antiquities Service boss, Gaston Maspero, wanted to meet and discuss Carter's 'future'. In the four years since Carter had left his post, there hadn't been much talk like that. So Gaston Maspero's request for a meeting was more than welcome.

It could be a lifesaver.

The distance from the Winter Palace Hotel to the Valley of the Kings was roughly five miles. If one stood on the great marble steps leading up to the hotel's main lobby, it was possible to gaze across the Nile towards the distant cliffs that formed the back of the valley. When there was no wind and the desert dust was not clouding the air, those cliffs seemed almost close enough to touch.

That's the way Howard Carter felt every day of his exile. A man less passionate about Egyptology would never have debased himself the way Carter had, standing out on the streets to hawk his wares to tourists. To supplement his modest living as a watercolourist, he also sold antiquities on the black market, thus sinking to the level of the men he'd once prosecuted for tomb robbery.

Adding insult to injury, his most beloved patrons of all, Lord and Lady Amherst, had been forced to sell Didlington Hall in 1907, and Lord Amherst was in poor health.

At the age of thirty-four, Howard Carter had become little more than a self-educated sycophant.

Enter, thanks to Maspero, the inimitable Lord Carnarvon.

George Edward Stanhope Molyneux Herbert, better known as the Fifth Earl of Carnarvon—or, more simply, His Lordship—was a pale, thin man with a hound's face pitted by smallpox. He smoked incessantly, raced cars, owned horses and otherwise revelled in living the life of a wealthy, self-absorbed *bon vivant*. Even the 1901 car crash that had almost killed him didn't stop Carnarvon from spending his money recklessly and living a life of entitled leisure that no one deserved—at least not in Carter's opinion.

His Lordship had first come to Egypt in December 1905; that visit and subsequent other 'tours' had whetted his appetite for all things Egyptian. Little by little, Carnarvon was transformed from a man consumed by the here and now into a man consumed by the past—the ancient past.

Now, like many wealthy men who'd become smitten by Egypt and treasure hunting, Lord Carnarvon wanted to fund his own excavation.

The successes of Carter and Theodore Davis were well known, and Carnarvon could easily see Davis's yacht *Bedouin* moored across the street from his hotel. British acquaintances also had minor concessions, and Carnarvon believed he would enjoy digging up an important bit of history. He thought it should be great fun indeed.

Unfortunately, his first season's results weren't promising. Or much fun. Arthur Weigall—who now held Carter's former job as chief inspector for Upper Egypt—had dismissed Carnarvon for the rank amateur that he was. He assigned Carnarvon to a rubbish heap known as Sheikh abd el-Qurna, with predictably dismal results. The sole find during that first six-week season was a mummified cat contained inside a wooden cat coffin.

Carnarvon, while disappointed, actually treasured the discovery. It was his first, after all. Egyptology was now officially in his blood.

The only problem, it seemed, was Carnarvon. Rather than hire an experienced professional, he led the digs himself. Each day he would sit inside a screened box that kept away flies and smoke cigarette after cigarette as his men, *not* a topnotch crew, worked in the heat and dust.

What Carnarvon needed—he was told repeatedly—was a seasoned professional to guide his digs.

And Howard Carter needed a wealthy patron with a concession to get him back in the game.

Between seasons, Carnarvon wrote to Weigall from England, asking for 'a learned man, as I have not time to learn up all the requisite data'.

The common thread in all of this was Maspero, who had arranged Carnarvon's concession in the first place.

So it was that Carter was summoned to the Winter Palace to stand before Carnarvon and Maspero to discuss the possibility of once again leading a full-scale excavation. His clothes were nearing the point of no return, and his ever-present portfolio was tucked under his arm, as if he had been called to sketch the moment, which, he believed, was a depressing possibility.

Did Carter want back in the game? he was asked.

The disgraced Egyptologist, thrilled that fate was giving him a second chance, hastily answered yes. He even managed to keep his famous arrogance and temper in check—for the first meeting anyway.

Amarna, 1333 BC

'What's wrong, Mother?' asked Tut.

The handsome little boy stood beside Nefertiti in a garden surrounded by fig trees and date palms and a rich green carpet of grass. His mother sat in the shade of a small palmetto. Her beautiful face was a tightly clenched mask. They both knew that she was unwell, and yet she pretended that nothing of the sort was true.

To be eight and faced with the prospect of losing his mother, so soon after losing his father, was something that no child could be prepared for.

But Tut was no ordinary child: he had royal blood; he was divine.

So he joined his mother on the small settee. He watched as she slowly leaned back and tried to relax, then flinched in pain as her skin came in contact with the hard chair.

'I'm dying, Tut, and I need to ask you to do something that you might think odd.'

'Don't say that, Mother. You're *not* dying.'

'I am. Either I am being poisoned or there is a sickness inside my body that Aten does not wish to remove. I have ordered my servants to hasten their preparations of my burial chamber, because there may not be much time for me.'

Nefertiti closed her eyes as pain shot through her body. Tut placed his hand on top of hers, but did so gently, so as not to hurt her.

This small act of kindness and compassion made Nefertiti smile. 'You will be a great pharaoh. I am sure of it.'

'Thank you, Mother.'

He paused, reluctant to say what was on his mind.

'What is it?' Nefertiti asked.

'Do you promise not to be angry?'

She let a moment pass as she weighed her answer. 'I promise. Now ask your question. You must always speak your mind, Tut.'

'Did Aye do this to you? I see the way he looks at you. It's hard to tell whether he loves you or hates you.'

'I think it's a little of both. But no, I do not fear Aye—though you should. You are just a boy and need to be protected from powerful, unscrupulous men who might want to see you harmed.'

'Do you think he wants to be pharaoh?'

'Yes, Tut, I do. And he is not the only man with a dream of ruling Egypt.'

'But he is a commoner.'

'So are you, Tut. Remember, your natural mother was of common birth. You are only half royal. Your sister is the only child in this palace who is full-blooded royalty. This is why I have asked you to come and see me.'

'What do you mean? What are you saying, Mother?'

'Ankhesenpaaten cannot reign as pharaoh because she is a woman. But for you to rule as pharaoh, and to produce an heir who ensures the succession of our royal blood, you must blend your blood with that of a woman who is fully royal. Do you understand?'

'But Ankhesenpaaten is the only such person.'

'That's right, Tut.' Nefertiti flinched once again from the pain. 'Ankhe is the only one.'

'So you're saying that . . .'

His voice trailed off in confusion, so Nefertiti finished the sentence for him.

'You must marry your sister.'

Luxor, 1909

Howard Carter was once again in the world that he loved more than anything else. A little older perhaps, a few belt holes thinner, but he was definitely back in the game.

As the sun rose over the Nile, he gazed out at a small army of workers, just as he had so many times before. True, he was digging in what many called the 'unfashionable district' of the Theban necropolis, where, at best, he could hope to find the tombs of nobles and wealthy businessmen instead of pharaohs. But after years of living hand to mouth, Carter didn't mind at all.

It was good to have a job. So Carter lit a cigarette and gave the order for his men to start digging.

Lord Carnarvon stood at his side, dressed smartly in a suit and boater.

Their relationship would clearly be different from the ones Carter had enjoyed with Lord Amherst and even Theodore Davis. The old days of Carter being stubborn to make a point were over. He was a hired man now and would not be treated as a member of the family.

But he didn't much care. He had plans in his head, plans to bring professionalism and accountability to Carnarvon's ragtag style of digging. With Carter's expertise and Carnarvon's money, there was a chance they might actually find something important.

And someday, if this all worked out, they would move into the Valley of the Kings and do some real digging, for *real treasure*.

Amarna, 1330 BC

There had been no public ceremony and no special words from the high priests to mark the moment of their marriage union.

Ankhesenpaaten had simply moved her belongings to Tut's side of the palace, where their father had once laid his head.

That had been three years ago. They had slept in separate rooms since then but had also become closer friends. Now, on the day they had put Nefertiti in her tomb, Tut would rule alone.

Ankhesenpaaten fumbled with her gauzy white gown as she and Tut prepared to share a bed for the first time. He wasn't yet a teenager, like his sister and bride, who was a few years older, but Tut had begun to develop physically into a man, and this wasn't lost on his wife.

It was time that they produced an heir—or at least, given their ages, began practising.

Tut untied the cumbersome false pharaoh beard from around his head and laid it on a bedside table. Nefertiti had coached them both, in individual discussions, and Tut thought he had a good understanding of how it all worked. But he had never visited a harem, and what was about to transpire was unnatural and awkward to him.

Ankhesenpaaten turned her back discreetly as she slipped her dress off her shoulders. Tut watched the fabric drop down past her narrow hips and land silently on the floor.

Ankhesenpaaten covered her budding breasts with one hand as she turned to pull back the bedcovers, then slid between the warm cotton sheets. He could smell the perfumed oils she used on her body and hair.

'Now you, *Pharaoh.*'

Tut felt butterflies in his stomach and was unnerved at the thought of shedding his clothes right there with Ankhe in the room.

'Did you ever feast as much as today?' he asked somewhat randomly, referring to the whirlwind of revelry surrounding Nefertiti's funeral. All the priests of Aten had fêted her. Aye had been there too, and Tut had noticed that the royal vizier drank quite heavily while huddling in the corner with Tut's generals.

'I don't think I've ever seen that much food in my life,' Ankhesenpaaten agreed.

'I wish Mother could have been there.'

'Now you can make your claim to the throne. No one can deny you.'

'Yes,' Tut said softly, feeling for the first time the crushing weight of being the pharaoh of all of Egypt. It pressed down on him like a block of limestone.

'We are alone, Tut,' Ankhesenpaaten whispered, realising a different sort of burden. 'Just the two of us in this difficult and complicated world. Not a parent to guide us. Just us.'

'It's scary when you say it like that.'

'Yes. But, Tut, let's promise that we will always look out for each other and protect each other from those who would do us harm.'

'I promise, Ankhesenpaaten. I will never let anyone harm you.'

'I promise too.'

The bedroom was still then, uncomfortably so. The warm desert air flowed in through the open window, and Tut could smell the faint and wonderfully familiar musk of the Nile.

Ankhesenpaaten took a deep breath, then she pulled back the sheets, unafraid to show herself to her husband.

In their many years together, Tut had never seen his half-sister naked, and now he gasped at the realisation that she was exceptionally shapely as well as beautiful.

'Take off your kilt, Tut,' she said.

The pharaoh did as he was told. And he was beautiful too.

Thebes, 1326 BC

Tut had now moved his palace back to Thebes, and the nights of passion were but a memory to Ankhesenpaaten these days. Still the young queen had never been more excited—or frightened. '*I'm late*,' she whispered, rolling over in bed and propping her chin on Tut's chest.

'How often have I heard that?' Tut replied.

'Tut,' Ankhesenpaaten whispered. 'I am three months late. We are going to have a baby. I'm certain of it. So think of a name,' she said softly.

'Nefertiti,' he said.

'What if it's a boy?'

'Nefertiti.' Tut laughed.

Ankhesenpaaten looked at him. 'We are going to have a baby,' she repeated.

THAT HAD BEEN five months ago.

Now, perched on a royal birthing stool, Ankhesenpaaten clenched her abdominal muscles and pushed one last time. As Tut stood by her side, clasping Ankhe's hand, their child finally joined them, delivered into the waiting hands of the royal physician.

It was stillborn.

The poor baby was obviously deformed, with one shoulder much higher than the other and a spine curved sideways, and just as obviously dead.

'Summon the royal magician,' the doctor said emphatically, speaking to a courtesan standing just behind Ankhesenpaaten.

The royal magician would be charged with healing whatever illness had caused the queen to miscarry, burning hot coals on the floor between her legs as she remained on the low stool, allowing the smoke to enter her womb and clean out all impurities.

'Is it a boy or a girl?' Ankhesenpaaten asked in a weak voice. She felt like crying but held back the tears.

'I do not think it matters, Queen,' said the doctor.

'Boy or girl?' barked Tut in a voice that indicated he would not brook such insolence.

The physician sat up straight, remembering his place. 'A girl, Majesty.'

Ankhesenpaaten held out her arms. The umbilical cord connecting mother and daughter was still intact, and now the queen pulled her dead child to her bosom and sobbed in anguish. She ran a finger over the baby's head, touching the small nose and stroking the soft black tufts of hair. The child's eyes were closed, and she kissed each one.

All too soon, she knew, the royal embalmer would mummify this newborn and place her in the royal tomb to await the death of her parents. 'We will get to know one another in the afterlife,' Ankhesenpaaten whispered. 'I love you, my darling Nefertiti.'

Egyptian Desert, 1324 BC

It was his time now, but was he ready—quite possibly to die? Tut stood alone in his tent, his stomach a knot of nerves and fear. Adrenaline raced through his body as he anxiously clenched and unclenched his fists, then bounced lightly on his toes half a dozen times. He was all of seventeen years old, and he was going to war.

Outside, he could hear swords clanking and horses whinnying as his great army assembled on the morning of battle. *His* army. *Egypt's* army.

Tut whispered a silent prayer to Amun. He strapped on his leather chest armour, slid a sword into the scabbard at his waist, then stepped out into the harsh desert sunlight to join his soldiers.

Unlike many of these men, whose wives followed the army, Tut had travelled alone. Sadness over the loss of their child had changed things between Tut and Ankhesenpaaten. Even though she had become pregnant again, things weren't the same. She was moodier, more grown-up.

Unlike his father, who stayed home with Nefertiti every day of his life, Tut began travelling. He hunted deer with Aye, whom he continued to distrust.

He also fell under the spell of General Horemheb, particularly on the subject of warfare. To be a real man, Tut decided he needed to do battle. He needed to be here with the army.

Now he had a chance to fight for the first time. He would test his mettle today, and perhaps he would die.

The great Egyptian army was encamped near the Canaanite city of Megiddo, a desert fortress surrounded by towering walls of mud and limestone. There was a good chance the Canaanites would refuse to come out and fight, preferring to endure an Egyptian siege than to be slaughtered in full view of their women and children.

Tut prayed that this would not be so. He ached for his first taste of battle.

The gleaming sword weighed heavily against his hip as he inspected his chariot team. Like soldiers before him, Tut vowed to be strong and to show no fear, but he worried that he might turn and flee.

'You have a talent for drawing, Pharaoh. Your images of the gods are so powerful that I feel the urge to bow down at the sight of them,' said Horemheb, who had stepped up to Tut's side. It was a snakelike compliment about Tut's passion for art, a not-too-subtle insinuation that the boy was timid like his father.

'Are you saying I should have stayed in Thebes, General?' Tut was unafraid to ask hard questions, even of men decades his senior.

Now he wiped the sweat from his brow. He surveyed his men—infantry, archers and charioteers assembling in long orderly columns. A simple sweep of the eyes brought into view an arsenal the likes of which few had seen before: powerful bows, maces, highly sharpened axes, spears, and daggers glistening in the sun.

Having so much power at his disposal excited Tut in a way that he never could have imagined. No, he was *not* his father's son. He was a warrior!

'I was paying you a compliment, Pharaoh,' said the crafty Horemheb.

'Then I accept your compliment. Tell me, General, what is our strategy today?'

The general squinted as he studied Megiddo's distant fortifications. 'May I speak bluntly, sir?'

'Of course you may. You know me well enough by now. I need to know the truth—always. Speak your mind.'

'I have conquered this miserable town before. It is a den of whores and thieves who don't understand anything except brutal domination. If they come out to fight, we will first launch arrows and then send chariots to scatter their army. Our fighting men will wade in and slaughter them like the weak little piglets that they are. The desert sands will be engorged with their blood, which will flow from their bodies like water over a raging cataract.'

Horemheb grinned maliciously. Instead of grovelling, he was now testing Tut for signs of squeamishness.

'When that moment comes, General, I will personally gut a Canaanite. I will use his innards to grease the axles of my chariot.'

'As you should,' said Horemheb, who seemed to approve of the pharaoh's words.

Tut stared at Megiddo again and then turned to Horemheb. 'And if they do not come out, what then?'

'Then there will be a siege. We will poison their wells and starve them. It might take months, but we will enter the city. I guarantee it. You haven't lived until you've plundered a city like this one. The women cannot refuse you. And the men know to bring the youngest and most beautiful. You, of course, will have your pick.' Horemheb paused, his sense of timing exquisite. 'That is, if you desire a grown woman. They can be tempestuous, Pharaoh. Particularly when reluctantly submitting to a victor.'

Tut resisted the urge to draw his sword and hack off Horemheb's arm to put him in his place.

'My wife is woman enough for me. You may have my share of tempestuous whores.'

Suddenly, Horemheb's eyes caught sight of something.

'What is it, General?'

Horemheb pointed a gnarled finger. 'The gates to the city. Look for yourself. They are opening! The Canaanites are coming out to fight.'

'HOLD!' YELLED HOREMHEB, the low timbre of his powerful voice cutting through the dry desert air. The highly trained Egyptian forces halted abruptly. Tut stopped too. Then he stared in utter amazement at the scene unfolding before him.

A mile distant, the Canaanite army poured forth from behind the city walls. The infantry marched three columns abreast, numbering perhaps 5,000 men. The archers were assembled on the wings, ready to fire on any Egyptian flanking movement.

Up in the very front, in a mirror image of Horemheb and Tut and the rest of Egypt's commanders, the Canaanite charioteers charged forward. There were two men in each chariot, a driver and an archer, which allowed arrows to be fired while racing into battle.

The Canaanites came fast, as if intending to take immediate control of the field. Their hulking shoulders and the great, dark beards that covered their chests made them look bigger and stronger than the Egyptians.

To his shame, Tut's throat instantly closed in terror. He vomited in his mouth. As he studied the Canaanites, he realised that their march had not faltered, nor had their pace slackened. They seemed to grow more terrifying as they closed to within 500 yards.

But their horses! Tut could see that they were ill trained and struggling to turn away from the fight.

Even the animals have the good sense to fear the coming battle, he thought. These were not the horses of victorious warriors, but horses that knew what it was like to turn and flee.

The realisation galvanised Tut, but the chaos in his stomach intensified. He bent over and vomited in his chariot, quickly wiping his mouth and standing up straight so that his men would not think their pharaoh weak.

But there was no hiding anything from Horemheb. 'I have done it many times myself, Pharaoh,' he said, his voice laced with sarcasm.

No, now would not be a good time to cut off Horemheb's arm. Later, perhaps. After the victory was assured.

'It will not happen again,' Tut barked, steel in his voice.

His schooling had included courses in tactics and warfare. Now, with Horemheb's taunt ringing in his ears, Tut took command. He removed the composite bow from his shoulders. Made of cherrywood and leather, its gleaming ivory decorations looked too beautiful for the battlefield.

'Give the order for battle formations!' he told Horemheb.

The general glared at Tut but said nothing at first. He was not used to being ordered about, especially by a boy. 'As you wish, my king,' he finally replied. Then Horemheb turned and faced the assembled army. 'Battle formations!'

The Egyptian column spread out, until they formed a wide but narrow line, shoulder to shoulder, twenty men deep, facing down the men of Canaan. The well-trained charioteers remained in front. The archers scurried to the right and left flanks.

Horemheb, and the entire army, awaited Tut's next command.

Conventional wisdom said that a wide open battlefield like this desert plain favoured the defender, so in this case it was best to wait for the Canaanites to make the first move.

But Tut knew that such tactics did not always work. As his adrenaline surged, flooding him with a new fearlessness, his instincts told him that this day the Egyptians must attack first.

'I do not wish to give them a chance to flee behind the city walls,' Tut stated evenly.

'As I said before, we will wait them out,' insisted the general.

Tut licked his lips. Holding tight to the reins of his chariot, he stepped from the chassis and turned to face his troops.

Their bodies glistened with sweat, and they looked tired from the two-week march from Thebes, but there was no mistaking their professionalism. They were reliant warriors, hungry for battle and the rewards of victory. They had trained and drilled for the sweet primal satisfaction of fighting man to man against a sworn enemy of Egypt. And then—plunder.

Tut's heart raced. He had never been so proud to be an Egyptian.

The troops watched him expectantly, awaiting the next command. 'General Horemheb, command the archers to open fire.'

NOW EVEN HOREMHEB had caught the fever, and when his words rang out across the desert, they were delivered with the same excitement as Tut's.

'Archers, take aim.'

The Canaanites could see the Egyptian archers draw arrows from their quivers, then pull back their bowstrings. A distant horn commanded the Canaanites to battle, and they flew at the Egyptians, daring their attackers to hold their lines.

Simultaneously, the Canaanite archers took aim.

Now Tut chose an arrow from his quiver, ready to fire the first shot of war. He launched it into the sky in a powerful arc, right on target. Only then did he call out to his men.

'Fire!' Tut commanded. His voice was thin and reedy, still that of a boy on the cusp of manhood. But there was fury in his tone, and a fearlessness that buoyed the Egyptian lines.

Tut's archers sent forth a volley that blackened the sky before descending into the Canaanite infantry and charioteers. Hundreds of them fell, screaming to the heavens, writhing in agony.

Tut watched in dismay as the Egyptian infantry refused to attack, preferring to hold their lines.

It was Horemheb who told him why.

'*They're waiting for you, Pharaoh.*'

Tut swallowed hard. How long had he been taking chariot lessons? Six years? Seven? He believed he could ride as well as any man, but he couldn't be sure. 'Be with me, Mother,' he whispered. Then the young pharaoh stepped back into his chariot.

'Sound the call, General.'

Horemheb signalled to the herald. The battle horn blared.

Tut slipped his bow back over his shoulders. He pulled his sword from its scabbard. The time had come to christen it with the enemy's blood. He slapped his reins down hard on his team's flanks and raced straight towards the Canaanites.

As one, the Egyptian army roared forward. Above them, another volley of arrows arced, then fell into the Canaanites' battle lines.

Horemheb and the other Egyptian charioteers galloped beside the young pharaoh. Within seconds they were trampling the bodies of many Canaanite warriors. Tut could hear the whoosh of swords meant for him.

Holding the reins in one hand, he swung out with his blade and was stunned to see it sever a man's head. He had killed his first victim.

The Canaanites retreated, dropping their shields and sometimes even their swords, running for their lives.

But Tut could see that the great wooden city gates were shut tight. They could not escape.

The women of Canaan had chosen to doom their husbands and sons rather than submit to the Egyptians. It was left to the pharaoh's men to finish the slaughter. Canaanite bodies soon littered the desert, most butchered beyond recognition.

Tut had finally tasted battle and become a man—and a true king.

CHAPTER 6

Thebes, 1912

The book that documented every large and small success by Carter was known as *Five Years' Exploration at Thebes: A Record of Work Done, 1907–1911*. Despite the lack of a valley concession, the partnership between Carter and Carnarvon had certainly been prolific.

Carter had refined his excavation techniques, bringing greater precision and professionalism to the task. He introduced photography as a means of documenting discoveries and continued to sketch elaborate drawings. With local work crews sometimes numbering close to 300, he and Carnarvon discovered tombs of nobles and other high-ranking functionaries.

But as well received as *Five Years' Exploration* proved to be, raising eyebrows in London and Cairo for the depth of the Carter/Carnarvon discoveries, the American Theodore Davis continued to overshadow them, and that galled Howard Carter.

Now a story making the rounds about Davis suggested that he had found not just a new tomb in the valley but the *last* tomb.

Theodore Davis believed he had found the elusive Tut.

It ALL BEGAN when Davis and Edward Ayrton discovered a hidden doorway made of mud bricks and stamped with the image of a jackal watching over nine captives. This seal for the necropolis guard signified that a mummy was inside.

Next to that was stamped another symbol, this one representing Tutankhamen.

They immediately kicked down the door and tore away the bricks with their bare hands, then entered a narrow hall.

A corridor led to the burial chamber. Rocks littered the floor. A piece of wood decorated with gold leaf showed the image of Queen Tiye, known to be the mother of the 'heretic king' Akhenaten.

What an amazing four days it had been. On January 3, Davis's workers excavated an ancient rubbish dump. Inside they found eight large sealed pots bearing Tutankhamen's name. As it turned out, the jars were filled with embalming supplies and leftovers from a long-ago feast, as well as floral collars stitched with berries and flowers.

Very likely, this feast took place after Tut's burial. The flowers were a sort that bloomed between March and April, offering a clue as to when this mysterious pharaoh had died.

Now this.

At the end of a hallway was the main chamber. It was heavily damaged by water, but the seals of Tutankhamen could be seen everywhere on the walls.

A casket lay on the floor.

Once it had rested atop a wooden platform, but time had rotted that away, and the coffin had toppled over. The lid had popped open, and when Davis looked inside, he was delighted to see a mummy staring back at him.

Portions of the bandaging were unwrapped. Davis could see hair and teeth and the remnants of a nose.

He plucked a hair, then wiggled a tooth, trying to determine the mummy's condition. Not surprisingly, it gave way in his hands.

Davis was dismayed, but only for an instant. Not even waiting for Ayrton's help, he lifted the mummy into his arms and carried it out into the sunshine as if it were a small child.

He stood there, dazzled, as tourists stared at him in utter shock and amazement.

A doctor happened to be walking by on the broad dirt path. Davis knew the man and beckoned to him. The doctor performed an inspection of the mummy—and determined that it was a woman.

Davis made a judgment: based on the evidence, he was holding in his arms the remains of Queen Tiye. He was now convinced that the tomb was that of Tutankhamen. All he had to do was dig deeper, and he was certain he would find the pharaoh himself.

Standing in the centre of the Valley of the Kings, cradling a 3,300-year-old woman, Theodore Davis was triumphant and flushed with acumen and success.

He was also dead wrong about everything.

Luxor, 1912
Carter and Carnarvon weren't the only Egyptologists to publish a book that year.

Carter leafed through the pages of Theodore Davis's *The Tombs of Harmhabi and Touatankhamanou*, and he was more convinced than ever that the elusive tomb of Tut was still out there somewhere in the valley.

Carter later wrote that he was 'quite sure there were areas, covered by the dumps of previous excavators, which had not properly been examined'. Looking forward to the day when Davis would abandon his concession, and he and Carnarvon might return to the valley, Carter added, 'I will state that we had definite hopes of finding one particular king, and that king was Tut.Ankh.Amen.'

Carter lit a cigarette and reread the descriptions of the tomb in which

Davis purported to have found Tut. In his opinion, the gold-flaked and alabaster objects present inside that tomb were of too low a quality for a pharaoh's burial chamber. More likely they had been placed there years later, when the tomb was reopened. Owing to the growing connection between Amarna and the tomb, it seemed plausible that Queen Tiye had been relocated from Amarna to the valley at some point after her death.

No, Tut hadn't been found. But other discoveries in the valley—jars of embalming fluid, the faience cup, remnants of a final meal bearing inscriptions showing it had been part of Tut's burial feast, seals bearing his symbol stamped on tomb doorways—clearly showed that he had existed.

'To explain the reasons for this belief of ours, we must turn to the published pages of Mr Davis's excavations,' Carter went on to write. 'Davis claimed that he had found the burial place of Tut.Ankh.Amen. The theory was quite untenable . . . We had thus three distinct pieces of evidence: the faience cup found beneath the rock, the gold foil from the small pit tomb, and this important cache of funerary material. Which seemed definitely to connect Tut.Ankh.Amen with this particular part of the valley.'

Now all Carter needed was an opportunity to find it. 'With all this evidence before us, we were thoroughly convinced in our own minds that the tomb of Tut.Ankh.Amen was still to be found, and that it ought to be situated not far from the centre of the valley.'

But he needed Davis to abandon his concession.

Two years later, the American did just that.

Valley of the Kings, February 8, 1915

Lord Carnarvon snatched up Theodore Davis's concession without hesitation. Just like that, after eight years of waiting, Carter was back in the valley. He finally began scouring the area for his long-hoped-for virgin tomb on February 8, 1915.

When Davis had walked away from his concession, saying that the valley was 'exhausted', few members of the Egyptology community disagreed. 'We remembered, however, that a hundred years earlier Belzoni had made a similar claim,' wrote Carter.

Carter clung to the belief that Davis had made assumptions about the discovered mummy's identity that couldn't be verified. 'Clearly enough, we saw that very heavy work lay before us and that many thousands of tons of surface debris would have to be removed before we could find anything.

But there was always a chance that a tomb might reward us in the end, and that was always a chance we were willing to take.'

So February 8, 1915, should have been a triumphant day for Carter, as what amounted to the pinnacle of his life's work was about to begin.

There was just one problem: the world was at war.

All digging in the Valley of the Kings had been stopped. Even worse, orders arrived from the British army conscripting Carter into service.

How dare the venal, tawdry modern world intrude on his search for an ancient king.

Egyptian Desert, 1324 BC

The bonfire lit up the night, its crackling flames reflecting off the pale tents of Egypt's great army. The pharaoh sat on his travelling throne, with sword-carrying sentries on either side.

Tut had drunk more wine than was prudent, but he didn't feel it that much. As he strapped a cloak about his shoulders to stave off the cold night air, Tut sensed the men watching him. He detected a new respect. Their eyes said that today, on the field of battle, he had behaved as a true king.

Women also ringed the fire, some of them quite beautiful. Several were camp followers who had endured the long trek from Thebes. But many were captured enemy women—the prettiest ones—bound at the wrists. Their faces were masks of terror, shame and loss. They had seen their husbands and sons slain. Now, once the fire died, they would be passed from man to man—a fate that made many wish that they had died too. Soon, a few would get their wish and go to the afterworld.

Tut felt one of the women gazing at him. Across the fire sat a solitary maiden with the most beautiful hair. Someone's daughter, thought Tut. She was his age, perhaps younger.

His stomach felt funny, a sensation that he at first blamed on the wine. But now he knew it was nerves, the same insecurity that had threatened to paralyse him before battle. Tut shrugged it off and turned away from the girl who dared to stare at him. He forced himself to think of Ankhesenpaaten, who was pregnant with their second child. His queen, his lover, his friend since childhood.

But then Tut found himself staring at the female prisoner. The girl tossed her hair to show her profile better. If she had to submit to an Egyptian, she clearly preferred to spend the night with a pharaoh.

He watched as the woman stood, the firelight revealing the sort of full-breasted figure that he had long coveted. Her skirt rode high on her thighs, leaving Tut's imagination free to wander, which it did. How could it not? He was far from home and had just won a great battle.

I am the pharaoh, Tut reminded himself. *What does it matter what others think? Let my wife be angry with me. My father had lovers, and so did his father before him. What does it matter if I take this woman to my bed—or take her for my wife, for that matter?*

Tut moved forward until he was sitting on the edge of his seat. By the look in her eyes, it was clear that the girl sensed that she was about to be beckoned. Her hard look had softened.

Tut rose and stared at her. He could feel a deep and powerful longing. He studied the girl—her face, lips, every curve—and then he turned and walked to his tent.

Alone.

He remained faithful to Ankhe.

Tut's Palace, 1324 BC

Ankhesenpaaten staggered into the throne room holding her bulging belly in both hands. She was six months into her second pregnancy.

Each morning she had said a quiet prayer to Amun that this time he would let the baby live. Those prayers had been answered so far, but now something was happening, something new that had her terrified.

'Tut,' she whispered from the doorway. 'Tut, please.'

Tut's advisers stood in a semicircle before his throne, midway through their morning discussion about an upcoming invasion of Nubia. The pharaoh wore just a royal kilt and a decorative collar, for it was summer in Thebes, and at midmorning the temperature was already stifling. When Tut had decided to move the capital back to Thebes, he had not anticipated such extremes of weather.

Tut walked quickly to his queen, not caring that his advisers might disapprove.

'What is it, Ankhe?' he asked. After he had returned from war, the two of them had become closer than ever.

'Tut, I can't feel anything.'

Tut glanced back at his advisers, who were trying—and failing—somehow to pretend that they weren't smug about the conversation.

'I'm sure the baby is just sleeping,' Tut said in a low voice.

Ankhesenpaaten shook her head. 'It's been a whole day. Usually he moves inside me all the time. Here,' she said, taking Tut's hand and placing it against the curve of her abdomen. 'Feel that?'

Tut nodded. 'That's his foot,' she told him. 'He normally kicks all the time, but that foot hasn't moved today.'

She suddenly gasped in pain and crumpled to the floor. The advisers rushed to the pharaoh and his queen.

'Guard!' Aye yelled. 'Send for the royal physician.'

Ankhesenpaaten's face had turned a sickly shade of pale. She cried out as a wave of excruciating pain coursed through her body.

'What is it?' asked Tut, holding her hand tightly. 'What is happening?'

'The baby is coming, Tut. Right now.'

And at those words, Ankhesenpaaten began to cry. She knew that no child should enter the world so early in a pregnancy. There was no way it would live.

It was as if Tut and his advisers did not exist now. Alone with the child, she curled into a ball on the floor and sobbed bitterly, pressing her face into the cool, smooth stone.

'I am so ashamed,' she whispered.

'My queen . . .' said Tut.

'I am not worthy of being called your queen,' she said, sitting up straight and looking deeply into Tut's eyes. 'I cannot give you an heir. Don't you see? I am incapable.'

The advisers said nothing to this, but none would have disagreed.

'Don't speak nonsense,' Tut said in an unconvincing voice. This was the moment he had feared since Ankhesenpaaten had announced that she was with child again. 'We'll put the child in my burial tomb. Much of it is already finished.'

'You're not listening to me,' said Ankhesenpaaten, just as a contraction sent a new wave of pain through her body.

'She's right,' Horemheb pronounced. 'She sees things clearly.'

Tut got to his feet and stood toe to toe with the general. 'Do you dare tell the pharaoh that he is in error?'

Horemheb didn't back down all the way. 'No, sir. I am merely agreeing with your queen. You heard her. She is telling you to take another wife. Listen to her.'

Tut bent to the floor and scooped up Ankhesenpaaten. Lovingly, he kissed her cheek as she wrapped her arms round his neck and he carried her to the royal bedroom.

'I will deal with you later,' Tut said to Horemheb. 'Egypt is a land of many generals. Do not forget it.'

Then, to Aye, he added, 'Send the doctor to the bedroom. And do it quickly, Scribe.'

TUT STRIPPED DOWN at his bedside, letting his kilt fall to the floor for a servant to clean in the morning. Many days had passed since Ankhesenpaaten had lost her second child.

He took off his eye paint, which was black and extended to his temples. He rinsed his mouth from a tumbler of water on the night stand, then slid into bed. The pillow was cool against his bare, shaved head, and the cotton sheets gently caressed his torso. Like most Egyptians, he was obsessed with hygiene and cleanliness. The hair on his body was regularly removed with razors and clippers.

Now he lay back and wondered what would happen next.

All night long the palace had been buzzing about the angry confrontation between Aye and the pharaoh.

'Egypt is once again powerful and prosperous,' the royal vizier had bellowed. 'This is due to me, Pharaoh. Not you. Not your queen. Your father ran this country nearly into ruin, and I have built it up again. Now you threaten all we have worked for by not producing an heir.' The vizier continued, 'This thing you two call "love" is a greater threat to Egypt than the Canaanites, the Nubians and all our other neighbours. These people'—now Aye threw his arm out towards the city—'deserve a pharaoh who puts the nation first.'

'I am pharaoh. I can do whatever I want to do. You are but a man, Scribe.'

As Tut entered his bedroom alone, after seeing Ankhesenpaaten to her room, he was aware that every person in the palace waited to see what would happen next.

Would Aye make good on his promise to bring a handmaiden to Tut's bed?

At midnight, with the full moon pouring into his open window, Tut got his answer. He heard two sets of footsteps in the corridor outside. The first was heavy and laboured and the other soft.

Then came a delicate rustle as the lighter footsteps tiptoed into his room. Tut could sense hesitation, perhaps fear, as the feet came closer and closer to his bed. He could almost feel the pounding of the young girl's heart.

What must she be thinking? Tut wondered, lying flat on his back, his eyes still adjusting to the near darkness. *She has come to have sex with the pharaoh.*

Tut rolled onto his side to have a look. His fierce loyalty to his queen almost caused him to send the girl away, but he held back for the moment, though he was unsure why.

Now he saw her.

The girl looked to be sixteen or seventeen. Tut remembered admiring her at a state dinner and thinking she might be the daughter of a local dignitary. That she was a great beauty, there was no doubt. She stood at the side of the bed, very demure, moonlight shining through her sheer robe. Tut was mesmerised at the sight of her: her shape, her long black hair, her dark eyes still painted.

'What is your name?' he said softly, surprised to feel the beating of his own heart, surprised that he cared about her feelings.

'Tuya,' she whispered.

'Take off your robe, Tuya. Don't be afraid. There's no need for that. Not here.'

Tuya did as she was told, pulling the fabric from her shoulders, letting it drop to the floor.

'Turn round for me. Slowly. You're very beautiful. Please, don't be fearful.'

She spun in a circle, her shoulders back and head held high. Then she took a tentative step towards him.

'Wait,' Tut said, seized by a sudden image of Ankhesenpaaten. What was his queen doing now? And what would she say if she could see him?

Tuya stopped and self-consciously placed her hands over her breasts.

Tut got out of bed then and walked to her. Her eyes grew wide at the sight of him, which only increased his arousal.

Next, he kissed Tuya's lips and found them to be soft, even more so than Ankhe's. Her breath was fresh and sweet.

The young pharaoh didn't think of his queen for the rest of that long sleepless night.

ANKHESENPAATEN COULDN'T SLEEP. The mere thought of what was happening in Tut's bedroom filled her with jealousy and more than a little sadness. From the time they were children, she had always loved Tut. And the men in the palace had always got in the way.

She stood and slipped on a robe, then walked quietly outside into the gardens. The air was cold, and she shivered from the chill. There was much on her mind. She thought of Tut again and that girl.

He's not enjoying it, she assured herself.

Oh, yes, he is, shot back an inner voice.

That night at dinner she'd overheard the servants laughing at her, scornful that a queen was incapable of bringing children into the world.

Yes, I can! she'd wanted to scream. *I have brought two wonderful children into this world. The gods have seen fit to send them to the afterworld, but I will bear more.*

Why does no one point the finger at Tut?

Why does he not endure the pain of childbirth, only to have the infant perish? Why is he allowed to take a woman to his bed to produce an heir, while I am left here alone? What if I felt like taking a man to my bed? What then? Maybe I do feel like it sometimes.

She paced. The queen was barefoot, and the path had many pebbles that dug into her feet, causing her to step gingerly. One sharp stone made her stop completely. Yet she revelled in the petty annoyance. This is nothing like childbirth, Tut! That was pain!

She considered racing to the other side of the palace and confronting the lovers, all tangled and sweaty in his bed.

You told him to do it, she reminded herself.

Yes, but I didn't mean it.

She would march in and claw the girl's face until her beauty was gone for ever. And then she would strike out at Tut.

No, I can't do that. I do love him. He is my king, the king of all of Egypt.

But he abandoned you. He is in another woman's arms this very minute.

He is a pharaoh, and pharaohs have harems. This is just one girl.

But we promised each other. We promised to be true. He would kill me if I broke that promise.

No, he wouldn't. He may never touch you again. But he wouldn't kill you.

I am the queen. I am of full noble birth. It was through marriage to me that Tut gained his throne. I can do the same with another man. Just watch me.

'It's *you*, Pharaoh,' Aye smirked.

They marched side by side to the royal stables, the air smelling of manure and sweet green alfalfa. Tut was late for his chariot ride.

Tuya had kept him up all night again and, rather than sleep the day away, he was determined to revive himself with a hard gallop across the desert on the east side of the Nile.

In truth, he was troubled and confused about Tuya—and about Ankhesenpaaten.

'What are you talking about?' he said.

'Tuya is not with child. The problem is not her, Pharaoh, and it is not your queen. You are the reason there is no royal heir. *It's you!*'

Tut flushed angrily. 'That is not possible! My manhood is beyond question.'

He had reached his chariot and now grabbed the reins from a young stableboy. The horses whinnied in anticipation.

'From the looks of things, there are no arrows in your quiver,' continued Aye.

That was the last straw. 'Guards,' commanded Tut. '*Seize him.*'

The contingent of six royal guards moved forward and towered over Aye, yet they were apprehensive, as if looking to Aye for leadership rather than Tut.

'*Now!*' Tut screamed, rage and humiliation pouring through. He was the pharaoh. He could impregnate every virgin in Egypt if he wished. It wasn't his fault that Tuya was having trouble bearing a child. Maybe Aye had chosen her because she was known to be infertile, all part of his scheme.

Aye didn't struggle as the guards clamped their hands on his arms and shoulders. No—all he did was smirk.

'I am the pharaoh, Aye. You will remember that from now on.' Tut stepped into his chariot. 'I am going for a ride,' he told the captain of the guards. 'By the time I return, you will have administered fifty lashes to the royal vizier. Am I understood?'

The smirk was gone from Aye's face now, much to Tut's delight. Even ten lashes would have been too much. Fifty would lay Aye's back open to the bone and leave permanent scars that would be a brand of shame for the rest of his life.

With a final glare, Tut whipped his reins and raced across the desert.

THE FORGIVING ELM WHEELS of the chassis provided the only shock absorption, but the terrain was smooth and so was the ride.

A lone man on a camel could be seen in the distance, but otherwise Tut had the desert to himself, as he liked it.

Within a few minutes, his forehead was sweating, and the dust from the horse's hoofs covered his chest. This was what he loved, but today even a fast chariot ride didn't help.

Tut was so caught up in thoughts of Aye's insolence and his own inability to produce an heir that he didn't notice that the desert had become more rugged in the few miles since his journey began.

And he didn't see the deep cleft that had probably been created by a flash flood. That is, not until it was too late to avoid it.

Hitting the rut, Tut was thrown headfirst from the chariot. He landed hard on the ground and was knocked unconscious for a time.

He came too slowly, moaning, and found himself staring up at the face of . . . a camel.

The rider was kneeling over Tut, checking for signs of injury, clearly unaware that the man before him was Egypt's pharaoh.

Instead, the robber—for that's what he was, Tut now realised—relieved the pharaoh of the expensive floral collar, then frisked the royal body for money.

Tut would have told the man who he was, except that—strangely—he seemed unable to utter a word.

Only when the man was sure that Tut wasn't carrying a purse did he leave, but not before stealing Tut's sandals and kilt.

Night was falling as Tut faded back into unconsciousness.

'WE NEED TO TALK.'

'I'm listening.'

It was an hour before dawn. The entire palace was astir. After the largest manhunt in Egyptian history, the pharaoh had been located in the desert west of Thebes. Tut had been robbed of all his possessions, no doubt by a nomad. The young pharaoh was still unconscious.

In addition to a high fever, his body was covered with bruises and abrasions. Now Aye and Horemheb stood on opposite sides of his bed, looking down at their comatose ruler. The cavernous bedroom was dark, save for the moonlight shining in the window.

Aye said, 'We should take this conversation into the hall.'

Horemheb pursed his lips. A long straight scar ran diagonally across his face, the result of a Hittite sword. When he was tense, it took on a reddish hue that made it stand out.

'If we go anywhere else, we will be observed. Obviously, the pharaoh cannot hear us. It's better if we talk here.'

Aye didn't like to be contradicted, but Horemheb was probably right. Besides, the royal vizier was still in great pain after enduring the humiliating lashes Tut had ordered. The guards had gone easy on him because of his status, but a few of the lashes had sliced into his skin. Now his back was a swollen mess, oozing blood and crisscrossed with whip marks.

'All right. Here then,' said Aye. He glanced about the room to make sure no one was there to overhear them. 'I am getting to be an old man. I have served my nation since I was an adolescent and learned the serpentine ways of the royal court. We both witnessed the ruin brought on by Akhenaten's reign, and we know that Tut is moving too slowly to fix the damage.'

'Are you saying—'

'Yes,' Aye stated flatly. 'And if you help me, I can ensure that you will be my successor. I will not live long, but in my short time as pharaoh I can return Egypt to her former glory. You will complete the task, General.'

Horemheb's scar was now a vibrant magenta. 'How would we do this? Look at him. He's a boy. No doubt he'll recover from his fall.' Horemheb sighed. He was nervous, yet he revelled in the notion of being pharaoh. 'I never thought the day would come that I would speak openly . . . of killing the pharaoh.'

Before Aye could respond, they heard sandals shuffling on the tiled floor. They turned to face the sound.

'Show yourself,' said Aye. 'Come out now. Who's there? *Who?*'

Yuye, the queen's lady in waiting, a tall girl with green eyes, stepped out of the shadows. She was just a teenager, and the palace knew her as Ankhesenpaaten's confidante. If anyone would tell the queen of their discussion, she would.

The girl was clearly terrified. 'I didn't hear anything, Vizier.'

'The issue is not whether you *heard* something, but whether you will *say* something.'

'I won't. I promise I won't.'

Aye grabbed the girl's wrist and yanked her towards him. His face was just inches from hers as he issued a quiet threat: 'I know.' He then turned to Horemheb. 'You think of a plan for him,' he said, nodding his head in the direction of Tut. 'I'll take care of the girl.'

AT FIRST YUYE was certain Aye was going to kill her and dispose of her body. He'd forcibly pulled her out of Tut's bedroom, his grip so tight that she thought her wrist might break.

There was a bedroom two doors down, and he led her inside. Then he threw her down on the bed.

'Listen to me,' Aye said simply. 'You will be my spy. Do you agree to do this?'

'I don't understand. What kind of spy?'

'You will tell me the queen's secrets. *That* kind of spy.'

'She will become suspicious. She is no one's fool.'

Aye was quiet for a moment. The muscles of his still-raw backside clenched, and he arched his back. Then he raised his fist and brought it down hard into the girl's ribs. It was more pain than Yuye had ever felt in her life. She couldn't breathe to cry out.

'Anything and everything that comes from the queen's lips will be reported to me. Am I understood?'

Yuye nodded. Of course she understood him.

IT HAD BEEN A WEEK since the pharaoh's chariot accident. Tut was well enough to sit up and take broth and sip a glass of wine that contained powdered eggshells, which the physician believed would help heal the shell of Tut's head.

But for the most part Tut slept, his every toss and turn watched by Tuya and the queen. The two women took turns attending him. Ankhesenpaaten had decided that they would be the ones to nurse him back to health.

Ankhe dabbed his forehead with a cool cloth, then bent down to kiss him tenderly. He had spoken a few words to her earlier, but she knew he wasn't safe yet.

The wounds would heal eventually, but his infections could worsen. She had seen this happen many times with the sick.

She kissed him again and then whispered, 'I forgive you.' She believed that she did. Tut had been unfaithful for the good of Egypt and only as a last resort. Most important, it had been her idea.

The queen stood up and smoothed her dress, leaving Tut to sleep.

Now Tut lay alone in the darkness, breathing softly. She had left the white cloth on his forehead, but otherwise his skull was uncovered. Was he healing? the queen wondered.

It was well past dark as the queen made her way back to her side of the palace. She was drowsy after a long day caring for the pharaoh.

Suddenly, a sound echoed down the hallway. 'Who's there?' she asked. 'I heard someone.'

There was no answer, so the queen continued to her room.

A moment after she passed, a bulky figure stepped out from behind one of several stone statues that decorated the hall.

Quickly, quietly, the man went into Tut's room and hurried towards the pharaoh's bed.

In his hand, a two-foot-long club. In his heart, murder.

CHAPTER 7

Valley of the Kings, 1917

Like a general commanding a small army, Carter barked orders, positioning his workers across the landscape in the spots where they would soon dig and dig, then dig some more. The men marched to their positions and leaned on their hoe-like *turias*, knowing that the work would not commence until Carter said so.

The forty-three-year-old Howard Carter, fluent in Arabic and knowledgeable about Egypt, had been deemed a vital resource by the British army. So, rather than searching for forgotten pharaohs, he'd spent the war in Cairo, labouring for the Military Intelligence Department of the War Office.

'War work claimed most of my time for the next few years,' he later wrote, 'but there were occasional intervals when I was able to carry out small pieces of excavation.'

But those were strictly reconnaissance efforts, not genuine searches for Tut or some other lost pharaoh. Then, on December 1, 1917, while war was still being waged in Europe, Carter was finally released from duty and allowed to return to his beloved Valley of the Kings.

'The difficulty was knowing where to begin,' he noted. 'I suggested to Lord Carnarvon that we take as a starting point the triangle of ground defined by the tombs of Rameses II, Mer-en-Ptah and Rameses VI.'

Just as so many soldiers in the trenches had longed for loved ones, so had Carter pined for the valley. To be standing here beneath the blazing blue skies, feeling a fine layer of dust settle on his skin—it was like falling in love all over again.

'Proceed,' he yelled, his words echoing.

The bare-chested army of diggers swung their *turias* into the earth.

Carter intended to clear the area around the tombs of Rameses II and Rameses VI right down to the bedrock, a task that would require removing tens of thousands of tons of stone and soil. He had already laid narrow-gauge tracks and arranged to have a small train haul away the debris.

The plan was ambitious, but after a decade of waiting, anything less would not have been acceptable to Carter or His Lordship. There was too much stored-up energy, too much deferred ambition.

But would he find his virgin tomb? Would he find King Tut?

Davis had said that the valley had been exhausted and, by the time he'd upped and left, the American had become its leading authority. For that reason, the experts had taken Davis at his word. But now Davis was dead, having keeled over from a heart attack just six months after abandoning the valley. Carter, however, was very much alive and hard at work.

He wondered about his diggers, those veterans with callused hands and broad shoulders who had moved so much earth in their lives. Did they also think the valley was exhausted? Did they believe they were digging all day long in the blazing sun with no hope of finding anything? Or did they believe in their hearts that they might help unearth a long-buried tomb?

Would they discover the elusive Tut?

Valley of the Kings, 1920

But Tut's tomb would not be found in 1917—or 1918 or 1919, for that matter.

Carter surveyed the Valley of the Kings with deepening frustration and little of his usual quixotic hopefulness.

Hundreds of workers had laboured on Lord Carnarvon's payroll for a number of long seasons—and for nothing of any real value. In Luxor,

Carter was something of a laughing stock, a sad man tilting at windmills.

Carter had found tombs that had been begun but never finished, caches of alabaster jars, a series of workmen's huts. And though his patience seemed inexhaustible, Lord Carnarvon's was not. 'We had now dug in the valley for several seasons with extremely scanty results,' Carter lamented. 'It had become a much-debated question whether we should continue the work or try for a more profitable site elsewhere. After these barren years, were we justified in going on?'

He looked out at the valley, searching for some sign of King Tut. As Carter explained it: 'So long as a single area of untouched ground remained, the risk was worth taking.' His rationale was simple: 'If a lucky strike be made, you will be repaid for years and years of dull and unprofitable work.'

His gaze rested on the flint boulders and workmen's huts over by the tomb of Rameses VI.

That would be his focus next year—if there was to be a next year.

Tut's Palace, 1324 BC

A solitary figure moved like a ghost through the pharaoh's bedroom—an angry, vengeful ghost.

He was a soldier in the Egyptian army, a man named Abdul, who had been conscripted at the age of eight and spent every day since in the service of the pharaoh. He had no wife, no children, and his parents had long since entered the afterworld. He had never risen above the rank of foot soldier. This warrior, in essence, was a nobody who had nothing.

Abdul was unused to the finery of the palace. He felt certain that he would be discovered at every turn in the hallway. But he'd seen only the queen leaving Tut's bedroom. It was as if the guards had all been told to take the night off. Had that been arranged too?

He had left his sandals at the barracks, knowing that his feet would be quieter on tile. In his hand he clutched a special implement prepared for him by one of General Horemheb's top weapon makers.

A smooth Nile stone the size of a grapefruit had been tied with leather straps to the end of a two-foot length of polished ebony.

By all appearances, it was a most attractive and suitable war club. Abdul knew, however, that the club was too pretty for combat.

But it would be perfect for murdering a young pharaoh.

Valley of the Kings, February 26, 1920

A discovery had been made, but what kind of discovery was it?

Carter bent down to be the first to examine the find. Lord Carnarvon was close on his heels, as was his wife, Lady Carnarvon.

They appeared to be inspecting a common debris pile—rocks, sand, chips of flint and pottery tossed aside during the excavation of a tomb long ago.

But peeking out, smooth and white, were alabaster jars—a dozen or more.

And the jars were intact.

Carter stepped forward to clear away more dirt, but the normally reserved Lady Carnarvon beat him to it. Though heavyset and past her prime, she dropped down to her knees and clawed fitfully at the soil. The Carnarvons had invested substantial time and money in the valley, and this was the first significant treasure they had to show for it. Lady Carnarvon would not be denied the opportunity to enjoy the discovery every bit as much as the men.

Carter and the workers stood back to watch as she cleared the soil away from each jar.

A tally was taken when she was done: thirteen. Perfect and near pristine, they were most certainly related to the burial of a king named Mer-en-Ptah and represented a decent find.

There were, however, no markings indicating that the jars had anything to do with Tut. As minor as the find may have been, something was better than nothing. And with the close of the 1920 dig season just a week off, it would end the period of labour on a high note.

'It was the nearest approach to a real find that we had yet made in the valley,' Carter wrote in his journal.

Once again, he was the hopeful Don Quixote of Egypt.

Highclere Castle, near Newbury, England, 1922

To be honest, Carter's time in the valley had been expensive and fruitless. He had found nothing to warrant the hundreds of thousands of pounds Lord Carnarvon had spent in the search for a great lost pharaoh—or even a minor one.

The alabaster jars had buoyed hope after the 1920 season, momentarily pushing aside memories of barren searches in years past.

But 1921 had yielded nothing important. There seemed no reason to think that the upcoming 1922 season would be any different.

Now the two men strolled across the sprawling grounds of Highclere Castle, Carnarvon's family estate back in England.

The mood was uneasy, and Carter had an inkling that he had been summoned for very bad news.

The two had become unlikely friends over the years. They had spent so much time together, fingers crossed, praying that their next effort would be the one to unearth some great buried treasure.

Tons of rock had been scraped away. But Howard Carter hadn't made a major find in almost twenty years.

The war hadn't helped. His Lordship's health had suffered in the absence of those warm Egyptian winters. And now he was ready to stop funding costly excavations that yielded nothing.

Carter quietly made his case anyway: he had located ancient workmen's huts near the tomb of Rameses VI, but because of heavy tourist traffic he hadn't been able to dig deeper. His plan was to start digging in early November to avoid the peak tourist season.

Carnarvon rebuffed him. He was through with the valley. There would be no more excavations with his money. 'I'm so sorry, Howard. I'm nearly as sad about this as you are,' Carnarvon said.

The news would have been crushing to Carter if he had not anticipated this moment and planned his next move. He cleared his throat. 'There's one last tomb to be found, sir. I'm sure of it. So sure that if you will allow me to make use of your concession in the valley, I will fund the next year of digging myself. Of course,' he added hastily, 'we would split whatever I find evenly.'

Carnarvon was astounded. 'You don't have that kind of money,' he exclaimed.

'I'll find the money, sir.'

'You will? To pay the wages of a hundred diggers? To pay for the guards? To feed yourself?'

Carter offered a rare smile. 'I'm not all that hungry, for food that is. I suppose I will need cigarette money.'

Carnarvon squinted. He was touched by this show of faith. 'I will fund one more year. But just one, Howard. This is your last chance. Find King Tut, or we're done.'

PART THREE

CHAPTER 8

Palm Beach, Florida, present day

'What are you smiling about, Jim?' asked Susan. My wife was standing in the doorway to my office.

I had just hung up the phone with Marty Dugard. 'My gut feeling is getting stronger. Tut was murdered, Sue. I just have to figure out who killed the poor guy.'

'A hunch doesn't mean very much if you can't prove it,' she said.

'Oh, I'll prove it,' I said with a grin. 'And thanks for the vote of confidence.'

'Anytime,' she called over her shoulder.

Sue had a point. How was I going to prove that Tut hadn't died from wounds suffered in his chariot crash? That was the most widely accepted theory about his death.

My most popular fictional character, Dr Alex Cross, lives by his hunches and instincts, quite possibly because I do as well. At that moment, I felt that I would soon know who was responsible for Tut's death—perhaps someone you might not expect. *That* was what had me excited now.

I had been making notes on a new Cross manuscript before the call from Marty Dugard. The pages were stacked in a pile on my desk, next to pages from a dozen other projects I had in the works. I have an ability, or a curse, to focus on several projects at once. But Tut was distracting me from all the other projects.

Ignoring the Cross manuscript, I reached for my list of pharaohs.

The New Kingdom, as the era spanning the Eighteenth to Twentieth Dynasties was known, had lasted a little more than 500 years. There were thirty-two pharaohs during that time, but the ones I was interested in were Tut and the man who succeeded him. It seemed reasonable to presume that the person who had the most to gain by Tut's death was the man ascending to the throne after him. Follow the money, follow the power.

I ran my finger down the list. I read the succession of kings out loud. 'Amenhotep II, Tuthmosis IV, Amenhotep III, Akhenaten, Nefertiti, Tutankhamen . . .' Then I stopped.

Not just the next name but the next *two* names held my attention. I had looked at this roster before, but only now was I beginning to realise what it could mean. These weren't only names—they were pieces of a puzzle that hadn't been solved for thousands of years.

Staring at them, I began to think that I wasn't studying a random act of murder but a cold-blooded conspiracy. There was that gut instinct of mine again—the reason, I think, that *Time* magazine had once called me 'The Man Who Can't Miss'.

We'd soon see about that, wouldn't we?

Valley of the Kings, November 1, 1922

The men were assembled for work. Carter knew most of them by name or sight after working the valley year after year. They carried their digging tools casually over their shoulders and wore thin sandals and flowing white shirts that extended to their ankles.

'*Mabrook*,' they called out in greeting, their smiles a sure sign that they were ready for a brand-new season with their demanding boss man.

Carter tried to appear upbeat, but even he was racked by self-doubt.

'We had now dug in the valley for several seasons with extremely scanty results,' he wrote in a rare candid moment. 'After these barren years, were we justified in going on with it?'

He had decided that they were and had convinced Lord Carnarvon to wager another several thousand pounds. Nodding to his foreman, Carter gave the official order to start.

They were beginning two months earlier than usual, hoping to finish their work before the tourist season began.

Near where he stood, just in front of the cavernous opening to the tomb of Rameses VI, rose a triangle of ruins first excavated five years earlier—a chain of ancient workmen's huts.

First, Carter's men would record the precise location and dimensions of each hut. Then they would remove the huts and dig down through the soil to the bedrock. Only when they struck bedrock could they begin stripping away the remaining sand and dirt to search for the seam in the earth that might lead to Tut and his tomb. A tomb architect would have cut straight down into the rock to create the most solid and long-lasting burial place imaginable. There would be a descending staircase, perhaps, or a long-buried passageway to mark the opening.

Or so Carter hoped.

'I had always had a kind of superstitious feeling that in that particular corner of the valley one of the missing kings, possibly Tutankhamen, might be found,' Carter wrote in a journal.

But a strong gut feeling was all he had to go on. Certainly, this was the very last part of the valley that had not been fully explored. But who could say if or when another lost treasure would be found?

Carter fell into the habit of watching the men working. They talked non-stop, gossiping about their friends and wives as their *turias* dug into the rocky soil. The tools clanked when hitting rock, and the work had a cadence that was almost musical to Carter's ear.

Despite their chattiness, his men were deliberate and precise. Years of toil in the valley had made them proficient Egyptologists in their own right. They knew when to proceed cautiously and when to move earth with abandon.

So there was little for Carter to do but stand and watch and hope this would be his year. No matter how fast his crew moved, excavating down to the bedrock would take days. He thought it might be better to return home, get out of the sun and unpack the food and wine that had just arrived from London.

But he stayed on at the site anyway, preferring to endure what he called the creeping 'doubts, born of previous disappointments' there than at his home.

He lit another cigarette and watched the dirt fly.

Valley of the Kings, November 4, 1922

It was dawn, three days into the season. The first day's optimism had already given way to grumbling and low morale. The diggers were still chatty but seemed subdued and disappointed, almost as if they had already given up.

A young boy, a worker's son, played happily in the loose sand. His job was to carry water, but the sun wasn't high enough yet for the men to be thirsty, so he contented himself by pretending to be one of the diggers.

The boy knew to keep away from the ancient workmen's huts where the men were, so he dug into the ground nearby with a pair of sticks. The sand was fine and not at all hard. It didn't take much effort for him to plunge his sticks into the ground.

One stick hit something solid. His heart beat a little faster as he wondered what it might be. He dropped his stick and started to use his hands to push back the soil. A solid object soon revealed itself. It was flat and smooth and made of stone. The more dirt he cleared away, the more the boy could see that the object was something very worth while indeed.

It was a step.

Here, not where the men were digging.

Someone long ago had carved the step out of bedrock. Time and the elements had covered it over until this young water boy, thousands of years later, reclaimed it from the earth with a pair of sticks.

Quickly, he pulled the sand back into the hole and carefully marked the spot. Then he ran off to tell Mr Howard Carter about the mysterious stairway.

Egyptian Desert, 1324 BC

'Halt the excavation!'

The voice echoed down the corridor above the din of hammering and chipping.

The overseer was furious. No one but the pharaoh could issue such an order.

He planted his feet, placed one callused hand on each hip, and turned to glare at this offensive idiot, whoever he might be.

He heard footsteps slapping down the corridor, then the angry cries of workmen who were being trampled on by the interloper.

A royal page skittered to a halt directly in front of the overseer. The overseer believed that the man worked for the royal vizier, though he wasn't certain. Either way, it was best to keep his temper in check.

'By what right do you barge into my construction site and issue such a decree?' the overseer said in measured syllables.

'By order of the royal vizier,' replied the page.

The overseer calmed down a little. 'I'm listening. By order of the vizier, *what*?'

'The pharaoh is dead.' The page leaned forward and whispered in a voice so low that the overseer could barely hear. 'There are rumours that he has been murdered and that more deaths will follow.'

The overseer's shock was evident, which pleased the gossipy page. 'Is this a secret?' asked the overseer.

'The biggest. If I were you, I would not repeat it.'

'You just did.'

'You are not me, gravedigger.'

There was a moment of strained silence. The overseer was so consumed with the astounding news that it took a moment for the ramifications to sink in.

'I can't finish this tomb in seventy days,' he said, alluding to the pre-scribed mourning, embalming and mummification period before a pharaoh would be sealed inside the ground for eternity. 'It is impossible.'

'That is why I have come. We will finish *this* tomb later. The pharaoh will be buried in the tomb at the centre of the valley.'

The overseer was once again astonished. 'That is no tomb for a pharaoh. It is a trifle. Just four rooms and the narrowest of hallways. It is a closet!'

'Yes, but it is a finished closet.'

'It still needs to be painted,' replied the overseer. It was customary to paint scenes from the pharaoh's life and his journey into the afterworld on the walls in vivid colours.

'Exactly. You had better get your men painting pretty pictures.'

'Stop the excavation!' roared the overseer. He paused, and then looked at the page curiously. 'Who will—'

'Inherit this tomb?' answered the page, anticipating the words.

The overseer nodded.

'The royal vizier has graciously offered to take it off the pharaoh's hands.'

Valley of the Kings, 1324 BC

Ankhesenpaaten stood at the top of the stone steps that led down into her husband's tomb. The funeral was more than two months away, but she wanted to see for herself where he would rest for eternity.

She nodded to Yuye, her lady in waiting, signalling that she did not want to be followed. Then the queen descended the steps.

The steps led to a hallway. She noted with disappointment the lack of decoration, the walls of bare rock. Ankhesenpaaten understood that time was short. Still, a few simple paintings would have been better and more fitting.

She turned back towards the light at the tomb entrance, checking to see if she had been followed. There was no sign of anyone.

Ankhesenpaaten breathed a sigh of relief. More than anything, she wanted to be alone right now. She had much to think about.

The hallway led into a large chamber, and a slightly smaller room lay beyond that. The way was lit by small lamps whose ghostly flickerings danced on the walls.

The queen was heartened when she finally gazed upon murals depicting Tut's life. At least he would be remembered here.

In the centre of the small room was Tut's throne, as if waiting for him to arrive. She walked to it, running her hand along the wood.

Ankhesenpaaten smiled as she examined the back of the chair, where scenes of their life together had been carved. There was one of her anointing him with oil. And another of them hunting together, his bow at the ready as she handed him an arrow and pointed to a fat Nile duck. She remembered the day, or one exactly like it, as if it were yesterday.

There was another reason she'd come here: Ankhesenpaaten was terrified for her own life.

She circled the throne, afraid of the emotions welling up inside her. She had never felt so alone before, had never so needed Tut's reassuring voice. He would have known what to do. She had seen him grow more and more confident in Aye's presence, so much so that Aye had little or no power over him. Tut had been fond of reminding her that Aye and his wife had been little more than glorified servants to their parents. Indeed, Aye's wife had been Nefertiti's wet nurse. The queen had nothing to fear from them.

Ankhesenpaaten took a deep breath, then allowed herself to settle onto the throne. She sat up straight at first, then settled back until she was relaxed in the chair. That was how Tut had sat there, not erect, like some tentative ruler, but slumped and secure.

She could almost hear his voice as she sat there. He would be speaking directly, unafraid to tell the truth to whoever needed to hear it.

Ankhesenpaaten felt power rising within her, as if Tut himself were giving her confidence. But it was too much. She broke down in tears, sobbing alone in the tomb.

Tut was gone from this world; there was no getting round it. How would she rule without him?

His voice came to her, strong and sure: *A woman cannot be pharaoh these days. You have two choices—either marry Aye and let him rule, or find a foreign king to occupy the throne.* Some of her sisters had married Asians. Why should she be different?

Because they were princesses, and I am the queen—and right now the pharaoh too.

Ankhesenpaaten stopped crying, but the grief in her heart was great. She didn't want to marry anyone else and certainly not Aye. But she was the queen, and she had no choice. Whatever plan she followed, it must be for the good of Egypt.

The queen gazed at the walls again. She needed to act quickly.

Ankhesenpaaten strode from the burial chamber, shoulders back and head high. In her mind she was already composing the letter that might set her free.

Or possibly get her killed—just like poor Tut.

EGYPT'S WEALTHIEST and most prominent citizens had travelled from far and wide to mourn the Boy King. They had dressed in their most colourful kilts and gowns and golden collars. The vibrant scene looked out of place amid the valley's desolation.

There were so many mourners, and the tomb entrance was so small, that only an elite few were granted the honour of entering it to see where the pharaoh would lie for eternity.

The sarcophagus was heavy, and the stairs were steep, making the journey to Tut's final resting place long and laborious. The sweat from the shoulders of the men made their burden slick, and it was obvious that they were struggling not to drop the pharaoh.

The crowds outside watched anxiously, unprotected from the sun. Even the wealthiest women were sweating and miserable, thick eyeliner running down their cheeks. Some were fanned by slaves, who provided just a whisper of relief in the still, hot air.

Yet no one dared leave to find a sliver of shade. That could wait until the pharaoh's body was sealed in the ground.

It was the overseer's job to safeguard the tomb's contents, for even the richest and most powerful person in Thebes might be tempted to grab a golden trinket if given the chance. Once the pharaoh's body had been placed in the tomb, the overseer quietly pressed through the crowd and descended the steps. His men were already using wood and plaster to seal the burial chamber.

Tut now lay inside a solid gold coffin, which was nested inside another coffin, which was nested inside another, which was then placed inside a sarcophagus made of yellow quartzite, with a lid of pink granite. The sarcophagus was housed in a burial shrine, which was encased in another, and then another, all of this hidden within the outermost shrine decorated in blue faience and gold.

The structure was so big it filled the burial chamber from wall to wall, with barely an inch to spare.

As the workers laboured, gangs of men began carrying Tut's possessions into the much larger room next to the burial chamber. No item of his was considered too small or insignificant—from childhood game boards to travel beds. The work went on for hours, as if Tut were moving everything he owned into a new residence, which, of course, he was.

'We're finished, sir,' said the mason, motioning with one hand for the overseer to inspect the work. The plaster was still wet, but it was clear that the job had been expertly done. For a tomb robber to penetrate that chamber would take an act of supreme will—and muscle. Getting to the pharaoh's body would require knocking down the entire new wall, then disassembling each piece of the elaborate sepulchre.

'You are safe now,' murmured the overseer, proud of his handiwork and professionalism. 'You were a good pharaoh.'

No one would bother the pharaoh ever again.

CHAPTER 9

Valley of the Kings, November 4, 1922

Carter was smoking a cigarette, his fifth or sixth already that day, and was again in a hopeful mood. He sat astride his brown and white mule as it sauntered into the valley. The dirt path wound between cliffs that climbed steeply, giving way to pale blue sky.

This was the same route Carter had travelled countless times in the past thirty years, and the day seemed as if it would be just another day, fraught with expectation but tempered by despair. Before going home the previous night he had ordered his foreman to finish clearing the soil down to the bedrock. Now he smoked and wondered how the work was progressing.

Thirty years—a long time for such unpleasant and unrewarding results. No wonder they laughed behind his back in Luxor.

He noticed the valley was quiet.

The valley was never quiet during dig season.

His curiosity aroused, Carter dismounted and tied the animal in the shade. The foreman found Carter almost immediately to tell him the news. 'I was greeted by the announcement that a step cut into the rock had been discovered,' Carter later recalled. 'This seemed too good to be true, but a short amount of clearing revealed that we were actually in the entrance of a step cut in the rock.'

Carter had seen this sort of staircase in many valley tombs and, he mused, 'I almost dared to hope we had found our tomb at last.'

HE ORDERED THE MEN to dig. The single step found by the water boy soon revealed more steps, leading deeper and deeper into the hard bedrock a dozen or so feet beneath the entrance to the tomb of Rameses VI.

Carter had worked the valley long enough to know that this was the sort of stairwell associated with tomb construction. The way the rock had been cut was a giveaway.

The men didn't need to be told what to do. All other areas of the job site were abandoned. As one group dug deeper, clearing away the hard-packed soil and limestone that covered the staircase, another worked at the top. Their job was to hack away the soil around the opening to reveal the stair-well's true shape and size.

Carter halted the work at nightfall. But the frantic pace began again at dawn, with the men back to jabbering.

By the afternoon of November 5, it was clear that they had found some kind of great underground structure. They just needed to dig until an entrance was revealed.

Even with the clang of *turias*, and dust choking the air, Carter's pessimism had returned. He began to ponder the status of the underground chamber.

Was it empty? Had it ever been used? Was it just a storage chamber, or was it actually a burial tomb? And if it was a tomb, how was it possible that it might have somehow eluded plunder?

The staircase was now a partially covered passageway, measuring ten feet high and six feet wide. Eight steps had been unearthed.

Then nine.

Ten.

Eleven steps.

At step twelve they found the uppermost portion of a door. In his journal, Carter described it as 'blocked, plastered and sealed'.

Sealed. That was a positive sign. Carter began to believe it was possible he had found an unopened tomb.

'Anything, literally anything, might lie beyond that passage,' wrote Carter. 'It needed all my self-control to keep from breaking down the doorway and investigating there and then.'

But he was done with investigating—at least for now. As the sun set on the Valley of the Kings on November 5, Carter ordered that there be *no more excavation.*

Instead, as much as he wanted to dig deeper, as much as he *needed* to, he ordered the men to fill in the stairwell.

Luxor, November 23, 1922

When the train from Cairo pulled into Luxor station, nearly three unnerving weeks had passed since the tomb's discovery.

Not a bit of work had been done since the staircase had been filled in on November 5. Sentries guarded the site night and day. As added insurance, boulders had been rolled over the opening.

These safeguards were vital. Rumours about the find had already sent droves of tourists into the valley, leading Carter to note wryly in his journal that 'news travels fast in the small town that is Egypt'.

Yet he refused to open the tomb.

'Lord Carnarvon was in England,' he explained. 'In fairness to him I had to delay matters until he could come. Accordingly, on the morning of November 6th I sent him the following cable: At last have made wonderful discovery in valley; a magnificent tomb with seals intact; re-covered same for your arrival; congratulations.'

Carnarvon replied by telegram that he would arrive in two weeks.

'We had thus nearly a fortnight's grace, and we devoted it to making preparations of various kinds, so that when the time of reopening came, we should be able, with the least possible delay, to handle any situation that might arise,' Carter wrote.

Carter spent those two weeks in a state of perpetual self-doubt and second-guessing. His entire life was tied up in this tomb.

'One thing puzzled me, and that was the smallness of the opening in comparison with the ordinary valley tombs,' he wrote. 'Could it be the tomb of a noble buried here by royal consent? Was it a royal cache, a hiding place to which a mummy and its equipment had been removed for safety? Or was it actually the tomb of the king for whom I had spent so many years in search?'

As the days slowly passed and the news rapidly spread round the world, Howard Carter became a public figure.

This terrified him. Not that he minded the fame—after years of failure and struggle, it was nice to have his ego massaged. But if the tomb was empty he would be a laughing stock everywhere, and his reputation for failure would only grow.

Carter tried the best he could to go about his business, spending night after sleepless night waiting for Lord Carnarvon and his family to arrive.

At last they were here!

As the train settled to a stop, the dapper earl stepped down from his first-class compartment. His daughter Evelyn, a twenty-year-old beauty, was at his side. She and Carter had enjoyed a clandestine enchantment the season before, despite the nearly thirty-year difference in their ages, though with Carnarvon spending night and day with Carter in Luxor, it was impossible for him to take the romance with Evelyn very far.

Carter greeted them both eagerly, handing Evelyn a bouquet of white flowers. Next, the three would mount donkeys for the six-mile ride to the Valley of the Kings. The path would take them through the lush green fields outside Luxor. They would then cross the Nile by ferry and continue down the dusty dirt path to the valley.

But even though Lady Evelyn was her usual radiant self, Lord Carnarvon was weak and tired. He needed rest.

The opening of the tomb would have to wait one more day.

A disappointed Howard Carter led his guests to his home, where he would spend yet another sleepless night.

Valley of the Kings, November 24, 1922

The following day, Carter, Lord Carnarvon and Lady Evelyn arrived at the site. For Carter this had been a thirty-year wait, but even for the Carnarvons the suspense must have been great.

The heavy boulders were rolled away from the tomb. Then Carter's men began clearing the steps. But this was not as simple as shovelling sand out of a hole, for as they dug deeper and deeper, ancient artefacts mixed with the soil.

Lady Evelyn was beside herself about the historical significance of it all, lovingly studying each new pottery shard or amulet—scarabs, they were called—that turned up in the mountain of dirt.

But Carter's spirits soon plummeted. In his mind these bits of rubble confirmed that he had found not a tomb but a royal rubbish dump. 'The balance of evidence would seem to indicate a cache rather than a tomb,' he admitted dourly, 'a miscellaneous collection of objects of the Eighteenth Dynasty kings.'

The shards were stamped with the names of kings he knew well: Amenhotep the Magnificent, Akhenaten, Tuthmosis. Less than pleased with what he was seeing, Carter passed the day looking down from the top step, thinking this might be the end of his career—and an ignominious final chapter at that.

Finally, 'by the afternoon of the 24th the whole staircase was clear, sixteen steps in all, and we were able to make inspection of the sealed doorway,' he wrote.

He was terribly disappointed by what he saw.

'The tomb was not absolutely intact, as we had hoped,' he wrote.

Someone had been there before Carter.

WITH THE DOOR now fully exposed to sunlight and air, there was clear evidence that the plaster seals had been tampered with. Tomb robbers had entered the tomb, then had taken the time to reseal the door when they had finished ransacking it.

Carter's mind raced in all the wrong directions. Would the break-in have happened in modern times? Impossible. The workmen's huts and loose soil above the bedrock dated the tomb to the time of Rameses VI, at the very least. This meant that whoever rifled through the tomb had done it in a 200-year window between the reigns of Akhenaten and Rameses.

There was one thing that gave Carter hope: the seal of Tutankhamen was stamped on the doorway.

This led to more questions: Was the seal evidence that this mysterious king, about whom so little was known, was buried inside? Or was it merely an indication that he had been present or in power when the remains or belongings of others had been relocated to this site? After all, the same seals had been found on the tomb that Davis had once claimed belonged to Tut.

As the light faded and work stopped for the day, the symbol taunted him. Carter's mind kept going back to the same question: *Could this be Tut?*

If so, this could be the greatest discovery of modern time.

In the morning Carter would get an answer. At dawn, he planned to be the first man in 3,000 years to break down that door.

Valley of the Kings, November 25, 1922

It was time. Well, almost time. Before the door could be destroyed, the royal seals had to be photographed for the historical record.

This singular honour fell to Lord Carnarvon, president of his local camera club back home in England. The earl now stood at the bottom of the narrow stairwell in the pale dawn light, fussing over shutter speeds and apertures, a very professional and dedicated amateur. The last thing Lord Carnarvon wanted to do was make a mistake that would lead to bad photos—or, worse, no photos at all.

Carter, on the other hand, was beside himself with anxiety.

Complicating matters, a much-loathed bureaucrat from the Antiquities Service had arrived to oversee the entry. Rex Engelbach, nicknamed 'Trout' by Carter and Carnarvon owing to his sallow countenance, was firm in stating that his job title gave him the right to be the first person to enter the tomb.

Carter had never liked Engelbach, with his high-handed arrogance and lack of Egyptology credentials, but on this morning Carter refused to let Engelbach bother him. After a career defined by hard work and failure, Carter was finally about to enter the tomb of Tut. This was no time to be arguing with civil servants. But there was no way that Engelbach was getting into that tomb first. No way in hell.

Carter descended the steps with his sketchbook to draw each of the seals and impressions. These would serve as a back-up for Carnarvon's photos, and now the two friends worked side by side at the base of the cramped stairwell.

Carter's sketches were precise in scale and detail. No aspect of the designs went unrecorded.

Only at midmorning, when he had completed the drawings, did Carter trot back up the stairway with Lord Carnarvon.

It was time.

Carter ordered his workmen to demolish the door.

'On the morning of the 25th,' wrote Carter, 'we removed the actual blocking of the door; consisting of rough stones carefully built from floor to lintel, and heavily plastered on their outer faces to make the seal impressions.'

The crowd gathered at the top of the steps strained to see what was on the other side. Shadows and debris made it impossible to tell.

Carter walked down the steps to have a look. He found himself peering into a long narrow hallway. The smooth floor sloped down into the earth, a descending corridor.

The hallway, Carter wrote, 'was filled completely with stone and rubble, probably the chip from its own excavation. This filling, like the doorway, showed distinct signs of opening and reclosing of the tomb, the untouched part consisting of clean white chip mingled with dust; whereas the disturbed part was mainly of dark flint.'

How far into the ground the hallway led, it was impossible to know. But one thing was certain: someone else had been there.

'An irregular corner had been cut through the original filling at the upper corner on the left side,' noted Carter. Someone had burrowed through there searching for whatever lay on the other side.

Carnarvon snapped a photograph of the rubble pile. Then a weary Carter gave the order for his men to clear it away, chips and dust and all. Sooner or later the tunnel would have to end.

With any luck, the tomb robbers hadn't taken everything.

Valley of the Kings, November 26, 1922

It was just after lunch, which had gone mostly untouched by Carter. He and Lady Evelyn were sifting through a basket of rubble, when a digger ran up the steps with the news: the workers had found a second door.

His heart racing in anticipation, Carter readied himself to go back down the steps to have a look and evaluate the new discovery.

It had been a tumultuous and nerve-racking twenty-four hours for everyone. The diggers had laboured into the night, hauling debris out by the basketful. Yet the corridor was still a seemingly endless repository of rubble when they finally stopped working.

Making matters worse, the rock was laced with what Carter described as 'broken potsherds, jar sealings, alabaster jars, whole and broken, vases of painted pottery, numerous fragments of smaller articles, and water skins'—

further signs that this could be an ancient rubbish dump, *not* a tomb.

Work had resumed at first light. Carter and Lady Evelyn carefully sifted through each new basket of debris, searching for historical clues. Carter was an Egyptologist, first and foremost. To him, this diligence was a matter of preserving history. Rather than simply dumping the rubble, as Theodore Davis would have done, Carter meticulously catalogued and recorded each new discovery, however small or seemingly insignificant.

To the anxious onlookers—desperate to see inside the tomb and literally baking in the desert sun—the record keeping was a monotonous waste of time that was slowing things down.

Excitement shot through the crowd as Carter now walked down the steps, trailed by Lord Carnarvon and Lady Evelyn. The three of them jostled for space with the diggers as they traded places in the slender passage.

Dust filled the air, as did 'the fever of suspense'.

The second door was an almost exact duplicate of the previous one. Faint seal impressions were stamped into the surface, bearing the name Tutankhamen.

But this door too had been penetrated in ancient times. The symbol for a royal necropolis was also stamped into the door, and Carter couldn't help being pessimistic. 'It was a cache that we were about to open, not a tomb,' he wrote.

Still, he stepped forward and began clawing a hole in the upper-left corner of the passageway. His hands trembled as he reached up to pull away thick chunks of plaster and rock.

Lord Carnarvon handed him a long slender iron rod. Grasping it firmly, Carter jammed it into the small opening until it poked clean through to the other side. He tested for further resistance. There was none—no wall of limestone chips or pottery shards, just air.

He had actually broken through to the next level.

Carter had no idea what might happen next, but the great moment had finally arrived. Was it a cache, or was it a tomb? There was only one way to find out.

'There lay the sealed doorway, and behind it was the answer to the question,' Carter recalled.

He clawed at the hole he had opened with the rod. Then he worked with his bare hands, the only digger.

He figured that he deserved as much.

CHAPTER 10

Tut's Palace, 1324 BC

The eyes gave them away—always.

So eyes were what Ankhesenpaaten studied whenever a member of the royal court entered her presence during these dangerous times. As she stood alone in her study, the morning sun barely brightening the large stone room, she steeled herself for another day.

If their eyes were slightly downcast, they thought she had killed her husband. The same was true of those who fixed strained smiles on their faces while avoiding her gaze.

She could not quite describe the look of those who believed her. But there weren't many in the palace who did. It seemed that she had already been tried and found guilty.

'You wanted to see me, Majesty?' said Yuye, her lady in waiting. The girl bowed as she entered the queen's quarters, making it difficult for Ankhesenpaaten to observe her.

Now that Tut was gone, the entire palace belonged to the queen, but she still kept to her rooms. It felt better that way. Safer. The only change she'd made to palace life was to banish Tut's lover.

'Take a letter,' the queen told Yuye. She peered over the girl's shoulder as she spoke, afraid of being overheard or caught at what some would call treason.

Yuye chewed on a fresh reed before dabbing it in an inkwell and pulling out a fresh sheet of papyrus.

'My dearest King Suppiluliuma,' the queen dictated, her voice unsteady.

Ankhesenpaaten appraised the girl before she continued. If she could trust anyone, it had to be Yuye. Still the queen wasn't sure that sending a letter to the king of the Hittites was a good idea. They were Egypt's enemy, and centuries of battle had bred significant distrust between the nations.

But Ankhesenpaaten had a plan, a forward-thinking vision that would benefit Egypt now and in the future. The Hittites were powerful, with a fine army and strong leaders. A marriage between the queen and one of the king's sons could strengthen Egypt for centuries to come.

She continued, 'My husband is dead, and I am told that you have grown sons. This is fortuitous for both of us. Send me one of your sons. I will make him my husband, and he will be king of Egypt.'

Ankhesenpaaten paused, searching for the proper words to end the letter. All she could do was blurt out the one thought endlessly racing around her brain: 'I am afraid for my life.'

Yuye looked up at Ankhesenpaaten, uncertain why the queen would say such a thing.

That is when the queen finally caught a glimpse of Yuye's eyes.

The lady in waiting clearly believed that the queen had murdered her husband.

ANKHESENPAATEN HAD BEEN badly afraid for exactly twenty-eight days in a row. She had counted each and every one. Now she walked the palace courtyard alone as the sun rose on the twenty-ninth morning following Tut's death.

The sound of water trickling from a nearby fountain gave her a false sense of calm, as did the sparrows flitting through the fruit orchard. But she hadn't touched her morning meal and was so nervous that not even a sip of water had passed her lips.

Today would be the day. She was sure of it. But she was certain about nothing else at the palace.

It took fourteen days for a messenger to travel from Thebes to the Hittite kingdom. If all went well, a prince would ride to her palace this day and offer his hand in marriage. She would accept, of course. Aye had grown more terrifying with each passing hour, imposing himself upon the palace as the pharaoh. But his claim would never be true if she did not marry him. Once the Hittite prince arrived, the matter would be settled. Aye would once again be a commoner, forced to live out the rest of his days as royal vizier. If that.

Just then she heard heavy footsteps. It was certainly not her lady in waiting.

Ankhesenpaaten turned to face Aye.

'Good morning, Highness,' he said stiffly. But there was something else in his look. A smugness.

'Vizier.'

'What troubles you?' he asked.

She took a calming breath. 'That is none of your concern.'

While the queen stood, Aye sat on a bench, ignoring proper protocol. That in itself was bold and insulting.

'Stand up,' barked the queen.

The vizier smiled, then stood and took a step towards her. 'Highness, there is still ample time before your husband's burial. But we must discuss the plan for succession. Do you have a plan?'

She said nothing.

'Highness, you need a king beside you to rule Egypt. You must understand that.'

'And I will have one,' she said.

'There is no one in the land more capable than I—'

'I said I will have one. Please do not discuss this delicate matter with me until my husband has been laid to rest.'

They were interrupted by Yuye, whose eyes hastily met those of the vizier. The queen noticed the look that passed between them. Could it be collusion? She pushed the thought aside. Yuye would never betray her. And yet she felt certain something was going on.

'There is a messenger to see you, Highness,' Yuye announced.

'Who is it?' demanded Aye.

'That is none of your concern,' Ankhesenpaaten said. Her heart was beating wildly. 'You are dismissed, Vizier.'

A dark-haired man was led into the courtyard after Aye departed. The visitor had left a small retinue behind at the gate. One look told the queen this was not a Hittite prince.

'What is the meaning of this visit?' the queen asked. She looked at Yuye in desperation. Yuye shrugged as the Hittite, clearly uncomfortable in the presence of the queen, struggled to explain himself.

'I have a message from my king,' he said. He handed it to the queen, and she read it quickly. Then the Hittite verbalised the message. 'Where is the son of the late pharaoh? What has become of him?'

Ankhesenpaaten nearly flew into a rage. 'Do you see a male child wandering the palace halls? Do you? Do you see a young prince on a chariot galloping about the grounds? Oh, what I would give for a young boy. Does your king think this is some sort of trick? Did my letter to him seem insincere or unclear?'

The Hittite shuffled his feet and lowered his eyes. 'What shall I tell my king?'

'Tell him this: "Why should I deceive you? I have no son, and my husband is dead. Send me a son of yours, and I will make him king of Egypt." '

The Hittite stood there, not sure what to do next.

'What are you waiting for?' asked the queen. 'We are running out of time! We have until my husband is buried, no longer.'

As the Hittite fled the palace, Yuye slipped away to find Aye.

The queen stood alone.

Egyptian Border, 1324 BC

The Hittite prince's name was Zannanza.

He and his entourage rode fine white horses down the dirt road to Egypt. He was pure Hittite by birth, his father's pride and joy. At the age of twenty-two, Zannanza had already demonstrated courage on the battlefield and shown confidence and diplomatic skill in the royal court. His impending marriage to the queen of Egypt would unify the two nations and make history. Zannanza would be the new pharaoh and would possess a level of power not known even by his father.

Now Zannanza drank from a water skin, then passed it to his vizier. 'Do you see them?' asked the vizier.

'How could I not?' Zannanza replied.

It seemed that the queen had sent a welcoming party. A small band of Egyptians waited at the border, taking refuge from the sun in a verdant oasis. Zannanza imagined they would have something to eat—fruit, perhaps. And fresh water. He had ridden hard all day.

Zannanza and his soldiers and courtiers galloped towards the waiting Egyptians. As they arrived, a small man with a pot-belly trotted forward on his horse to welcome them.

'Greetings. I am Horemheb, the queen's general. She sends her best wishes, Prince.'

'I am Zannan—'

The Hittite prince's words ended abruptly. He had not seen the archers behind the tents, nor the arrow racing towards him straight and true that would pierce his forehead. He toppled off his mount, royal blood flooding onto the sand in a massive pool.

His entourage suffered a similar fate. Anyone who escaped the arrows was chased down and hacked to bits. As buzzards circled, Horemheb dismounted and walked over to Zannanza.

With his sword, he severed the prince's head and held it high. Horemheb's men cheered and then raced to loot the other bodies.

'For the queen,' Horemheb said with a sneer, throwing the head into a bag for its trip back to Thebes.

Tut's Palace, 1324 BC

The throne room was dark and depressing. Ankhesenpaaten and Aye had argued for hours, beginning just after dinner. Now it was midnight, and the queen and the royal vizier spoke by the light of the moon. This same debate had raged for more than a week, and this night the words chosen were no different.

The queen's protestations were heated and loud, unmuffled by draperies and potted plants. Anyone still awake in the palace could hear her frantic voice, and she knew it.

'Make no mistake: I will rule as king. And you will be my queen,' said Aye. His sagging neck and paunch made him look more like her grandfather than a man capable of fathering a royal heir.

'I will not do it,' she shot back. Ankhesenpaaten paced up and down, trying to buy time.

Yuye entered the room, as if on cue.

'What is it?' asked the queen. 'Do you have news? Tell me.'

Aye burst out laughing. 'Yes, she has news. Tell her the news. Tell her the fantastic news about her Hittite prince—who is riding here to save the queen and become pharaoh.'

Ankhesenpaaten glared at him. 'You knew?'

'Of course I knew.' He laughed some more before turning his attention back to Yuye. 'Your lady in waiting has been a useful spy. Please, Yuye. Tell the queen the news she has so longed to hear.'

Shame coursed through Yuye's body, and she couldn't meet the queen's gaze. When she spoke, it was in a low monotone. 'The Hittites received your missive, Majesty. Their king sent a son to Egypt to marry you and serve at your side as king.'

'And?' asked Ankhesenpaaten.

'And this prince, whose name was Zannanza, was met at the border by General Horemheb. The prince and his men were slaughtered. A courier galloped here this day with the news—and this.'

Yuye placed a leather bag on a table. Aye stepped forward and emptied the contents onto the floor. The prince's severed head hit the tiled floor with a loud thud.

Ankhesenpaaten staggered backwards. She could barely breathe as she looked at the head, then faced the vizier.

Aye showed no deference to her now. He mocked her openly. 'You are a traitor. I control the priests, I control the money, and I control Horemheb,' he declared. 'Choose wisely, Majesty. You can either marry me and keep your life, or you can choose to die, just like your husband.'

Aye turned and paraded from the room, sandals slapping softly. He took the girl Yuye with him, and that night, to be safe, he made certain she would keep quiet—by slitting her throat. If the lady in waiting could betray the queen, she could betray him as well. And the stakes were too high for that.

THE WEDDING RING was made of glass and glazed in blue. Inside the band were inscribed the cartouches of the newlyweds: Aye and Ankhesenpaaten.

The queen slipped the ring onto her finger and pretended to be blissfully content. The banquet hall was filled with revellers, and the party would continue well into the night. Bulls had been slaughtered, then roasted over open fires. Beer was served in copious amounts. Try as she might to be a quiet bystander, Ankhesenpaaten was the queen of Egypt. Her every move was being watched, and the country's more illustrious and well-connected residents were curious as to whether she was truly in love with her new husband.

Hence the importance of wearing her ring and appearing radiant and happy to all.

Aye stood across the room with Horemheb, looking very much like the old and prosperous pharaoh he now was. He was forty summers older than his teenage bride, and he already had a possessive wife his own age.

How much longer Aye would live was anyone's guess. And then what? Would Ankhesenpaaten be forced to marry yet again? And who would her next husband be? A foreigner, perhaps?

The only solution, she decided, was to become pregnant with Aye's child. There was no other way to protect herself.

As the party grew louder and more festive, Ankhesenpaaten suddenly felt feverish, clammy. A wave of nausea swept over her. Within seconds she was on her knees, vomiting all over the floor.

Servants rushed to the stricken queen. Aye gazed at her from across the room, but he did not go to Ankhesenpaaten's aid.

It was then that the queen locked eyes with her new husband. She saw his look of conceit and triumph and did her best to return it.

When that failed, Ankhesenpaaten waved away the servants and rose unsteadily. But she crashed to the floor again, this time banging her head and losing consciousness.

The Hittite prince had been carrying a plague virus. That virus had made its way to the queen. That was the story Aye would tell and then record for all history.

A few days later, Ankhesenpaaten was dead. Bowing to his older wife's wishes, Aye refused to bury Ankhesenpaaten in his tomb—or even in Tut's.

Instead, the queen's body was taken downriver and fed to the crocodiles.

CHAPTER 11

Valley of the Kings, November 26, 1922

Carter clawed at the hole once again, trying to enlarge it enough to see through to the other side. He was sweaty and winded, and his tobacco-stained fingertips were raw from pulling at the coarse plaster and jagged chunks of rock.

Behind him stood Lady Evelyn, along with her father. Further up the hallway a handful of diggers waited, all hoping for the financial reward that would come if a great discovery was made here today.

Notably absent was Trout Engelbach. He had left to inspect another dig site several miles away. Carter was supposed to await his return before entering a chamber or tomb. But that was not to be.

When the hole was cleared from the ceiling down to eye level, Carter lit a candle and held it to the opening, checking for foul gases. The candle flickered as air that had been trapped for millennia whooshed from the chamber.

When the flame stopped sputtering, Carter slid the candle through the hole. Next, he pressed his face to the opening, feeling the dust of the centuries against his skin. With one arm inside, holding the candle steady, and his face now looking directly into the chamber, he studied what he could make out in the darkness.

'At first I could see nothing,' wrote Carter. 'But presently, as my eyes grew accustomed to the light, details from the room within slowly emerged from the mist. Strange animals, statues and gold—everywhere the glint of gold. For the moment—an eternity it must have been to the others standing by—I was struck dumb with amazement.'

'Can you see anything?' Lord Carnarvon asked impatiently.

'Yes,' Carter responded. '*Wonderful things.*'

'Let me have a look,' the earl demanded. 'It's my turn to see.'

Carter not-so-politely ignored him. He had waited too many years for this incredible moment. If anything, it was even better than he could have imagined. He had finally done it! *Wonderful things*.

Carter exchanged the candle for a torch. He played the beam slowly over the contents of the chamber, spellbound. 'Never before in the whole history of excavation,' Carter later wrote, 'had such an amazing sight been seen as the light of the electric torch revealed to us.'

This tomb—or cache or whatever it was—did not merely hold a few stray pieces of antiquity. Rather, it overflowed with gold and other priceless treasures.

Carter's eyes now began to distinguish shapes, and he mentally catalogued the amazing contents. Straight ahead were 'three great gilt couches, their sides carved in the form of monstrous animals, curiously attenuated in body, but with heads of startling realism'.

'Next, on the right,' he would later write, 'two life-sized figures of a king in black facing each other like sentinels, gold-kilted, gold-sandalled, armed with mace and staff, the protective sacred cobra upon their foreheads.'

There was so much more: inlaid baskets, alabaster vases, bouquets of golden flowers and leaves, and a gold and wood throne with a delicately carved inlay.

The room was packed floor to ceiling with furniture, statues, pottery and all the accoutrements of a wealthy Egyptian.

Carter felt a pair of wiry hands yanking him backwards.

It was Carnarvon.

Planting his feet firmly on the stone floor, the surprisingly powerful earl took hold of Carter's shoulders and muscled him aside. The earl was not in good health, so the effort left him breathless.

Yet all was forgotten as he snatched the torch from Carter's hand and pressed his nose through the opening.

Once again, Carnarvon was rendered breathless.

Behind Carnarvon stood Carter, slouched against the wall and beaming at Lady Evelyn. Her eyes were riveted on Carter, in awe of the great discovery, but even more, of Carter's passion for his work. Lady Evelyn was a woman destined for a life of wealth and status. Howard Carter was many steps beneath her on the social ladder. Yet the attraction between Carter and her had become intense. Lord Carnarvon had taken to keeping a close eye on them.

Only now he wasn't looking. So Carter and Evelyn locked eyes in the dank hallway, 'the exhilaration of discovery' bubbling between them. They were struggling to hide their emotions.

A dazzled Lord Carnarvon finally turned round, gesturing that it was Evelyn's turn to look inside. 'Come, come. It's amazing, my dear! You must see for yourself.'

Only then did Carter's focus return, allowing him to ask himself the most obvious question: *If this is a tomb, then where is the mummy?*

UNFORTUNATELY, THERE WOULD BE a major problem in looking for the mummy.

The wording of Lord Carnarvon's concession to dig in the valley implied that a tomb's discoverer had the right to enter first. However, as Trout Engelbach had made abundantly clear before, the Antiquities Service's understanding was quite different.

Acting under orders from his boss, Engelbach now demanded that a member of his staff be on hand for the opening of any chamber. The penalty for ignoring that order was severe—Carter and Carnarvon could forfeit much of their claim to the treasure inside.

After all those years of searching, impatience now could mean they'd end up with nothing.

And though Engelbach had left Carter's dig site, he had designated his Egyptian deputy, Ibrahim Effendi, to carry out that task in his absence. But as Carter and his group stood before the second doorway, Effendi too was no longer in the valley. He had returned to Luxor, awaiting news from Carter.

Now Carter and his group were faced with a dilemma: send for Effendi, or break on through to the other side without him.

Carter did both.

Swearing everyone in the tunnel to secrecy, including the Egyptian diggers, Carter wrote a hasty note informing the Antiquities Service of what he'd found. Then he handed the note to one of the diggers and ordered him to wait until nightfall before delivering it.

Next, he again turned his attention to the wall. He enlarged the hole even more.

He was going inside to find the mummy.

LADY EVELYN was the smallest of the bunch and was the first to wriggle through the opening. She found herself transfixed by ghostly alabaster vases, and Carter enlarged the hole so the more portly Lord Carnarvon could also squeeze through. Then he entered what would become known as the antechamber.

The room was a small rectangle, twelve feet deep by twenty-six feet wide. The ceilings were low to the point of claustrophobia, and the walls undecorated, which was odd, Carter thought. *Why hadn't the chamber been properly finished?*

The air smelled not just of dust and time but also of perfumes and exotic woods. 'The very air you breathe, unchanged through the centuries,' marvelled Carter.

Carter was surprised to find himself humbled by the timelessness of the moment. There were footprints in the dust from thousands of years earlier, and a container still held the mortar used to build the door. 'The blackened lamp, the fingermark upon the freshly painted surface, the farewell garland dropped upon the threshold—you feel it might have been just yesterday,' Carter mused.

The three modern-day intruders shone the torch about the room, setting aside all historical propriety to hold the golden relics in their bare hands.

Carter opened a small casket painted with images of a pharaoh—*Tut?*—slaying his enemies in battle. Inside were a pair of ancient sandals and a robe festooned with brightly coloured beads.

Lady Evelyn gasped with delight as she came across a golden throne with images of a pharaoh and his queen depicted in lapis lazuli. The pair were obviously very much in love, as demonstrated by the tender way the queen seemed to be touching her king. To Carter's eyes, it was 'the most beautiful thing that [had] ever been found in Egypt'.

Outside, darkness fell. The workers and any remaining spectators had finally left for home. Inside the antechamber, Carter's group continued to revel in discovery after discovery.

But Carter was still not satisfied. A great mystery remained unsolved. He probed the walls, searching for signs of other chambers.

At one point he came upon a tiny hole and pointed his torch through the opening. On the other side lay a very small room, also overflowing with treasure. There was no sign of a mummy, so Carter resisted the urge to tear down the doorway.

He continued searching, running his hands along the smooth walls, looking for signs of a concealed opening. At last, he found one! On the far right wall, two statues loomed on either side of yet another sealed doorway.

The statues were apparently sentinels, standing guard over the opening, as they had for centuries. 'We were but on the threshold of discovery,' he would write, still trying to wrap his mind around the stunning evidence. 'Behind the guarded door there would be other chambers, possibly a succession of them, and in one of them, beyond a shadow of a doubt, in all his magnificent panoply of death, we shall see the pharaoh lying.'

Once again, Carter was faced with the dilemma of whether or not to wait before making a hole in the wall.

Once again, Carter chose to ignore the possible political consequences and see what was on the other side. He hoped only that his decision wouldn't prove disastrous at some future time. But of course, it would.

At the bottom-right corner of the hidden doorway, Carter found a three-foot-tall hole that had been plastered over at some time in antiquity. This was a sign that tomb robbers had preceded him.

For the third time that day, Carter chipped away at some thief's ancient plasterwork, pulled back the stones that had been used to build an impromptu wall, and shone his light through.

At first it didn't look like much. A narrow hallway?

Carter slid through ahead of the others. He went feet first, dropping down into a sunken room. He scanned the narrow walls with his torch.

At first it appeared that the light was playing a trick on him.

Then he realised that one of the walls was not a wall at all. He was inside a stunning square chamber, not a narrow hallway.

The low wall that confused him was actually a shrine. It was decorated in blue faience and gold.

He had found the burial chamber.

As Lady Evelyn and Lord Carnarvon hurried to join him, Carter examined the shrine.

He was facing a pair of mighty wooden doors secured with an ebony bolt. Inside, as Carter well knew, would be several smaller shrines like this one. Only after each shrine had been opened would he be able to see the sarcophagus, coffins—and the mummy itself.

At this thought, Carter's heartbeat quickened. *There was definitely a mummy here.* There was no way tomb robbers could have stolen the body without destroying the shrines, and these shrines were in pristine condition.

With Carnarvon's help, Carter slowly and carefully slid back the bolt. The doors swung on their hinges. A linen shroud decorated with gold rosettes was draped over the next shrine. He lifted the shroud and saw further evidence that the mummy had not been disturbed: on the bolts of yet another opening, to yet another shrine, was a royal seal. It was the royal necropolis stamp, with a jackal and nine bound captives, signifying that a pharaoh lay within.

By now, it was almost morning. The group explored a while longer, but soon they left. The Carnarvons needed rest. They weren't used to the heat or the manual labour. Even Carter needed a break, though for him a short one would suffice.

They climbed the steps, walking from the ancient past to the cool predawn air of the present in just a few seconds.

Carter's men were still standing guard. They helped secure the tomb for the night and would remain there to protect it from possible invaders.

The greatest day of Howard Carter's life was over.

Valley of the Kings, December 1922
Back at 'Castle Carter', as the news of his discovery sped round the world via cable and telephone, Carter took a moment to think about what he had found and the consequences of that discovery.

The spectre of Tut's death hung over Carter as he peered out at the valley from his home's lofty viewpoint. He struggled to make sense of the findings inside the tomb—the toy sailing boats, the chariots, the golden shrines and *shabtis* and jewelled amulets—and wondered how a young man so full of life had come to die. Even more mysterious to Carter: Why was the tomb located where it was? And where was the queen buried?

'Politically we gather that the king's reign and life must have been a singularly uneasy one. It may be that he was the tool of obscure political forces working behind the throne.'

Carter mentally catalogued the valuable artefacts he had found. He wrote of a 'painted wooden casket found in the chamber, its outer face completely covered with gesso'. He noted cosmetic jars portraying 'bulls, lions, hounds, gazelle and hare'. Most touching, he thought, were 'episodes of daily private life of the king and queen'. But where was *her* coffin?

He was struck by a painting that depicted Tut accompanied by a pet lion cub and shooting wild ducks with bows and arrows, 'while, at his feet, squats the girlish queen'. Another such scene showed the young queen offering Tut 'libations, flowers and collarettes'. Still another showed the pharaoh pouring sweet perfume on his queen as they rested together. He had the sense of how young they both were—and how much in love.

Carter was astounded by the gold and jewels found inside the tomb, but he was also stunned by what seemed to be an arsenal.

In the room off the burial chamber, the one with unpainted walls that Carter referred to as the treasury, and in the small room off the antechamber known as the annexe, he had discovered a stockpile of weapons: thirteen composite bows, three self bows and two quivers; 278 arrows, many with bronze arrowheads; and an elaborately carved bow case decorated in gold leaf.

The largest bow suggested that Tut was a man of some strength, as it was more than six feet in length.

Certainly, Tut was no peaceful king. And, just as certainly, he had a fondness for pursuits other than archery. The annexe also contained several shields; a leather cuirass that would have protected Tut's chest and shoulders; and swords, boomerangs, clubs and daggers.

Tut clearly was not his father's son. 'The possessor of the bow could bring down the fleetest of animals and defend himself against the enemy,' Carter noted.

In one corner, lost amid the towering bows of the hunt and war, was one Tut would have shot as a child. It was just a foot and a half tall, and its lone arrow was six inches long.

Carter again found himself wondering about the circumstances surrounding Tut's death and concluded that it might not have been an accident. 'The sense of premature loss faintly haunts the tomb. The royal youth, obviously full of life and capable and enjoying it, had started, in very early manhood—who knows under what tragic circumstances?—on his last journey from the radiant Egyptian skies into the gloom of that tremendous Underworld,' he wrote.

Valley of the Kings, February 16, 1923

Time to open the burial chamber.

Carter had never told Trout Engelbach that he had already entered the chamber, so when the day of the 'official' opening arrived, he had to pretend to be curious about what might be inside. And he had to be convincing. As news of the great discovery had spread around the world, pandemonium had erupted in Luxor. Suddenly, Howard Carter was a star and a significant historical player.

Beyond that, a certain divisiveness had set in, with Egyptian bureaucrats and foreign hangers-on all trying to get a piece of the action.

'Telegrams poured in from every quarter of the globe. Within a week or two the letters began to follow them, a deluge of correspondence that has persisted ever since,' noted Carter.

Letters of congratulation gave way to 'offers of assistance; requests for souvenirs—even a few grains of sand would be received so thankfully; fantastic money offers, from moving picture rights to copyrights on fashions of dress; advice on the preservation of antiquities; and the best methods of appeasing evil spirits'.

For a man like Carter, so fond of introspection and relative quiet, things were getting completely out of hand. No one could have predicted this, least of all himself or his detractors in Luxor.

'The Winter Palace is a scream,' noted Egyptologist Arthur Mace, whom Carter had recruited to join the excavation party. 'No one talks of anything but the tomb; newspapermen swarm, and you daren't say a word without looking around to see if anyone is listening. Some of them are trying to make mischief between Carnarvon and the Department of Antiquities, and all Luxor takes sides one way or the other. Archaeology plus journalism is bad enough, but when you add politics, it becomes a little too much.'

An unexpected problem arose for Carter because of a decision made by Lord Carnarvon. Seeking to make as much money off Tut as possible, the earl signed an exclusive agreement with *The Times* of London that gave the newspaper the rights to publish all details of the discovery. This infuriated not only the Egyptian press but also newspapers and magazines from around the world that had been clamouring for a piece of the century's greatest discovery.

Perhaps worst of all, the Antiquities Service and the Egyptian government began trying to take control of the tomb. That would prove to be an ongoing struggle that would plague Carter for years.

And then there was Lady Evelyn. As Lord Carnarvon became more and more suspicious about a relationship between Carter and his daughter, tensions between the men deepened. This, combined with Carter's new fame, drove a wedge between the two long-time partners and friends.

And yet, both men were present as politicians and bureaucrats from Egypt and Britain crowded round the tomb opening. Carter led the group inside. The statues in the antechamber had been pushed to the perimeter to safeguard them from haphazard elbows and hips. A platform had been built along the wall that divided the burial chamber from the rest of the tomb. It looked very much like a stage, and that day Howard Carter was the star.

He climbed on top of the platform, stripped off his jacket and shirt, and then placed a chisel blade against the wall.

With a mighty blow of his hammer, Carter began knocking the wall down.

Arthur Mace stood to one side, and as work progressed Carter handed him bits of rock that he had chiselled away. These were in turn passed to a chain of Egyptian workers who collected them, then carried them out of the tomb.

Slowly, the hole widened. After two hours, Carter was 'dirty, dishevelled and perspiring'—and playing his part perfectly.

Carter squeezed inside and beckoned the others to follow. The alabaster jars, Canopic shrine with figures of four guardian goddesses, and spangled shroud were clearly visible now.

The effect on the visitors was profound: they threw their hands up and gasped, dazed by the vision before them.

Carter could only stand back and watch. By now he was exhausted, from both the physical labour of opening the hole and the mental exertion of his daily jousting with Carnarvon and the press. He was privately making plans to reseal the tomb and shut himself in his house for a week of quiet and solitude.

When the momentous tour of Tut's burial chamber was over, Carter and Carnarvon said their goodbyes. Carter prepared to get down to the hard work of cataloguing the tomb's many contents, a job that could take him years but one he couldn't wait to start. He believed it would be the pinnacle of his life's work.

Carter and Carnarvon resolved most of their differences before the earl left on February 23. But just six weeks later, Lord Carnarvon was dead. The cause seems to have been septicaemia, which arose after he nicked a mosquito bite with his open razor.

Carter was left to deal with Egyptian politics and bureaucracy on his own. He couldn't do it. Less than a year later, he was evicted from Tut's tomb and from the valley.

One last time, his temperament and stubbornness had done him in.

CHAPTER 12

Cairo, 1931

The wedding ring was made of glass and glazed in blue, and it was still very beautiful. Inside the band were inscribed the names Aye and Ankhesenpaaten.

Ironically, it was Perky Newberry, now a veteran of forty years in Egypt, who turned it over in his hand. He was in Cairo, at the legendary souvenir shop of Englishman Robert Blanchard.

Rather than garish knock-offs of Egyptian tomb relics, Blanchard sold the real thing—purchased from tomb robbers, of course.

European tourists were the favoured clientele, but Egyptologists sometimes stopped by to see if some new curio had made its way onto the market—a sure sign that tombs were being raided somewhere. Perky already had an extensive collection of amulets and was pecking through the display racks in the hope of adding a new treasure.

He had accidentally stumbled upon the ring, but he immediately understood its significance.

He reread the elaborate inscription to make sure he had the names right before allowing himself a satisfied smile. The ring he held in the palm of his hand solved a mystery that had bothered Howard Carter since Tut's tomb had been opened. Namely, what had happened to Tut's beautiful young queen?

There had been no mention of Ankhesenpaaten or any other wife on the walls of Tut's tomb. And Aye's tomb, which had originally been intended for Tut, had a painting of his first wife but lacked any indication that he'd taken another.

'Where did you find this one?' asked Perky, trying not to sound excited, lest Blanchard jack up the price to a more exorbitant sum.

'Eastern delta,' Blanchard replied with a disinterested shrug.

Perky was careful not to show his surprise.

How had the ring made the journey all the way from Thebes, down past Cairo, to the mouth of the Nile? That was odd. Then again, it had been 3,000 years. Anything could happen in that time, couldn't it?

Perky went to pay for the ring but discovered that he had forgotten his wallet. He pulled out his pocket notebook and carefully copied the inscription. Then he placed the ring in the display case and raced to his hotel, intending to hurry back to complete his purchase.

First, he dashed off a quick note to his old friend, who was now back in England.

'My dear Carter,' the letter began, 'I have just seen a finger ring at Blanchard's that bears the cartouche of Ankhesenpaaten alongside the prenomen of King Aye. *This can only mean that King Aye had married Ankhesenpaaten, the widow of Tutankhamen.*'

Perky mailed the letter, then hurried back to Blanchard's to buy the ring.

He was too late.

It had just been sold.

Valley of the Kings, 1319 BC

General Horemheb mourned his friend and ally, Aye. The two had known each other since they were young men. As Aye was sealed inside the tomb once reserved for Tut, a wave of sadness filled Horemheb's heart. The scar on his face turned a bright crimson.

How odd, thought Horemheb, that I can stab a man through the heart and still mourn him.

He scanned the crowd gathered round Aye's tomb, making eye contact with a few old friends in the process. The tomb was located in a rather obscure spot, far removed from the Valley of the Kings.

Horemheb could understand why Aye would want to be buried there—the location was concealed and remote, which might prevent tomb robbers from finding it. But he also cursed his compatriot for selecting a spot so far from Thebes. The sun was going down, and it was a two-hour journey back to the city in the dark.

Finally, though, he smiled. These were good problems to have. For at the end of the ride, he would not return to his old home or to an army barracks. He would ride triumphantly into the palace.

General Horemheb was now pharaoh.

As the servants collected the plates and wine urns from the final meal, Horemheb picked his way down a rocky trail towards the temporary stable. A long procession of mourners trailed behind him. He could hear the accents of Memphis and Amarna in some of the voices. The high priests led the way.

Despite the death of Aye, the mood today was festive. Perhaps that was on account of the wine or maybe it was because Aye was far from beloved.

Still, Horemheb hoped it would be like this when he died, with celebrants coming from all over Egypt. He loved a good party.

In the distance, Horemheb could hear the whinny of horses and knew that his groom was hitching his chargers to the chariot. He was in a mood to bring the reins down hard on their flanks and race all the way back to Thebes at top speed.

What sort of pharaoh will you be? he asked himself.

Magnificent. Like Amenhotep III.

Yes. I will be magnificent. Let them attach it to my name.

Horemheb instantly knew what he must do next: wipe the slate clean.

Then and there, the fierce general resolved to level Amarna, the city that had been erected by Akhenaten.

The entire city.

All of it.

Gone.

And wherever the names of Tut and Aye were carved on the temple walls, they would be chiselled off. His name alone would remain.

His soldiers would search throughout the land. The job might take years, but the names of Horemheb's predecessors would be obliterated. Pharaohs like Tut would moulder in their tombs, edicts undone and commandments overruled. It would be as if Tut and that pretty young wife of his had never existed.

Horemheb was deep in thought as he took hold of the reins to his chariot.

Now that he was pharaoh, a procession of bodyguards travelled with him, but he did not acknowledge them. Instead, as he raced down the dusty road back to Thebes, all Horemheb thought of was his plan to erase history.

For more than 3,000 years, it actually worked.

Palm Beach, Florida, present day

I sat in my office looking out at the view of Lake Worth, but my mind was lost in the desert. When I am writing a draft of a book, I occasionally scribble the words *Be There* at the top of a page. This reminds me to make each chapter come alive for the reader, to place myself in the scene. I knew this story was vivid—in my imagination at least. And nothing could be more stunning than what happened to poor Tut in 1925, more than two full years after his tomb was discovered. I could hardly believe it myself.

The investigation would have been impossible without Howard Carter, of course. It had taken him years just to extract Tut's remains from the burial chamber. The process began the moment the plaster wall separating the anteroom from the burial chamber was knocked down. Reporters clustered outside the tomb and breathlessly awaited news. Doubters in the Egyptology community still believed that Carter had found nothing more than an elaborate closet. And still there was no sign of Tut's mummy.

Poor Carter! And it only got worse for him.

Once his workers had prised the wood apart at the joints and hauled away the protective panels, he was surprised to be looking at another, smaller shrine. This too had to be disassembled, piece by piece.

But inside was another shrine. And then another.

In all, there were four shrines, one within the other, like Russian dolls.

Finally, however, Carter reached the sarcophagus. He saw that the lid was made of pink granite and cracked across the centre, as if someone had struck it with a hammer or stone club. But who would do such a thing? And for what reason?

At least Carter was fairly certain he had found Tut. The two outer coffins were opened. Politics intruded. Carnarvon died mysteriously. And the Egyptians expelled Carter for a year.

He returned in October 1925 to open the final golden coffin. The mummy was coated with black unguent. When Tut was seen for the first time in modern history, he was covered in black resin and so was *still* cloaked in mystery.

What happened next was as shocking as anything else in the story.

Dr Douglas Derry of Cairo University was brought in to examine the body. As a professor of anatomy, he was seen as a more suitable choice for this task than Carter. That was debatable. With Tut stuck inside the tomb, Derry got extreme, to say the least. First he tried to chisel Tut out. Then he used hot knives to melt the resin. And then Derry did the unthinkable: *he took a saw and cut Tut's body in half.*

Tut's Palace, 1324 BC

The soldier, Abdul, tiptoed silently into Tut's bedroom. He had stood behind a statue as the queen left her ailing husband, right on schedule. He knew that he had only a few minutes to do the deed and escape the palace.

The young pharaoh looked so innocent and helpless as he lay in his bed, like a child. A sliver of remorse flitted through the soldier's mind but was quickly replaced with grim resolve and the knowledge that what he was about to do was for the good of Egypt. The general had promised him money and a promotion in rank. The royal vizier had sweetened the deal with a land grant and some cattle.

So the cold-blooded assassin walked to the edge of the pharaoh's bed. He planted his feet wide. Now balanced and stable, he grasped the club with two hands and brought it up high over his head.

Could it really be this easy to murder a pharaoh? He kept waiting for a guard to spring out from hiding or for Tut to rise up and catch him in the act, to forbid his own murder.

The soldier felt the smooth ebony in his hands, and the heft of the stone seemed right for what he was about to do—not so light that it would bounce off the king's head, and not so heavy that it would throw him off-balance as he swung.

He was startled as the pharaoh spoke softly in his sleep.

'Mother,' Tut said.

The soldier put down the club. It wouldn't be right to kill the pharaoh like this. Instead, he placed his strong hands firmly on either side of Tut's windpipe and applied great pressure.

Tut's eyes opened wide. He tried to fight back but was too weak. And then he was dead.

The soldier picked up his club and left the room as quickly and quietly as he'd entered. Later that night, the soldier himself was hacked to death.

Palm Beach, Florida, present day

The paintings inside the tomb were what told the true story and helped to solve the murder mystery.

On the walls of Tut's tomb are images of Aye peering down at anyone inside the burial chamber. He is shown performing the Opening of the Mouth ceremony and wearing a king's crown. This was the job of the new pharaoh. So not only did Aye perform the task, but he was pharaoh soon enough after Tut's death to commission an artisan to paint his own likeness on the wall of Tut's tomb.

Ironically, these two men, mortal enemies in life, were now linked for eternity inside this dank chamber. Tut would never be able to escape his tormentor.

My research showed similar paintings on the walls of Aye's tomb. As with Tut's burial chamber, there was an ochre and yellow painting of twelve guardian baboons, representing the twelve hours of the night. There was a painting of Aye hunting in the marshes. Upon Tut's death, Aye was in charge of the wall paintings for the young pharaoh's tomb and, of course, his own.

More important, Aye didn't have Ankhesenpaaten depicted on the walls of Tut's tomb. This was unusual since pharaohs almost always had their favourite wife painted on the tomb walls. Ankhesenpaaten was Tut's favourite and *only* wife. But Aye wanted her all to himself so he could claim the royal throne. His plan was clearly to make Ankhesenpaaten his queen, almost as if Tut had never existed.

So who was responsible for the murder? Who conspired to kill Tut? And why?

They *all* killed him. Remember, the queen actually ruled as pharaoh immediately after Tut's murder. She clearly wanted power—witness her attempt to marry the Hittite prince. That was treason of the most desperate sort. And for what reason? The power to rule Egypt.

All three of them—Ankhesenpaaten, Aye and Horemheb—succeeded Tut to the throne. Aye double-crossed Ankhesenpaaten by killing the Hittite prince. He was getting on in years, after all, and knew he wouldn't have another shot at the throne. First he murdered the Hittite prince, and then he killed Ankhesenpaaten. The queen had agreed to Tut's murder. No doubt worried that he might die anyway, she believed she could marry her Hittite prince, produce an heir and continue to sit on the throne.

Ankhesenpaaten had no idea she would be double-crossed by Aye and then murdered.

Nor did Aye know he would be killed by his ally, General Horemheb, who would then succeed him as pharaoh.

Tut was killed by a conspiracy of the three people closest to him in life—Ankhesenpaaten, Aye and Horemheb. Hundreds of thousands have visited the Tut exhibits, many millions believe they know the story, but few understand the sad tragedy of the Boy King.

Case closed.

Today, Tut's mummy resides in a plain wooden tray that Carter had built for him. Investigators over the years have discovered that he had a broken right ankle that seems to have been in a cast; he had suffered a fracture of the right leg that was severe and possibly infected; he even suffered from an impacted wisdom tooth.

But Tut was murdered.

London, March 2, 1939

Howard Carter died alone, attended only by a niece who stood to inherit the treasures he had found while toiling more than thirty seasons in the Valley of the Kings.

Four days passed between his death and the burial, long enough for *The Times* to eulogise him as 'the great Egyptologist . . . who gained fame for his part in one of the most successful and exciting episodes in the annals of archaeology'.

Eulogies in *The Times* were a privilege. Usually only the rich, famous, eccentric, and overachieving were granted the honour.

Carter had once been all four. But the romantic flavour of this eulogy, written by his friend Perky Newberry, belied the fact that Carter's celebrity had long ago diminished—and that Perky was his only close friend. In fact, the funeral was embarrassing for its air of sloppiness and apathy: just a handful of mourners gathered round the grave; the birth date etched on Carter's tombstone was off by one year; and, saddest of all, he was buried in a simple hole in the ground.

For a man who had spent a lifetime exploring the elaborate burial tombs of the pharaohs, it seemed a most unfitting way to bid the world adieu.

But there was one saving grace.

Years after breaking off their affair, the one love of Carter's life appeared at the graveside. Lady Evelyn was a small woman, expensively dressed, wearing a broad black hat. Her father had been furious with Carter about their clandestine romance. And when Lord Carnarvon died quite suddenly, just months after the discovery of Tut, she had done 'the right thing'. Lady Evelyn, daughter of the Fifth Earl of Carnarvon, had turned her back on Carter and found a more socially—and financially—appropriate groom. They were married just months after the public opening of Tut's tomb.

Now Lady Evelyn stood on the spring grass, gazing at a simple coffin and a deep hole in the earth, just as she had once gazed into another burial site while at Carter's side. Maybe that was why she had come. For no matter how far apart Carter and Lady Evelyn had drifted, neither could escape the fact that on one glorious November morning, seventeen years earlier, they had been the first people in 3,000 years to gaze inside the tomb of the Boy King known as Tutankhamen.

Together they had made history and been toasted around the world.

'I see wonderful things,' Carter had said breathlessly after his first peek. Now Carter breathed no more.

The vicar of Putney closed his prayer book, and Carter was lowered into the ground. Lady Evelyn threw a fistful of earth into the chasm, then walked slowly back to the gravel drive, where her car and driver were waiting.

It was Hodgkin's lymphoma that killed Carter at the age of sixty-four. Tut was barely eighteen when he died, though the cause of his death had mystified Carter right up to the end. It was a mystery that Lady Evelyn had pondered over the years too, a great missing piece of the puzzle of King Tut.

Now in a grave far less noble, Carter slept, never to be disturbed.

EPILOGUE

Valley of the Kings, 1300–500 BC

The mystery of King Tut, the teenage Boy King, deepened slowly, one sandstorm and deluge at a time.

First, the desert winds whipped tons of sand across the Valley of the Kings, sending the tomb robbers living in caves high above the valley floor to scurry deep inside their homes. The door to Tut's burial chamber was sealed and hadn't been tampered with for hundreds of years.

And as the sand covered the lowest step leading down to the doorway, then another, and another, the doorway had an even better seal.

Now it was entirely buried by rock and grit, hidden from the world.

Rain didn't come to this valley often, but when it did, the water fell with such intensity that massive chunks of earth slid from the walls to the valley floor. The water turned the sand and limestone into a form of cement, so that anything lying beneath it was encased in a hard rocky crust. In this way, the final steps leading down into Tut's tomb were covered over.

Soon it was as if they had never existed.

Each successive sandstorm and torrential downpour heaped on another layer, until the tomb steps were more than six feet below the surface of the earth. The burial site's location was not just obliterated but forgotten.

Deep below the ground, Tut, the Boy King, rested. The walls were sturdy and did not crumble or crack from the new weight above.

Nor did his treasures suffer from rain or humidity—if anything, they were more protected now than they had been before.

Tut lay alone year after year, century after century, as if waiting for the day when some explorer would scrape off those layers of dirt and limestone.

And, perhaps, unearth the secrets of his life and untimely death.

james patterson

No one would dispute that American author James Patterson is an extraordinary storyteller. He currently holds the *New York Times* best-seller list record with forty-seven chart-topping titles, and in 2007 alone his book sales were greater than those of John Grisham and Stephen King combined. His fame reaches far beyond America, too, bringing him millions of fans.

The secret of Patterson's success can be attributed, in part, to three best-selling detective series. In the first, he introduced Alex Cross in *Along Came a Spider* and *Kiss the Girls*, both of which were adapted for film and starred Morgan Freeman. He is also the creator of the Women's Murder Club series, from which the ABC television dramas of that name were made. A third series launched his New York City police detective, Michael Bennett. But James Patterson writes children's books, too, and is the passionate driving force behind readkiddoread.com, a website that helps parents, teachers and librarians connect their children with books that will turn them into lifelong readers.

Since Patterson is so prolific, it's no surprise that he works with co-authors on almost every book. This time his writing partner was Martin Dugard, who has published many nonfiction books and writes for magazines such as *Esquire* and *Sports Illustrated*. Describing himself as a writer, producer and adventurer, Dugard regularly immerses himself in his research to understand characters and their motivations better. He sailed from Genoa to Spain aboard a tall ship, in the manner of Christopher Columbus, before writing *The Last Voyage of Columbus*, and swam in tiger shark-infested waters off Hawaii to re-create Captain James Cook's death for *Farther Than Any Man*.

But Dugard is also a family man and, realising that his three young sons at home in California were growing up fast during his absences, he decided to indulge his passion for history closer to home. His attempt at a more tranquil domestic life was not entirely successful. Once again, he diced with death in Tanzania while researching Stanley and Livingstone for his book, *Into Africa*. 'I became something of a research fiend in the process, though,' Dugard confesses, 'especially at the British Library. I rarely saw the inside of a library when I was in college. Now you can't get me out of them.'

The Murder of King Tut saw Dugard travelling to Egypt to unravel the centuries-old mystery of who murdered Tutankhamen, Egypt's legendary boy king. He and Patterson dug through X-rays, Carter's files, forensic clues, and stories told through the ages. Here, Patterson describes how the team went about unearthing the truth:

'I don't think I've ever done more research for a book. From the instant the idea hit me and I teamed up with Marty Dugard to write this story, it's been total immersion in ancient Egypt. The book is a murder mystery, but the plunge back in time added a whole other layer of detective work. We didn't just need to know the players in our drama; we also needed to know what foods they ate, the clothes they wore, how they loved, and, ultimately, the ways they might have killed each other.

'Marty's historical legwork involved trips to London and to Tut's tomb in Egypt's Valley of the Kings. I lost myself in books and online research. We then combined our notes and began writing. One astounding fact about Egyptian history is that so much of it is still unknown. So when we came to a gap, we went back to the research for answers. Then we put forth our theory as to what happened. We constructed conversations and motives and rich scenes of palace life—all grounded in long hours of research.

'It's nothing new for histories to be speculative, but there's a difference between guessing and basing a theory on cold hard facts. We chose the facts. As for Howard Carter, he is almost a contemporary, so his life was much easier to document. I resisted the temptation to speculate about his relationship with Lady Evelyn Herbert, though I thoroughly hoped to find a steamy journal entry that would allow me to muse at will. You can draw your own conclusions.'

In search of fame and glory

In 1922, Howard Carter (right) made one of the greatest archaeological finds of the 20th century when he opened King Tutankhamen's tomb. It was the success that this obsessive, driven man had craved for three decades. Shunned for his lack of genteel upbringing, but determined to be taken seriously, Carter had battled to raise funding. Then, in 1915, he met the risk-taking, adventure-loving Lord Carnarvon whose wealth underpinned Carter's digs, bringing fame and glory to both men.

PRESENT DANGER

DANGER

STELLA RIMINGTON

MI5 officer Liz Carlyle is surprised to receive
orders to go to Northern Ireland, where a breakaway
Republican group, calling themselves the Fraternity,
seem determined to disrupt the peace process.
Why has MI5 sent her with such urgency?
Then a colleague disappears, and Liz finds
herself up against some cold and ruthless men
with interests far beyond Ireland . . .

1

Aidan Murphy was woken by a loud knocking on the front door. He lay still, trying to decide whether he had a hangover or was just tired. There was another, louder knock. He rolled over and looked at the clock radio: 10:31. Why didn't his mother answer the door? The knocking turned into a hammering and someone was yelling his name.

He climbed out of bed, grabbed a T-shirt and went slowly downstairs. Two men were outside. The older one was Malone. The other he didn't know. Heavyset, with dark stubble and swarthy skin, he looked Spanish.

'Boss wants to see you,' said Malone flatly.

'What, now?' Aidan was confused. He was due at work at three—couldn't it wait until then?

'Yeah, now,' Malone growled. The dark man said nothing.

Aidan shrugged. 'I'll get dressed,' he said, and went back upstairs to his bedroom. The second man stayed by the open door while Malone stood at the foot of the stairs, keeping an eye on the door to Aidan's bedroom.

What's this about then? Aidan wondered. He felt a flicker of alarm. Stay calm, he told himself; you've done nothing wrong.

He threw on a fresh shirt, neatly ironed by his mother. There were benefits to living at home, even when you were twenty-three years old. He finished dressing, then grabbed a jacket and went downstairs.

He followed the stranger to a red Vauxhall Vectra with racing tyres, parked in front of the house. He didn't like the way Malone walked close behind him. The two men got into the front seats, Malone driving. Aidan relaxed—if he was in trouble one of them would have sat in the back with him.

Malone pulled out sharply and they sped down the monotonous terrace of red-brick houses, heading towards the city centre. Neither man spoke, and to break the silence, Aidan asked, 'Did you see Celtic on the box?' Malone shook his head, and the other man didn't even do that. Aidan sat back silently with folded arms and looked out of the window.

They turned into Divis Street, past the flats where his father had died, shot in a stairwell by British soldiers. He'd been an IRA sniper, and he'd died doing his job. Aidan had wanted to follow his father into the Provos, to avenge his death by killing British soldiers, but they were on cease-fire now, so instead he'd found the Fraternity. Or they'd found him.

Dermot O'Reilly had recommended him—old Dermot, who had been interned in the Maze with Aidan's father; Dermot, who had been tried twice on arms charges yet somehow had avoided another stretch in prison. There was no questioning *his* nationalist credentials, and when he'd said that the Fraternity wasn't what it said it was, giving Aidan a wink, Aidan understood his meaning at once.

The Fraternity purported to be a 'political consultancy', which Aidan took as code for carrying on the fight. It put up a good enough phoney front, with smart new offices in the centre of town, and an Irish-American who called himself Piggott at its head, a strange man who had more degrees than you could shake a stick at.

Aidan soon learned that the Fraternity's moneymaking business had nothing to do with consultancy, but everything to do with supplying: drugs, guns, even women. However much he tried to gild it, his own job was courier: he delivered packages to pubs, bookmakers and sometimes private homes. From the bits and pieces he'd overheard from other members of the Fraternity, Aidan knew that he carried cocaine, Ecstasy, methamphetamine, crystal meth and occasionally a gun, and on his return journeys, lots of cash in large, sealed bags, which he never, ever looked inside.

None of this had bothered him at first, since O'Reilly assured him these transactions were funding the war against Ireland's enemies. But Aidan never got near to the real business, and he knew that his father, who like all good IRA men passionately disapproved of drugs, would have skinned him alive if he'd known what Aidan was up to.

They approached the usual turn to the office off Castle Street, but Malone drove straight on. 'What's going on?' asked Aidan, unable to disguise the fear in his voice.

'Relax, kid,' said Malone with a glance in his rearview mirror. 'We've got a bit of a drive. Sit back and enjoy it. They say the sun will be out soon.'

But it stayed grey and gloomy as they headed south on the dual carriage-way. Where were they going? Aidan decided not to ask. Then he remem-bered two of his colleagues had mentioned that Piggott had a place down on the coast in County Down. It was an odd place for a Republican activist, if that's what he was, for it was Protestant country; but perhaps chosen because it would be the last place the security people would expect to find him.

Aidan wasn't scared. Why should he be? Helping with the distribution of the goods, he had no responsibility other than to follow orders, which he had been doing faithfully. It was true he'd made it clear to some of his friends and associates that he wasn't happy with the Fraternity. He'd told them it was all moneymaking and no action, as far as he could see. But he'd been careful to whom he complained: just a few close mates in the back room of Paddy O'Brien's pub. Dermot O'Reilly was sometimes there, but he could be trusted.

In the distance ahead he saw the Irish Sea, rocky outcrops and slits of sandy beach, the Mourne Mountains miles to their right. They drove along the coast for several miles, through a grey stone village, its long street prac-tically deserted, its ice-cream hut shut up for winter.

At the end of the village the car slowed and turned sharply down a narrow track that skirted a bay. The tide was out, revealing a vast expanse of wet sand gleaming in the grey light. They crossed a narrow bridge and came up to a closed five-bar gate. Malone pressed a button on an electronic device he held in his hand and the gate creaked open, allowing them in to pass directly in front of a small, high-gabled Victorian house, the gatehouse to an estate that ran up the gentle slope of land away from the sea. Past the house, the road turned into a track and Malone drove slowly along it.

A quarter of a mile further on, through another gate, the track ended in front of a large stone house. The car stopped with a sudden crunch of tyres against gravel. Malone led the way to the front door and knocked. An elderly woman wearing an apron tied round her waist let them in, keeping her head down and her eyes averted as they walked into a large hall.

Malone said, 'Wait here,' and Aidan stood with the Spaniard while Malone went through a doorway to one side. When he returned a minute later, he gestured towards the back of the house.

'Come on,' he said, leading them down a hall, through a large kitchen with a massive Aga at one end. In the short hall behind the kitchen, he flicked a light switch and they followed him down a steep flight of stairs.

They were in a cellar; a damp, empty room with exposed brick walls and a rough concrete floor. Fastened to one wall was a metal cabinet, which Malone opened with a key. He pulled down a switch and, immediately, with a high-pitched whirring noise, the far wall of the cellar moved slowly to one side, revealing a room behind it.

This room was furnished almost lavishly. The floor was carpeted in sisal, topped by a few Oriental rugs, and at the far end sat a mahogany desk with a green-shaded desk lamp at one corner. Floor-to-ceiling bookcases held leather-bound volumes and on the other walls hung landscape paintings.

The room could be the study of a wealthy, bookish man, but if that's what it was, thought Aidan, why go to such effort to hide its existence?

'Sit down,' said Malone, pointing to a wooden chair that faced the desk. He sounded tense.

As Aidan sat down he heard steps on the hard floor of the cellar behind him. He watched as the tall, thin figure of Seamus Piggott walked round the desk and sat down in the leather chair behind it.

'Hello, Mr Piggott,' said Aidan, managing a weak smile. He had spoken to the man only once, when he had first been taken on by the Fraternity, but he'd seen him several times when he'd been in the Belfast office on errands.

Piggott, with his rimless glasses and cropped hair, looked like a professor. Aidan knew he was a brilliant scientist, an aerospace engineer who, when he was young back in the States, had designed handheld rockets, which the IRA had used to try to bring down British Army helicopters. But they said he was weird, too clever to be normal, and the way he was staring now, coldly, almost analytically, made Aidan understand why.

'Are you happy in your work, Aidan?' he said, his voice soft.

What was this about? Aidan didn't believe that Piggott was interested in his job satisfaction. But he nodded vigorously. 'Yes, I am, Mr Piggott.'

Piggott continued to stare at him. Then he said, 'Because as CEO of this organisation I need to feel my staff is fully on board.'

'I am on board, Mr Piggott. I'm treated very well.' Aidan was scared now.

Piggott nodded. 'That's what I'd have thought. Yet you've been heard complaining.'

'Me?' asked Aidan. Oh Christ, he thought, thinking of his indiscretions in Paddy O'Brien's. Who on earth could have shopped him?

'Aidan, you are a very small part of my operation, but even from you I require complete, unquestioning loyalty, and I haven't had it. You've been complaining,' he repeated. Piggott leaned forward in his chair. 'Why?'

Rather than denying it, Aidan found himself saying, 'I'm sorry, Mr Piggott.'

'Sorry,' said Piggott, his lips pursed as he nodded his head. 'Sorry's a good place to start,' he added mildly, then his voice grew cold. 'But it's not where things end.' And for the first time he took his eyes off Aidan and nodded sharply at the two other men.

As Aidan turned towards the Spaniard next to him, he felt Malone's hand suddenly grip his arm. 'Don't,' he started to protest, but now his other arm was gripped as well. The dark man grunted, looming over him.

'What?' Aidan asked, unable to keep the fear from his voice.

'Give him your hand,' said Malone.

And as Aidan raised his left hand from the arm of the chair, he found it gripped by the Spaniard's hand. It felt as if his fingers were in a vice that was starting to turn. The pressure increased, then Aidan felt and heard his third finger crunch as one of the bones broke.

Agonising pain filled his hand. The Spaniard let go at last, and the hand flopped like a rag onto the chair arm.

Tears welled up in Aidan's eyes and he could barely breathe. He looked down at his fingers, red and compressed from the strength of the Spaniard's grip. He tried to move them one by one. His third finger wouldn't move.

Piggott stood up, brushing the sleeve of his jacket, as if to rid it of an unwanted piece of fluff. He came out from behind the desk and walked towards the open wall into the cellar. As his footsteps rang out on the concrete floor, he called back, 'Before you take him back to Belfast, break another one. We don't want him to think that was just an accident.'

LIZ CARLYLE WAS SURPRISED to find the church full. It sat in what had once been a proper village but now formed one link in the chain of affluent suburbs that stretched south and west from London along the River Thames.

Judging by its fine square tower, she guessed the church must be Norman in origin, though the prodigious size of the nave suggested a later expansion. She reckoned from a quick count of the rows that there must be three or four hundred people present.

Liz had known there would be many colleagues from Thames House at this memorial service, for Joanne Wetherby had been with MI5 over ten years and had never lost touch with the friends she'd made then (and of course her husband had continued with the service). The Director General was here, along with Director B, Beth Davis, responsible for all personnel and security matters. Virtually every other senior member of MI5 was present and a number from MI6.

Ahead of her she could just see Charles Wetherby in the front row, flanked by his two sons and others, presumably relations. There was a woman in the row behind them, smartly dressed in a dark blue suit with an elegant black hat. She was leaning forward whispering to Charles's younger son, Sam. She must be another relation, thought Liz.

She hadn't seen Charles since Joanne's death and she felt a sudden pang seeing him now, so obviously bereft. She had of course written to him, and he'd written back, thanking her. The boys, he'd said, had been pillars of strength, though naturally he worried about them. Charles ended by saying how much he was looking forward to returning to work.

Liz hoped that meant he was looking forward to seeing her as well. She had missed him at work, both as a boss and as . . . what exactly? She had only recently acknowledged to herself how strong her feelings were for Charles, yet they had never exchanged so much as a kiss. She wondered if that would change now, then immediately felt guilty about envisaging a future with Charles that Joanne Wetherby would never now have.

Next to Liz, her mother's friend Edward Treglown put the order of service paper neatly folded on his knee, and whispered something to Liz's mother on his other side. Liz had been astonished by the coincidence that Edward, who had known her mother for only a couple of years, was a childhood friend of Joanne Wetherby. It turned out that they had grown up together in the same town in Kent. As adults they had lost touch, but came back into contact— because of Liz, curiously enough.

After Liz had been badly hurt several months before, during an investigation into a plot to derail a Middle East peace conference, she had gone to her mother's to convalesce. Concerned about her safety there, Charles Wetherby had contacted Edward; the two had immediately taken to each other, even before discovering Edward's earlier friendship with Joanne.

The Bach Prelude ended, and the only noise in the church was that of light rain thrown by the wind against the stained-glass windows. Then the vicar stood before the congregation and the service began. There were two readings, given by the sons; Sam's voice quavered as he reached the end of Keats's 'Ode to Autumn', a favourite of his mother's as he'd told the crowded church, but resolutely he gathered himself together and finished with a strong, resonant voice:

> '*The red-breast whistles from a garden-croft,*
> *And gathering swallows twitter in the sky.*'

A final hymn and the service concluded, and the congregation began slowly filing out. The rain had stopped, and the sky had lightened slightly as Charles stood outside the church with the boys next to him. Liz let Edward and her mother go first to offer condolences. Then it was her turn.

'Liz,' said Charles, gripping her hand firmly. 'It's lovely to see you. Thank you so much for coming. How have you been?'

'I'm fine, Charles,' she said as brightly as she could. It was characteristic of him to ask how *she* was.

'You've met Sam before,' he said, turning slightly to include his son. The boy smiled shyly and shook her hand. The woman in the black hat Liz had noticed in church came up to the other son, laying a comforting hand on his arm. Was she an aunt? Charles said, 'Liz, I want you to meet Alison.'

The woman looked up and smiled. She had a striking but friendly face, with high cheekbones, a sharp nose, and unusual violet eyes. 'Liz,' she said. 'I've heard so much about you.'

Really? thought Liz with surprise. From Charles? Or from Joanne?

Charles explained, 'Alison lives next door to us. We've been neighbours for years.'

'Yes. Joanne brought me a cake on the day we moved in.' She looked fondly at Sam. 'You weren't even born then, young man.'

Other people were waiting to speak to Charles, so Liz moved on. She had been invited with others for refreshments at the Wetherby house several miles away, but she couldn't face a large gathering just now—she wanted to see Charles, but she wanted to see him alone.

So, saying goodbye to her mother and Edward, she left, having decided to drive straight back to Thames House and get on with her work. She'd see Charles there soon enough. If he needed someone to talk to today, Liz sensed that his neighbour Alison would be happy to stand in.

SOMETHING WAS HOLDING them up. Their driver tapped his fingers impatiently on the wheel and Beth Davis looked out of the window at the patchy woods that lined the A307 south of Richmond. She wondered if she'd be back in time for the meeting she'd planned for that afternoon.

She glanced at DG sitting next to her. God knows how many meetings he must have scheduled, yet at the gathering after the service at Charles's house, he had been a model of tact: solicitous of Charles, polite to the array of friends and relatives he'd been introduced to, never giving any indication that he had pressing business elsewhere.

The car inched forward, tyres churning the slushy piles of leaves in the gutter of the road.

'Lovely service,' DG said with a small sigh.

'The boys read beautifully,' said Beth.

DG nodded, then after a moment he said, 'Our lot made a good show of it, I thought.'

'Yes. Thames House must have been seriously undermanned for a few hours.'

'I didn't see anyone leaving the service, so let's hope there were no crises.' DG smiled, then grew serious. 'I didn't see Liz Carlyle.'

'I did; she was at the church, with her mother. She didn't go on to the house though. She must have had to get straight back.'

DG nodded and looked thoughtful. Beth sensed what he was thinking—it was no secret that Liz and Charles were close, though no doubt the two of them believed no one else had noticed. But how could you fail to observe their obvious mutual attraction? The way Charles's face would light up when Liz joined a meeting he was chairing. The rapt look on Liz's face when Charles was speaking. You would have been blind to miss it.

The couple's feelings for each other would not have been a problem if Liz had worked for anyone else. But now she was reporting to Charles again, since he had taken over the counterespionage branch, and that's where matters grew complicated.

It was not an unknown, or even uncommon situation. It was understood within the service that the secrecy of the job made it hard to forge relationships with anyone 'outside', and that therefore office romances were inevitable. What was expected, however, was that the participants declare themselves at once, and that one of the pair would have to be moved. The power of love might be accepted, but its inevitable impact on working relations couldn't be.

As far as Beth knew, Liz and Charles had nothing to declare. Charles was far too upright, too devoted to his wife to do anything like that. And Beth simply couldn't see Liz in the role of mistress, waiting restlessly by the phone for a call from her married lover. Beth was sure that with these two, there had been no illicit affair: everything was bubbling beneath the surface.

DG sighed again, this time more loudly, usually a sign that his thoughts were about to find vocal expression. They were in Putney now, about to cross the river. DG said, 'I think we've got a bit of a problem on our hands.'

Beth nodded. She waited patiently until he added, 'It could be very difficult for them both.' He threw up a hand to indicate his own ambivalence. 'I mean, there's nothing stopping them now, is there?'

'I suppose not,' said Beth.

'Though my father used to say "Forbidden fruit looks less attractive once it's off the tree".'

Beth gave a small snort. 'With all respect to your father, I don't think the mutual attraction's going to diminish. It's other things that will get in the way.'

DG fingered his tie soberly. 'Like what?'

'Like guilt, unjustified though it might be. And I suppose the fear that what you've wanted so long could finally be yours; that somehow you don't deserve it. It's just too much—the prospect of having what you've desired for so long is too daunting.'

'You think it could be that bad for those two?'

Beth shrugged. She was paid to understand people, but had long learned that such understanding was precarious. 'I'd like to think not.'

'But you're not sure,' said DG, and it wasn't posed as a question. 'In which case their work will almost certainly be affected. So I think they might profit from a break from each other.'

What now? Beth thought warily. Personnel and postings were her responsibility, and he rarely interfered directly. But she could see DG had made his mind up.

He said emphatically, 'I think Liz should be posted—at least temporarily, while Charles settles back in at work.'

'Where do you want to put her?' she asked. Counterterrorism, she imagined. That's where Liz had been before. Working for Charles when he had been director there.

'We'll have to work that out,' he said, rather to her surprise. If he'd already decided, he clearly wasn't ready to say. 'It's got to be something challenging. I don't want her to think it's in any way a demotion.'

'No, though—' and Beth hesitated to say any more. When DG looked at her questioningly, she sighed. 'She's going to see it that way, I fear.'

'Probably.' DG shrugged. 'But so long as we make sure her new posting is tough enough, she'll soon get stuck in. She's too good an officer not to.'

THE CALL CAME out of the blue and Dave didn't recognise the name.

'Phil Robinson,' the man on the end of the phone repeated, with an English-sounding voice. 'I'm a warden with the National Trust. I was in contact with the RUC Special Branch in the past. I was told to ring you.'

Dave Armstrong had been in Northern Ireland for a couple of months. He was part of the team that was gradually filling up the smart new MI5 offices in Palace Barracks, the army HQ a few miles north of Belfast city centre. With power-sharing in Northern Ireland taking its first staggering steps, the new Police Service of Northern Ireland had handed over intelligence work in the province to MI5. With that transfer of power went all the records of the large stable of agents—the human sources that had fed the RUC with information from inside the Republican and the Loyalist armed groups during the Troubles. Dave and a couple of colleagues in the agent-running section of the MI5 team had the job of sorting through the list of sources they'd inherited, closing down the many who were of no future use and getting to know the few who might continue to be of value.

Although the so-called 'peace process' was well established and the security threat in Northern Ireland had changed, it hadn't gone away. The Provisional IRA might have disbanded its armed groups but there were still those among its former ranks—and Loyalists on the other side of the divide—who did not support the peace process. For them the war was not over, which meant Dave and his colleagues were monitoring several renegade groups determined to do all they could to keep the war very much alive.

Phil Robinson. The name now rang a bell. It had stuck out of the list of old sources because of the National Trust link. It had seemed an unlikely connection, but Dave knew that National Trust properties had been the target of IRA attacks in the past. In 1973 two young IRA volunteers had blown themselves up in the Castle Ward estate with a bomb they were trying to plant. After that, the security forces had paid more attention to the Trust's properties in Northern Ireland, and Robinson had been one of the people who'd been recruited to advise them.

'How can I help?' asked Dave now.

'Something's come up. I wonder if we could meet.'

'Of course,' said Dave, thankful to have something active to do. He was finding the routine job of reviewing old files and standing down old cases tedious. 'How about this afternoon?'

THEY HAD ARRANGED to meet in the middle of the city. Dave took one of the operational cars from the garage and drove into the heart of Belfast, busy even in midafternoon. When he'd first arrived, it had been a pleasant surprise to find the city centre lively, vibrant, humming with activity. The images Dave had grown up with—soldiers with automatic weapons, barricades and barbed wire, apprehensive people—had been replaced by teeming shops, pedestrian areas and a buoyant nightlife. It was hard to believe that not so long ago the city had been to all intents and purposes a war zone.

Dave was living in one of the flats the service leased in the suburb of Holywood, just outside Palace Barracks. It was an area of the town that had been comfortably safe in the Troubles but now, for someone living on their own like Dave, it was rather dull. He had a girlfriend in London, Lucy. They'd been together for two years, which for him was a long time. He was serious about her but it was difficult keeping it going when they were so far apart. He was too busy to hop over to England every weekend and there wasn't much point in Lucy coming to see him if he had to work.

But he'd just heard some news that had lifted his spirits. Michael Binding, the head of the MI5 office in Northern Ireland, had told them all that morning that Liz Carlyle was coming out to head the agent-running section. Dave knew that Binding didn't have much time for Liz, or she for him. But Dave had both affection and respect for her, though he wondered, now that she was going to be his boss, if their relationship would change. Not that they had been very close for the last couple of years. Liz had been transferred from counterterrorism, and it was only a fluke that they had recently worked together—in Scotland, at Gleneagles, where they had managed to abort a plot to ruin a vital peace conference. It had been good working with her; she was formidable without being aware of it, straightforward, clear, decisive.

That wasn't all, of course. For a time, five or six years ago, they had been not only good work colleagues but close friends, too. They might even have been more than that, but some mutual hesitation had held them back. More 'mutual' for her than me, Dave thought sadly. Getting together was out of the question, now. For one thing he was with Lucy and for another, he knew that

Liz's heartstrings were tied somewhere else—to Charles Wetherby. When Joanne had died two months ago, Dave's first thought had been that Liz and Charles would be together. So why on earth was Liz coming to Belfast?

Whatever the reason, he was delighted. And only partly because he was looking forward to seeing her dealing with Michael Binding.

PHIL ROBINSON WAS a tall man with greying hair. He spoke without a hint of Ulster brogue in his voice and, with his tweed jacket and checked Viyella shirt, looked completely English. He seemed out of place in Northern Ireland, thought Dave, and, as if in answer to the thought, Robinson told him that he had come over to Northern Ireland from England for the National Trust on a temporary posting thirty years before—and stayed.

'I fell in love with the place despite myself,' he said with a small grin. 'Then I met my wife, and fell in love with her as well.'

They were sitting in a coffee shop in St George's Gardens, round the corner from the Europa Hotel, which, after years of being the most bombed hotel in Europe, now seemed to be flourishing. When Dave had walked past it, a long line of Japanese businessmen had been queuing for cabs, while foreign guests of every conceivable race and nationality—Indians, Arabs, Orientals—went in and out of the big revolving doors.

Robinson then explained that he now worked only part-time for the National Trust.

'Consulting?' asked Dave politely.

Phil Robinson gave a self-deprecating laugh. 'Hardly. I help with the migrant bird counts up in Antrim, and my wife and I look after the holiday cottages on the Drigillon Estate in County Down. There are three of them and they're let for a week or two at a time, or sometimes for short breaks of two or three nights. It's a fair amount of work, particularly in the summer when they are occupied all the time.'

'So why did you want to see me?'

'One of the cottages—it's not really a cottage; it's a house, the old gate-house to the estate—has a gate in front of it which is usually closed. If you have a remote-control device it opens electronically and then closes behind you. Some local members of the National Trust who like to walk on the estate have remotes to open the gate and anyone staying in the cottages is given one. In the last six months or so, several people who've been staying at the gatehouse have complained that people were opening the gate at odd hours in the night—it's noisy and makes rather a crash as it closes—and driving cars up past the house into the estate.'

Dave nodded, but inwardly wondered why this necessitated a call to MI5.

Robinson seemed to sense his scepticism. 'I know, it may be nothing at all,' he said modestly.

'But something tells you it's not?' Dave asked gently.

Robinson nodded, and said, 'Yes. My wife and I stayed in the gatehouse for a couple of nights, between lets. Val thought I was mad, but it seemed the best way to find out if anything was going on. And, sure enough, one night the gate was opening and shutting and there were cars driving by at four o'clock in the morning. Then, after breakfast, two of them came back down the track. I was out walking our terrier.'

Dave nodded. 'Are there any other houses on the estate where they might be going?'

'Just the old farmhouse. But that's not owned by the Trust. Whoever does own it had a lot of work done to it a year or so ago. There were builders' lorries going up and down the track then. But not in the middle of the night.'

Robinson continued, 'When the two cars came down the track after breakfast, I was just by the gate. They slowed down to wait for the gate to open and I recognised one of the men in the cars. I'm pretty sure it was Terry Malone, an old IRA hand. I doubt you've heard of him, but he used to be well known over here. He was fairly high up in the Provisionals, and he had a brother, Seamus Malone, who went with the other side when the IRA split in the seventies—he was Official IRA. When Seamus was murdered in Dublin, the crack was that his own brother—that's Terry—fingered him for the killers.'

While Robinson finished his coffee, Dave thought about this, then asked, 'What are you suggesting? Do you think there might be some renegade IRA outfit in this farmhouse?'

Robinson shrugged. 'All this coming and going could mean anything. An awful lot of former Provisionals are finding life pretty difficult—all the organisation's money goes on Sinn Fein election pamphlets these days, instead of Armalites. These guys are up to all sorts of stuff to try to raise money to keep the war going.'

'Is the gatehouse occupied at the moment?'

'Yes it is, until the middle of next week. But then it's empty. I could let you have a key if you wanted to see for yourself.'

'Thanks,' said Dave. 'I think that could be very useful.'

2

When the tyre blew, Liz's car suddenly veered right at a forty-five-degree angle. She knew that at fifty miles an hour the car might go out of control, but there was a chance that she could manage the situation if she acted forcefully and immediately.

Instinctively Liz braced her forearms, struggling to hold the steering wheel as it fought her with enormous torque. The car slewed across the slow lane, cutting in front of a black van, which braked with a squeal.

She used all her strength now, and the skidding car just missed the concrete barrier on the road's hard shoulder; then, as if it had a mind of its own, the vehicle moved right, back out into the road. Narrowly avoiding a sports car, it headed this time towards the central barrier, but just before hitting it at speed, Liz managed to turn the car away sharply, then rode the resulting skid once, twice, then three times, weaving through the lanes as other cars swerved desperately to avoid her. At last the vehicle slowed down, and Liz brought it to a tremulous stop back on the hard shoulder.

She sat for a moment, trembling violently, waiting for the drumroll in her heart to slow before getting out. Inspecting the damage, she saw that one of the rear tyres had virtually disintegrated, its vulcanised rubber now hanging in shreds from a black lump round the metal wheel.

As her fear subsided, it was replaced with anger. The car had been left for her to pick up at the airport by her new colleagues in the Palace Barracks office. What the hell were they doing, leaving her a car with dodgy tyres? She grabbed her mobile phone and dialled Michael Binding's secretary. As she punched in the numbers she looked down the road and saw a sign facing the traffic. Its cheerful message read: WELCOME TO BELFAST.

SEVEN DAYS BEFORE, Liz had sat in Director B's office on the third floor of Thames House. The low winter sun had glanced through the windows; she could see, half a mile down the river, the postmodernist headquarters of MI6 bathed in golden light.

Beth Davis had been friendly, praising her recent work, but then she had dropped her bombshell—Liz was being posted to the MI5 headquarters in

Northern Ireland. 'We need you there to take charge of the agent-running section. You'll have much more responsibility, Liz. The agent runners will be reporting to you. They have a big job to do—there's a lot still going on over there—and we need someone with your background to decide where the priorities lie.'

She continued for a few minutes, couching her words carefully, but Liz found it hard to understand why she had been chosen. She knew that of all the service's new regional offices, Belfast was the most important, because it was going to act as a back-up HQ in the event of a terrorist attack on Thames House in London. But even though she'd done short stints on the Northern Ireland desk when she'd first joined the service, she'd never actually been posted there.

'When do I start?' she asked, thinking of the arrangements she'd have to make.

'Michael Binding's expecting you next week.'

Oh God, thought Liz, trying not to react. She and Binding had crossed swords on more than one occasion; she imagined he would relish being in a position to tell her what to do.

Beth said, 'Call in on the postings team this afternoon, Liz; they'll sort out the details.'

Nice of Beth to take the time to build me up, Liz thought sourly as she left. Then she told herself to get a grip. There must be a reason for this posting, though for the life of her she couldn't see what it could be. And why so fast? Charles was due back at work any day now, and she was longing to see him. It was almost as if Beth Davis was keen to get her out of the way before Charles returned.

Don't be so silly, Liz told herself. They couldn't have any idea of her feelings. She'd never told anyone about them, and had made a point of always acting completely professionally with Charles. Something else was going on to account for this posting.

While she was ruminating about this, a car drew up beside her on the hard shoulder and she recognised Maureen Hayes from A4 at the wheel, with a younger man sitting next to her.

'Hello, Liz. I got your message from Michael's secretary. That looks pretty nasty. Are you OK?'

'Well, I am now,' said Liz. 'It's good to see you. Have you got many cars over here with ropy tyres?'

'I'm amazed,' Maureen replied. 'This one was serviced last week and I drove it myself to the airport to leave for you. It seemed fine then. Get in and I'll take you to the office. Let's bring your luggage, and Tom here will wait for the pick-up truck. It's on its way.'

'I THOUGHT YOU'D LIKE to see your office first,' said Michael Binding's PA, a thin young woman with spiky, ash-streaked hair. She led Liz down a corridor until she stopped at an open door. It was a good-sized room, but with its bare desk, steel cupboard and two upright chairs it looked utterly cheerless.

Liz looked out of the window at the view of the half-empty barracks. In the distance she could see the A2, where the traffic was speeding along towards Belfast ten miles away.

'Michael wanted to be here when you arrived, but he's been called over to Stormont unexpectedly. I'll let you know as soon as he's back.'

'Dave Armstrong around?' Liz asked, suddenly keen for a familiar face.

The girl shook her head. 'I know he wants to say hello, but he's out meeting someone. He said to tell you he'd see you tomorrow. Some of the agent runners are in—their office is just along the corridor.'

An hour or so later Liz was feeling better. There were several familiar faces in the agent runners' room and the welcome had been warm, as had the coffee. Then the PA stuck her head round the door.

'Michael's back.'

Liz followed her along the corridor, past the centre lift shaft, until they came to a large office in the corner.

'Ah, Liz,' said the tall, wide-shouldered man as he got up from his desk, and shook her hand without a smile, 'I was sorry to hear about your car accident. Driving here is usually so safe.'

He looks different, thought Liz. Michael Binding had always favoured the country squire look—tweed sports jacket and highly polished brown brogues. But now he was wearing a long-sleeved khaki pullover, with leather patches on the sleeves, and brown suede shoes. His hair, previously short and neat, was now curling up off his collar. Liz realised that he had changed from squire to military officer. She sat down and waited to see what the new image portended.

She knew Binding as a clever but impatient man, whose impatience was at its worst when he had to work with female colleagues. More than impatience, in fact, since he patronised them in a manner so anachronistic and breathtakingly rude that he somehow got away with it. He had become famous for it throughout Thames House and, far from taking offence, most of the women he worked with put up with it and treated it as a joke.

Liz had never had to work for him before, but a few years previously she had had to interview Binding during an investigation—the same one that had unearthed a mole at a high level of MI5. Binding had been difficult, obstreperous, objecting to her questioning, until Liz had warned him that she'd bring in DG if Binding did not cooperate, which sulkily he then had.

After that, when their paths had occasionally crossed he had treated her with cautious resentment. So she watched warily now to see how he would react to her joining his staff.

'I must say,' he opened, 'I was hoping to be sent someone with Northern Ireland experience. I understand you have very little.'

Liz gazed at him levelly. 'Not much,' she said in a bright, cheerful voice. 'But, as I'm sure you know, I have a lot of agent-running experience and I assume that's why I was chosen for this particular job.'

Binding said nothing for a moment. Then, changing tack, he said, 'It's busier here than you may think.' He spoke defensively. 'I know there isn't much coverage on the mainland of things over here, but the Troubles have far from gone away. With no Northern Irish background you may find yourself at a disadvantage in understanding the current situation.'

Liz forced herself not to respond and kept her face expressionless.

'Our estimate is that there are over a hundred paramilitaries still active on the Republican side. They are not particularly well organised, thank God—they belong to almost as many splinter groups as there are members.'

'Still, a hundred individuals could do a lot of damage,' said Liz.

'Precisely,' he said in the pedantic tone Liz remembered, designed to make her feel like a pupil being marked on a test. 'Equally worrying, they can trigger a reaction on the other side. For now, the Loyalist groups have laid down their arms, but a few sectarian murders could change that overnight.'

'Where are these fringe people getting the resources to carry on? Is there still any foreign support?'

'Not that we know of. Al Qaeda aren't moving in, if that's what you're thinking,' he added with heavy sarcasm.

'I wasn't, actually,' said Liz drily. 'I was thinking about funding and weaponry—from the States, the Basques, North Africa, wherever.'

He looked a little surprised that she knew anything about the past sources of IRA arms. 'Their funding is local now, as far as we know. But none of it's legitimate. Crime of all sorts—drugs, prostitution, robberies.'

'How's our coverage of their activities? Have we any decent sources?' asked Liz, moving the conversation on to her own area of responsibility.

'Reasonable,' said Binding. 'I gather you've met some of the agent runners just now. I've had Dave Armstrong acting in charge of the team. But Dave is an action man. He prefers to be out running his own cases.'

What does he think I've done for most of my career? thought Liz. 'I've worked with Dave before,' she responded. 'He's good. I'll certainly need his input until I get up to speed.'

Binding looked at his watch with undisguised impatience. 'Well, then, why don't you get settled in, talk to Dave? Then in a day or two, we'll meet up again and you can give me your first impressions.'

And you'll let me know where they are wrong, thought Liz. Different posting, different place, different clothes. Same Michael Binding.

'I'M GOING OUT,' Dermot O'Reilly shouted as he left the house. This was as far as he kept his wife posted on his whereabouts, a habitual secrecy that had originated during the Troubles, when it was safer not to let her know what he was up to.

She'd had a good idea, nonetheless, and when the knock on the door had come that day in 1975 and five RUC men had taken him away, she wasn't very surprised. 'Cheer up,' she'd said on her first visit to the H-Blocks at the Maze. 'Think of it as a holiday from me.'

The 'holiday' had lasted two years and had been especially hard on Cath. He knew he was a gruff man to live with, but he was devoted to his wife in his way and understood how long-suffering she was. Especially since after he'd been freed he'd waited less than forty-eight hours before resuming the activities that had got him interned in the first place.

He'd been the munitions officer of Company B of the Belfast Brigade, with a weird farrago of firearms stored in half a dozen safe houses and under the floors of barns and sheds in the early days of the conflict. That was before Colonel Gaddafi of Libya had sent them ships full of the latest of everything and cash to go with them.

The Irish-Americans had been a steady source of revenue too. Did all those drinkers in the bars in Boston really believe that when they dropped their cash into the collecting buckets, it was going to go to widows and orphans of the struggle? Seamus Piggott would know all about that, since the boss of the Fraternity was from Boston.

Dermot didn't trust Piggott. What was an American doing carrying on the struggle? What was he hoping to get out of it? But Dermot had joined the Fraternity because it seemed the best resourced of the breakaway groups. At first he had been chief targeting officer. The plan was to kill a cop in the new PSNI—to show them that though they might have renamed themselves, to true Republicans like him they were still the enemy. Piggott had got hold of a list of addresses and Dermot had spent some cold, damp days on surveillance, watching policemen and their families coming and going, planning the best way to attack. He was glad when Piggott had acquired a couple of surveillance vans in which he could sit in comparative warmth, parked up, with his camera trained through a slit in the side. The vans were repainted frequently so they didn't get noticed.

He walked under the bypass and into Andersonstown. Ahead of him he saw Paddy O'Brien's bar on the corner. The barman was already pulling a pint of Murphy's before Dermot was through the door. With a wooden paddle he cut off the towering creamy head and placed the pint on the bar.

Dermot grunted thanks and looked around the pub. He liked coming here; it was an informal meeting place for many of the former Provisional IRA volunteers he had served with, especially those who were down on their luck. A few were in here already, nursing a pint through lunchtime. I'll be like that soon, he thought with an intense bitterness. He wasn't going to work today, not after his last conversation with Piggott.

Above the bar there was a framed black-and-white photograph of the hunger striker Bobby Sands, with a one-word caption underneath: *Loyalty*.

Loyalty: the word turned to ashes in Dermot's mouth. Once it had been the maxim of his professional life—loyalty to the cause, to the organisation, to his superiors in the hierarchy. It was a principle he'd carried over to the Fraternity, squashing his doubts about Piggott; helped, he had to admit, by the fact that the money was so good.

Dermot had never had money before, and he realised how easily he had got used to a comfortable life: the satellite dish on the roof; the holidays on the Costa Brava each February, getting away from the grey, dank cold. And the prospect of retirement to that small cottage in Donegal he and Cath had often dreamed about. Two more years with the Fraternity and he would have been free and clear. Only now he'd been pushed aside.

Piggott had been clinical. 'I need a younger man in charge of operations. You'll be running security from now on.'

When British intelligence was everywhere, security had been an important job. Now it meant making sure Piggott's driver showed up on time, or locking the office's desks. It was a dogsbody job, and Dermot was sure he'd be as badly paid and treated as Malone, who was nothing but a thug.

The barman was suddenly there again, though Dermot had barely touched his pint. He looked up at him from his bar stool.

'Sorry to hear about Aidan Murphy,' the barman said, polishing a glass.

'How do you mean?'

'Oh,' said the barman, putting the clean glass on a shelf above the bar. 'I thought you'd have known. Being as you work together and all.'

'Why don't you spit it out, seeing as you know so much and I don't?' Dermot said angrily.

The barman raised an apologetic hand. 'Sorry, Dermot. His hand got all smashed up. He said he'd had an accident . . .'

Dermot stared at the barman. 'What are you saying? If it wasn't an accident, what was it?'

The barman shrugged. 'All I know is that they—' He caught himself. 'Is that his hand was broken half to smithereens. He won't ever have full use of it again.' The barman sighed loudly. 'And him so young.'

He went down the bar to check on another customer, while Dermot took in what had been said. He reached for his pint glass and drained half the contents. Christ, he thought, what had they done to the kid? All right, he had a big mouth, and he should learn to keep it shut—but not this way. He didn't need teaching a lesson.

It's Piggott, he thought. *He doesn't give a shit*, he realised, with an anger he hadn't felt for years. Well, we'll see about that, he told himself.

THE FLAT WAS on the first floor of a red-brick house just a quarter of a mile from the university, on a quiet side street that stopped in a dead end.

On the ground floor a door led to another flat, but Liz went straight on up the stairs and let herself in through her own front door.

She put her bags down and did a quick recce of her new quarters. Two bedrooms—room for her mother to visit, she thought—a large living room, with a kitchen and a small breakfast alcove. Perfect—nothing too large to keep tidy; nothing so small to feel cramped. Someone had even come in and put tea and coffee on the kitchen top, and fresh milk in the fridge.

The bigger bedroom had a pleasant view of the park, where children were playing on swings and slides. She started to unpack and was just finishing when she heard a faint creaking from the door to the flat. Then a step.

Liz tensed, listening. She must not have closed the door properly. She took a deep breath and went out of the room and into the hall.

A little girl with a mop of brown curls and big brown eyes was standing there, staring at Liz. She wore pyjamas decorated with colourful lollipops.

'Hello,' said Liz with relief. 'Who are you?'

'I'm Daisy,' she said, and with great formality extended a hand.

Liz shook hands, with a smile. 'Pleased to meet you, Daisy. I'm Liz. Do you live downstairs?' she asked, gesturing with her head towards the floor.

'Yes,' said Daisy. 'Are you going to live here now?'

'I am. We'll be neighbours.'

A woman appeared in the doorway, white-haired, too old to be this girl's mother. She looked at Liz with a worried frown. 'I'm sorry, miss,' the woman said, with an accent that marked her out as local. 'She was just being curious. Come along, Daisy. I've got your supper ready.'

But Daisy didn't move. Looking at Liz she said, 'Are you the lady Mummy knows?'

'I shouldn't think so,' said Liz, wondering who her mother was.

A voice came from the hallway. 'Don't be so sure about that.' It was a woman's voice, followed by a laugh that could only belong to one person.

'Judith,' cried Liz, as a tall, elegant woman came into the room. 'I had no idea you were living here.'

Judith Spratt had worked with Liz in counterterrorism. She was widely respected within the service for her acumen and relentless pursuit of leads. She and Liz had become good friends before losing track of each other— Liz had been moved to counterespionage, and Judith had gone on extended leave after marital problems. Liz had heard vaguely that Judith had come back, but she hadn't seen her in Thames House—and now she knew why.

'I've been here over a year,' said Judith, as if amazed herself. 'Time flies when . . .' She paused, then grinned. 'When you're as busy as I am.'

By now the white-haired woman had a firm grip on Daisy's hand, and with a nod to Judith marched the little girl out of the flat. Liz and Judith went into the kitchen, where Liz put the kettle on.

'And of course that's Daisy,' said Liz, remembering the tiny child in

London. 'My, she's grown,' she added. 'How old is she now? Five? Six?'

'Almost six.' Judith's expression darkened. 'I'm divorced from Ravi, you know. He went back to India for a while; God knows where he is now. I haven't heard a monkey's.'

'I'm sorry.' She had always admired Judith's ability to juggle career, marriage and a child. It had been a big shock when things had fallen apart for her friend. Yet from the look of her now, Judith had picked herself up.

'Don't be sorry. I'm all right now, Liz, and so is Daisy. She's at a very good school here and doing well. Mrs Ryan collects her every day and looks after her until I get home. Don't be fooled by the white hair—she's quite feisty. But I like that. I've come to rely on her—it's busy at the office.'

'So Michael Binding was telling me.'

Judith gave an understanding smile. 'I know you've never been keen on him, Liz. Nor me. He hasn't changed much, but at least he lets us get on with it. Have you seen Dave?'

'Not yet. They told me he was away on a case.'

Judith nodded. 'Yes, he seems to think he's onto something new.' Her handsome, composed face suddenly broke into an unrestrained grin. 'Dave's so glad you're here. And so am I. There really is a lot more going on than people in London realise. I don't know what you're feeling about this posting, but I promise you one thing. You won't be bored.'

'THEY COULD EASILY stop it doing that,' said Technical Ted Poyser to his companion, as the gate closed behind them with a long-drawn-out squeal.

'Good job they didn't. We wouldn't know there was anything going on.'

'If there is,' said Ted sardonically.

Ted, the service's master of all things electronic, had decided they would go into the gatehouse in daylight, dressed to look like National Trust visitors, letting themselves in with the key that Robinson had provided.

'I wouldn't mind a few days here,' said John Forrest as he finished unpacking his drills and looked out of the dining-room window at the bay. The tide was in now, and little football-like heads of seals were popping up inquisitively from the ripples.

'Well, we haven't got a few days,' replied Ted, 'so let's get on with it.'

A couple of hours later, after some muted drilling and hammering, Ted was on the phone to the office at Palace Barracks. 'There's a woman with a dog just coming up to the gate now. How's the focus?'

'Clear as a bell,' came back the answer. 'But hang on there till a car comes past—we need to check the angle.'

A minute or two later, a small hatchback came out, driven by a woman with a small child in a car seat at the back. 'You need to adjust the angle. Just a few degrees down and to the left.' Ted relayed the instruction to John Forrest in the loft and the adjustment was made.

As the two men started to pack up, they heard the engine of another car coming down the track. Ted stood at the side of the dining-room window, half concealed by the curtain, and watched as a red Vauxhall Vectra with racing tyres slowed as it reached the gate. There were two men sitting in the front and another in the back seat. As the gate clanged shut and the car drove away he thumbed in a number on his phone. 'Did you get that?'

'Brilliant. Front seat, clear enough for *Hello* magazine. But we're not going to be able to get the rear-seat passengers, I'm afraid.'

THE CAMERA at the gatehouse had been busy. There were photographs of walkers, and several of a black Toyota hybrid car, which had been identified by Phil Robinson as belonging to holiday tenants. But Liz was staring at several pictures of a red Vauxhall.

'The owner is called Malone,' said Dave Armstrong, standing behind her and looking over her shoulder. 'That's him driving. He has form.'

'What kind of form?' asked Liz, still looking at the photographs.

'Six years in the eighties for the attempted murder of an RUC officer. He left his fingerprints all over a bomb that didn't go off underneath the policeman's car. He's got a list of convictions for violence. Lately he's calmed down. He's middle-aged, like we'll all be soon.'

'Speak for yourself,' said Liz. 'Who is the other guy in the front seat?'

'Don't know,' said Dave.

'What do you think's going on down there?' she asked.

Dave shrugged. 'Hard to say. But I doubt it's above board.'

'Do we know who really owns the farmhouse?' asked Liz.

'It's a company in Belfast. I've got the directors' names, but none of them has a trace in the files.' His face brightened. 'I was planning to go out there this morning to have a snoop around. Why don't you come too?'

'Are you talking about trespassing on private property?'

'Of course not,' he said, though from the glint in his eyes Liz was sure that was exactly what he was proposing.

SHE WAS SURPRISED how quickly they moved out of the city into country-side. A dreary grey sky hung like a lead lining above them and a gusty wind was throwing rain against the windscreen in short, erratic bursts.

'Not a great day for a stroll in the country,' said Liz, ruefully contemplating her walking shoes and wondering if they really were waterproof.

Yet half an hour later, when they had reached the Irish Sea and were driving along a deserted shoreline, a watery sun had broken through and was sparkling on the waves. 'Pretty?' asked Dave mildly.

Liz nodded. 'I hadn't realised how beautiful the countryside round here is,' she said.

'Neither had I. I thought it would be all council estates with "Up the IRA" and "Brits Out" painted on the walls.'

At the end of the village street, Dave turned sharp left round the bay and over a narrow bridge, from where they could see the closed gate into the National Trust estate.

'How are we going to get in?' said Liz. 'Don't we need a gadget to open the gate?'

'Got one,' said Dave, slowing down and fishing in his pocket. 'Ted made a copy of the one Phil Robinson lent us.'

They passed in front of the stone gatehouse. The black car was parked outside, indicating that the paying visitors were at home.

The wind had picked up now and Liz, shivering in her city raincoat, resolved to go shopping for some outdoor clothes as she followed Dave, warm in his fleece-lined parka. The footpath ran from the small car park through pine trees towards the sea. Seagulls were swooping over the water and a number of small birds were picking something off the low bushes, keeping just ahead of Liz and Dave as they walked. The path ran parallel to a crumbling dry-stone wall, beyond which Liz could see the foundations of what must have been an enormous house, the centrepiece of the estate. The path stopped at the corner of the wall, but Dave kept walking on until they crested a mound and suddenly faced a farmhouse, less than 100 yards away.

It was a long, two-storey structure with neatly painted stucco sides. The roof tiles had been re-laid recently and had yet to lose their gloss. Behind the house at one side was an outbuilding, a squat windowless brick structure about the size of a double garage.

Dave took a small pair of binoculars from his pocket but suddenly swung round and faced the sea, still with his binoculars to his eyes. Then quickly dropping them back in his pocket he turned towards Liz, threw both arms round her and kissed her full on the lips.

Furious, Liz was about to dig a fist into his ribs, when Dave disengaged just enough to whisper, 'Someone's coming.'

She understood and hugged him back fiercely.

Then a voice rang out. 'This isn't a Lovers' Lane.'

Dave and Liz let go of each other and turned together to face a man in a long waxed coat. He was tall and lean, with short greying hair, square features and rimless glasses. Behind him stood a shorter, dark-skinned man in a black leather jacket. His hands were deep in his pockets and he was looking at them with dull, expressionless eyes. Liz felt pretty sure she knew what was in the pockets, and her backbone crawled.

'Sorry,' said Dave, in an uncanny approximation of an Ulster accent. 'The footpath just seemed to disappear.'

The man looked at Dave, then moved on to Liz, giving her a probing stare, a soulless once-over that had nothing to do with her being a woman. He pointed sharply in the direction from which they'd come. 'The footpath's there. This is private. Didn't you see the notice?' There was no trace of an Irish accent, but something flat about his pronunciation didn't sound English. The man looked back at Dave. 'You're on my land.'

'Not for long,' said Dave. 'Our apologies.' He took Liz's arm and started walking quickly back towards the corner of the wall.

When they were well down the path towards the beach, Dave stopped and looked behind them. 'That shorter, heavyset guy followed us to make sure we left,' he said. 'Did you recognise him? He's the man in the front seat in a couple of those pictures.'

'Not exactly a pleasant encounter.'

As they retraced their steps to the car, Dave said, 'Still, it had its upside.'

'You mean we got a sight of the inhabitants?'

Dave grinned. 'No. I was thinking of our clinch. Wait till I tell them back in Thames House. My stock will go through the roof.'

'Don't you dare,' said Liz. She added with a smile, 'That was strictly business and don't you forget it, Dave Armstrong.'

IT HAD BEEN almost two weeks since her arrival and Liz was finding a rhythm to life, driving to the office each morning and returning against the rush-hour traffic at six—or at seven or eight when there was lots to do.

She had settled into her flat, supplementing the few belongings she had brought with her with the odd find at the Saturday flea market, so the place was beginning to look slightly more lived in. Not that she had done it single-handed—one afternoon, Mrs Ryan, Daisy's childminder, had bearded her in the hall. 'Would you be needing a cleaner, Miss Carlyle? You work hard—you're just as bad as Mrs Spratt. You need to take it easy when you've got a minute to relax, like. And not be worrying about washing your smalls and vacuuming your sitting room.'

Liz smiled, seeing the truth of this. 'Would you know of someone?'

'I'll do it myself, miss,' the woman said firmly. 'It won't take long at all, and I'll charge you just the same as I do Mrs Spratt.'

'Well, if you're sure you have time—'

Mrs Ryan waved this away with a hand. 'Time's the one thing I have got, miss. My poor husband's been with his maker these last five years and I've only my son Danny to look after, and he's out at work all day.'

So now Liz was living in unaccustomed cleanliness and order, which she had to admit to herself was rather pleasant.

Judith had asked her down to supper, after Daisy was in bed, and the two women had stayed up late, catching up with each other. How eventful Judith's recent life had been, thought Liz, and how well she had picked herself up from her failed marriage. What had Liz to report in return? Nothing really. There was still no one man in her life, no marriage, no children; only the solace of doing work she enjoyed and knew she was good at.

The sole news she'd had of Charles had come in a letter from her mother, and it was not what she wanted to hear. Her mother and Edward had been to have supper with him, and Charles seemed very well. Her mother went on to tell her that Charles was busy again with his garden, and that he had help from one of his neighbours—that nice woman, Alison, who'd been at the funeral. She had also been a big help with the boys, apparently. There was no mention in her mother's letter of whether Charles had asked after Liz, which made her sad.

She had explored the city centre extensively, and found that there were still plenty of signs of the sectarian divide that had caused the Troubles in the first place, although they seemed like memories of the past rather than evidence of imminent hostilities.

But she thought again about her surroundings after a meeting with Michael Binding. The chief constable was concerned about an increase in activity by breakaway Republican groups. There were signs that policemen, current and retired, were being targeted for assassination. Binding had said, 'If one of these groups succeeds in killing a target, it could endanger the entire peace process.'

He looked worried for the first time. 'We don't want to make too many waves, but potential targets are being advised to increase their personal security. And we all of us need to be careful too. Make sure that if you take a car from the pool you keep it parked at the garage of your flat, or here in the car park—don't leave it on the street. And if you detect any sign of surveillance, please report it to A4 and me immediately.'

He looked at Liz with a thin smile. 'But of course I don't need to tell you any of this, with all your counterterrorism experience.'

Then why did you? thought Liz, trying her best to smile back.

Binding seemed to remember something, for he said suddenly, 'By the way, I've heard from A4 about that car you drove in from the airport. The wheel was damaged, but they think that's because you drove on it—the tyre was completely shot.'

'But what caused the blowout?'

Binding raised both hands in a 'Who knows?' gesture. 'It could have been anything. A nail on the road, broken glass, even the way you were driving, I suppose. There wasn't enough of the tyre left to tell.'

Liz bristled at the suggestion that her driving had caused the blowout. And how could Binding sound so certain it had just been an accident? But she resisted the urge to challenge him, knowing it would just confirm his view that women were hysterical.

3

Dave poked his head round Liz's office door. 'I'm going to see an old RUC Special Branch contact this afternoon. Maybe he can cast some light on things. I'm taking the photographs from the camera to show him.'

'Where are you meeting him?'

'At his house. He didn't want to come here.'

'What's his name?'

'Jimmy Fergus. He's retired but he's still winding up some of the old RUC cases. He's supposed to be a mine of information.'

'I know him,' said Liz. 'He was a big help when I was on that mole case a few years ago. I'd like to come, too.'

JIMMY FERGUS LIVED in a comfortable suburb on the north side of the city. As they drove there Dave asked, 'How's it going with Binding?'

Liz shot him a look, but Dave kept his eyes on the road.

'He seems to think I screwed up that pool car,' she said. 'Apparently my inferior driving skills caused a blowout.'

'That's ridiculous,' said Dave.

'He didn't think so. He also gave me a lecture on security—he seemed obsessed with where I parked my car.'

'Well,' said Dave, 'Binding's got a point, even if it kills me to say it. On the surface it's all sweetness and light, but just twenty years ago any IRA man in Ulster would have given their eyeteeth to kill either of us.'

He turned now onto a quiet, tree-lined road with detached red-brick houses set back behind high hedges and no parked cars by the kerb. Only a van delivering laundry disturbed the peace.

He's lost weight but he's hardly aged at all, thought Liz, as her old acquaintance opened the front door. She was surprised to find him still working for the police service. But he'd married again—wife number four, if Liz remembered right—so maybe he needed the salary.

'Liz,' Jimmy said, beaming, and gave her a big kiss on the cheek. She introduced Dave, who then sat silently, shifting in his chair as they talked of old times. Eventually, bored with a conversation in which he had no part, Dave opened his briefcase and laid out the photographs on the coffee table.

'I know three of them,' said Jimmy, leaning back in his comfortable chair and surveying the enlarged prints now strewn on the table. He scratched a finger against his pockmarked cheek. He was a big man, whose suits never quite fitted his powerful frame, and whose tie always slid an informal inch down his shirt front. But the ruffled sloppiness of his appearance was misleading; Liz knew he was an excellent policeman, with an intuitive feel for a case and a nose for what people were really like.

'This guy,' he said, pointing at the photograph of the driver of the car that had passed the gatehouse several times, 'is Terry Malone. Long-time Provo volunteer. Enforcer type. Nothing sophisticated.' He paused to contemplate the photographs again. 'These other two are called Mickey Kinsella and John O'Sullivan. Small-time villains basically, not as heavy as Malone. This fourth guy. Don't know him—looks Spanish? What do you think?'

'Maybe he's black Irish,' said Dave facetiously.

Jimmy ignored him. 'Come to think of it, we had a tip-off that someone had come here from the Costa del Sol. A hit man named Gonzales. Terry Malone was never an angel, but this guy's reported to be seriously hard.'

'Who's he working for then?' asked Dave. He seemed a bit prickly with Jimmy, while Jimmy was as easy-going as Liz remembered.

'Nobody seems to know—but you don't bring in somebody all the way from Spain unless he's got a role to play. Where were these pictures taken?'

Liz explained, telling him about the tip-off from Phil Robinson and their reconnaissance of the farmhouse.

Dave broke in, 'We've checked who owns the farmhouse. A company—Fraternal Holdings. It's a private enterprise, Belfast based, with offices just off Castle Street. They describe themselves as consultants.'

Jimmy snorted. 'Who doesn't these days? Every retired copper I know says he's a "private security consultant". It usually means they work the door at the local disco.'

'This is different,' Dave said testily. 'I drove past the offices—they've got an entire floor in a new building.'

'Who runs the business?'

'The managing director is one Seamus Piggott.'

'Ring any bells?' asked Liz.

Jimmy thought, then shook his head. 'Can't say it does.'

Liz reached for one of the photographs and pushed it towards Jimmy. It was of an Audi that had passed the gatehouse, with the man named Malone at the wheel. Sitting beside him was a thin man in a suit. Liz said, 'I'm pretty sure the man in the passenger seat is the same man who confronted us when we were looking at the farmhouse.'

Jimmy peered carefully at the still. 'I don't recognise the guy. I don't know the name either.' He sounded puzzled. 'I thought I knew all the players, but I don't know anything about this guy. And that worries me. If a foreign hit man's involved, there must be something going on, and normally I would expect to have picked up at least a hint of it. But I haven't.' He gave a modest smile. 'Sorry. Maybe I'm getting past my sell-by date.'

'Well, it's not your responsibility any more,' said Liz. And it was true. Any case with even the faintest whiff of sectarian politics had been transferred to MI5. She returned to the business in hand. 'What if this mystery man Piggott isn't local? If he's the same character we met, he didn't sound any sort of Irish.'

Jimmy shrugged. 'He could be from the mainland. First- or second-generation Irish there.'

Dave said, 'We've done some basic checking. Couldn't find anyone of that name in our files, and Dublin hasn't got anybody either.'

'What about the States?' Liz asked. 'That might account for his accent.'

'Wait a minute,' Dave protested. 'How do we know Seamus Piggott is the guy in the picture, or the same guy we saw the other day?'

There was silence in the room, and Liz saw both men were looking at her.

She said, 'We don't know, Dave. But what else do we have? Three small-time crooks and a Spanish hood. That doesn't explain a swanky set of offices in downtown Belfast, or a suspiciously expensive-looking farmhouse with an owner who is paranoid about outsiders. There's something going on, and I'll feel much better once we know who Seamus Piggott is.'

ANTOINE MILRAUD stepped out of the tall double doors of his apricot-pink villa set high up above the little Provençal town of Bandol. He stood at the point where the drive, winding upwards through the garden from the security gates, ended on a tarmac apron. He was waiting for his driver, who was late, and he was annoyed. Milraud liked to be in control but there were some things he couldn't do for himself. He needed the chauffeur; it wasn't only driving that he required from him.

From where he stood Milraud could see over the tops of the umbrella pines towards the harbour, where large white motor launches and yachts were moored alongside the art deco casino. If he turned to his left, he could look across the pine-clad hills towards the naval base at Toulon, but today he could see no further than the first headland, for the clouds sat low on the hills, threatening rain. The mimosa flowers that covered the trees along his drive were being tossed by a January mistral. His car and driver should have been visible but there was still no sign of them. Shivering a little, he turned and went back into the house, firmly closing the doors behind him.

Milraud did not often think about his past. There had been too many episodes he would prefer to forget. After eleven years in Paris with his former bosses, chronic mutual fatigue had set in. The salary had been negligible, the suburb that was all he had been able to afford had not matched his self-image, and when his employers had accused him of overreacting, of using hammers to crack nuts, it had become increasingly obvious that his prospects for promotion were nil. He had managed to extricate himself from his post most advantageously, and the eight years since he had left had been good ones for Milraud.

He had his shop in Toulon, another in London's Camden Market, and a third in Belfast. They did well: there was a growing demand for antique weapons, swords, pistols, cannons, all Milraud's speciality. His shops brought in good profits, enough to justify employing a manager for each one, and now there was a thriving online business as well. His profits would have satisfied any antique dealer, but Milraud wanted more: to pay his chauffeur's salary and maintain the Mercedes limousine he was paid to drive; to keep up the villa in Bandol and to employ the staff who ran the place; to pay for the designer clothes that his wife (still asleep upstairs) loved to flaunt in the local restaurants and clubs.

So, although his antique business was successful, it did not underwrite his current lifestyle; nor was it the reason why his driver carried a 9mm automatic pistol under his dark blue uniform suit.

His second business, for which his antique shops provided cover, was one that required him to take extensive precautions to protect himself: electric gates to his property, razor wire on top of its perimeter wall, a movement-sensor alarm and cameras, and a driver who doubled as a bodyguard. Yet to date the greatest danger he'd had to face had been flying through a sandstorm in a prop plane to the desert redoubt of a customer in the Emirates.

But recently he had begun to wonder whether someone was paying him unwanted attention. The telephone in his house had gone out of order and since the line had been restored, he seemed to hear a strange echo in the background whenever he used it; his banker, located in Lausanne, had told him of an enquiry from France that had been withdrawn when challenged; a *permis de construire* had been issued for an extension to his house but only after an unnecessarily detailed inspection of the interior.

Was someone probing his affairs? And if so, who? It might be anyone—including his former employers, of whom it had been said that, though you could choose to leave them, you could not guarantee they would leave you.

Conceivably, all this suspect activity could be entirely innocent. Milraud had been trained long ago to be suspicious of coincidences, but after all, he told himself, one must avoid paranoia. A life of fear was not a life.

The buzzer sounded in the hall. Milraud stepped outside again as the Mercedes rolled to a halt. The driver got out to open the car's door.

'You're late.'

'I beg your pardon, *monsieur*. There was traffic coming out of town.'

'Leave earlier next time,' Milraud said brusquely, and slid smoothly into the cream-coloured luxury of the rear seats for the short journey.

It was a drive of only fifteen minutes to Toulon, where Madame Dipeau would be opening up the shop at any moment. The route took them parallel to the coast for twelve miles, and then down into the town. The car swung past the long, arcaded Maison des Cordes, past the elegant pink and white naval headquarters building behind its massive security gates manned by tough-looking sailors, past the great pillared doors of the Musée de la Marine, and into the avenue de la République, where it drew up at the end of a small side street of eighteenth-century buildings: the rue d'Alger.

Here Milraud got out and leaned down to speak through the front window. 'Come back at twelve,' he ordered. 'I am having lunch in Marseilles.'

He walked halfway up the street, through a weathered stone doorway and into the shop where Madame Dipeau was bringing out a pair of fine silver duelling pistols from the vault. She was a widow of indeterminate years who had made herself expert in eighteenth-century weapons. Even more important from Milraud's point of view, she was careful and discreet.

'*Bonjour, monsieur*,' she said quietly. 'There has been a telephone call for you. A Monsieur Donovan. He said he would call again.'

'*Merci, madame*,' he said, and went to his office in the rear of the shop, closing the door behind him. Then, sitting down at his desk with yesterday's local paper, he lit a Disque Bleu, and waited.

Twenty minutes later the phone on his desk trilled faintly. He picked it up at once. '*Oui*,' he said.

'It's me,' said the man calling himself Donovan. Though the name was unfamiliar to Milraud, the flat accent was unmistakable. Milraud knew immediately who his caller was.

'*Bonjour*,' said Milraud. 'It's been a while.'

'Too long. It would be good to meet. Were you planning to be over here any time soon?'

'*Franchement non*.' He'd visited Northern Ireland at Christmas and his next trip was planned for June. Business there was not what it had been.

'That's a pity.'

'I can always alter my plans,' said Milraud, reaching for his diary. He respected Piggott. Piggott didn't waste time. His own or other people's.

'It could be worth your while. I may have some business for you.'

'Would this be a distance requirement, or close by?' he said, carefully avoiding any word that might trigger a listening device.

'Both, actually. Not a big deal but important to make it happen.'

The best, thought Milraud. He knew what 'making it happen' meant, and it would cost the other man. He looked at the open page of his diary. 'I can be there the day after tomorrow. How does that sound?'

'Good. Ring me when you've arrived.' And the other phone went dead.

DAVE WAS WALKING carefully to his desk in the agent runners' room, balancing surveillance photographs on top of a mug of coffee, when the phone on his desk began to ring. The flashing red light indicated that the call was coming in on one of his agent lines. In his haste to get to it before it stopped ringing, he banged into the corner of his desk and lurched forward, dropping the photographs all over the floor and spilling coffee on his hand. Cursing under his breath, he grabbed the handset and said, 'Seven eight two seven.'

'I've got something for you,' said a hoarse Ulster voice that he didn't recognise. It sounded middle-aged, certainly not young.

'Who's this?' asked Dave, his pulse quickening.

'You don't know me, but I've got something for you.'

'What sort of thing?' Dave pressed the buttons that activated the recorder and the call-tracing mechanism.

'Information. I'm not saying any more. I need to meet. It's about what's going on now.'

'What do you mean, going on? Going on where?'

'I'll only talk if I can see you.'

'Just give me a steer. What are we talking about here?'

'I was a Provo volunteer. We're supposed to be on cease-fire. But there's things happening. I know what's going on and who's doing it.'

'You mean the breakaway groups?' Dave was desperately trying to keep him on the line.

'It's just for you, not the police. You can't trust them. I'll ring again at twelve o'clock and you can give me the meeting place.'

The phone clicked and the light on Dave's handset went out.

Hooray, thought Dave, picking up the photographs from the floor. This was what he liked. Action.

He turned on his computer screen and pulled up the list of available operational premises—safe houses suitable for meeting a source.

IT WAS A COLD, sparkling morning and the sun was glancing through the window onto Liz Carlyle's desk. The new offices were well heated, almost overheated. She was feeling hot in the thick polo-neck sweater she had put on earlier and was just contemplating removing it, wondering whether the T-shirt she had on underneath was decent enough to reveal, when Dave walked into her office.

'You look very bushy-tailed,' she said, observing his flushed cheeks. 'What were you up to last night? Do I detect the effect of lovely Lucy?'

'No, I haven't seen Lucy for weeks. It's strictly work,' Dave replied with a wide grin. 'I've had a phone call.'

'Lucky you! Sit down and tell me more. Who from?'

'That's the interesting part. I don't know. But I'm going to find out pretty soon.' He gave Liz the gist of the message from the anonymous caller. 'Call came from a phone box, of course. He's calling back in'—Dave looked at his watch—'two and a half hours.'

'What are you going to say to him?'

'I'm going to meet him in Blue Lagoon,' Dave replied, giving the code name of one of the safe houses.

Liz was turning over the situation in her mind. She was not used to being Dave's boss and she hesitated to start throwing her weight about at this early stage, but she felt uneasy at Dave's breezy approach.

'How did he get your number?'

'I don't know. It's a number I've used for some time and it's known to the police. The caller said he'll only talk in person.'

'I can't say I like the sound of this. What back-up are you planning?'

'I don't need back-up. There is a cease-fire on, you know.'

Liz hesitated. She was a new arrival and Dave, who'd been here longer, must have a better feel for the situation. But, though she rated Dave very highly, she knew that he had one flaw as an agent runner—impetuosity. This didn't feel right to her; it could easily be a set-up.

So she said, 'There may be an IRA cease-fire, but your caller's offering information on the breakaways. And they're certainly not on cease-fire. I think you should have full antisurveillance back-up for this meeting and that means meeting him out in the open, not in a safe house.'

'He'll be looking for surveillance. I don't want to scare him off.'

'You're not going to. You know how good A4 is. He'll never see them. You should meet him somewhere he's got to make a bit of a journey to get to, so we can watch him—make sure he hasn't got anybody else with him.'

Dave looked at her unhappily. 'That will take a lot of resources, Liz. I'm not sure Binding will agree to it.'

'Leave Binding to me; I'll go and see him straight away. You line up A4 and I'll meet you in the briefing room in half an hour.'

'OK,' said Dave unenthusiastically. 'But I hope we don't blow this.'

I hope not too, thought Liz. If this didn't go right, her reputation as head of the agent runners would be mud that would stick for a good long time.

LIZ HAD NOT yet been to Bangor, up the coast of Northern Ireland from Belfast, but thanks to Google Maps she was beginning to feel she knew it pretty well, at least the layout of the streets in the centre of the town, which she and Dave had pored over with A4 the day before.

Now she was in the Bangor A4 control room, the domain of Reggie Purvis, operational controller. Sparkling clean, its comprehensive equipment looked almost unused. There was only one blot on the newness and that was the old, saggy-bottomed armchair that was parked by the door, kept for case officers to sit on when an operation was in progress. Liz stood carefully positioned where she could see all the monitors, but well out of Reggie's way.

Michael Binding had proved surprisingly amenable when Liz had asked for approval for resources for this operation. Indeed he'd been so interested in this new source that Liz had worried he would insist on taking over the operation. Fortunately he'd been called to a meeting in Thames House.

Little squirms of tension were chasing each other round Liz's stomach. Reggie's jaws were moving rhythmically as he chomped on a wad of chewing gum. Each of the monitors in the bank in front of him was flickering. Everything was ready for Operation Brown Fox to begin.

Suddenly a voice said, 'The eleven thirteen has arrived at platform three.' It was A4 agent Mike Callaghan, sitting at a café table on the concourse of Bangor railway station, with a copy of the *Belfast Telegraph* and a large cappuccino.

Reggie Purvis spoke into his mouthpiece. 'Brown Fox should be wearing a green anorak and carrying a Marks and Spencer carrier bag.'

'Got him. He's heading towards the main exit.'

Suddenly, on one of the monitors, Liz could make out the figure of a man, walking rapidly past the concourse café. The image was transmitted by Callaghan, using a miniature device that looked like a standard mobile phone, but which sent at high bandwidth and resolution. The image was slightly blurred, nonetheless, and the man passed by Callaghan too quickly for Liz to see much detail.

'OK. Bravo, he's yours now. You'll see him in ten seconds.'

Maureen Hayes, the A4 operative who had picked up Liz after her incident with the blown tyre, was parked in one of the short-stay bays, engine idling. 'I have him. He's walking up towards the roundabout.' And then, after a pause, 'Brown Fox has turned left on Dufferin Avenue. He's clean.'

'As instructed,' Reggie said, turning towards Liz. 'So far so good.'

Liz looked down at Reggie's desk, where a laptop showed the satellite map of this area of Bangor. They'd chosen it because it was outside Belfast, yet easily accessible. As she stared down at Dufferin Avenue on the laptop screen, ten miles away Agent Terry Fleming walked slowly down that road towards the station. When he saw the man across the street walking in the other direction, he said in a voice barely louder than a whisper, 'Brown Fox moving north. There's no one behind him.' The miniature microphone under the lapel of his overcoat relayed this instantly to the control room.

At the corner of a residential road called Primrose Street, the target turned right. A couple in a parked Mini, 200 yards down the street, stopped squabbling and reported that Brown Fox had stopped at a public phone box.

The phone on the desk in front of Reggie Purvis gave a long, low buzz. He pressed the button and spoke in quiet, controlled tones. 'Listen carefully. Walk back down Primrose Street, then continue right on Dufferin Avenue. Turn right onto Gray's Hill Road and walk towards Queen's Parade and the harbour. There's a large car park right next to it—go in from your end and walk towards the fountain in the middle. You'll be contacted.'

The caller said nothing and hung up. Seconds later, Maureen Hayes reported, 'All clear on Dufferin Avenue. We're across from the harbour now.' She had collected Fleming and driven along another street to the car park.

'OK,' said Reggie. He spoke over his shoulder to Liz. 'It all looks quite clean, but let's get an overview, shall we?'

He flicked a switch on the console and suddenly a *phut phut phut* came over the speakers. 'Air Three, can you hear me?'

'Loud and clear. We've circled the harbour and are coming inland to turn.'

The helicopter appeared to be searching for something off the coast. The manoeuvre gave the pilot and his A4 passengers an unrivalled view of the network of streets that lay between the flotilla of yachts in the basin and the railway station less than half a mile away.

In the control room, the camera positioned on the helicopter's front right strut began transmitting to the second monitor. It was like a moving version of the satellite map, but infinitely sharper—Liz could see individuals walking on the streets below. Including a lone figure approaching the car park.

A minute later, a voice spoke over the chopper's fluttering. 'All clear on Queen's Parade and back up Gray's Hill Road. No sign of hostile activity.'

By then another parked car had reported that Brown Fox had entered the car park. On the third monitor a misty view of the car park appeared, shot through the windscreen of Maureen Hayes's vehicle. Liz watched the man in a green anorak walking towards the little fountain that sat in a miniature garden in the middle of the car park.

Maureen zoomed her lens and the image grew sharper and closer—the target, a man in his late sixties at least, with a pinched face and short grey hair.

The watchers in the control room heard a car starting up and a metallic grey saloon appeared beside Brown Fox. He turned and stepped to one side to allow it to pass, but as it drew alongside it slowed and stopped. Brown Fox looked startled as the passenger door opened. Then Liz heard Dave's voice on the audio say, 'Good morning. I'm your contact. Climb in.'

4

Dave had re-parked his car in an uncrowded corner of the car park. It gave him a clear view in all directions; equally, it allowed the two A4 cars discreetly stationed to cover the exits a clear view of him and his passenger. Further up on Gray's Hill Road another car sat, watching for new arrivals, whether on foot or by car. Above them all, the small unmarked helicopter flitted in and out of the area quite unobtrusively.

'I'm Simon Willis,' said Dave, offering his hand, which his passenger slowly shook.

'Patrick.'

'Patrick? That's a fine Irish name. Have you got one to go with it?'

'Not one you need to know.'

'OK.' Dave sounded confident, thought Liz in the control room. 'You said you needed to talk to me.'

'No—you need me to talk to you.'

'Well,' said Dave, 'I'm certainly interested in hearing what you have to say. And why you want to say it to me.'

'That's my affair,' said 'Patrick'. He sounded surly, and Liz wondered just what his motivation was. He clearly wasn't acting out of any affection for the security services. This was confirmed when Patrick announced, 'I am not here to betray the cause I served for twenty-five years. I'm here because someone else is doing the betraying and I want it stopped. All that's different now is that you people and I have the same interests—*temporarily*.'

'I'm listening,' said Dave. Then he added, 'Do you mind if I take notes?'

'I certainly do,' said Patrick sharply.

Liz smiled at the classic ruse for distracting the agent from wondering whether he was being recorded.

'That's fine. I have a good memory,' said Dave easily.

Patrick took a deep breath. 'When the Provisional Army Council decided to sign the Belfast Agreement and go along the political route, not all of their followers went with them. Some wanted to continue the struggle. You will be familiar with the groups I'm talking about. The splinter groups.'

'Continuity IRA. The Real IRA,' said Dave.

Patrick must have nodded, and he went on, 'The fact is, things have changed. Now that the leaders are taking jobs as government ministers and drinking coffee out of china cups in Stormont, we can't carry on the war like we did.' He added venomously, 'Not that most of us don't want to. But we've sworn loyalty to the leadership and the leadership's come down hard on splinter groups. So we've had to find something else to do.' He added with a suggestion of embarrassment, 'There's also the problem of earning a crust.'

Dave said, 'I've often wondered how people have managed.'

'It's been hard,' said Patrick harshly. 'While the bigwigs ponce about in Downing Street and Stormont, the rest of us have been left out in the cold.'

Dave stayed silent, and Patrick continued. 'The problem was how to stay loyal to the Movement while not getting left out. There weren't many options, and when you saw an opportunity you had to grab it quickly.' Suddenly he dropped the third person. 'So I did.'

'Tell me about the opportunity.'

'A new company in Belfast needed some technical assistance. It was a consultancy,' he added, 'and I guess you'd say I became their consultant.'

'Consultant in what?' asked Dave slowly.

'Technical aspects of security,' said Patrick a little grandly. 'Several of the employees of the firm were old colleagues of mine.'

'Where is this company?'

'Right in the centre of Belfast—just off Castle Street.'

That's about the first concrete information he's offered, thought Liz. And Castle Street rang a bell. You had to admire Dave's handling of this man: a good agent runner never hurried the agent and took care never to prick the balloon of his ego. Dave was doing well on both counts.

'And are you happy working there?' asked Dave.

'I was at first, especially as I was told that the firm's profits were going to help the Cause. It was a legit business but also a holding action, if you see what I mean, until the struggle began again.'

His agenda's clear at any rate, thought Liz, wondering how many former Provos shared his views. The thought was depressing and frightening—former terrorists waiting for the fragile peace to crack so they could come in and finish the job, starting the futile spiral of violence all over again.

Dave was asking, 'Can you tell me about your technical work?'

'No!' The man called Patrick was almost shouting. 'I'll tell you what you need to know.' There was an edge to his voice now.

'Fair enough,' said Dave steadily.

'The business turned out to have a retail side I hadn't been told about.'

'What are they selling?'

'What *aren't* they selling is more like it. They flog stolen lottery tickets, stolen booze and foreign women.'

'Any guns?' asked Dave quietly.

There was silence in the car; for a moment, standing in the control room, Liz worried that the audio connection had been lost.

Then Patrick said, not answering Dave's question, 'Worst of all, they sell drugs. We never touched drugs. It was a punishable offence to have anything to do with them. They could destroy our communities.'

'So this consultancy is really just a front for criminal activity?'

'Looks like it.'

'Why are you talking to me?' asked Dave, sounding more assertive now. Liz reckoned he was probably thinking what she was—that this wasn't a matter for MI5, but for the new Northern Ireland police service, the PSNI.

Patrick seemed to bristle. 'If you're not interested, just say so, and I'll be on my way.'

Dave ignored him. 'You know as well as I do that this sort of stuff is a matter for the police. So why did you want to tell me about it?'

Patrick must have decided he had been opaque for too long. He said, 'The company I'm talking about is called Fraternal Holdings.'

Bingo, thought Liz. Things were starting to fall into place.

'The boss isn't Irish, but he calls himself a Republican. He says we've all been let down by Adams and McGuinness. What he really wants to do is kill policemen—and he wants to kill one of your lot, too. He says that will demonstrate that the war goes on.'

'*What?*' exclaimed Dave, unable to contain his surprise.

'That's what I'm telling you,' said Patrick, and Liz could imagine him with his arms folded, smugly certain that he had justified this rendezvous.

'Let me get this straight,' said Dave. 'You're telling me you've gone to work for a boss who claims to share your nationalist ideals, only to discover he's running rackets of every conceivable sort all over Belfast. And now you're saying he wants to kill policemen and an MI5 officer. I don't get it.'

'What's there to get? If you don't believe me, say the word and I'll be off.' Liz heard him shake the door handle.

'Hold your horses. I'm just surprised. You would be too in my position.'

'Not very likely,' said the old man, giving a caustic laugh.

'I need to know more. This man isn't exactly the only guy in Northern Ireland who'd still like to kill a policeman or shoot a British intelligence officer. Wanting is one thing; doing it is another. Has he made any plans?'

'If you're asking if this is just some fancy he's got, you're wrong. This guy is serious. He's got plans all right and I know he's called in external help for the job.'

'Where from?'

Liz recalled the man she'd seen at the farmhouse; Jimmy Fergus had identified him as a Spanish hit man. But Patrick said emphatically, 'France. There's a Frenchman visiting while we're sitting here talking.'

'Have you got a name?'

There was a pause. Then, 'His name's Milraw or Milroe, something like that. He's supposed to be a dealer in antique weapons. He's got a legit shop here but I think you'll find he sells modern weapons as well.'

'And he would supply weapons to your boss?'

'He's not here to sell him a blunderbuss.'

Dave nodded. 'There's still something I don't understand—why you are here. Is there something personal about your reasons?'

'Personal?'

'Well, I wouldn't have thought you'd give two hoots if a cop got shot or someone like me got topped. So what's this to you?'

For the first time Patrick let his taciturn front drop. 'What's it to me?' His voice rose. 'I'll tell you. I haven't worked my guts out for thirty years to have some little American prick come over and tell me what to do.'

'This guy's American?'

'Boston-Irish. University fella, clever, but just as bad as the rest of them. You know what I mean: all those brave guys sitting on bar stools in Boston, throwing in a dollar or two when the NORAID bucket went round, acting tough but doing sweet F-all. Piggott's just as bad—only instead of getting sloshed in Jerry Kelly's Shamrock Saloon, or whatever phoney name they call it, he was sitting behind a computer dreaming up the perfect missile. But it never worked, as far as I know. While we were literally *dying* over here.'

'Did you say *Piggott*?' Dave gave stress to the surname—for her benefit, Liz realised, in case the audio had not been clear enough.

'Why? Do you know the man?' asked Patrick suspiciously.

'Never heard of him. Is he related to the jockey?' Dave gave a small laugh.

Patrick didn't join him. He must regret losing his cool like that, thought Liz. He was nursing a grudge. That was clear now. What Piggott had done to him was anyone's guess, but Liz didn't believe it was just his American citizenship that had set the Irishman on a quest for revenge.

Dave said, 'This is extremely helpful, Patrick. But it would be even more helpful if you could find out more. Next time we could meet up in Belfast.'

'No.' Patrick's voice was unequivocal. Liz heard him open the car door. 'You've had all you're going to get from me. It should be enough for you to put Piggott away. And if you can't catch him, and one of you gets blown away . . .' His voice suddenly assumed a gross caricature of an Irish voice. 'Well, faith and goodness, wouldn't that be a terrible shame?'

JIMMY FERGUS WAS an easy-going man, famously affable, a lover of women, pubs and convivial company. His sunny front to the world masked his serious commitment to the RUC, which had been responsible for the breakdown of his first three marriages. Determined not to let this happen to his fourth, he was now working only part-time for the Police Service of Northern Ireland.

Fortunately, Moira, his bride of just over a year, understood how attached he was to police work, and it was she who had encouraged him to defer retirement. Not for her a life in Ibiza or some other stultifying resort, where former policemen sat pickling themselves in sun and booze.

As it turned out, he had found that it was an exciting time to be in the police force, which made him even more pleased not to have hung up his boots. The newly formed PSNI had recruited more Catholic policemen than many old RUC hands would have dreamed possible.

Jimmy welcomed the changes, particularly the transfer of the intelligence work from the old RUC Special Branch to MI5, since it meant policemen could focus on fighting good, honest crime. But though he was optimistic about Northern Ireland's future, he wasn't naive. The old policeman had a sceptical view of human nature and he knew that in this bit of the island of Ireland, above all, the past never really died.

It was this knowledge, heightened by a well-honed instinct for self-preservation, that made him notice the laundry van the first time. It had been two weeks before, and the van was parked at the corner of the quiet side street where he and Moira lived. There had seemed nothing odd about the van's presence—its driver, wearing white overalls, was sitting behind the wheel ticking things off on a clipboard. And when Jimmy saw it again the following week, with the same driver (same clipboard, too), he had reckoned it must now be making regular pick-ups.

This morning he emerged from his house earlier than usual; he was due at Stormont by eight to discuss the transfer of old RUC files. As he backed his ancient Rover out of the garage and slowly down the gently sloping drive, he saw over his shoulder that today the laundry van was parked right beside his gate, partly blocking the road. He was just starting to get out of the car, when he noticed that the driver of the van was getting out. Then he saw there was another man in white overalls getting out of the van as well.

Alarm bells were ringing loudly in his head. 'Excuse me,' the driver shouted out, walking towards Jimmy. He had a smile pasted on his face that the policeman distrusted at once.

The man stopped, standing about fifteen feet away, and Jimmy saw that the second man was also coming into the drive. He had his arms down by his sides, but Jimmy could see that he held something in one hand. Reflexively, he reached for the Glock 9mm pistol he always carried holstered under his jacket. As he grabbed it, a bullet caught him high in the chest on his right side. He lost his balance and began to fall, knowing that he mustn't let go of his gun—*Don't drop it*, he told himself, *or you've had it*.

He hit the drive heavily, landing on his side, and tried immediately to roll behind the open car door for protection. But waves of pain were seizing him just below the shoulder. His fingers still gripped the Glock, but when he tried to lift the pistol and fire, his arm did not obey.

The man with the gun was coming round the rear of the car now, and the van driver stood back to give him space. He turned to face Jimmy, who was still lying sprawled on the drive. His gun was a semiautomatic and, as he raised his arm to fire, Jimmy could only think, *This is it*.

Suddenly a scream broke through the air, like the sound of shattering glass. Through his pain, Jimmy realised it was Moira, coming out of the front door, wearing the pink housecoat he had given her for Christmas.

The man with the gun jerked sideways, obviously startled.

'Get back,' Jimmy tried to shout. He saw the man turn to face Moira, who was running towards them down the path, still screaming. To his horror, the man raised his weapon. And then Jimmy found his fingers could move after all, and he managed to lift the Glock an inch or two off the ground with his hand, pointed it and fired.

The gun kicked with enough force to fall from his hand. As its sharp crack echoed in the air, Jimmy heard a muffled shout—'*Agghh!*'

He saw his would-be executioner reaching down, to where a dark stain was seeping through one leg of his pristine white overalls.

In obvious agony, the man dropped his gun. The driver of the van ran forward and put a rough arm round his wounded accomplice, then half ran with the hobbling, bleeding man to the cab of the laundry van. Seconds later the van's engine started up. With a long squeal of tyres, it turned a sharp 180 degrees and shot off down the road.

Then a hand was gently stroking his hair, and as he slumped down he heard Moira sobbing. 'Jimmy, Jimmy,' she was saying through her tears. 'Can you hear me? Are you all right? Oh, please, God, tell me he's alive.'

'Leave God out of it,' gasped Jimmy, 'and ring the ambulance.'

'HOW IS MRS RYAN working out?' asked Judith Spratt. She was sitting in Liz's office, waiting for Dave to join them.

'I haven't lived in such order since I left my mother's house. I hardly ever see her though, and when I do she's not exactly chatty.'

In her first weeks working for Liz, Mrs Ryan had reorganised almost everything in the flat, from the pan cupboard to Liz's underwear drawer.

Judith took a last swallow of her coffee. 'She never says much to me either. But thank goodness she and Daisy seem to get along. Daisy says she talks to her all the time; that's her excuse for not doing her homework.'

Dave hurried into the office. It was clear from his face that something had happened. He looked at Liz grimly and didn't sit down. 'There's been an incident. One of the PSNI officers has been shot. I don't know who.'

'Oh my God!' exclaimed Liz. 'When?'

'An hour ago. The man's in surgery. They don't know if he'll make it.'

Liz exchanged a look with Dave. What had Brown Fox said? Had the threat been carried out, and so soon? She mentally shook herself. Until they knew more there was no point in jumping to conclusions.

'OK, we'd better get on with things here. Judith, are there results from the Fraternal Holdings investigations?'

'Yes,' said Judith, taking her cue from Liz and passing folders round.

Liz looked at the first sheet in her folder. 'This is a mugshot of the walk-in Dave met yesterday, Brown Fox. What have you found out about him?'

Judith consulted her notes. 'He's Dermot O'Reilly, a long-time Provisional IRA volunteer. Interned in the Maze in the 1970s. After he was released he stayed involved, though he managed to escape prosecution for terrorist activity. But he's got convictions for two criminal offences: a drunk and disorderly outside a pub—got a fine for that, and a charge of receiving stolen goods—suspended sentence.'

'So what is he now, a crook or a terrorist?' mused Dave.

'It looks like a bit of both,' said Judith. 'He lives just off the Falls Road. We checked his credit history. He's had cars repossessed, mortgage arrears, credit-card debt. But starting two years ago his situation improved dramatically, suspiciously so, I'd say. He wiped out the credit-card debt, paid off half his mortgage, and now has over ten grand in the bank.'

Liz said, 'He's been working for Fraternal Holdings. They must pay well. Do we know anything more about this man Piggott who runs the show?'

'Not much,' said Judith, with a puzzled shake to her head. 'He owns a flat here in Belfast, and that farmhouse in County Down. He's got a local driver's licence. The Audi we've seen him in on the camera at the National Trust gatehouse is registered to Fraternal Holdings. That's it.'

'O'Reilly said he's a Yank, Boston-Irish, a university type who designed missiles that didn't work,' Dave remarked. 'Though all that may be just sour grapes. O'Reilly's obviously got a big grudge against him.'

'I'll speak to Peggy Kinsolving at Thames House and get her to work her magic. She can see what's in the files and perhaps get onto the Americans,' Judith said. 'If that stuff's true—about designing missiles for the IRA—there's sure to be information in the files.'

Liz nodded. 'If there's anything to find, Peggy'll find it.'

A shadow fell across the open door. Liz looked up and saw Michael Binding, his face pale. 'You've heard about the shooting?' he said.

'Yes,' Liz said. 'Do we know who it was?'

'Yeah. Some chap who was supposed to be at my meeting in Stormont. He's an old RUC officer, semi-retired. His name's Fergus—Jimmy Fergus.'

'Oh, no, not Jimmy,' said Liz. 'I know him. Dave and I went to see him last week—he's helped me before.'

'Do they know what happened?' asked Dave.

'He was just setting off for work, backing out of his gate, when the gunmen attacked—two of them. A neighbour said they were in a laundry van. Fergus managed to fire back: we think he hit one of them. There was blood where the van had been parked.'

'Is he very badly hurt?' Liz could hear her voice shaking.

'He took a bullet in the chest.' Binding's voice softened. 'That's all I know. I'll keep you posted.' He gave a little bow of the head and left.

'I wonder why they chose Fergus, if he's semi-retired?' asked Judith. She sounded shaken too. 'Do you think it's someone settling an old score?'

Dave stood up and walked to the window. 'God knows,' he said.

There was silence in the room. Dave stayed by the window, shifting from foot to foot, looking agitated. Judith was obviously stunned. Liz remained sitting at her desk. She felt as if all her energy had gone.

Judith broke the silence. 'I'll come back later, Liz, if you like.' She stood up and started to gather together papers. The movement triggered something in Liz and she felt a great surge of anger.

'No,' she said. 'Don't leave, Judith. We're going to find out who's behind this and what it's all about. So let's get on with what we were doing.'

'I just thought you'd want to be alone. I know you were close to Fergus.'

'No,' Liz corrected her. 'I wasn't close to him. But I was very fond of him.' Then she realised what she was saying. 'I *am* fond of him.' She took a deep breath. 'Look,' she said, 'there's nothing we can do to help Jimmy Fergus right now, so let's just try to stop thinking about it.'

Pulling herself together she said, 'What do we know about this Frenchman that O'Reilly talked about?'

'He's Antoine Milraud. He flew in from Paris the day before yesterday. I checked with Interpol but they've got nothing on him. So to cover all the bases, I rang the DCRI. You know, it's the new French internal service. They've just had a reorganisation. I thought it might be difficult to find the right person to speak to, so I wasn't expecting anything.'

'But?'

Judith pursed her lips, musing for a moment. 'Well, I got through to a senior officer called Isabelle Florian. Her reaction was a bit strange, I must say. Her English was even worse than my French, though she managed to get across that they knew Milraud, or knew of him anyway. But she wouldn't tell me anything. When I pushed a bit she said they did have information about him, but someone would have to go and talk to them about it. Shall I ask the MI6 station in Paris to contact her?'

'Why the secrecy?' wondered Liz aloud.

'You know, it sounds as if he's an agent of theirs,' said Dave. 'That's how we'd respond if someone asked us about a source.'

'This is getting really complicated,' said Liz, frowning. 'Who's at the MI6 Paris station, Judith? Do you know?'

'I don't know who the head is, but the deputy is Bruno Mackay.'

Dave looked at Liz. 'Your favourite old Harrovian, Liz,' he said with a grin. 'Speaks fluent French as well as Arabic, I'll be bound.'

'He may speak fluent French, but he's the last person to put into a delicate situation,' responded Liz crossly. 'I'll go myself.'

DANNY RYAN WISHED Sean would shut up. 'Oh my God, oh my God,' Sean was saying, again and again, in between great shuddering racks of sobs. Danny couldn't concentrate. He was trying not to drive too fast, or do anything to call attention to the white laundry van he was driving.

More than one policeman was going to be looking for them soon enough. He needed to get off the road before the call went out across the radio bands with a description of the van. Even though no one had been around, they must have been seen, especially after the guns had been fired.

He looked sideways at Sean, sitting bent over in the passenger seat. Blood had completely soaked the leg of his jeans. He had to get him to a doctor fast, or the poor bugger was going to bleed to death.

'Hang on,' he urged him, 'we're almost there.' But they weren't: rush hour was just starting and he didn't dare run the risk of driving through the centre of Belfast. He wasn't going to sit in traffic, waiting for the PSNI to pick them up. So he took the Knock Road south through Castlereagh, until the road swung west and brought them to Andersonstown. Here Danny drove fast, under the A1 and into the large industrial estate built on the edge of the Catholic neighbourhood. He turned the van into a side street running round the back of Casement Park, then pulled off at St Agnes's Way, where a row of eight lockup garages occupied one end of a small plot.

'Hang on, Sean,' he ordered as he pulled up and the groaning started again. 'Help's on the way.'

Danny got out of the van and, without looking around, unlocked and lifted the steel shutter of one of the garages, then ran back to the van and drove it inside. Once he'd turned on the lights and pulled the door down again, he did his best to make Sean comfortable, lying him across both of the front seats. Then he stood by the steel door to make sure the signal was strong, and dialled a number on his mobile.

'Hello.'

'Mr P, it's Danny. It didn't go according to plan. We got the bastard, but he got Sean and—'

'Where are you?' The voice was terse, emotionless.

'At the lockup. I'm sure we were spotted. But Sean's bad—'

'I told you not to go back to the lockup.'

'We've got to get Sean help, Mr P.'

'Sean can wait. He's cocked it up.' There was fury in his voice. 'Now, listen. Wait there till I send someone over. He'll take care of Sean. Then you drive that van out of there, find a place and torch it. Do you hear me?'

'I hear you, Mr P.'

'Good. And don't call me again, understood? Just sit tight, then do it.'

TWENTY MINUTES LATER, there was a sharp rap on the steel door of the garage. Danny peered through the window slit and saw the Spaniard,

Gonzales, in his black leather jacket, standing to one side. He reached down and slowly pulled up the shutter.

Gonzales pushed by him and walked to the van and looked in. He nodded, satisfied.

'He's hurt bad,' said Danny. 'He needs to see a doctor right away.'

Gonzales appeared not to hear, and went out and got into his car. Starting it, he reversed halfway into the garage, forcing Danny to jump to one side. As he got out he opened the rear passenger door, then walked over to the van. Without saying a word, he reached in and put his arms roughly under Sean's back, propping him up.

'Mind his leg!' Danny shouted. 'He's been wounded.'

The Spaniard ignored him, pulling Sean backwards out of the door until only his legs remained on the seat. Then he hoisted him out of the van, leaving his legs dangling on the floor. Sean screamed as the Spaniard lowered him onto the back seat of his car, where Sean fell, moaning continuously.

'Jesus, will you take care?' Danny shouted. 'He's been shot!'

Gonzales turned suddenly and stared at Danny. There was a cold menace in his look that frightened the younger man. In heavily accented English, Gonzales said, 'You know what to do with the van. Get going.'

AN HOUR LATER, Danny was driving through County Armagh. This was border country, traditionally sympathetic to the IRA. He took a spur, halfway between Portadown and Armagh, which led to the old Moy Road, and stopped a mile short of a farm where he'd been taught how to fire a pistol by three veteran Provos. He turned onto an old cart track, muddy from the winter rains. It wound up a tree-lined hill, ending suddenly in a small sandy lay-by sheltered from view by a small copse of young oaks. Locals had used the slope behind the remains of an old crofter's cottage as a tip. Wedged halfway down, against the trunk of an ancient tree, were the charred, skeletal remains of a burnt-out car.

Danny parked the van at the top of the slope. He was anxious to get the whole business over with, before anyone came. He checked the inside before getting out, to make sure he'd left nothing important in there.

Taking a full can of petrol out of the van, he sloshed half of it over the floor at the back, then over the cab, making sure the vinyl seats were soaked. Finally, he stood back, struck a match and tossed it onto the driver's seat. It went out as he threw it. Anxious now, he took a dirty handkerchief out of his trouser pocket and dangled the corner into a pool of petrol lying on the cab floor. Retreating a little, he lit the handkerchief and tossed it into the open window of the cab. Flames jumped up with a sudden *whoosh*, and he backed off a good twenty yards. Soon the whole van was ablaze.

Danny set off down the track, heading for the old Moy Road, where he'd hitch a lift into Moy itself. From there a minicab could take him to Portadown, where he'd catch a train for Belfast. He'd booked the whole day off, so no one at work would be wondering where he was. His mother would be worried, but she'd known he was up to confidential business anyway.

As he reached the road there was a loud boom. The van's petrol tank had just exploded. He gave a small, satisfied nod.

5

O'Reilly was restless. That bastard Piggott was always on his mind, and he was going to get him one way or another. But how? The meeting with the MI5 man had gone well. O'Reilly was pleased that the Englishman had got no more out of him than he'd wanted to give. But what would the Brits do with the information? Would they do anything?

He needed to be sure. He wanted to tie Piggott up in knots; have him looking over his shoulder, not knowing who he could trust. Then he'd start to make mistakes and that would be the end of him.

But Piggott was clever. And he wouldn't listen to anything O'Reilly said to him—especially not now that he'd as good as sacked him. He'd have to find another way to unsettle him and wipe that sneer off his Yankee face. But what way?

Then an idea came to him—an old-fashioned solution, the kind he liked best. No computers, nothing technical. And it should work.

HIS WIFE CAUGHT HIM by surprise. She was supposed to be out having her hair done, but there she was, standing in the kitchen doorway. 'What's going on?' she said, pointing to the mess on the table.

'Just give us a few minutes, will you? I'll clear it all up, but I need to be private now. It's work.'

'Work?' she asked with disbelief.

He put a warning hand up, and she knew better than to argue. She shut the kitchen door, and he could hear her go upstairs.

On the table he had a week's worth of newspapers, some scissors, a few sheets of A4 paper and a glue stick. He examined his handiwork so far:

YouR Man Mil*raud* **is a** *t***out.** Seen with *Brit***ISH INTELLIGENCE**e at *rendez*vous **IN** Ligoni*e***L** *Park***.**
   W**a**tch *youR* b***ACK* . . .**

Thanks to the *News of the World* and the *Irish News*, his message could hardly be more anonymous. With luck, Piggott should read it as it was intended—a warning from a Republican sympathiser that his new French 'mate' wasn't what he said he was. Piggott would certainly take it seriously: it was just too likely to O'Reilly's mind that Milraud, a foreigner, was a plant.

At the very least it would get Piggott thinking. Which meant that sooner or later the two worlds would collide: with luck Simon Willis would be contacting the Frenchman before he left Northern Ireland, and when Piggott got the message he would be watching for him as well. The two strings O'Reilly had pulled would start winding round each other; if there was any justice in the world, they would leave Piggott trapped in the knot.

TWO DAYS LATER, Liz woke up in a small hotel on the boulevard Malesherbes, just round the corner from the British Embassy. She had arrived late the previous evening to a wet and windy Paris, having eaten nothing since breakfast but a sandwich. Now, as she contemplated a day in the company of Bruno Mackay, a black cloud of gloom descended.

Liz had crossed swords with Bruno several times during her career. With his public-school manner, perfectly cut suits and permanent tan, she would have liked to be able to treat him as a bit of a joke. But she had to admit to herself that, for some reason, he got under her skin.

Determined not to be outdone by him, Liz had brought her smartest outfit: a designer suit bought in the sale at Brown's in South Molton Street. The dark navy-blue put colour into her cool grey eyes and, with its tight skirt and short jacket, the suit emphasised her slim figure. The outfit had actually been bought for Joanne's funeral and, as Liz dressed, she found herself wondering how Charles was coping, and wishing she could see him.

It was clear from the hissing of the car tyres on the busy street outside her window that the rain of the night before was still falling heavily. Thank goodness she had brought a mac, though she realised with dismay that she had forgotten her umbrella.

Half an hour later, as she walked the short distance to the embassy, the rain had turned to a light drizzle, plastering her hair damply to her head. Sitting in the embassy waiting room, she mopped drips from her forehead.

The door opened and in sauntered the tall, lean figure of Bruno Mackay, wearing an impeccably cut grey suit with a dark blue shirt and a tie.

''Morning, Liz,' he said breezily and, before she could prevent him, he leaned down to plant a kiss on her cheek. He stood back and, casting an eye over her bedraggled hair, remarked, 'Raining, I see. Never mind. We'll dry you out and I'm sure you'll come up a treat.'

Liz clamped her jaw shut. She wasn't going to let Bruno annoy her.

He led her up the sweeping flight of stairs, then along a carpeted corridor lined with portraits of kings and statesmen. He flung open an enormous mahogany door and showed her into a spacious, high-ceilinged room, in which a large antique desk faced inwards, centred between two floor-to-ceiling windows overlooking the back garden of the embassy.

Bruno turned and smiled at Liz. 'Do sit down,' he said.

A pot of tea and china cups and saucers bearing the royal crest were brought in by a young woman. When she'd left, Liz took a sip of her tea, then said, 'As you know, Bruno, I have an appointment at the DCRI in an hour.'

'Ah, the new Direction Centrale du Renseignement Intérieur,' Bruno said rapidly, showing off his impeccable French accent. 'Excellent. You're seeing Isabelle Florian. She's very good. We'll go over in my car.'

'I'm sure you're very busy, Bruno. I can take a cab.'

'I insist.' When she was about to object, he gave her his sweetest smile. 'Good French, have you, Liz?'

She hesitated. Six years at school, O level, a reasonable reading ability, the usual difficulty with understanding the language when spoken at speed. 'Pretty rusty,' she admitted. 'But, presumably, they'll have an interpreter?'

He shook his head. 'They'll expect you to bring an interpreter.'

Liz ground her teeth. He was right, of course—and it was essential that she and Mme Florian understand each other. If Bruno was the only conduit for communication, then Bruno it must be. She would have to brief him about Milraud, though she decided to tell him only what he needed to know. Experience had taught her that Bruno was not entirely trustworthy.

He had a habit of putting his fingers into every pie that came his way.

An hour later they both sat in an office high up in the headquarters of the old Direction de la Surveillance du Territoire, the DST, the French counterpart of MI5, which had recently been merged with other intelligence departments to form the new DCRI. The building was a stone's throw from the Seine and, through the window, the Eiffel Tower was just visible.

Isabelle Florian was not at all what Liz had expected. Far from the chic Parisienne in a sharp black suit of her imagination, Mme Florian turned out to be a businesslike woman in her forties, wearing jeans and a pullover, and with her hair scraped back in a band. It was clear that both Liz and Bruno were definitely overdressed for this visit.

Liz began by explaining the background to the enquiry about Milraud, with Bruno translating. When she had finished, Isabelle replied in a torrent of French, hardly taking breath and not pausing for Bruno to translate.

When at last she stopped, Bruno turned to Liz and said, 'Well, the gist of all that is that we are in the wrong place. She says that they do have a very considerable file on Milraud here. He was a part of some operation involving her service, but the foreign service, the DGSE, were leading it, and she is not at liberty to reveal any details to us. She has spoken to the DGSE about our enquiry and they have agreed to talk to us.'

Liz sighed. She knew that the headquarters of the Direction Générale de la Sécurité Extérieure were on the other side of Paris. 'Can you ask her who I should speak to there?' she asked, a little impatiently.

Mme Florian understood her, for she replied in English, looking directly at Liz. 'Monsieur Martin Seurat. He iz expectant of you.'

'*Bon*,' said Liz.

Mme Florian smiled. She went on, '*Il parle anglais couramment. Vous n'aurez pas besoin d'un interprète.*'

'*Bon*,' replied Liz again.

They shook hands and thanked Mme Florian as she showed them out of the building.

'Bit of a drive now, I'm afraid,' said Bruno as they stood outside. 'The DGSE's halfway to ruddy Charles de Gaulle.'

'Well, really,' said Liz. 'I can't think why she didn't say all that over the phone to Judith days ago and save me the trouble of coming here.'

'Of course, she wanted to know why you were interested in him,' replied Bruno patronisingly. 'She wasn't born yesterday, you know.'

'Well, at least I won't need to trouble you any more. I'll take the Métro.'

'But, Liz,' he protested, and his surprise was a pleasure to watch. 'You'll need me. You don't understand French.'

'I understand enough to know I won't need an interpreter. Isabelle Florian said Seurat's English is fluent,' and she stalked off towards the Métro, leaving Bruno standing on the pavement.

'*ENCHANTÉ*,' SAID THE MAN, shaking Liz's hand. 'I am impressed you have found us all on your own. When I spoke with Isabelle Florian, she said you were accompanied by Monsieur Mackay.'

'I decided I could manage without an escort,' Liz said. In fact it would have been much easier if she had allowed Bruno to drive her. The price of her irritation with him had been a complicated journey on the Métro.

The DGSE was an imposing compound of white stone buildings protected by a gatehouse manned by armed guards in military uniform. One of the guards had led her to Seurat's office, a small corner room overlooking a gravelled courtyard, which looked as though it had once been a parade ground. Seurat was a man in his mid-forties, five or six years older than Liz. With his greying hair cut very short and his checked tweed jacket and grey turtleneck, he had an indefinably military appearance.

'I will see Bruno some other time, I'm sure,' Seurat said now with a wide smile, motioning Liz to sit down. 'Isabelle Florian tells me you are interested in Antoine Milraud. How can I help?'

'I gather he is known to you?'

Seurat pursed his lips. 'Yes. *Bien connu*. But what is your interest?'

'We have recently come across him in Northern Ireland—in Belfast, where I'm based at present. You may have read that all is now peaceful in Northern Ireland, but though the IRA has declared a cease-fire, there are still some former members who want to continue the struggle. We call them breakaway groups. We're looking at what we think may be one such group, led by a man we believe to be an American calling himself Seamus Piggott. He's running a security business but we have recently been informed that it's a cover for one of these breakaway terrorist cells. The same informant also told us that Antoine Milraud is in some way involved in all this. We traced him with the DCRI and my visit to you is the result.'

Seurat was leaning forward in his chair, watching her face with close concentration. When she stopped talking there was a momentary silence, then he said, 'Well, Milraud's a businessman who lives near Toulon. Not to be confused with Toulouse. He has a successful antiques business there; he also has a shop in London. And also, which of course is relevant to your story, one in Belfast.' He looked at his watch. 'I don't know about you, Miss Carlyle, but at this time of the day I am usually halfway through lunch. Why don't you join me? The bistro's just round the corner.'

Her heart sank. She was hungry, but she thought she could see what lay ahead—three courses, wine, a lot of small talk, and yet further run-around about the mysterious Milraud.

Seurat seemed to sense her frustration. 'It will be possible to talk freely at lunch. And in case you are wondering why I know about an antiques dealer from Toulon, Antoine Milraud has not always worked in that trade.'

'No?'

'No, he had a long career doing something different altogether.' He seemed amused. 'The last time I saw him, he was sitting in the very chair you are occupying.'

'Oh, really?' She wished this man would stop playing games.

'Yes, he used to come in for coffee and a chat almost every morning. You see, Antoine Milraud was once an officer of the DGSE. Perhaps now you can see why your enquiry is a little difficult for us. Shall we go to lunch?'

THE VIEUX CANARD was a small bistro near the Métro, on rue Haxo. Seurat led her into a small, dark room in the back, which had one scrubbed wooden table set for two. They were greeted by Madame Bouffet, a petite, black-haired woman in an apron, who kissed Seurat warmly on both cheeks, before shaking Liz's hand.

As they sat down, Seurat said, 'We all have our vices; mine is having a proper lunch. I eat here almost every day. Now, there is a *prix fixe* set lunch, or, if you prefer, I can ask for a menu—'

'No, no. The set lunch is fine,' said Liz.

They started with pâté with brioche—simple but delicious—and, while she ate, Liz listened as Seurat told her about Milraud.

'Antoine Milraud was a good friend for many years, but he was also what I think you might call a troubled soul.'

Liz smiled at the phrase, and Seurat grinned back. Suddenly, for the first time since she had landed in France, Liz felt relaxed. She had begun to enjoy the company of this man, so different from the arrogant Mackay.

Seurat seemed comfortable with himself, self-assured but without the need to dominate.

'As I say, Milraud was troubled, discontented, moody. So one day, when he announced quite matter of factly, "I am not happy, Martin. I am not sure how much longer I can stay in this job"—well, *franchement*, I thought nothing of it. I had heard the same before from him. I can see now that Milraud had perhaps grown fed up with his small salary. And his wife has always had expensive tastes. You know the type, perhaps?'

Liz smiled as he filled her glass from the *pichet* of red wine. Seurat went on, 'At his best, Milraud was a very good officer.' He gestured with his hand. 'Other times he was not so good. I think he was right to sense that his prospects for promotion were slight. He lacked . . . judgment.

'Then Milraud went on an operation and disappeared. It has taken me seven years to piece together what happened, but I think at last I know.'

Liz waited while Madame Bouffet took away her plate, replacing it with a fresh one bearing a simple steak and *frites*. A bowl of béarnaise sauce and a green salad in a white crockery dish were placed between them.

'Milraud was assigned to an operation near the Spanish border, helping to infiltrate the Basque extremists who were operating with impunity on our side of the border. He was posing as an arms dealer, a middleman between the Basque extremists and some vendors from Russia. Milraud made the arrangements for an arms transaction, which would take place on neutral ground in Switzerland, near the French border.'

He sighed, cutting into his steak, then chewed thoughtfully. 'But then someone talked too freely: just as the deal was about to be done, thirty armed officers of the Swiss Federal Criminal Police, alerted by a phoned tip-off, swooped in. Unfortunately, the raid was premature—neither the guns nor the cash to be paid for them were discovered. The Swiss deported both the Russians and the Basques summarily. In the aftermath, the Russians believed the Basques had taken possession of the weapons but not paid the cash; equally, the Basques were furious, thinking the Russians had taken their money without delivering the guns.'

He gave a wry smile. 'Possibly because they were embarrassed at the hash they'd made of things, the Swiss authorities told us that they had managed to confiscate both arms and money. And I have to say that this is what many of my colleagues were happy to believe. Milraud disappeared and it has taken me quite a while to work out what he had done.'

A thin sliver of *tarte Tatin* came next. Seurat, pouring the remaining contents of the *pichet* into their glasses, went on, 'Milraud seems to have held on to the three hundred thousand euros he had been holding as the escrow agent, and the small arsenal of automatic weapons, which put him in an unparalleled position to become an arms dealer for real.'

He took a mouthful of tart, then put down his fork. 'And that is what he has been doing ever since. He is an international dealer in arms. He has many enemies, not least the Russians and the Basques whom he cheated, but most of them are now either dead or in prison.'

'And you can't stop him?'

He gave a rueful smile, then said with sudden intensity, 'We are investigating his activities. One day we will have enough to arrest him. But he was always clever, and he has lost none of his cleverness in his new profession.'

Dessert was cleared and Liz pondered all this over coffee. It was an intriguing story, and she had no reason to doubt any of it. She sensed in Seurat's account a feeling of betrayal, which she well understood.

'So, tell me, are you very often in France?' he asked.

She shook her head. 'Sadly not. I like your country very much—and I love Paris. But . . .' and she waved a hand helplessly.

He laughed, a low chuckle she was coming to like. His looks would make him attractive to any woman, but it was his mix of the urbane and the unaffected that appealed to Liz. 'And your husband? He likes Paris as well?'

He knows full well I'm single, thought Liz. He had greeted her as Miss Carlyle when she first arrived, and in any case she wasn't wearing a wedding ring. But she was flattered by the unsubtle query. 'If I ever have a husband, he will be required to love Paris,' she declared firmly.

'Ha! That's excellent. My wife cannot stand the place.'

'Oh, really?' said Liz, disappointed in spite of herself.

'Yes, perhaps that is why she took herself off to her mother's house in Alsace. I believe she is living there still,' he said, flashing his infectious grin. Then he said more seriously, 'It is funny that you should be here asking about Milraud. I was thinking of him just the other day.'

'Why was that?'

He shrugged, nodding at Madame Bouffet as she plonked the bill down on the table. 'How long have you been with your service?'

'Long enough,' she said, ducking the question, but it was in fact almost fifteen years now.

'Then you'll understand me when I say that sometimes we all have our Milraud days. The kind of day when everything seems . . . would the word be "thankless"? You work hard, the money seems very small, and your personal life is *absolument zéro, n'est-ce pas*? Does that make sense?'

'Of course,' she said at once. What he was describing was familiar enough.

'It never lasts, and please do not misunderstand me—I like my work. My point is, *au fond*, that in those moments I can see what came over Milraud.'

'You can empathise then?'

'You mean "share" his feelings? *Non!*' He was suddenly emphatic. 'I can sympathise, but that's all. And not for long. For his so-called freedom, Milraud has helped many people to be killed. None of them he knew; none of them he ever saw. But it is killing just the same.'

There was a bitterness, which suggested a personal as much as professional resentment. Liz said nothing as Seurat paid the bill, then they left the café and walked slowly towards the Métro.

When they reached the station, she held out her hand. 'That was a wonderful lunch. Thank you very much. And you have been extremely helpful.'

'Excellent.' He seemed genuinely pleased. 'Now perhaps you can help me with two requests. The first is to please keep in touch as you investigate what Milraud is up to in Belfast. It goes without saying that if we can be of any assistance, you must not hesitate to say so.'

'Of course,' Liz said, wondering what the second request would be.

Seurat looked hesitant. 'The other is perhaps not quite so professional. Would you have dinner with me this evening, Liz?'

'Oh, Martin,' she said, suddenly realising they had slipped into first names, 'I would love to. But I have to get back.' An image of Jimmy Fergus flickered briefly in her mind.

'Another time then,' said Seurat mildly.

There was something disappointed in this gallant acceptance of her rejection; it made Liz want to reassure him. She touched him lightly on the arm. 'There will be another time, I'm sure,' she said. 'I have a feeling Monsieur Milraud will see to that.'

HE WAS SUSPICIOUS of the letter from the start. Block capitals on the envelope—SEAMUS PIGGOTT—and the office address, then at the bottom: PRIVATE. His secretary had obeyed the instruction and placed it unopened with the rest of the morning's post in his in-tray.

He slit the envelope cautiously. Letter bombs were bulkier than this, but it paid to be careful. A man with his background had many enemies, and he knew they were out there, just waiting for him to drop his guard.

There was no bomb inside the envelope, just a folded piece of A4 paper. He extracted it slowly and carefully, holding the corner with his fingertips and flicking it open with the point of a pencil. He was startled by the bizarre appearance of the message, and surprised by what it said.

Watch your back. Well, he'd spent thirty years doing that. Yes, he took risks, but only necessary ones; he had never been impetuous, and every step he took was carefully calculated beforehand. He didn't need some anonymous coward to instruct him to take care.

But the real thrust of the message—its warning about Milraud—was more puzzling. He didn't believe for a moment that Milraud was talking to British intelligence. He and the Frenchman went back a long way. He knew what Milraud's previous profession had been and why he'd changed it. It was inconceivable that Milraud would betray him to MI5.

Still, he'd learned long ago that any allegiance was vulnerable; everyone could be seduced by something: money, women, power, fear, ideology. There were many people in this little island whose lives were governed by ideology—be it Irish Republicanism or so-called Loyalism to the British Crown.

Piggott himself was happy to pay lip service to the ideology of Irish Republicanism. His credentials as a long-standing IRA supporter had helped to establish him in the Belfast underworld. But his true ideology, the only thing he really cared about, was revenge. He had one desire: the burning urge, fuelled by anger, to get even with the people who had hurt him. To injure them as they'd injured him. That was what was driving him on.

He picked up his mobile and thumbed the auto-dial. After three rings a reedy, youthful voice answered. 'Hello?' it said shakily.

He knew Danny Ryan was terrified of him. Good—he was going to keep it that way. 'Danny, listen carefully. I've got a job for you.'

'Yes, Mr P,' he said, like a junior mobster speaking to *il capo*.

'Here's what I want you to do,' said Piggott mildly. Then he added in a voice of steel, 'And this time you'd better not screw it up.'

'Where's Liz?'

Judith turned from her cupboard clutching a pile of papers to find Dave standing beside her.

'She's not back from Paris yet,' she said, dumping the papers on her desk and looking up at Dave. Judith had known Dave for years and they'd worked together often before they both came to Northern Ireland. His cheerful, breezy approach to life had buoyed her up through some difficult times at work. But now she stared at him, shocked by his appearance. He looked drawn and tired.

'Dave, are you OK?'

'Yes, I'm fine,' he replied flatly, sitting down in her visitors' chair.

'Well, you don't look it. What's happened?'

He rubbed a hand over his face. 'I expect you'll hear on the grapevine, so I might as well tell you. I've broken up with Lucy.'

Lucy was a second lieutenant in the Intelligence Corps stationed outside London. Judith knew that she and Dave had been an item for two years or so and Dave had even hinted that they might get married.

'It's not been easy being apart,' Dave continued, 'but I thought everything was fine. Then last night I phoned her and she said that she wasn't sure about us. She was thinking of leaving the army, she didn't want to be hitched to my job, she needed time to think and she didn't want to see me again until she knew her own mind.' He looked at Judith glumly. 'I think it's the end for us. She's probably met someone else and is trying to let me down lightly.'

'Oh, Dave. I'm so sorry. I thought you were both so happy.'

'We were,' said Dave. 'But I think I'd better get used to the idea of life without her now. Anyway,' he said, shaking his head and standing up. 'I was looking for Liz to tell her that I'm seeing this bloke Milraud this afternoon.'

Judith's eyes widened. 'Where?'

'At his shop.' He looked at her. 'What's the problem?'

'Who's watching your back?'

'No one. It's just a social call,' he added. When she didn't smile, he said, 'It's no big deal. I've told him I'm a collector of antique derringers wanting to look at what he's got. I've got all the guff on them from the Internet.'

'Don't you think you should check with Liz first?'

'That's why I was looking for her, but I'll have to go ahead without her.'

'I think you should wait. Liz might have learned something useful about Milraud in Paris.'

'Yeah, but he's here now and I don't want to miss him.'

Judith hesitated, looking at Dave's drawn face. She could see that he needed to be active to take his mind off his troubles. But she felt uneasy. 'Shouldn't you at least talk to Michael Binding?'

'Binding's virtually living at Stormont these days,' he replied impatiently. 'It'll be OK, Judith. Stop worrying.' And he walked off.

LATER THAT DAY Dave drove into Belfast and parked in the car park at the Castlecourt shopping centre. Milraud's shop was in a terrace of two-storey Georgian buildings of yellowing stone, halfway down a narrow side street full of coffee shops and clothes boutiques. In a long, low window fronting Milraud's establishment, a beautiful antique pistol was lying on a red velvet cushion, flanked by a pair of wooden-handled, eighteenth-century derringers propped decoratively against each other. Looking through the window, Dave could see a large glass cabinet against a far wall, where more antique pistols hung from iron hooks.

Putting his hand on the highly polished brass handle, Dave took a deep breath and pushed. The opening of the door triggered a bell, and a slim, middle-aged woman looked up from behind a display counter. This was obviously no ordinary shop and she no ordinary shop assistant. She had beautifully cut grey hair and was dressed in a plain black silk suit, a thin gold necklace her only jewellery.

'Can I help you?' she asked, with a smile at once formal and genteel.

'Good afternoon. My name is Simon Willis. I have an appointment with Mr Milraud.'

'Good afternoon, Mr Willis. Please follow me,' the woman said, and led him through to an office where a man sat at a small mahogany desk.

Milraud's face beneath his short hair was Gallic, with dark questioning eyes and olive-tinted skin. He wore a maroon turtleneck sweater under a grey plaid jacket. When he rose to shake hands, though he was much shorter than Dave, his body was more muscular, and Dave sensed an icy element behind the façade.

'Would you like coffee, Mr Willis?' Milraud asked as they both sat down. Dave shook his head. 'Thanks, but I'm fine. It's good of you to see me.'

Milraud shrugged, as if to say this was his business after all. 'You said on the telephone that you have an interest in antique arms. What sort of arms are you looking for?'

'Derringers, at least to begin with. Eighteenth- and nineteenth-century. Continental ones especially.'

'Belfast is not perhaps the ideal place to look for French and German weapons,' Milraud said with a mild enquiring tone.

It was Dave's turn to shrug. 'You never know where things will turn up, thanks to the Internet. Have you anything here that you can show me?'

'Of course,' said Milraud, smiling. 'Even some Continental items.'

He stood up and, motioning for Dave to stay where he was, left the room, returning a minute later with a cherrywood box, which he put down on the desk. Lifting the lid, he exposed a small derringer sitting on a cushion of black velvet. He took the gun out with both hands and handed it to Dave.

'It is made by Sabayone,' Milraud declared. Dave looked down the barrel, doing his best to act like a true aficionado.

Milraud chuckled lightly. 'Probably the only one to be found in this part of the United Kingdom. Are you an admirer of his pistols?'

'Absolutely,' said Dave. 'A master craftsman.' He handed back the pistol carefully. 'What would you ask for such a piece?'

A shadow of a frown flitted across Milraud's face, as if the intrusion of money into their conversation had a soiling effect. He said quietly, without looking at Dave, 'Seventeen thousand pounds.'

'I see,' said Dave. 'Do you guarantee its authenticity?'

'Of course,' said Milraud with a tolerant air.

'I'd like to think about it. When could we meet again?' asked Dave.

'Well, tomorrow would be possible, I suppose. After that I will be back in France. Although Mrs Carson'—he gestured towards the front of the shop and the lady in the suit—'can always negotiate on my behalf.'

Dave shook his head to show a surrogate wouldn't do. 'I'll come back in the morning, if that's convenient.'

'*À demain*, then.' They both stood up and shook hands.

Dave said, 'And perhaps we could talk about more modern armaments.'

Milraud raised his eyebrows a fraction. 'Why not?' he said with an almost imperceptible shrug. 'If you wish.'

A LITTLE WHILE LATER Milraud's mobile rang and he answered it cautiously. '*Oui?*'

'It's me.'

'James.' He continued to use Piggott's old names.

'Listen, my friend, I've had a communication. Someone's suggested you've been talking to my old British friends.'

'How interesting,' Milraud said non-committally. He had done business with Piggott for many years and they trusted each other. But Milraud was always cautious, and this was a lethal accusation if it were believed.

Piggott said, 'I was wondering whether anyone unusual had crossed your path lately. I mean, if I'm supposed to believe this message, someone should be making an appearance, if they haven't already.'

'Mmm. I think we should meet.'

HALF AN HOUR LATER the two men sat down at a table in a nearby café.

'I had a man in the shop just before you rang. He phoned me out of the blue, claiming to be interested in antique derringers. I showed him a lovely example and he made all the right noises, except for one. I told him the gun was made by someone called Sabayone. He agreed that Sabayone was a brilliant gunsmith.'

'And?'

'There wasn't a gunsmith called Sabayone. I made him up to test him.'

Piggott snorted. 'That sounds like our man. What was he really after?'

'He dropped a heavy hint about modern weapons. I've arranged to see him again tomorrow morning. I'm sure he'll come.'

'Oh, so am I,' said Piggott. 'You should see him, by all means. That'll give us a chance to see him, too.'

Piggott walked away from the café, relieved. He hadn't ever really thought Milraud would double-cross him. Yet he hadn't come entirely clean with his old associate, for he'd avoided telling Milraud that Danny Ryan had reported back to him an hour before.

'We watched the shop, just like you said Mr P. There was only one customer this afternoon; he was inside for about twenty minutes. We got a good photo when he left. I followed him as best I could—you said it was better to lose him than get spotted.'

'So you lost him?'

'Not there. He was parked at the Castlecourt shopping centre. I picked him up as he left and trailed him as far as the harbour. He was heading towards the A2 when he got away from me.'

'M2 or A2?' The difference was important.

'A2, Mr P.'

And Piggott nodded to himself. The A2 went north. Towards Holywood and Palace Barracks, he thought. He'd have put money on it.

6

Bruno was waiting for Liz when she got back to the embassy. He made a show of looking at his watch. 'How did you get on?'

'Very well. Seurat was most helpful.'

He extended a fistful of paper. 'This came in while you were gone.'

She cast a quick eye at the pages. It was a long message from Peggy Kinsolving in London, marked *Strictly Confidential*. 'Anything urgent in this?' she asked drily, as he had obviously read it.

'Not that I can tell. Though this chap Piggott sounds a handful. You'd better come into my office, Liz.'

Upstairs she went through the document carefully. Peggy had been her usual thorough self and had unearthed a gold mine of information on Piggott. A prefatory note declared: *Liz, the following summary is based on our own files, which have drawn heavily on information from the FBI. Please also see the note I've attached at the end. PK.*

Piggott born James Purnell in 1954 in Boston, Massachusetts. Changed his name to Piggott by deed poll six months before moving to Ireland three years ago.

Purnell was the child of two first-generation Irish émigrés, and eldest of two sons. Grew up in the working-class neighbourhood of Dorchester—his father was a clerk in a law firm. Educated at the prestigious Boston Latin School after winning a scholarship. Attended MIT and took a Bachelor of Science in a combined mathematics and physics degree, followed in 1974 by a PhD. A brilliant student but references from teachers describe him as headstrong.

Purnell's advanced degree was of particular value in the military area of high-grade missile technology. Purnell was offered a position with Arrow Systems, a group specialising in missile control and retrieval software systems. Its contracts were predominantly with the US Defense Department. Accordingly, Purnell was successfully vetted before being offered the post.

In 1985 Purnell left Arrow Systems and established his own consultancy (The Purnell Group—or TPG), employing his younger brother

Edwin as chief finance officer. Edwin was a trained accountant, but also very active in IRA fundraising—his name appears in FBI files on NORAID (Northern Ireland Aid) activities, and he visited Northern Ireland on several occasions.

Where Arrow Systems had specialised in antiradar aspects of large-scale missile systems, TPG focused on rocket-propelled grenades (RPG), and surface-to-air missiles (SAMs). Until the late 1990s revenues were almost exclusively derived from Department of Defense contracts, but cuts in procurement at the end of the Clinton administration forced TPG to look for other clients. These included US government-approved customers, Israel, South Africa and Pakistan, but an FBI file suggests Purnell may also have been doing business with a range of illegal clients, including Somalian rebels and both sides of the Rwanda civil war—the Hutu and Tutsi.

In 1999, at the instigation of MI5, the FBI began to investigate a gun-running scheme to smuggle arms, including handheld missile launchers, by ship from the coast of Maine into Northern Ireland. Three men were eventually arrested, including Edwin Purnell. The trial of the Mattapan Three (named by the press after the South Boston neighbourhood where all three lived) took place in 2001.

All three men were convicted and Edwin Purnell was sentenced to six years for his part in the plot. He was due for parole in 2004 but died of kidney failure in a federal prison in Louisiana in 2003. Despite our suspicion that James Purnell was involved, the FBI was unable to link him to any part of the conspiracy.

After his brother's death, James Purnell closed down his company, changed his name, and moved to Northern Ireland.

When she had finished reading, Liz looked at the note Peggy had attached to the end of the document:

Liz, the FBI special agent in charge of the Boston investigation of 1999/2000 was called Daryl T. Sulkey, Jr, and the same man is the new FBI legate in London. I phoned him and he could meet you first thing tomorrow—8.15 a.m. at Grosvenor Square. Please let him know if you can't make it; otherwise he will be expecting you. PK

'Interesting,' said Bruno, when he saw her look up at him. 'But what's the connection with this man Purnell and Milraud? And why did Purnell move to Northern Ireland?'

Liz sighed. 'Ask me no questions, Bruno, and I'll tell you no lies.' Not that Liz knew the answers to his questions. She was hoping that the FBI man rejoicing in the name of Daryl T. Sulkey, Jr, might supply them.

BACK AT HIS DESK, Dave was feeling uncomfortable. In the calm aftermath of the meeting with Milraud his depression over the breakup with Lucy had returned. Judith had looked in to see how the meeting had gone and he'd assured her that it was all just fine and he was writing it up.

But had it really all gone fine? The more he thought about it, the more he wondered if Milraud had been playing him along. He was worried about Sabayone. He'd pretended to know all about him but he'd never heard of him. And when he'd got back to the office he'd looked him up on the Internet and had found no trace of a gunsmith of that name. Whatever game Milraud had been playing, Dave was now convinced that he was not merely a prosperous dealer in antiques.

He ought to talk to Liz about it before he went back for another interview. She would want to discuss with Michael Binding just how far out on a limb Dave the Derringer Collector should go.

But yet again Liz wasn't in her office. She was coming back via London, Judith told him, because of something she'd learned in Paris. He ought to wait; she might have found out something relevant. But it would be another day before she was back and with Milraud's departure imminent, Dave felt there was no time to lose. The investigation of the attempt on Jimmy Fergus meant that there would be no spare A4 resources available at such short notice to provide adequate back-up support for a meeting with Milraud the next morning anyway. And then Milraud would be back in France, leaving the shop in the charge of the woman in the black silk suit, who would profess to know nothing about anything except antique weapons.

And that would be that. All the hard work he'd done since the initial call from Brown Fox would go down the drain. No way, thought Dave. He couldn't bear the thought of his investigation joining his private life in ruins. Besides, Milraud had been receptive so far.

'THE DERRINGER is very appealing, but—'

'But?' asked Milraud with a knowing smile. 'I can move on the price to fifteen thousand, but no more, I am afraid. One reaches a point . . .'

They were in the back office again, and small talk had been kept to a minimum. Milraud wore a tie today, and a suitcase in the corner suggested he would leave for the airport immediately after seeing Dave.

'I understand,' Dave said. 'The price is not the issue.'

'Ah. Then if I may ask, what is your position? Do you wish to buy?'

Dave hesitated. But then 'nothing ventured, nothing gained', he said to himself. Milraud hadn't thrown him out of the shop yesterday when he'd mentioned modern weapons. 'Perhaps other things might be included too.'

The Frenchman looked at him thoughtfully. He raised his eyebrows a fraction. 'Well, of course, Mr Willis, I deal in a wide range of weapons. I assume we are no longer talking about derringers?'

'No. Modern weapons as well.'

Milraud seemed to consider this, clasping both hands, elbows on the desk in front of him. 'It's conceivable. What kinds of weapons?'

'All kinds. Automatic weapons. Handguns and larger items. Possibly associated ordnance too. Grenades, mortars, RPGs.'

Milraud narrowed his eyes, and his hand wandered beneath the edge of the desktop; Dave tensed. Then it re-emerged, apparently from the upper drawer of the desk. Milraud popped something in his mouth.

'I assume, Mr Willis, that you are talking about legitimate weaponry? What my clients want, I try to find, that is true. But I would need to know more about who they are, and their reasons for making such enquiries. Particularly, if I may say so, in this town.'

Dave was beginning to feel uncomfortable. He had a suspicion that Milraud was playing with him. So he said, 'To be more precise, what I'm interested in is information. And we may well be talking about sums greater than fifteen thousand pounds.'

'I should think so, *mon ami*,' said Milraud, staring levelly at Dave.

There was a tap on the door. When it opened Mrs Carson stood there. 'Monsieur Milraud, I beg your pardon for interrupting. But could I see you for a moment,please?' She threw a small smile in Dave's direction. 'I'm so sorry. A rather awkward customer in the shop.'

Dave waved an arm in understanding, relieved at the opportunity to gather his thoughts. As Milraud left the room, he wondered what to say next. He was pondering his next move when he heard the door behind him open. 'Everything all right?' he asked.

'Could not be better, my friend,' said a foreign-sounding voice. It didn't belong to Milraud.

AT FIVE FOOT EIGHT INCHES Liz thought of herself as tall for a woman; even so she was used to having to look up at American men. But Daryl Sulkey was huge, probably a foot taller than Liz. She could see him waiting for her on the far side of the daunting security post at the American Embassy in Grosvenor Square. After her bag and jacket had gone through the X-ray machine and she had been patted down by an unsmiling uniformed female guard, she emerged on the other side to a warm welcome. Liz was thankful that the power of Sulkey's grip, as his right hand engulfed hers, did not match the size of his hands.

As she followed him to his office, she noticed that he moved his right leg awkwardly and that his right foot was crooked, and she wondered if his size and the length of his back and his legs had affected his movement. She was relieved when he finally sat down behind his desk and she was able to see his face on something like a level with hers for the first time. It was a thinner, more lined face than she had expected.

Crossed flags were draped behind the desk and on the walls hung framed photographs of Sulkey with the director of the FBI, Sulkey shaking hands with a former president of the United States, and several of Sulkey sitting with a group of equally enormous men, obviously a basketball team.

'I used to play ball,' said Sulkey, seeing Liz eyeing the photographs, 'until I got my injury.'

Liz smiled sympathetically, but thinking it more polite not to pursue the question of the injury, she broached the reason for her visit: Seamus Piggott, once known as James Purnell.

'Your colleague, Miss Peggy Kinsolving, told me on the phone that Purnell is now in Northern Ireland and causing you guys some concern.'

'Well,' said Liz, 'we're not entirely sure what he's up to yet. On the face of it he's running a perfectly legitimate business, but we've had some information from a source recently that Purnell is leading a breakaway group of ex-IRA people who are out to kill police and intelligence officers in Northern Ireland. Our files show that you were the special agent in charge of the investigation in Boston, and when I heard that you were here, it seemed a good opportunity to pick up some background on him.'

'Nothing he'd do would surprise me,' Sulkey said. 'Let me tell you a bit about him.' At first, there was little in what he said that Liz hadn't already read in Peggy's memo—the super-bright young Irish-American, who ultimately became an expert in missile technology.

'I gather you first came across him through investigating his brother,' Liz interjected, trying to move things on.

'That's right. And they couldn't have been more different.' Sulkey gave a wry smile. 'Edwin Purnell was James's younger brother by eight years. Their parents died when Edwin was still quite young and James looked after him. Edwin was an OK student but he dropped out of college and got in with the hard core of the Boston-Irish crowd. After a series of dead-end jobs he ended up working for James when James formed his own company.'

'Were they brought up to support the IRA?'

'Not really—that's the funny thing. Neither of their parents was political, but the local Irish culture was political all right, and that's where Edwin picked it up. He grew more and more pro-IRA as the years went by, and James got drawn in when Edwin was asked to help smuggle arms for the IRA. By then James's company was heavily into developing missiles— handheld, surface-to-air. It was a legitimate business—but it was also just what the IRA was looking for in those days. I don't think James got involved out of nationalist conviction, so much as for the money and trying to keep his brother from getting caught. If James was the genius, Edwin was the dumbo. James clearly felt the need to look after him.'

'But they got caught.'

'They did. Somebody in Northern Ireland talked to you guys in MI5. There was enough detail in the information that we knew what was going to be smuggled out—RPGs and SAM missiles—and where it was going from: Gloucester, a fishing town thirty miles north of Boston. We staked out the harbour and two months later we caught them red-handed.'

'But not James?'

'Nope.' He shook his head emphatically. 'He was the obvious source of the stuff, but we couldn't get evidence that would hold up in court. If you ask me, he would have taken the fall for his brother if he'd had to—he was that devoted to him—but it was too late. From James's point of view, there was no point going to prison if it wasn't going to keep his brother out.'

Liz said, 'And then Edwin didn't come out.'

'That's right. It was a freak thing. A kidney infection that was mistreated.'

'And James?'

'He was devastated. Well, as much as he was capable of feeling emotion. You see, this is a guy who was known as a loner, who has never married, has no record of close relationships with anybody. Except his brother. Once his brother was gone, there was nothing to care about except avenging him.'

Liz said, 'It makes sense in a strange kind of way.'

Sulkey nodded. 'Yeah. So, because it would give him a better chance to avenge his brother, James goes all Irish. He becomes Seamus, moves to Belfast and, from what you tell me, starts to act like an IRA hood. I've spoken to a lot of people about Purnell over the years and the words they've used to describe him were "single-minded", "ruthless" and "cold-hearted".'

Liz felt a chill run down her spine. 'Then if he's decided to kill a police officer and one of us, he's going to keep going till he succeeds,' she said quietly. 'Or until we catch him,' she added. 'And you make that sound difficult.'

Sulkey gave a grim nod. 'Let's just say I never succeeded.'

Liz looked up at Sulkey's lined face. 'Thank you. I think I understand what's driving him much better now.'

They stood up together and, as they shook hands again, Liz said, 'There's just one more thing. Didn't Purnell also nurse a grudge against the FBI? After all, it's you who put his brother in the prison where he died. I'd have thought he'd have tried to get his revenge on you chaps first.'

Sulkey gave a short laugh. 'Funny you should ask. He tried to kill the officer in charge of the investigation.'

'A colleague of yours?'

Sulkey looked at Liz. 'No, it was me. Someone tampered with the wheels of my car—I reckon it was Purnell. Two of my tyres blew out when I was doing seventy on Interstate 95.' He looked down at his leg. 'I was lucky to survive. All I got left with was this limp.'

'LIZ. THANK GOD you're back,' said Judith, coming out from her flat into the hall as soon as Liz opened the front door. 'Have you heard from Dave? He's gone missing.'

'What do you mean, missing? Tell me. Let's go upstairs.'

'No, I can't leave Daisy. Mrs Ryan's gone home. Come in here.'

Dumping her bag in the hall, Liz went into Judith's sitting room. It looked unusually untidy. Daisy's toys were still spread out all over the floor and there were papers, an empty wineglass and a coffee mug on the table. Now that she could see Judith clearly in the light of the room, she saw that her eyes were two dark pools of worry.

'Tell me what's wrong while I put the kettle on,' said Liz, walking into the kitchen.

Judith sighed and her shoulders slumped. 'I can't reach Dave.'

'Since when?'

'Since this afternoon. Yesterday, while you were in Paris, he had a meeting with Milraud. He went to his shop.'

'Really?' said Liz sharply. She'd assumed Dave would wait for her to report in before taking any action. 'I hope he had good back-up.'

Judith shook her head. 'No, he said he didn't need it. He was pretending to be a gun collector. He'd researched it all on the Internet. He was fine—but when he returned he was absolutely certain Milraud was dodgy.'

'He *is* dodgy.' Liz put tea bags in two mugs and poured the boiling water, then came back into the sitting room and put the mugs down on the table. 'I found out a lot about him in Paris. Milraud is ex-DGSE and a gun runner. Dave's lucky he didn't see straight through him.'

'That's just it, Liz. I think he probably did. But Dave insisted on seeing him again. He was planning to proposition him. He said Milraud was going back to France later today and he couldn't afford to miss his chance.'

'Oh God. What happened? Surely he had police back-up, A4 . . .?'

She saw at once from Judith's face that he hadn't. 'Couldn't you stop him, Judith? That was crazy.'

'I know. He wouldn't listen to me. I'm not his boss,' she added.

'No, but Binding is. Why didn't you bring Michael in on this?'

'I tried. But he was tied up at Stormont. He'd left word with his secretary that he wasn't to be disturbed. I even tried reaching you over in London, but no one knew where you were.'

Of course Liz's mobile had been switched off in the US Embassy and she had never switched it on again.

Judith said quietly, 'I'm sorry.'

Liz sighed. 'It's not your fault, Judith. I just don't understand what's got into Dave. It was bad enough him seeing Milraud the first time without waiting to hear what I'd learned . . . but then to go back again? And without back-up.' She shook her head in exasperation.

'He wasn't thinking clearly. He'd rung Lucy the night before and she'd told him she was having doubts. She said she wanted to cool things down for a bit. He told me all this yesterday morning. He was upset.'

'So his girlfriend has a wobble and he throws all caution out of the window? That doesn't sound like Dave.'

'I think it was more than a wobble. He seemed to think she was telling him it was all over. They were practically engaged to be married.'

Liz groaned. She said, 'I know Dave—he would have plunged himself into work.' She thought for a second. 'Did he say he was coming back to the office after meeting Milraud?'

'Yes, he did. And I made him promise to ring me if for any reason he got delayed. I got that much out of him.'

'And you've tried ringing him?'

'Only about a hundred times,' Judith said. 'On his mobile, at his flat, and I've got everyone alerted at the office to let me know if he shows up.'

'I'm going to phone Binding,' said Liz, putting down her mug. Now she was worried too.

OVER THE PHONE at Michael Binding's house, Liz could hear the clink of cutlery and glasses and the sound of conversation—he must be having a dinner party. He seemed reluctant to leave his guests and speak in private—Liz had to shout to make herself heard. 'Yes, Dave's missing,' she found herself saying for the third time. 'I'm going to alert the police.'

'Hang on a minute,' Binding said. After a pause his voice came again more clearly. He must have moved into his study.

'OK. Now tell me exactly what's happened.'

She gave him a quick summary of what she'd learned in Paris about Milraud, explaining that Dave had gone to see him for a second time, with the intention of propositioning him and without any back-up. 'Milraud would have seen Dave coming a mile off. He's a trained intelligence officer. And now Dave's disappeared. We've got to do something, Michael.'

'Why wasn't A4 brought in on this meeting? Didn't you insist on that before you swanned off to France?' he said irritably.

'We can deal with that later. Right now I want to find out where Dave is, and make sure he's OK.'

'Have you any reason to think this Milraud character would do Dave any harm, even if he did see him coming? He's not a terrorist, is he, or a murderer? Stop panicking, Liz. Have a strong drink and go to bed. You may not have heard, but Dave's had a bit of a setback in his private life and he's probably just gone off to lick his wounds. Leave it now. And you do not have my authority to bring in the police. He'll turn up tomorrow right as rain.'

And before Liz could say any more, he rang off, leaving her angry and more worried than ever.

THROUGH THE CLOTH BAG over his head Dave couldn't see a thing. But he knew where he was, and that scared him.

During the drive from Milraud's shop, as he lay with his mouth taped and his hands tied behind his back in the boot of the car, he had concentrated hard on the sounds of the vehicle on the road. The journey had taken about an hour by his reckoning, first on fast roads, then for about twenty minutes on smaller ones, where the car stopped and started at junctions or traffic lights. Then it had turned onto a rougher surface—some sort of track.

They could have been anywhere in the countryside of Northern Ireland. But then, just before the car stopped and he was bundled out, he heard a sound that he recognised. It was the squeak and bang of the gate on the National Trust estate that he'd heard when he was with Liz.

He must now be in Piggott's house in County Down—the house of the man who, as Brown Fox had told him, wanted to kill an MI5 officer. Until then, Dave had thought he was either the victim of a kidnapping or of mistaken identity. Now he realised he could be about to die.

He'd been lifted out of the boot of the car, put on his two feet and led into a house, bumping his shoulder against what felt like a door frame. Then he'd been walked down a flight of stairs and deposited unceremoniously on a hard chair. He'd now been sitting there for a minute or two, not sure who was around him, trying to get his bearings and cope with the fear that was growing with each second he waited.

Rough hands removed the bag from his head. He looked up into the face of the man who had walked into Milraud's shop and pulled a gun on him; the same man he had seen here, outside this house, when he and Liz had walked on the headland. Piggott's foreign-looking henchman.

Dave blinked in the sudden light and looked around the room, taking in the comfortable furnishings, the large desk, the leather-bound books in the bookcases and, incongruously, the camp bed in the corner.

He cursed himself for having gone to see Milraud without any back-up. Not just once, but twice. How could he have been so stupid, acting like a complete amateur? He should have listened to Judith and waited for Liz to get back. But it was too late for regrets. They hadn't killed him yet—could they believe he was just a harmless collector? Maybe the dark-faced thug had not recognised him from their earlier encounter?

For a moment, he nursed these seedlings of hope, but he was too much of a realist to let them take root. If they really did see him as harmless, then why had he been held at gunpoint and taken forcibly from the shop?

Suddenly, he felt agonising pain splay across his face as the foreign-looking man ripped the tape roughly from his mouth. Then, pulling a flick knife from his pocket, the man reached down and swiftly cut the cords binding Dave's arms, though he left his hands tied tautly together.

The blood rushing back into Dave's joints hurt a lot, and his muscles ached from his cramped position in the boot of the car. He gingerly moved his legs, but he stayed sitting in the chair while the dark face watched him expressionlessly, holding a gun pointed directly at his head.

He heard footsteps behind him and the tall, spare figure of Seamus Piggott appeared with another man. Dave recognised his face from the A4 surveillance—Malone. The man was carrying an old-fashioned doctors' bag. Turning his head, Dave saw for the first time that Milraud was also in the room, standing in the corner, looking studiously detached.

Piggott said nothing and didn't even look at Dave as he walked over to the desk. Malone put the bag down and Piggott rummaged in it for a moment, then his hands emerged holding a rubber tube in one hand and a syringe in the other. He handed the tube to Malone, who walked over and grabbed hold of Dave's right arm from the side.

Now Dave panicked. He shouted, 'No!' and tried to wriggle free from the strong grip on his arm, but his legs felt like jelly and he hadn't the strength even to try to stand up. His shirtsleeve was swiftly forced up above his elbow and Malone tied the rubber tube tightly round his upper arm. Dave struggled frantically as Piggott walked briskly from the desk and plunged the syringe directly into the bulging vein of his bicep. As the liquid moved into his bloodstream, Dave felt a cold sensation in his arm, followed almost immediately by a gentle lethargy. He was only partly aware of being frog-marched over to the bed, then put prone on the mattress and strapped to the frame. He found himself incapable of resisting, and he didn't even want to.

As THE DAYLIGHT was fading, a strong wind was gusting across the bay, whipping the sea into white-crested waves and blowing open Milraud's grey checked jacket. The fine cashmere sweater he wore underneath was not designed to cope with these temperatures and he shivered as he walked down to the wooden jetty, which jutted out into the small cove.

A substantial, rigid inflatable dinghy was moored up, rocking in the water's chop. Much further out, in the mouth of the bay, a large motor cruiser was anchored. At first sight, with its gleaming white paint and aluminium rails, it looked like the sort of rich man's toy that is ten a penny in the Mediterranean, but Milraud recognised the wide bow and strong lines of a boat designed for longer trips than cruising the Mediterranean. He knew that this boat made regular voyages to pick up the goods that Piggott imported and sold, under the cover of his consultancy company.

As he gazed out to sea, Milraud's mind was racing. He was used to dealing with the unexpected and turning it to his advantage, but the events of the last twenty-four hours had thrown him off-balance. Ever since Gonzales had marched into the shop, he had been trying to keep things under control.

The Spaniard had been told to wait for Simon Willis to leave, then follow him to find out who he was. But Gonzales had got his signals crossed and had come into the back room where the Englishman had been sitting. At that point it would still have been possible to terminate the meeting and let him go, but Gonzales had pulled a gun. He'd said later that he could tell that the man recognised him, as if that somehow justified what he had done.

After that, there was no way they could let Willis leave. Milraud had alerted Piggott, and the American had instructed Gonzales to bring the Englishman down here to the house in the bay. They'd bundled him, hands tied, head enveloped by a sack, his mouth covered in thick strips of parcel tape, out of the back door of the shop and into the boot of the car brought round by one of Piggott's men. He was now lying, half comatose and strapped to a bed in the basement room.

It was a fallacy that 'truth serum' could flush out of the brain all those things an undrugged person would never admit to. But in the hands of an intelligent practitioner, it could be just as revealing. Willis had not told them *anything* directly, but nor had he shown the blanket ignorance he should have displayed if he had been the innocent collector he claimed to be. And he'd nodded drowsily at names he should not have found familiar. Any lingering doubt about Willis's true vocation had been dispelled.

But what was on Milraud's mind now was how to get out of this situation where he was party to the abduction of a British intelligence officer. And possibly to something worse than abduction, if he could not control Piggott.

As Milraud turned to go back inside, he saw the American coming towards him from the direction of the house. His leather jacket could not have given him much protection from the wind, but he walked upright, apparently impervious to the cold. It struck Milraud that the man seemed indifferent to so many things: clothes, food, women—all the aspects of life that Milraud enjoyed most. He knew there were things his associate cared about—there had to be, since nothing else could explain his actions. But the Frenchman did not know what those passions were.

Piggott said, 'There's a simple way of dealing with this, you know.'

Nothing was simple any more, thought Milraud, but he made a show of being willing to consider this. 'What's that, James?'

'Let Gonzales take care of the problem. There's no danger then of Willis ever talking. And we don't have to worry about what to do with him.'

Milraud looked out to sea, rough enough that day to keep most craft firmly on shore. 'Too late for that,' he said tersely, though just the idea of killing Willis made him feel sick. Milraud had a large, successful business that was now in peril; the last thing he needed was the prospect of a life sentence for murder. He said to Piggott, 'Listen, James, Willis's people will soon find out that he came to see me. It won't take them long to get onto you, too, and then they'll be swarming over this place. I have to get out of here and I suggest you do too.'

He wondered how long he could count on Mrs Carson back at the shop to play dumb. Probably longer than he feared, but not long enough. He'd have to write off the shop and stay out of Northern Ireland. If he could get back to France, it would be a while before the authorities here caught up with him. Eventually, the British would find him in Toulon and send someone over. But they had no evidence of anything substantial.

He should be all right. Unless he listened to Piggott. The man had drawn him into some vendetta of his own, and Milraud resented that. Phoning him with that preposterous accusation that Milraud was working with MI5, and now suggesting a course of action that would have the British authorities down on them both like a ton of bricks. If the British could connect him with the murder of Willis, Milraud would be looking round corners for the rest of his life.

But recriminations were pointless, as well as potentially dangerous—Milraud sensed an only half-submerged menace in the American, which he was wary of. If they were ever to cross swords, he wanted it to be on his home ground. Another good reason for his plan.

'We should make Plymouth on the first day and I reckon we'll be through the Strait of Gibraltar in five days and in Toulon within a week. It gives us some breathing space.'

'But why take this extra baggage with us?' asked Piggott. 'Wouldn't it be simpler if we just left it behind?'

'Listen,' Milraud said sharply. 'If we kill an MI5 man, we'll put everything at risk.' He looked at Piggott and saw that he was unmoved.

'What are we going to do with him in France, then?' Piggott went on. 'And are we going to keep him drugged for six days on the boat?'

'We may not need to. We can lock him up. He can't go far at sea. Think of him as a commodity,' said Milraud. 'With considerable value.'

'To MI5? You think we can ransom him to his own people?'

'That's possible, but much better to sell him off to the highest bidder. Let someone else hold him. That will take the heat off us soon enough.' Milraud had contacts in several countries who might well be pleased to buy Willis. 'But meanwhile, we need to move our commodity to a safe place.'

'When do you want to leave?'

'The next high tide is just after midnight. We should go then.'

Piggott thought about this, but his face showed no expression. Finally he gave a curt nod in agreement. 'I've some business to attend to before we leave. I'll send Malone back into town to bring down another "commodity". But this one will be staying here. Permanently.'

And seeing the set expression on the other man's face, Milraud decided not to argue. At some point he would have to find a way of betraying Piggott to the authorities, or else Piggott would drag him down with him. But Milraud was going to pick the time and place for that.

PADDY O'BRIEN was pulling him a second pint of stout. Normally Dermot would have contented himself with a single glass, but he'd been by the office of Fraternal Holdings twice in the last three days and there was no sign of Piggott, and no instructions left for Dermot. He'd caught sight of Terry Malone, but when he'd asked where the boss was, Malone had shrugged and said he had no idea, though Dermot didn't believe him. There was something going on, he was sure of that, but whatever it was, he, Dermot, wasn't part of it. At least there was no sign of that bloody Frenchman, Milraw or Miroe, or whatever his name was. Dermot hoped his letter had had its intended effect.

He'd had the first sip of his second pint when 'Danny Boy' suddenly blared out from his trouser pocket. He extracted his mobile and answered with a voice that he hoped sounded stone-cold sober. 'O'Reilly.'

'Dermot, it's Piggott here. Where are you?'

O'Reilly looked around him guiltily. 'I'm just off home, boss.'

'I'll need you about half past six. All right?'

'Of course,' said Dermot, breathing an inward sigh of relief. 'Shall I come to the office, then?'

'No, I'll pick you up. Be at the memorial park on the Falls Road.'

'OK,' said Dermot, puzzled. It seemed a strange time and place to meet, but clearly something was up. He wondered if it had to do with his letter, though he couldn't see how Piggott could suspect that he had sent it.

'Right, then,' said Piggott, and Dermot waited for him to ring off. But Piggott added, his voice uncharacteristically soft, 'And, Dermot, we'll need to talk about your new responsibilities. See you at six thirty.' He rang off.

Dermot sat staring at the pint of stout, watching as the creamy head of foam settled in his glass. He felt a growing satisfaction as he reviewed the phone call. Whatever Piggott had made of the letter, he clearly didn't think Dermot had sent it. And he had work for him, too, which was good news.

'Pint all right?' asked Paddy O'Brien, pointing to Dermot's glass.

'It's fine, Paddy. Just fine.' He pulled a fiver from his pocket. 'Why don't you have one on me?'

DERMOT HAD NEVER liked the Remembrance Garden on the Falls Road. It was neat and well tended—when flowers passed their best they were quickly replaced with fresh ones—but it was a gloomy enclave, particularly in the early dark of a winter's evening, and it depressed him now as he sat on one of its low brick walls, waiting for Piggott.

A man came in off the street, bulky in a duffle coat, walking without hesitation straight towards Dermot. As the man approached, Dermot saw it was Terry Malone. 'Ready?' he said.

Dermot nodded and stood up. 'I thought the boss—'

'He's waiting in the car,' said Malone.

Piggott was in the back seat and motioned to Dermot to join him. To Dermot's surprise, when Malone started the engine, he did a 180-degree turn and headed towards the outskirts of Belfast.

'We're not going to the office, then?' Dermot ventured cautiously.

Piggott said, 'No. I need your help at the house.'

They drove in silence, punctuated by the frequent calls Piggott made on his mobile phone. Dermot gathered he was going on a trip somewhere.

Once out of Belfast they made good time, and in less than an hour they were through the gate, passing the National Trust gatehouse and driving up the private lane to the house. Then, instead of stopping on the gravel at the front of the farmhouse, Malone drove into the low brick garage in the yard behind. The mystery deepened when Piggott left them in the big sitting room on the ground floor and went downstairs to his office by himself.

Dermot sat down in one of the soft chintz armchairs and looked around at the antique furniture. He felt ill at ease, like a messenger treated by mistake as a guest. Malone had stayed standing near the door, as if he were guarding someone. Then it occurred to Dermot that Malone might be guarding *him*, and his nervousness increased.

Footsteps sounded and Piggott reappeared, followed by another man. It was Milraud, and Dermot looked away.

'Here's my friend Antoine. Are you surprised to see him?' asked Piggott.

Dermot's heart began to race. 'We've never met,' he said at last, looking directly at the man. 'But I heard you were around.'

'Really,' said Piggott coldly. 'You know, I had a letter in the post a few days ago and I couldn't figure out who'd sent it. It was warning me that Antoine here might not be my friend after all. The odd thing was that the letter wasn't signed. I found that cowardly. I don't like poison-pen letters. What do you think, Dermot?'

'I don't know anything about that, boss,' said Dermot, trying to look respectful and baffled at the same time.

'Fortunately, Antoine here and I go way back—we've done business together for over ten years, and in as many countries. If he was going to betray me, he would have done it long ago. Even so, after a letter like that you can't help but feel a tiny bit of doubt.'

Piggott looked at the Frenchman, who was sitting in a wing chair in the corner, and for a moment Dermot's hopes rose. But then Piggott turned his grey eyes back onto Dermot and his icy gaze extinguished the optimism.

There was a noise from the back of the house, then more footsteps. The Spaniard, Gonzales, loomed in the doorway, and Dermot's agitation increased dramatically. He'd been set up, he could see that now. But how had Piggott discovered he'd sent the letter? He couldn't have any proof. Dermot had never told that MI5 man his name. Then he saw the Spaniard nod quickly at Piggot.

'He's out, then?' Piggott asked.

'Like a baby,' said Gonzales.

'Let's keep him that way,' said Piggott. He turned to Dermot and said, 'We've had a visitor staying. Name of Simon Willis. Ring any bells?'

Dermot shook his head.

Piggott went on, 'He wasn't meant to be here, but he's already been useful. While I was figuring out what to do with him, we had a little chat. Funnily enough, your name came up in our conversation.'

Dermot tried not to show fear; he told himself again that MI5 didn't know his name. 'Why was that?' he managed to ask.

'Because I brought it up.' Piggott watched his reactions, then added, 'Along with a lot of others. I was trying to understand why this Willis guy had made an approach to Antoine just after someone had tried to stitch him up. Not a coincidence, I think you'll agree. So someone in the organisation must have talked to Willis.'

'I don't know the man, I'm telling you.' In spite of himself, Dermot's voice was rising in panic.

Piggott nodded, but it was not reassuring. 'It's only fair to say he didn't seem to react to your name—or anyone else's for that matter.'

Thank God, thought Dermot. Piggott added, 'Then we tried showing him some photographs. And I have to say, yours was the only one he reacted to.'

Jolted, Dermot exclaimed, 'For the love of God, Mr Piggott. I don't know the man you're talking about. You say someone's been trying to stitch up Milraud here. Well, it looks as though someone has stitched *me* up, good and proper.'

There was silence in the room. Dermot sensed that Piggott was considering his appeal. After all, what evidence did he really have? Then Piggott said suddenly, 'How did you know Antoine was in Belfast?'

'The boys were talking about it.'

'I see,' said Piggott neutrally, and he sat down in another of the chintz chairs, across from Dermot. '"Loose talk risks lives", they used to say. I would have thought you knew the truth of that expression.'

'I do, boss. It wasn't me who was doing the talking.' He felt his mouth drying, and he wanted to wet his lips with his tongue.

'I suppose it was "the boys", then. Which one in particular?' asked Piggott. He dipped his chin a notch, and Malone moved into the room.

'I think it was Sean McCarthy,' said Dermot carefully, picking the first name he could think of.

'You sure?'

Dermot paused. He had nothing against young Sean, it didn't seem right to land him in it, but what could he do?

He nodded emphatically. 'That's right, Mr Piggott. I remember it clear as a bell. I saw him at Paddy O'Brien's saloon the day before yesterday. Why, he even bought me a drink—that's rare enough not to forget.' He tried to smile at his weak joke.

Piggott seemed to understand; you could tell the man's mind was churning over the news of who had been talking. He said, 'I tell you what, Dermot. Why don't you go with these two'—he jabbed a finger at Malone and Gonzales—'and walk down to the cove. There are some cases on the speedboat that need unloading. Put them on the pier, and Antoine and I will bring the cars down in a little while so you can load them up. I've got some calls to make first.' And with a wave of his hand, he dismissed them.

OUTSIDE IT WAS DARK. In the cold, fresh air, Dermot breathed an enormous sigh of relief. He felt a little bad about Sean McCarthy, but his regret was dwarfed by his exhilaration at getting away with it.

'This way,' said Malone, and they crossed the small square of lawn that slanted downwards towards the beach. A line of low lights marked the path, which led through a small copse of trees to the cove. They were halfway through the copse when Dermot saw the low mound at the edge of a tiny clearing on one side of the path. The earth had been freshly turned. Malone just ahead of him stopped, and Dermot almost bumped into him.

'What's that?' Dermot asked, pointing to the mound.

Malone turned to face him. 'You said back there that you'd been speaking to Sean McCarthy the day before yesterday. But you couldn't have been.'

'Perhaps I got that wrong,' Dermot said. He sensed that behind him Gonzales had taken a step back.

'You did, Dermot. And it wasn't a wise mistake to make.'

Behind him Gonzales gave a harsh laugh. 'Cheer up, *señor*. Soon you can talk to Sean McCarthy for as long as you like.' Dermot looked again at the mound, and realised it was a grave. His eyes turned to Malone beseechingly, but Malone wouldn't catch his eye.

There was a metallic noise behind him; Dermot knew it was Gonzales clearing the chamber of an automatic.

Malone said, 'Sorry, Dermot.'

7

By 9.30 the next morning, Binding's dismissive cool of the night before had gone and he seemed to be operating in a kind of frenzied overdrive, constantly on the phone, making increasingly tense calls. By eleven, when there was still no sign of Dave, he strode into Liz's office.

'I've spoken to DG. He's very concerned. As am I,' he added, conveniently wiping the slate clean of the previous evening's conversation. 'I'm going to ask DG to send an investigative team over asap.'

Liz nodded. She was glad to see that Binding was taking the situation seriously, but was alarmed by how far he'd now swung the other way.

'I wonder if it might be better to wait a little for that?' Liz kept her own voice mild, knowing how much Binding disliked dissent.

'Don't you realise time is of the essence? We need all the help we can get.'

That was more than Liz could take. 'If you remember,' she replied icily, 'I wanted to inform the police last night. In my opinion an investigative team getting involved now would just complicate things. There's nothing they can do at the moment that we can't—except get in our way.'

Binding had gone red in the face, but Liz could see he was considering what she'd said. He said slowly, 'We can't be sure Dave's absence has anything to do with this Frenchman, Milraud, can we?'

'We should check at Milraud's shop,' said Liz. 'Our airport source is looking to see if he caught his flight to France yesterday, but we need to confirm that Dave did actually meet the man.'

'The CCTV in the area will show if he went to the shop.'

'There's no camera on the street where Milraud has his place. We've got someone going through all the CCTV in the area, but that's going to take some time.' She stood up to leave, planning to go to Milraud's.

But Binding had other ideas. 'Send someone else,' he said sharply. 'I need you close by. Things are getting tense.'

You mean *you* are, thought Liz.

IT WAS THE SMELL that made him stop. Every three days or so, Constable Frederick Hughes drove along this lane as part of his shift. He was used to a variety of pungent odours as he passed the farms, from pigs' slurry to freshly cut hay and the woody smoke of smouldering piles of leaves. But not in midwinter. And anyway, this smoke was acrid.

He pulled over just past Docherty's farm, once a notorious haven for IRA men on the run, heading for the border. A decade ago, he would not have been patrolling here at all. What patrolling there was in South Armagh in those days was done by the military in helicopters or armoured cars. But that was the past. Now he and his colleagues were far more likely to be hurt in a car accident than in an assassination attempt.

He rolled his window down and sat sniffing like a gun dog. There—he smelled it again. He got out of the car.

The smell was stronger still outside. Turning round, he felt the wind sting his cheeks and he shivered slightly. It was blowing from the northeast, across the unploughed dun-coloured fields. So he got back into his car and drove towards the source of the smell, taking the first right turn he came to, along an old track he didn't recognise.

The track climbed gradually round Davitt's Hill, the highest point in this small stretch of valley. From here you could almost see the border with the Republic, the safety line for so many fleeing the law in the North. Once across the border the Provos had a habit of disappearing into thin air.

The track stopped suddenly in a small lay-by in front of what had been a crofter's cottage. From behind the decayed ruins, smoke rose in a twisty wisp before dispersing in the wintry winds. It was only when he walked behind the cottage that he saw the remains of the white van. One of its tyres was still smouldering.

THE FORENSIC TEAM moved fast—everyone did when a policeman had been shot. They checked for prints, but none had survived the fire, which was so hot that the steering wheel had been reduced to a metal spoke.

Over the course of the next two hours, the team extracted what remained of the engine from the vehicle's charred carcass. After applying acetic acid with a paintbrush, they could make out enough of the chassis number to allow a technician at the lab to run a software program used for identifying stolen vehicles. Its algorithm came up with four possibilities, of which only one was a vehicle large enough to be the burnt-out van found in South Armagh.

It had been a laundry van belonging to O'Neill's Laundry and Linen Service, a cleaning business run out of Sydenham in East Belfast. It had been reported stolen two days earlier. Twenty minutes later, two officers had driven to the home of the company's managing director, where they found Patrick O'Neill still irate at the theft of the van from his fleet.

Did he have any idea who might have stolen the van? No, he replied; he'd assumed it was local villains who'd taken it out of the yard. Had anyone recently left his employ? Well, yes, a guy called Sean McCarthy had quit a few days before. Short, with dark hair. He was a laundry collection and delivery driver, who'd never settled in the business. Was this before the van was stolen? Yes, come to think of it, it was just before the van was stolen . . .

The PSNI had a suspect now, and they soon learned from their own database that Sean McCarthy had a string of minor convictions as a juvenile. McCarthy's file also showed that he had been an associate of several members of the Provisional IRA. There was no recent information about that strand of his life and one recent informant had opined 'the boy's gone straight', though evidence for that appeared to be confined to McCarthy's being in full-time employment—at O'Neill's laundry service.

He was said to live in the house he'd been brought up in on the edge of Andersonstown—but a visit to his home found only his mother in residence. She seemed unconcerned about the absence of her son, and didn't seem to know anything about his friends or associates. The interviewing PC believed her—probably because he found her too drunk, at ten thirty in the morning, to lie convincingly. This was her usual condition, according to a neighbour.

JUDITH SPRATT STOPPED for a coffee at a Starbucks two streets away from Milraud's shop. This was a part of the city she did not know well, a small oasis of galleries, restaurants and boutiques in what had once been a commercial area of small factories and warehouses.

She needed to collect her thoughts before she went into the shop. It had been decided that no publicity was to be given yet to Dave's disappearance, so Judith had to find some excuse for enquiring about him at the shop. She had been taken aback when Liz had asked her to do this job; she was not used to direct contact with the public and role-playing was not her strength. Before she had joined the service she had been an analyst at an investment bank. Her current job, at which she excelled, was the processing and analysis of information once it had been collected; when the pieces came streaming in she liked nothing better than to use her mind like a prospector's sieve, throwing out the dross and making sense of the few gold nuggets that remained.

She finished her coffee and walked down the narrow street to the door of Milraud's shop. She was wearing an ankle-length knitted coat with a fringed shawl draped round her shoulders, and flat shoes. The look she was aiming at was arty, bohemian, slightly ditzy, but definitely genteel. As far away as could be imagined from an intelligence officer. She stood outside the shop for a moment and took a deep breath to calm her nerves, then she opened the door and went in. A bell tinkled discreetly.

'Good afternoon.' A woman stood up from a chair behind a low glass cabinet. She was middle-aged, smartly turned out, with elegantly coiffed grey hair and wearing a dark wool dress with a choker of pearls.

'Is Mr Milraud in?' Judith began, walking towards her with a smile.

'Monsieur Milraud is not available, I'm afraid. He's out of the country.' Judith adopted a puzzled frown. 'Did you have an appointment?'

'That's the thing. I don't know, and I'm not sure if I have the right day in any case. My cousin Simon asked me to join him here. He collects little guns, you see, and he said he was coming to see Mr Milraud about buying one. He asked me to meet him here this afternoon because we have to go down to the country after Simon has finished here. At least I think it was this afternoon, but perhaps I've got the wrong day—or the wrong time.' She gave a small sigh, and went on talking. 'He wants me to hold his hand while he negotiates with Mr Milraud. You know, to stop him spending too much.'

Judith saw the look of doubt in the woman's eyes and wondered if she was overplaying her role.

'As I said, Monsieur Milraud is not here. Let me have a look at the diary. Perhaps I can see when your appointment might be.' The woman went through a door marked 'Private' at the back of the shop, returning a moment later with a leather-bound desk diary. 'Your name is?'

'Crosby. Heather Farlow Crosby.'

Judith watched as the woman consulted the pages of the diary. 'I see nothing here,' she said.

'Oh, how silly of me,' said Judith. 'It wouldn't be my name at all, would it? It would be my cousin Simon's.'

'Simon?' the woman said, her expression suggesting she was having to work hard to keep her patience.

'Willis. His mother was the Crosby, which is why my cousin and I have different surnames.' And she continued prattling while the woman ran her finger up and down the page, until she stopped at one line.

'A Mr Willis was here,' the woman said slowly. 'Yesterday, in fact.'

'Ah,' said Judith with relief. 'So at least I was close.' Her smile went unreturned. 'And was I right about the time?'

'The time?' The woman was watching her carefully.

'Yes.' Judith glanced at her watch. 'Two o'clock?'

The woman made a show of looking at the diary. She seemed suddenly nervous. 'Yes, that is correct.'

'Did he make a purchase? I'm wondering if he went off to the country by himself. Do you remember when he left?'

'They left . . .' and the woman paused.

Judith pounced. '*They?*' There was nothing ditzy in her voice now. 'Did he and Monsieur Milraud leave together then?'

The woman said carefully, 'No. Your cousin left, then Monsieur Milraud left shortly afterwards. He had his plane to catch.'

'What time was that?'

'It must have been about two forty-five that your cousin left. Monsieur Milraud left at about three fifteen to catch the plane.'

'And my cousin left alone? You're absolutely sure of that?'

'Quite sure,' replied the woman tersely, dropping her mask of politeness.

'It's very important,' said Judith levelly, returning the woman's stare.

'I can assure you that he was on his own when he left. And I'm afraid I cannot help you further.' Judith was being ushered firmly towards the door.

Outside on the pavement, Judith found that her nervousness had been replaced with anger. It was obvious that something had happened to Dave and that this woman knew more about it than she was letting on. Now the woman also knew that someone was looking for Dave, and Judith doubted she believed for a moment that it was his cousin.

LIZ STARED OUT at the old barracks parade ground as the last flicker of sun gave way to the chill dusk of the February afternoon. Information was beginning to seep in but so far it was all negative. She still had no idea what had happened to Dave.

No results yet from the various CCTV cameras in the car park and the area around Milraud's shop, but at least she now knew, thanks to Judith's thespian efforts at the premises, that Dave had actually been there. If the shop assistant was to be believed, he had left safely and on his own at 2.45. But that might not be true. Judith thought that at the very least the woman was not telling all she knew, and, in spite of what she had said, Milraud had certainly not taken the flight to Paris on which he had a reservation. Nor had he been found on any airline manifest leaving Ireland in the last forty-eight hours. Preliminary checks with the ferry services in the North and in the Republic had come up with the same result: no sign of the man.

The main interest had come from analysis of the photographs taken by the camera on the gate of the National Trust property in County Down. There had been an unusual amount of movement in and out since the previous afternoon. Timed at 3.44, the red Vauxhall Vectra had gone in, with the dark-faced thug and the man identified as Malone in the front seat. At 4 p.m., Piggott had gone in driving his Audi, with an unidentifiable back-seat passenger. At 5.30 the Audi had gone out again, driven by Malone, and had returned at 7.30, again driven by Malone. Nothing more had happened until 7.30 the following morning when the Audi had been driven out by Malone, possibly with a back-seat passenger.

At the offices of Fraternal Holdings in Belfast, where A4 had been on watch since 8 a.m., very little had happened. At 9 a.m. the female receptionist had let herself into the offices with a key. She was now sitting in the reception area, clearly visible to two MI5 agents in their observation post across the street. She was painting her nails.

Two policemen had been to Piggott's house on the National Trust estate during the morning. The old housekeeper who had answered the door said that her employer had left the previous day and had not told her where he was going or when he would be back. After walking round the surrounding land and seeing nothing to arouse their suspicions, they had left.

As Liz was turning all this over in her mind, Michael Binding appeared in her office doorway, eyebrows raised in a questioning look. Liz shook her head. 'Nothing firm yet,' she said flatly.

'I promised DG a progress report this evening,' he said, coming into the room. 'All I've got is a *lack* of progress report. It won't do.'

Liz didn't reply. It wasn't quite true. The threads of an investigation were beginning to emerge. The problem now was making sense of them and deciding what to do about it, without precipitating a situation that might put Dave in more danger than he was already in.

Binding wasn't finished. 'You were supposed to be in charge here, Liz. You go away for two days and your people end up all over the place. God knows why Dave felt he could just go charging off on his own.'

'He certainly didn't have my permission to do that.'

'So you say,' Binding replied infuriatingly. 'Right now we need to do something. I want to talk to the police and put out an all-persons alert.'

'For Dave? Or for Milraud?'

He looked momentarily flustered. 'For Dave, of course.'

Liz turned away. What was he proposing to say? *Have You Seen This Man? He's an MI5 Officer and We Can't Find Him.* This was ludicrous. She decided to ignore it and said, 'I've been thinking over the leads we have.'

'None that I can see.'

'That's not entirely true. Remember, our informant Brown Fox said Seamus Piggott wants to kill policemen and an MI5 officer. Jimmy Fergus got shot three days ago and now Dave's disappeared. We know he went to Milraud's shop and we're pretty sure from what Brown Fox told Dave that Milraud is working with Piggott, probably supplying him with arms. It might all be coincidence, but if we can link the attack on Fergus to Piggott, that will let us grab Piggott, assuming we can find him, and that should lead us to Milraud. And with luck to Dave.'

He looked at her as he considered what she said. 'It's a tenuous chain you're building there.' But he said this quietly, always a good sign with him.

'I know it is. But we have to start somewhere. I want to put telephone intercepts on Milraud's shop and we need to identify the woman who works there. Also all the communications to and from the Fraternity offices need to be on check, and I'm wondering if we shouldn't ask the police to go back to Piggott's place and go in. As you said before, Michael, time is of the essence.'

Binding sat down heavily. There was a pause. Eventually, 'You're right,' he conceded. 'We need to work on the assumption that Dave has been taken by someone. We'd better get that investigative team over.'

'No. We do need reinforcement but not an investigative team. I still think that would cause delay and confusion. I want to get Peggy Kinsolving from counterespionage over here. If there is anything to find out to connect all this, she'll do it.'

'Well, if that's what you want, and if you can persuade Charles Wetherby to release her, then go ahead.'

SO LIZ NOW HAD two phone calls to make and she realised that she was looking forward to one much more than to the other, and not in the order she would have expected.

First she rang Charles Wetherby in London.

'Hello, Liz. It's good to talk to you. I hope you're being careful over there—I heard about Jimmy Fergus getting shot. And we're very concerned about Dave. Is there anything I can do to help?'

On any other occasion Liz would have taken the opportunity to tell Charles everything that had happened and ask for his advice. But she seemed no longer to feel the unspoken understanding that they'd had in the past. She didn't want to prolong the conversation, so she just asked if she could borrow Peggy Kinsolving. When Charles readily agreed, she rang off.

Why had she done that? It seemed that rather than getting closer, as she had expected they would after Joanne's death, they had got further apart. And she had cut short the conversation with Charles because she wanted to get on with her next call. This was the one she was looking forward to.

'Ah, Liz, how nice to hear from you.' The warm Parisian tones were what she wanted to hear.

'Martin, I need your help. Or at least your advice. I'm trying to find our friend Milraud, but he seems to have disappeared.' She explained how they could find no trace of the arms dealer having left Northern Ireland.

'That is puzzling, but perhaps he took another way back—a private plane even. Is this urgent?'

'It is, I'm afraid. One of my colleagues has disappeared. He had an appointment with Milraud at his shop here but he hasn't been seen since.'

'When was this?'

'Yesterday.' She heard his small exclamation of surprise, and she went on, 'I know, it hasn't been very long. But our man isn't one to take off like this. Our observations had confirmed our suspicions about your old colleague. He was here to do business with Seamus Piggott, the American I told you about.'

'I recall. And Milraud's disappearance is connected in some way, no?'

'Yes,' she said, relieved that Seurat understood. 'We have a source who claims that Piggott wants to kill a policeman and an MI5 officer. He's looking for revenge for something that happened in the past. And just before I came to Paris, a senior policeman was shot outside his own house—he survived, but they were definitely trying to kill him.'

'Liz, if it's any consolation, Milraud is not a murderer. Remember, I know the man well. It's not that I view him through—how do you say it? Rosy spectacles?'

'That'll do,' said Liz with a laugh.

'It's rather that I know he's too ambitious to risk spending the rest of his life rotting in prison. For Milraud, his business, legitimate or not, would always come before revenge.'

'I'm glad to hear that. The problem is, we can't find Piggott either. And he may not have Milraud's scruples.'

'Is there anything I can do to help?'

'I was hoping you might be able to locate Milraud.'

Seurat paused. 'Hmm. As you know, we have our own interest in Milraud, though we've never had enough evidence to place him under any surveillance. What I can do is speak with Isabelle in DCRI—you met her, yes?'

'Of course.' Isabelle Florian, the woman in jeans whom she and Bruno had visited in the office near the Eiffel Tower.

'I would ask her as a matter of urgency to discover if Milraud has returned to Toulon and, if not, find out if someone there knows where he is.'

'That would be very helpful, Martin.'

'It may not help very much at all. But it's at least a start.'

'THAT'S DAVE!' Judith exclaimed. They were huddled round a monitor in Michael Binding's office. It was ten in the evening and a pile of pizzas lay in their boxes untouched on a table in the corner.

Dave was easily recognised from his familiar loping stride as he strolled along the shopping centre's main walkway. He didn't seem to be in any hurry. The time on the screen was 1.48, so there were twelve minutes to go before, according to the woman, he had arrived at Milraud's shop.

The tape was a composite of all the relevant segments located by A4, after a search through hundreds of hours of CCTV film. As Dave disappeared from view along the long row of shopfronts, he suddenly reappeared, crossing a small concrete courtyard full of shoppers. The time on the screen was 1.55. The figure reappeared on a broad street lined by office buildings. It was less busy here, and Dave was easy to pick out, until he turned left at a corner.

'That's Milraud's street,' said Judith. 'Look, it wasn't quite two o'clock when Dave went down it. That confirms what the woman in the shop said. But none of these cameras show him returning. We've checked others that cover the opposite end of Milraud's street, and there's no sign of him.'

Binding was unusually quiet. He had changed his clothes at some point during the day, and was now back in his quasi-military garb.

Liz asked, 'Do we know how he travelled there?'

'We're pretty sure he drove. His car's not at his flat,' Judith said.

'What's your point, Liz?' asked Binding.

'If he drove, he must have parked somewhere. If we find the car, we'll know he didn't come back.'

Binding's silence seemed assent. Liz said, 'So, since we first see him at the shopping centre, I suggest we check the car park there.'

Twenty minutes later Maureen Hayes and Mike Callaghan located the car, a Peugeot 305 from the car pool, which Dave had been driving for the past two weeks. It was on the upper level of the shopping centre car park. They approached it cautiously, then Callaghan lay down on the concrete and peered underneath with a mirror and a torch. When he stood up, he gave Maureen a nod and she opened the passenger door with the reserve key.

The inside was empty, except for a street map of Belfast lying on the driver's seat, and a half-drunk bottle of water.

By the time they phoned back with news of their discovery the meeting in Binding's office had broken up and Liz was sitting alone in her own office. She asked for the car to be brought back to the A4 garage. As she put down the phone she reflected that it was now overwhelmingly clear that Dave hadn't gone AWOL. Something bad had happened to him, and she was trying not to assume the worst.

Ten minutes later she and Judith reconvened with Michael Binding in his office. It was almost midnight now, and Binding stifled a yawn as Liz reported on A4's discovery.

'I think he's been taken,' said Binding, and Liz just nodded in agreement. 'It seems the only possible explanation. I'll tell DG in the morning.' He looked accusingly at Liz. 'Then he will want to send a team over.'

'Perhaps,' said Liz, unperturbed. 'In any case, Charles has agreed to send Peggy Kinsolving. She's coming tomorrow.' She added, 'Have we got a press officer here?'

'Of course,' said Binding, as if she'd challenged his competence. 'But why are you talking about press officers? The last thing I want to do is talk to the press.'

'I know that, Michael. The problem is that the press may want to talk to you. Chances are they won't hear anything, but it's not something you can count on. As we broaden the investigation, knowledge of Dave's disappearance will inevitably get to the police, for example. If the media get the faintest suspicion that one of our officers is missing, you can be sure they'll be all over the story. We'll need to be ready for that.'

Binding looked horrified. 'Can't we slap a D-notice on the story?'

Liz shrugged. 'You could try. But I imagine there are still some foreign reporters around. A D-notice won't stop them.'

He said nothing, which she took as agreement.

'What I don't understand,' said Judith, 'is what Milraud would want with Dave. If he saw through Dave's cover story, why didn't he simply refuse to see him again?'

Liz answered. 'I'm afraid it's unlikely to be Milraud who's taken him. When I spoke to my contact in the DGSE in Paris—he's the man who used to be a colleague of Milraud's and knows him well—he said violence isn't Milraud's style. He may have told Piggott about Dave.'

'But why kidnap Dave?'

Liz and Binding exchanged looks. Liz said softly, 'They may not hold on to him for very long.'

'You mean they'd—?' Judith started to ask, then stopped as she saw the answer to her own question.

'HERE I WAS, expecting the grim reaper to come through the door, and in walks the most beautiful girl in the world. Or have I died and gone to heaven?'

Liz was glad to find Jimmy Fergus back in buoyant form. After the shooting it had been touch and go for the first twenty-four hours. He was still hooked up to all manner of machines—an IV feed attached to his arm, wires linking him to monitors. But at least there was some colour in his cheeks, thought Liz, and he was sitting propped up in bed.

She kissed him on the cheek. 'This place looks pretty five star.'

'Appearances can be deceptive. You haven't tried the food.'

'I should have brought you a takeaway but perhaps these will help.' She handed him a box of chocolates tied up with a ribbon and sat down in the chair by the window.

'So how's business? It would be nice to hear about something other than my potassium levels.' He gave a derisory wave at the rig of wires and monitors around him.

'We've found the van your attackers used. It was burnt out in South Armagh, about five miles east of Moy.'

Fergus nodded. 'Provo country. Can't say I'm surprised. There are plenty of people in this world who would like to shoot me—including an ex-wife or two—but only the Republican renegades would actually go and do it.' He sighed. 'It's depressing when you think that ninety-nine point nine per cent of the population is keen to have peace, and yet we can't stop a few lunatics from jeopardising everything. Any progress finding the villains?'

'We're getting there,' she said with a confidence she didn't entirely feel. 'We think we know who one of the guys was—he worked part-time for a laundry service; that's where they got the van. His name's Sean McCarthy, and he's disappeared.'

Jimmy Fergus scratched his cheek thoughtfully. 'That name rings a dim bell but I can't put a face to it.'

'Actually, I was hoping you could give us a description of them both.'

'I'll try, but I only got a good look at one of them—that was the driver. He was young, maybe twenty, light short hair, skinny, about six feet tall.'

'That can't be McCarthy. The laundry owner said he was dark-haired and short.'

'Sounds like the guy with the gun. I got a quick look at him.'

'Hopefully, if we find McCarthy we'll find the other guy.'

He looked at Liz. 'But they're just small fry, aren't they? This was well planned; I don't think two youngsters could have done it all by themselves.'

'Your colleagues think the Real IRA are behind it, but McCarthy's never been associated with them. I'm wondering if it may have something to do with our mysterious Mr Piggott.' Liz told Fergus what they'd learned about Piggott, and about Milraud. She didn't mention Dave's disappearance.

Jimmy Fergus pointed a finger down at his chest, where the bullet hole lay buried under a blanket of bandage. 'I'm glad this happened before Milraud and Piggott finished their business.'

'What do you mean?'

He managed a wan smile. 'Piggott would have been buying better firepower from Milraud, I bet. Powerful, accurate weapons. Compared to them the little pistol that put me here was a peashooter.' He was silent for a moment. 'The funny thing is,' he mused, 'those two guys didn't even bother to hide their faces.'

Liz said nothing.

'What is it?' asked Fergus, disconcerted by the look on her face.

'I think they weren't expecting you to be able to provide a description.'

Fergus gave a satisfied grunt. 'In that case, they really were amateurs.'

8

The winter mistral was blowing strongly at Marseilles Airport as Martin Seurat waited with Isabelle for her colleague to bring the car from the car park. Isabelle was shivering beneath her raincoat. She had left behind her customary scruffy garb of sweater and jeans and was dressed smartly in a short skirt and cashmere cardigan.

At the last minute Seurat had decided to join Isabelle on her visit to Toulon. Strictly speaking, this kind of domestic investigation was not the business of his service, but he had been stirred into action by the intriguing phone call from Liz Carlyle. This was the first firm lead in a long time that might put Milraud away. If he was honest with himself, he'd also taken the trouble to come down to Provence because he had been so taken by his lunch with the British woman. She'd struck him as straightforward, clever and amusing, but with a modesty too. It was an unusual combination of qualities and he found it, and her, very attractive. He hoped he would see her again.

Martin Seurat had been an intelligence officer a good long time and he had recently had to admit to himself that the adrenaline was beginning to run thin. He'd been wondering if it was time to leave his service. But today, standing in a cold wind on a Saturday morning, he realised with surprise that he felt excited at the prospect of catching up with his old colleague, Antoine Milraud. The man had always sailed close to the wind but it looked as if this time he'd gone right over the line and got himself involved in the kidnapping or murder of a British intelligence officer. This was so out of character that Seurat was convinced there was more to it than met the eye.

For fifty miles or so, the motorway to Toulon cut along the side of the coastal hills, white outcrops of rock pushing their way through the pines and eucalyptus. From time to time the Mediterranean came into view, sparkling blue, dotted with white-crested waves. Within the hour they were driving into Toulon, past the big iron gates of the naval headquarters and the Préfecture Maritime and along the avenue de la République to the big car park on the quay, busy with shoppers attracted in by the Saturday market.

Leaving their driver with the car, they strolled through the Place Louis

Blanc, with its tall, blue-and-grey-shuttered eighteenth-century houses, into the market, which was still in full swing. As she paused to sample an olive, Isabelle said, 'Do you think it's likely Milraud has come back here?'

'It's possible. Though our British colleague said she thought it unlikely.'

'Ah. The charming Mademoiselle Carlyle?' she said, with a hint of amusement.

'Yes. The officer from MI5 you sent to see me. It's she who wants to know Milraud's whereabouts.'

'You explained the MI5 urgency, but I hadn't realised it was the same officer. They're sure Milraud is linked to their missing colleague?'

'She sent a message yesterday saying that it looked that way. Something unexpected must have happened. Milraud has done a lot of bad things in recent years, but it makes no sense for him to get involved in this.'

'There's a woman in charge at his shop—I had an officer look into it. Her name is Claire Dipeau. I doubt she'll tell us anything but let's call on her.'

At the shop, Seurat held open the heavy oak door for Isabelle and followed her inside. Behind a counter, a white-haired woman in a black jacket and skirt was polishing a beautifully chased metal scabbard with a cloth.

Madame Dipeau, thought Seurat. She looks very respectable. Clever of him—no one would suspect that a woman of mature years, formidable demeanour and decorous dress would be colluding in anything shady.

The woman looked up and nodded politely, then greeted them in the strong nasal tones of the region. '*Bonjour, m'sieurdame. En vacances?*'

'No. We were hoping to see Monsieur Milraud.'

The woman shook her head. '*Pas possible. Monsieur* is away.'

Seurat said, 'Really? When we spoke on the phone he mentioned a trip to Ireland, but he said he would be back by now.'

'He called to say he would be away longer than planned.' Her expression made it clear that this was a matter of indifference to her.

'Was he still in Ireland when you spoke to him?'

'I don't know where he was, *monsieur*. I did not enquire.' Madame Dipeau spoke sharply.

'Possibly Madame Milraud would know where we can find her husband,' suggested Isabelle. The woman gave an elegant shrug. 'Do you have an address and perhaps we could call on her?'

'I am not authorised to give out personal information, *madame*,' she replied coldly.

'Even if we are old friends of the Milrauds?'

Madame Dipeau raised both hands palms upwards to show that she remained unable to help.

There was a pause. 'You're right—we're not old friends,' said Isabelle, speaking brusquely now, fishing in her bag and producing a warrant card. 'Nor new ones, either. But I suggest you give us the home address of Monsieur Milraud right away. Otherwise, I will have the *gendarmerie* here in ten minutes. Not to mention an inspector of taxes, who will wish to inspect every item in your inventory, see every invoice, check every bill that's been paid. I am sure that when Monsieur Milraud returns, he will be pleased that he's left his business in such safe hands. *C'est compris, madame*?'

The woman looked hard at Isabelle. She said nothing, but, reaching for a pad, wrote down an address and pointedly handed it to Seurat.

'Bandol,' he said with a smile, reading the address. 'Antoine has certainly come up in the world. *Merci beaucoup, madame*.' Isabelle had reached the door but he paused and, pointing at the scabbard, said, 'That looks as if it belonged to one of Napoleon's marshals.'

'It belonged to Napoleon himself, *monsieur*,' Madame Dipeau said tartly.

As THEY WALKED back to the car, Isabelle said, 'She'll be on the phone by now to Madame Milraud. What's the next move?'

She didn't need to ask—this was technically her turf; she dealt with the French mainland, not Seurat. But she seemed to have guessed that Seurat had some sort of an issue with Madame Milraud and decided that if he wanted to handle the interview himself, she wouldn't stand in his way.

So Seurat said, 'If it's OK with you, I'll go on my own. But you're right. That woman in the shop will be phoning both the Milrauds probably. Now that we've put the cat among the pigeons, I think we need phone interception on the shop and on the Milraud house. Could you organise that while I go and talk to Annette Milraud?'

She nodded. 'I'll take the car back to Marseilles and start putting things in motion. You can take a taxi and we'll meet up again in Marseilles. Here's the address of our office there.'

He slid out of the back seat and walked across to a taxi rank. He was glad she had taken it that way. From what he knew of Annette, in the days when he and Milraud had been working in Paris, he was sure that woman to woman would not have been the right approach.

THE TAXI TURNED OFF the Toulon–Marseilles motorway and began to coast down the winding side road to Bandol. Eventually, it came to a halt at the gates of a big villa facing east towards Toulon. Seurat got out and rang the bell at the tall black security gates. A camera zoomed round to observe him as he gave his name to a disembodied voice. A pause, then the gate opened and the taxi drove in, up a steep drive bordered with carefully pruned conifers and flowering acacias.

As he got out of the car, the front door opened and a uniformed maid took his card and ushered him into a large hall furnished with two sofas and an ebony table. Marble floor; pale grey sofas; mimosa-yellow cushions. An interior design job, reflected Seurat.

Typical of Annette, he thought to himself as he waited. She'll make her entrance after she's given me time to take this in, and not before. He grinned at the thought of the shabby little suburban flat she'd last occupied in Paris. She'd be surprised he'd turned up here but delighted that he'd seen the luxury in which she now lived. But softly, softly, he told himself. That was the way to deal with Annette.

The door to the hall opened. She hadn't aged much; she still swept rather than walked. The tan was smooth, professionally correct like the room. She was dressed too young, he thought, looking at her short skirt and low-cut top.

As they touched cheeks, she put both her hands lightly on his, as if to suggest a physical intimacy that he was certain she didn't feel.

He said, 'It's wonderful to see you. I was hoping to see Antoine as well. Is he away?'

She nodded thoughtfully, as though reviewing the possible reasons for Seurat's arrival. 'Yes, he's away. He's often away. He doesn't always tell me where he is. I don't enquire.'

Seurat could not help admiring the adroit way in which she had taken the bull by the horns and wrong-footed him.

'Is there any particular reason for your asking about him?'

'Well, yes. I need to talk to him.'

'That's obvious enough. I don't expect you came here just to chat me up, Antoine, pleasant though we might both find that. Or did you?'

'Annette—look. He's got himself into a difficult position. I don't want it to get worse for him. It needn't do that—if I could speak to him. You must know either where he is or where he might be. It would help him if you would tell me.'

She smiled, slowly took a cigarette from a silver box on the ebony table, lit it, blew out smoke, tapped her foot on the floor and said, 'I dare say he's amusing himself. There are plenty of places where he could be doing that.'

Seurat ground his teeth. She knew perfectly well where the bastard was.

'Well, then, how long has he been gone? What's he up to at the moment—I mean, business-wise? How long is he usually away?'

'That's rather a lot of questions, Martin.' She smiled seductively. 'Do you always tell your wife what business you are on? Oh, I'm sorry, I forgot you're divorced now, aren't you? Fond as I am of Antoine, I do actually appreciate his reticence, even his absences, for that matter.'

Checkmate, thought Seurat. We're getting nowhere.

'*Eh bien*. You have my card. Please tell him to call me. Tell him I can help him. Tell him I understand his difficulty.'

'Do you? Well, of course I will tell him that. When the possibility occurs, naturally. I'm sorry you should have come so far for so little. I'm sure he'll get in touch. Sooner or later.'

Seurat gave up. There was no point in deliberately antagonising her. 'I'll say *au revoir* then, Annette.'

'Lovely to see you again. I'm sorry there's been nothing I could tell you.'

'WE WERE THE FIRST,' Otto Perkins declared, and it took Judith Spratt a moment to understand what he was talking about. 'Concrete barriers, armed police patrolling the terminals, sniffer dogs checking the luggage—we had them all years ago. It took 9/11 for the rest of the world to catch up.' Judith wondered if this was a lead to be proud of, but Otto's enthusiasm made it seem churlish to demur.

The little man was full of irrepressible energy, waving his arms about when he talked and walking around his tiny office in the Portakabin in the car park so it vibrated with transferred energy. He had been manager of the Davis Hire car rental agency next to Belfast Airport for eleven years, he told Judith. Throughout those years he had also been on the books of the RUC Special Branch as an agent, transferring his services to MI5 when they'd taken over the old police force's counterterrorist duties.

Otto was a useful source; he seemed to know everyone who worked at or around the airport. More specifically, the rental-car depot was a convenient location for parking cars safely when MI5 officers travelled. It also served (in the form of Otto) as a conduit for messages, a temporary repository for keys, and a fount of information on his customers when, as now, that was needed.

Judith got down to business. 'You had a customer from France last week called Antoine Milraud, who hired a Renault Mégane.' She gave Otto the registration number and he began to tap at the terminal on his desk.

'Got it!' he crowed suddenly, like a man whose horse had won the race. 'The maroon Mégane.' He swivelled in his office chair and pointed out of the grimy window towards the car park behind. 'It's over there at the back.'

'When was it returned?' asked Judith.

'Hang on,' said Otto, resuming his manic attack on his keyboard. 'It was the day before yesterday—early in the evening. Just when it was due. No damage to the car and the petrol tank was full.'

'You don't remember who brought it back, do you?'

He looked slightly puzzled. 'I assume it was Mr Milraud himself. But I can't say for certain—I was off duty at the time.'

'Who would have served him when he returned the keys?'

'It might not have been anyone. An awful lot of people use the express service—they put the keys in the box outside. We never see them. Let me look.' He flipped through a large file box of recent receipts. 'You're in luck; the keys were handed back in person.'

'Who would have dealt with it?'

'It was one of the mechanics in our garage.' He pointed to a low building on the edge of the car park. 'We do most of the servicing for the cars ourselves. And any minor problems—dents, broken wing mirrors, that sort of thing.' He picked up the phone on his desk. 'Let me give them a ring.' Someone answered right away and Otto said, 'Danny, you worked the evening for me day before last, didn't you?' He listened for a moment. 'I thought so. Right, can you come over for a minute?'

Judith waited, while Otto regaled her with tales from his past years at the airport, until a tall young man in blue overalls pushed open the door and came in. Motor oil was streaked down his cheek and his sandy-coloured hair was flopping in his eyes. His face was unmemorable, except that Judith remembered it, though she didn't know from where.

'This is Danny,' said Otto.

'Hello. Have we met before somewhere?' she asked, trying to place him.

'Don't think so.' He looked at Otto. 'You wanted to see me?'

'That's right, Danny. The maroon Mégane. It was rented out last week by a customer who brought it back two nights ago. I was off, and you would have dealt with him. A man named Milraud—he's French.'

'Don't remember him. He might have used the express service.'

'Not this guy,' said Otto, and pushed the receipt across the counter at the mechanic. 'See, you initialled it right there.'

'Oh, yeah,' he said slowly. 'But I don't have time to really look at them. I just take the keys, punch in the mileage, hand them a receipt.'

'You've got CCTV in here,' said Judith, looking up at the camera in the corner of the office. 'Perhaps we could look at the tape for that night.'

There was a short silence. Otto looked embarrassed. ''Fraid it's not working. Went off about a week ago and we're still waiting to get it fixed.'

Judith sighed in disappointment, still trying to think where she had seen the mechanic before.

Danny looked at Otto. 'Is that all?' he asked.

Otto turned to Judith, who shook her head. 'Thanks, Danny,' said Otto, and the mechanic left. Otto looked at Judith and shrugged. 'Ryan's a nice enough fellow, though he's not exactly a threat to Einstein.'

But Judith wasn't really listening, for a picture was beginning to take shape in her mind. It was of this same man who'd just been in the office, standing outside a door. Her door, at her flat in Belfast. What had he been doing there? she wondered. Delivering a package? It didn't seem likely. Then Otto's words echoed and she asked sharply, 'Did you say "Ryan"?'

'That's right. Danny Ryan.'

Now she knew where she'd met him—outside her door, all right, one evening when Mrs Ryan had stayed late, and her son had come round to give her a lift home. What a coincidence, she thought. She shifted her attention back to Otto. 'While I'm here, there's something else I wanted to ask you about. One of my colleagues collected a car here a few weeks ago, then had a bad blowout on the A1.'

'I heard about it. Your Mr Purvis paid me a visit.'

'Did my colleague collect the keys to the car from you?'

He shook his head. 'No, I wasn't here.' He seemed embarrassed again, as if afraid Judith was beginning to think he was always taking time off. 'It was Danny Ryan. He's normally the one who stands in for me. He's the senior of the boys in the garage. I know it was him, because Mr Purvis talked to him. Danny told him the car had seemed in perfect condition when your colleague took it away. Believe me, Danny would know—he's an excellent mechanic; I'm scared I'll lose him to another garage one of these days.'

JUDITH FOUND LIZ poring over reports.

'Well, I've found Milraud's rental car,' said Judith. 'What I don't know is whether he returned it, or someone else did.'

Liz grimaced. 'Since he didn't fly from the airport, chances are it was someone else.'

'It's the weirdest thing. Otto Perkins, the manager at the car-hire place up there, wasn't working when the car was returned. One of the staff in the garage handled it. His name's Danny Ryan.'

'So?' asked Liz absently, her mind on something else.

'He's Mrs Ryan's son.'

Liz looked at her with surprise. 'Our Mrs Ryan?' When Judith nodded, she asked, 'Are you sure?'

'Absolutely. I thought he looked familiar, then I remembered where I'd seen him before. He picked his mother up from the flat one evening, not long after she started working for me. Isn't that a coincidence?'

'I'll say,' said Liz, looking down grimly at the reports on her desk. She was still only half paying attention when Judith said, 'By the way, you've met Danny Ryan too. It was he who gave you the keys of that car you picked up at the airport the day you arrived.'

Judith had all of Liz's attention now. 'The car that had the blowout?'

'That's right,' said Judith. They looked at each other.

'Did you speak to this Danny Ryan?'

'Not really. I saw him. Otto called him into the office to confirm that he'd been on duty when Milraud's car came back. He wasn't much help; he said it had been too busy for him to remember any individual customer. The CCTV camera in the office is broken too, so there's no photographic record of who came and went.'

'I don't like this,' said Liz slowly. 'What does Danny Ryan look like?'

'Young, light hair, quite tall, lanky—his mother would probably say he needed feeding up. What are you thinking, Liz?'

'I'm thinking he fits the description Jimmy Fergus gave me of the gunman's accomplice.' Liz was biting at the side of one of her fingers. Judith knew that habit of Liz's. It meant that her mind was racing; she was slotting information and events into position like a computer.

'I tell you what, Liz. Why don't I give Otto Perkins a ring and ask him if Danny Ryan was working on the day Jimmy Fergus got shot?'

And three minutes later Judith Spratt put the phone down and looked wide-eyed at Liz. 'Otto looked up his duty roster. Apparently Danny Ryan had the day off when Fergus was shot.'

'I don't like this at all,' said Liz.

'That's the good news.' Judith paused. 'Danny Ryan went home ill just after I left their office this morning. Otto was mystified. He said Ryan's never been off ill before, and he looked perfectly well earlier in the day.'

'We'd better find him fast.'

'We know he lives with his mother. I've got her address in my book. Do you really think he's involved in all this?'

'I don't know. But there are too many coincidences to be just chance. Danny Ryan's been involved with Milraud's car; my car; he fits Jimmy's description; he was off work at the right time and the moment you ask him a question, he goes off sick.'

'So do we have him pulled in?'

'Not yet—there's nothing firm enough. But we need to talk to him.'

'I think I should go to their house. He should be alone because his mother will be at my place cleaning up before she collects Daisy—' Judith suddenly went very pale. 'Liz, if Danny Ryan's involved in this—what about his mother? Do you think she knows anything about it? She's looking after Daisy . . .' Judith's voice was rising. 'She'll be collecting her from school in an hour.'

Liz put a calming hand on Judith's arm. 'You'd better go to the school and be there when she collects Daisy. Just tell her that you decided to take the rest of the afternoon off and spend it with Daisy. Try to act normal. Meanwhile, I'll go round to the house to see if Danny Ryan's there. But this time I'm taking the police with me.'

'I MUST TELL YOU, Miss Carlyle, that we were surprised to hear that you and Mrs Spratt have got Annie Ryan working for you.' Detective Inspector Kearne spoke matter-of-factly but his anger was close to the surface. 'She's from an old IRA family. Her husband was Tommy Ryan—served five years for a plot to kill a Special Branch officer. Tommy was the intelligence officer—the one who did the background research for the hit men.'

'My God,' said Liz. 'I didn't know that. I took her on from Judith. I think she got her from an agency. I can't imagine she wouldn't have had her checked out but I'll certainly find out. Where's Tommy Ryan now?'

'He was shot dead twenty years ago trying to ambush a patrol.'

The car pulled up outside a small, red-brick, terraced house. As soon as Liz knocked, the door of the next-door house opened. Their arrival had clearly been observed by the grey-haired woman who now stood at her open door, hands on hips.

'There's no one in. Never is at this time of day. She picks a kiddy up from school and the lad'll be at work. There hasn't been an accident, has there? Can I give her a message?' she asked eagerly.

'No, thank you, madam. It's just a routine enquiry,' replied Kearne.

'I'll tell her you called.'

I bet you will, thought Liz as she climbed back into the car.

'What now?' asked the inspector.

'Just a minute.' Liz got out her mobile phone. 'I'll see if I can find out where Mrs Ryan might be.'

Judith answered immediately. 'Yes. I've got Daisy. I don't think Mrs Ryan suspected anything. She said she'd go back to the flat and tidy up. I didn't tell her not to as I didn't want to alert her to anything.'

'OK. Stay out for the moment and I'll ring you when I've talked to her.'

At her house, Liz let them in with her key and knocked on Judith's door. They waited tensely, but no one answered. Kearne looked at her questioningly; she was listening to something. Then, motioning him to follow, she climbed the single flight of stairs to her own flat. Through the half-open front door came the sound of a vacuum cleaner. Liz paused; pushing by her, Kearne went in first.

Mrs Ryan was in the sitting room with her back to them, vacuuming the carpet. Liz called out, but her voice was lost in the din. Looking around, she saw where the plug was pushed into the socket and switched it off. The vacuum gave a strangled moan, then went silent. Mrs Ryan looked round and jumped when she saw Liz and Kearne standing in the doorway.

Putting a hand on her breast, she said, 'Oh, you've frightened me, miss. I wasn't expecting anyone.'

'I wasn't expecting you either,' said Liz. 'I thought you'd be at Judith's today with Daisy.'

'I should've been, but Mrs Spratt picked Daisy up herself. I knew you'd been away so I thought your place could stand a bit of sprucing up.'

'That's very thoughtful, Mrs Ryan. Thank you. It's lucky you're here because I wanted to speak to you. This is Detective Inspector Kearne.' Beside her, Kearne nodded.

'Why don't we all sit down?' said Liz, motioning Kearne to take one of the chairs and gesturing at the sofa for Mrs Ryan. She crossed the room to close the front door and, as she passed the open doorway into her small study, she saw that the stack of files on her desk still lay where she'd left them, but the top file was open—and Liz knew she had left it closed. She'd never brought secret documents home—so Mrs Ryan's snooping, if that was what it was, would have been rewarded with nothing more interesting than her electricity bill.

Back in the sitting room, Kearne and Mrs Ryan were sitting awkwardly across from each other, neither speaking. Liz pulled up a chair next to Kearne and smiled reassuringly at Mrs Ryan. But the woman avoided her gaze. She never looks me in the eye, Liz thought, alert now in the light of her new information about Mrs Ryan's background.

'Is there something wrong, miss?' asked Mrs Ryan.

'Inspector Kearne and I have a few questions about your son, Danny.'

'Has something happened to him? Is he all right?' Her concern was real.

'I don't know, Mrs Ryan. I was hoping you could tell us. We wanted to talk to Danny but we can't find him.'

'Isn't he at work at the garage?'

'He left there earlier. He said he was going home ill. But he's not at home.'

'How do you know?' For the first time she looked straight at Liz, her voice rising in agitation. 'Have you been round there causing a fuss? What's Danny supposed to have done?' she demanded, looking at the policeman.

'That's something we're wanting to talk to him about,' Kearne said. 'Where do you think we could find your son?' he asked sharply. 'We have reason to believe that he may have been involved in a serious offence. If you fail to provide information, you may be charged with obstructing the police and it will be worse for him.'

'Worse?' Mrs Ryan stared at Liz, her eyes filled with hatred. 'How could it be worse? You murdered my husband. Are you saying you're planning to murder my boy now?'

Liz said, 'Calm down, Mrs Ryan. This has got nothing to do with your husband. Listen, this entire country's having to learn how to live with its past and move on. You should be helping Danny to accept that.'

Mrs Ryan sat straight, colour rising in her cheeks. 'Don't you lecture me about the past—or the future. This is our country and you've got no right here. Peace agreement my backside,' she said bitterly. 'You think you've won, don't you? But just wait and you'll see what we think of your peace process.'

Her voice was shrill, and Liz raised a hand in a calming gesture. But Mrs Ryan was having none of it. There was no deference now, just loathing so deep it chilled Liz. 'Don't you shush me!' the woman shouted. 'Oh, it's all sweetness and light on the surface—you and your friend, with her spoiled little brat.' She leaned forward and glared at Liz. 'Look at you: you haven't even got a husband, much less a family. How dare you lecture me. You haven't got a clue what it's like raising a child on your own, without a penny to spare, and the man you loved gone because a soldier decided it was his turn to die. How am I supposed to move on from that, *Miss* Carlyle?'

Inspector Kearne had heard enough. 'That'll do, Mrs Ryan. I think you'd better come with me down to the station. I should warn you—'

'Suit yourself,' she broke in. 'You can do what you like to me. You'll never catch my son. He's a clever boy.'

'We'll see about that,' said the inspector, putting his hand on her arm and manoeuvring her towards the door. When they'd gone, Liz sat down heavily on the sofa. The sudden transformation of Mrs Ryan from deferential cleaning lady to hate-filled harridan had left her thoroughly shaken.

9

'Peggy, I can't tell you how glad I am to see you,' Liz said to Peggy Kinsolving, who had arrived the previous evening and was now installed at a small table in the corner of Judith's office.

Peggy had been in the office since 7.30 and had already mastered the main facts of the case. Her table was strewn with papers and Liz could see that she had drawn up a list of questions. The two women had worked together for the last few years, both in counterterrorism and in counterespionage, ever since Peggy had transferred from MI6. They were perfect foils for each other: Liz the quick-thinking, inspirational case officer, who to Peggy's admiring eye always seemed to know what to do; and Peggy, with her enquiring mind, the scholarly lover of detail who took nothing at face value.

When Liz had finished bringing Peggy up-to-date with the previous day's events, she said again, 'It's such a relief to have you here, Peggy. Not that Judith's not great. But this business with Mrs Ryan has really knocked Judith for six. And to tell you the truth, I'm beginning to wonder if Michael Binding's having some kind of a breakdown. You never know what sort of a mood he'll be in. He swings from seeming almost eerily calm one minute to getting in a rage in the next. I just don't think he can take the strain.'

'Why don't you ring up Charles and tell him what's going on? He sent you his best, and I'm sure he'd be happy to help—he'd want to know if it's that bad with Binding. And he'd tell DG, without making a big fuss.'

Liz flushed. She had avoided asking Peggy about Charles, though part of her had wanted to. Since Joanne's funeral Charles had said hardly a word to her and Liz had finally decided that she would move on, knowing that for now she had nowhere to move on to. Never mind. She certainly wasn't going to run to Charles for help.

'Oh, there you are, Liz,' said Binding, poking his head round the door and nodding in Peggy's direction to acknowledge her arrival. 'Any news? It's been three days now and you've turned up precisely nothing.'

Liz and Peggy both stared at him. He looked flustered, sweating slightly, his tie hanging crookedly from his unbuttoned collar. He went on, 'I'm not happy about this at all. I've got to brief DG and the minister this afternoon. Is there anything for me to tell them, other than that you and Judith have been employing a known IRA sympathiser in your households?'

Liz resisted the urge to shout back at him and said soothingly, as if speaking to a child, 'Michael, why don't we go into my office where we can all sit down and I'll tell you what I make of what we now know?'

'I don't have time for a lot of chat, Liz,' said Binding, but she ushered him along the corridor to her office and sat him down. Peggy followed them in and Liz began to set out the case.

'Firstly, we know from Brown Fox that Seamus Piggott's intention was to kill policemen and an MI5 officer. It can't be coincidence that there's been movement on both fronts—Jimmy Fergus got shot and Dave's'—she paused—'Dave's been taken.

'Secondly, we know from Brown Fox and A4 surveillance that Milraud is involved with Piggott, probably supplying weapons. We know from CCTV and the woman in the shop that Dave made it to see Milraud, though from the absence of any CCTV coverage of him leaving—and the fact that his car was still in the shopping-centre car park—I think we can assume that

Dave disappeared *from* the shop. I'd say we can assume Milraud was involved with his disappearance, and I don't think it's too much to argue that Piggott was as well. Now we can't find Piggott or Milraud—or Dave,' she added. 'We don't know whether Piggott and Milraud are together but it's a fair assumption that one of them has Dave.'

'What do the French say?'

'They're looking for Milraud, but they don't see him as a kidnapper. Then there's Jimmy Fergus—at least we've got a lead there. A man named Sean McCarthy has been linked to the van that Fergus's attackers were driving. The problem is, we don't have anything to tie McCarthy to Piggott, and he hasn't been found yet either.'

When Binding sighed, Liz held her hand up. 'I haven't finished. McCarthy had a sidekick—the man who drove the van. Jimmy Fergus's description of him resembles Danny Ryan, the son of Mrs Ryan, Daisy Spratt's minder and our cleaning lady, whom you've heard about. He's disappeared.'

'And what has Mrs Ryan said about it all?'

'Nothing. She's not talking.' Liz went on. 'Danny Ryan works at the Davis Hire agency at the airport. He was in charge the night Milraud's car was returned, and apparently he signed it off. Finally, it was he who handed me the keys of the car I drove when I first arrived. The one that had the blowout.'

'Oh God, Liz, are you still obsessed with that flat tyre?'

Liz found it impossible to restrain herself any longer. 'How *dare* you?' she said angrily, rising from her desk. 'My close friend and colleague has disappeared, and you have the nerve to imply that I care more about a flat tyre, as you call it, than what has happened to Dave?'

Binding stood up and, just for a moment, Liz thought he was going to explode. She tensed, but then, to her relief, his fists slowly unclenched, and he sat down again. 'I'm sorry,' he said, barely audibly. 'I didn't mean to suggest . . . What should we do next?'

Liz sat thinking for a moment. 'Everything points to Piggott. Dave's informant Brown Fox—Dermot O'Reilly—worked for Piggott; Milraud was doing business with Piggott; and I'd bet my bottom dollar that when we track down Danny Ryan we find there's a connection there as well.'

'But you can't find Piggott. Or any of these other people.'

'A4 has Piggott's flat in the city under twenty-four-hour surveillance. And the police have been to his house in County Down.'

'Where is that?' asked Peggy.

'It's about thirty miles south of here. On the coast.'

'On the coast?' repeated Peggy. 'If all these people have gone to ground, maybe they're not still here. I wonder if they've left Ireland altogether.'

'We've checked all the obvious possibilities,' Binding said. 'Airports, trains to the Republic.'

Peggy was nodding vigorously. 'Yes. But what if they've gone out by sea? Has Piggott got a boat? That would have been the easiest way out.'

'I should have thought of that,' said Liz. 'I think we need to have another look at the County Down house.'

'I was just about to suggest that,' said Binding importantly. The *entente cordiale* had been too good to last.

THE RAIN WAS STREAMING down the jacket of the policeman who opened the National Trust gate and waved their car through. The gatehouse seemed to have become a temporary police post. Further up the drive two patrol cars were parked and, as their car swung round to park on the gravel apron in front of Piggott's house, a sergeant came out to greet them.

'We're inside, sir,' he said to Binding, as they moved quickly to the front door. 'There's no one here except the housekeeper.'

'Have you got a warrant?'

'Yes. We're going room by room now, but so far nothing unusual has shown up. I've got two men searching the grounds as well. The housekeeper claims she hasn't seen Piggott for days.'

Liz was surprised by how almost unnaturally clean the inside of the house was. On the ground floor a large sitting room ran the full length of the front of the building, its tall, oblong windows giving a dramatic vista of the shore. The sea was rough, filling the bay with white-crested waves, which came crashing onto the beach of the little cove.

Across the hall was a dining room with a large oak table and matching chairs, and behind it a small room with a modern desk. Its drawers had been forced open but they seemed to have contained nothing more exciting than a telephone directory. Upstairs, more policemen were combing the three bedrooms. All were pristine, and so devoid of anything personal that it was impossible to make out in which of them Piggott slept.

When they came downstairs they found the sergeant in the kitchen, where the elderly housekeeper was sitting at the table drinking a mug of tea.

'Is there a cellar?' Liz asked the sergeant.

'Yes. There is. But there's nothing down there. Do you want to see?' He led her down a flight of stairs by the back door into a small, empty room, with a rough cement floor and cold brick walls.

'Not even a rack for wine,' said Binding, who'd followed them down.

Liz was looking around. 'When do you think this house was built?'

Binding shrugged. 'Maybe thirty, forty years ago. Why?'

'Well, an old house would have a cellar—a wine cellar, cold rooms for storage, that sort of thing. In a house this age, why go to the trouble of digging out a tiny little room like this. What's the point of it?'

'You're right, Liz,' chipped in Peggy, who had joined them in the little room. 'You'd make a basement. Rooms you could use.'

'Meaning what?' asked Binding.

'Meaning we've been looking for even one room that showed signs of Piggott using it, and there haven't been any. So maybe there's another room. Hidden. One that we haven't found yet.'

Binding's lips tightened, but he said nothing.

'What do you think that's for?' asked Peggy, pointing to a metal box on a bracket halfway up one of the brick walls.

The sergeant poked at it, trying to open it. 'It's locked. There's no sign of a key anywhere here. Perhaps the housekeeper has it. I'll go and ask her.'

'Don't bother with her,' Binding ordered. 'Break it open.' And ten minutes later, with the aid of a crowbar from the boot of one of the patrol cars, the small metal door was off its hinges.

Inside was a switch, like the switch in a fuse box. It was up. The policeman looked questioningly at Binding, who nodded. 'Here goes then,' said the policeman, and pulled down the switch.

Immediately, there was a low grinding noise and the entire far wall started moving on tracks, opening to reveal a room on the other side.

Liz moved forward slowly, taking in the comfortable furnishings. There was a desk, on which lay a neat stack of files; she picked up the top one, labelled *Fraternal Holdings Q4*. This must be Piggott's office.

The sergeant was pointing to something in the corner.

'Yes, what is it?'

'It's a camp bed.'

Binding said, 'Surely Piggott didn't sleep here?'

'I suppose he might have done. Or possibly,' Liz said grimly, 'it's where they kept Dave.'

Just then a young constable came running down from the kitchen. 'Sarge,' he said breathlessly, 'they've found something in the grounds.'

'What is it?' asked Binding.

'It's graves, sir. Two of them.'

LIZ COUNTED seventeen people, all of them male, including two pathologists and a deputy superintendent of police. Three hours had elapsed since the policeman had run down the stairs to the cellar, time that seemed endless to Liz as she waited for what she felt was certain to be bad news.

The wind had dropped and the rain had turned to a steady drizzle as she and Binding and Peggy stood huddled together under one of the tall oaks. Someone had produced coffee in plastic cups and they warmed their hands as they waited for news in the fading light. Not fifty feet from them, two white tents had been erected over the graves—temporary morgues. Inside them the grisly work of disinterment proceeded.

At last a policeman beckoned and Liz went forward. Binding touched her arm, but she shook her head—she'd do the identifying, since she was more likely than he to recognise the second body. They would all be able to identify one of them, she thought grimly.

She stooped down to enter the tent and was momentarily blinded by the dazzling light of the halogen lamp hanging from the top pole. A curious, sickly, chemical smell hung in the air. The pathologist looked eerie in his white suit and surgical gloves. A sheet covered the body on the ground.

'Ready?' asked the pathologist.

Liz nodded, taking a deep breath, trying to prepare herself for the worst. The constable pulled back the sheet and she looked down.

She allowed herself to breathe out. It wasn't Dave. A young man with dark hair lay on his back. He could have been asleep, were it not for the hole in his temple. The bottom of one of his trouser legs was darkly stained.

'Do you recognise this man?' asked the constable.

'No,' said Liz quietly, and saw out of the corner of her eye that Michael Binding had come into the tent. 'But I think I know who it is. Tell me how tall he is. I can't judge, looking down at him like this.'

'Between five six and five seven,' said the pathologist.

Liz turned to Binding, who was still blinking as his eyes adjusted to the harsh light of the overhead lamp. 'It's almost certainly Sean McCarthy. He was the gunman who shot Jimmy Fergus. Jimmy hit him in the leg when he fired back at him. He told me that the man was short and dark-haired.'

Binding nodded, looking stunned. Liz took another deep breath. 'Right. Now let me see the other one.'

They followed the pathologist in a sombre procession, outside through the drizzle and into the adjacent tent. Again, a sheet covered a disinterred corpse lying on the ground.

Liz stepped forward, gritting her teeth. Why hadn't she rung from Paris, or London? Anything to avoid this. She waited as the pathologist pulled back the sheet, bracing herself for how the familiar features would look.

'No!' she shouted. For the face that stared up at her was not Dave's. Someone else lay on the ground. A much older man than Dave. But the face was familiar.

'What is it, Liz?' Binding demanded, seeing her astonishment.

'This is Dermot O'Reilly.' Her voice trembled with a mixture of relief and horror. 'It's Dave's informant, Brown Fox.'

NAUSEA. WHENEVER IT SEEMED to subside, it would quickly come back. Dave couldn't think about anything else, as fresh spasms gripped him.

He felt the floor beneath him rocking gently, and heard a smacking sound—water slapping against wood. He must be on a boat, below deck, in some kind of hold. The throbbing background noise was the engine.

Dave had no idea where he was, but he knew that he had been out of it for a long time. He wanted to flex his arms, but as he tried to lift one he found it held fast to his side. He was lying on a low camp bed and he saw that he had been tied up—very neatly, like a painstakingly trussed chicken.

So he was a prisoner. But whose? Gradually coming to, he tried to remember how he had got here. Images were flickering in a bewildering sequence through his head. A man, speaking with a strong accent—a foreigner, who had been trying to sell Dave something. A voice behind him, guttural, and a bulky man with a gun in his hand. Then some sort of library and the cold unfeeling eyes of the man who'd injected him in the arm.

Suddenly the hold door swung open and Dave was half blinded by a rush of light. He blinked and made out a figure looming in the doorway. A familiar man with a dark face was holding a tray, which he put carefully on the floor. Reaching down, he grabbed Dave with both hands and flipped him over like a fish, so that he flopped off the bed and lay face down on the floor.

He could feel the man fiddling with the rope that bound his hands. When he'd untied the knots he hauled Dave roughly up onto his knees and put the tray down with his free hand in front of Dave.

'Eat,' he said tersely.

Dave looked down at the plate, where a watery stew lay on a small pile of mash. It looked revolting. He clenched his jaw, but there was nothing he could do to stop himself as he vomited.

The foreign man stepped back in disgust, then quickly left the hold. Dave moaned and retched again, propping himself on his hands and trying to still the spasms in his stomach. I need to get out of here, he told himself dimly, realising that his legs were still tied.

The foreigner returned. He held a syringe in one hand and a pistol in the other. He pointed the gun at Dave, then leaned down and plunged the syringe into Dave's arm before he had time to object.

'*Sueños dulces*,' the man said.

PEGGY PUT THE PHONE down at the end of yet another call. She lifted her head for a moment to look out of the window and realised that it was morning. A brilliant red sun like a perfectly round tomato was just appearing over one of the barracks buildings. She had been working all night.

The discovery of the bodies buried at Piggott's County Down house had energised everyone. The forensic teams were still hard at work, but one thing had been discovered straight away. When Dermot O'Reilly's body had been disinterred, in his trouser pocket they'd found his mobile phone. The pathologist had said that O'Reilly had been dead a few days and that he had been buried soon after death, so Peggy had trawled through the phone's memory of calls.

It was the final call that the phone had received that interested her most. And, after a night spent in conversation with a variety of contacts in different agencies, she now knew that the call the phone had received at 5 p.m. four days ago had been made from a mobile phone that had been at that time somewhere in County Down. O'Reilly's phone had been in Belfast.

It seemed a fair assumption that the call had been connected to Dermot's visit to Piggott's farmhouse, and could have been the call summoning him to his death. As she contemplated her night's work, Peggy had the satisfaction that, although she didn't know who had made that call or even whose phone it was—it was a pay-as-you-go phone, bought at a shop in Belfast— if that phone came on the air again, anywhere in the world, she would be immediately notified. At last there was a chance of getting somewhere in the search for the people who had taken Dave.

As Peggy sat at her table, her eyes drooping now, Judith Spratt came into the office.

'Good morning, Judith. I wasn't expecting you. Who's looking after Daisy?' asked Peggy.

'DI Kearne's wife, Bridget, is taking her to school. Daisy's taken a real shine to her. I told her Mrs Ryan had to stay at home because her son was ill. It's funny how you tell lies to kids without a second thought.'

'Well, that seems reasonable enough. You could hardly tell her that Mrs Ryan hated us all. Or that her son had tried to kill Liz.'

'No. That's true,' said Judith. 'By the way, you probably haven't heard, but A4 now think that Liz's car was tampered with. Apparently the nuts holding the wheel bearing had been overtightened; if you do that the bearing can collapse and the tyre shreds. It's the kind of mistake an amateur can easily make, but not an experienced mechanic.' Judith shook her head. 'It's difficult to imagine how someone as young as Danny Ryan could feel that level of hatred for someone he'd never met. Anyway the police have got him now—he was caught speeding just outside Newry yesterday.'

'Good. Maybe they'll get something out of him,' said Peggy, yawning. 'Though if his mother's anything to go by, he'll keep his mouth firmly shut.'

'Peggy, you've been here all night, haven't you? Go and get some breakfast. I'm going to start working on this boat theory.'

'BOAT?' SAID PHIL ROBINSON. He was in Antrim, cleaning up the National Trust hides on the coast, ready for the bird count that would begin in April. He sounded confused by Judith's question. She had explained again that she was talking about the National Trust property in County Down and the neighbouring house. Had he seen a boat moored at the jetty there?

Then, 'Ah,' he said with sudden comprehension. 'Yes, indeed. I have seen a boat there sometimes. One of those rigid inflatables. It's the dinghy from a big motor cruiser that I've noticed anchored just offshore where the sea's deeper. One of those glitzy things you see in the Caribbean.'

'It's the motor cruiser I'm interested in. Can you describe it?'

Robinson thought for a minute. 'I'd say it was a good thirty metres long, maybe longer. White with chrome railings all round, and a big open space on the rear deck. You could see it had several cabins below. Then there was a small upper deck, with a glass window surrounding it. I suppose that's where it's steered from.'

'Was there anything else about it you remember?'

'Yes, it had a squashed bow—it was wide, like a hammerhead shark.'

'I don't suppose you noticed its name by any chance?'

Robinson laughed. 'I did, now that you mention it, because it sounded so peculiar. *Mattapan*, with a Roman numeral III next to it—so I guess you'd say 'Mattapan the Third'. Not an emperor I've ever heard of.'

No, thought Judith as she thanked Phil Robinson, thinking of Liz's meeting with Daryl Sulkey of the FBI. It was *Mattapan III*, the trio of Boston-Irish gun runners sent to prison, of whom only Piggott's brother had failed to come out again.

Peggy was now back from breakfast, looking much brighter.

'Let's suppose they've gone off in *Mattapan III* and taken Dave with them. Where might they be going?' asked Judith.

'America?' suggested Peggy hesitantly.

'Surely even a boat like Phil Robinson described couldn't sail all the way to America at this time of the year, could it?'

'Probably not,' Peggy admitted. 'What about France? Milraud's base is at Toulon. Let's phone round to see if anyone has had sight of *Mattapan III*.'

Several hours later, they had come up with nothing. None of the obvious port authorities had any record of the boat putting in for fuelling.

'It can't have disappeared, unless it's sunk,' said Peggy gloomily to Liz, who had joined them. The lack of sleep was beginning to catch up with her. 'Do you think we should ask the RAF to put up a Nimrod?'

'No. We can't do that,' Liz responded. 'Binding is still insisting we keep the enquiry low-key. If Dave's disappearance leaks out, or Piggott and Milraud detect us close behind them, they may just kill Dave.'

'If they haven't already,' said Peggy, now close to tears.

'Peggy, go home and go to bed,' ordered Liz. 'We'll have to hope the police get something useful out of Danny Ryan or the French come up with some development. They've got Milraud's wife under close surveillance, so perhaps we'll get a breakthrough from that.'

ON THE SIXTH DAY they cast anchor in midafternoon just off the coast near Marseilles. It had been a steady enough voyage, though they had lost half a day by putting in at a small harbour on the Portuguese coast to avoid a late winter storm that had moved in from the Azores. *Mattapan III* was well known there and Piggott had arrangements with the harbourmaster.

Later, as they were passing the Balearic Islands, Milraud had decided to take a risk and ring his wife. The rule they had was no communication when he was away on business, unless he initiated it. He had not spoken to her since he left France. '*C'est moi*,' he'd announced when Annette answered the phone. 'Have you missed me, *ma chérie*?'

Usually she replied in kind to his endearments, so he'd been surprised by the urgency in her voice. 'Listen, Antoine. There's been a visitor here.'

'Yes?' He was impressed but not surprised that the British had moved so quickly. '*Un anglais?*'

'*Au contraire*. A Frenchman. Someone you used to know very well in Paris. Your closest colleague—'

'Enough!' he said sharply, cutting her off. If the British had already roped in Seurat to help in the search, things were serious. Seurat would have all angles covered and that meant that the phone line at the Bandol house was being intercepted. 'Tell me later. Is all well otherwise?'

'A bit lonely *toute seule*, and worried. Your colleague seems determined.'

I bet he is, thought Milraud.

TWO DAYS AFTER THE CALL, as the sun began to go down, Milraud started up the engine of a small but powerful motor yacht moored in an unremarkable boatyard in the Marseilles docks. He steered the boat gently out to come alongside the larger and more splendid craft, lying at anchor off the harbour. On the offshore side, a swarthy man helped a pale-skinned, ill-looking figure to transfer from the larger to the smaller boat, which then in turn dropped an anchor. The large cruiser sailed slowly and carefully into the boatyard and slotted itself with some difficulty into the vacant mooring. Then two men in a dinghy sailed out to the smaller boat; the dinghy was hauled on board and, in the gloom of the evening, the smaller boat sailed on southeastwards, hugging the shoreline until it passed Toulon.

Twenty minutes later Milraud could make out the shape of the island, then the hazy glow of light from the houses in its one hamlet on the north side. He sat in the pilot's seat with Piggott next to him. As they moved sharply south to the side of the island farthest from the mainland, the lights receded into the night-time black. Here, on the south side, the island was uninhabited, its shoreline composed of rocky crags rising sheer from the sea. As they neared the southeastern tip of the island, Milraud turned on the boat's spotlight and saw what he was looking for—a small, sheltered cove, the only possible landing place. He knew that near the shore a boom lay across the mouth of the cove, designed to keep craft from landing. But this was not the first time he'd landed here and he knew the trick of moving it.

Two hours later, Milraud sat on the rickety porch of an old farmhouse perched 100 feet above the cove. The house, the only one on this side of the island, was reached from the cove by a twisting path. It had taken Piggott and Gonzales twenty minutes to climb, half carrying their barely conscious prisoner, while Milraud took his motor cruiser round to the other side of the island and moored it in the small marina. He then walked back across the island, along familiar paths, guided by a torch.

The house had woods on either side, but on its inland-facing north end a small meadow fronted onto a now-wild vineyard that had been untended since the death of Annette's father. When Annette had inherited it, Milraud had persuaded her to hang on to the property, and its outbuildings had proved an excellent site for storing items that would never be displayed in his antique shops. His boat, kept normally in the Marseilles boatyard, though modest in appearance, was fast and roomy. It could hold a dozen crates of assorted weapons, and sat so lightly in the water that it could come in close enough to shore for his North African employees to load and unload his cargoes, wading waist deep, carrying crates on their heads.

Milraud took another sip of his Calvados as he considered his next moves. The MI5 man was safely confined to the cellar. Upstairs, Gonzales sat playing patience in his shirtsleeves, with a holstered 9mm pistol under one arm. Piggott was in the sitting room, with his laptop open.

As he finished his drink, Milraud pondered the situation. Ever since Gonzales had pulled a gun on Willis in the Belfast shop, he had been managing a fast-unravelling crisis, acting by instinct. Now, for the first time, he had a chance to look calmly at what had happened and to think what to do next.

Maybe if Willis had admitted to being an MI5 officer, the situation could have been saved. But Willis had denied it, putting on an almost convincing performance. Once in the same profession, Milraud had recognised the drill.

Piggott had wanted to kill Willis without more ado and Gonzales was just waiting to pull the trigger. But Milraud knew that if they had killed him there and then, the sky would have fallen in on all of them. And if Piggott had allowed Gonzales to kill Willis, why wouldn't they have killed him too?

He didn't think for a moment that his long working relationship with Piggott would have saved him if he'd been in the way. Milraud wanted to get control of a situation that was rapidly running away from him. He had put it to Piggott that a better plan was to transfer Willis to another group as a hostage. The publicity that would then result, he had persuaded Piggott, would ruin the reputation of MI5 for good.

Piggott had bought the plan and agreed to come here to the island house, which Milraud had painted as a safe base while he arranged the onward transfer of Willis. He had mentally drawn up a list: the FARC—the Colombian rebels with their long-standing links to the IRA; the Basque separatist movement ETA; an al Qaeda cell who would be natural customers, though he had little faith in their internal security.

But this would take time to arrange, and even from his short conversation with Annette it was clear that the British were on their tail. There was no time for the complexities of a hostage transfer, though he had no intention of telling Piggott that. Particularly because he was convinced now that Piggott was unhinged. The Irish-American had started ranting in an excited fashion. 'We've struck a blow against the Brits they won't forget,' he'd crowed as he stood at the helm of *Mattapan III*.

No. Milraud made up his mind. There was only one way out for him and that meant acting fast. He'd need Annette's help. Probably she was already under surveillance, but the encrypted email he'd send her in the morning would warn her of this, and tell her that they needed to meet, but only if she could be confident she wasn't being followed. She should make a trial run, he'd tell her, just as far as Toulon to flush them out, see if they were onto her already, and more important, see if she could shake them off.

10

Martin Seurat put down the phone. The poor girl. She sounds distressed, he thought, looking out of the window of his office at the thin sprinkling of late snow. Not surprising. She seems to have a mass murderer loose in Belfast, bodies buried in the countryside and her colleague still missing. Unfortunately he had nothing new to tell her. There had still been no sign of *Mattapan III* in French waters.

Liz Carlyle had wanted to know if Milraud had a boat. There was nothing on his files about a boat, though given where Milraud lived and the business he was in, he must have one.

Seurat was just about to pick up the phone to the DCRI, to pass on the enquiry to Isabelle, when his phone rang again.

It was Isabelle herself. 'I have some news for your Liz Carlyle. Milraud has been in touch with his wife. The call came from Majorca, so yesterday he was in the Mediterranean region.'

'Many thanks, Isabelle. I'll pass that on. Just before you phoned, she rang to ask whether Milraud owned a boat. I have no record here of such a thing. But could Milraud have been at sea when he made that call?'

'Possibly. But I have something else for your Liz. Tell me, how well do you know the wines of Provence?'

'What?' he said, puzzled. 'What's that to do with Liz?'

'Have you ever come across a wine called Chateau Fermette?'

A small farmhouse chateau—the name a joke, he supposed. He sighed. 'No, Isabelle, I haven't. Are you doing a crossword puzzle?'

'Martin, you sound cross. Don't be. The wine I'm referring to was made on the Ile de Porquerolles. The island lies just off the coast in the south. The vintner was named Jacques Massignac. He had a daughter, something of a beauty. She inherited the vineyard but she moved to Paris, and had no interest in making wine. Chateau Fermette is no more.'

'I'm beginning to get your drift. You are talking about Annette Milraud, aren't you? She once told me she had southern roots.'

'I am. Monsieur Massignac's daughter is Annette. When he died she inherited the *fermette* for which its wine was named. It seems she was going to sell it after her father's death, but according to the tax people she didn't.'

Now they were getting somewhere. 'Isabelle, tell me everything you know about the Ile de Porquerolles and this *fermette*.'

CASCADING RAIN, lightning, ear-shattering thunder—no film version of a storm could have been more dramatic. The clouds that had been hanging over the hills for hours had finally come east, and stayed put. In her office, Liz was wondering if the storm would ever pass.

The phone rang and she reached for it mechanically, her eyes on the display outside. 'Liz Carlyle.'

'Liz, it's Martin Seurat again. I think I may have some news for you.'

Liz listened raptly as Seurat recounted Isabelle's discovery that a farm-house and vineyard on the Ile de Porquerolles belonged to Annette Milraud.

'Where is this exactly?'

'Just off the south coast and only a few miles by sea from the harbour in Toulon. The island is not very large—about seven miles wide, perhaps three across. Said to be very pretty and quite unspoiled. Very few people live there all the year round. There is one village, also called Porquerolles, on the north side of the island, near a fort, with a small harbour. There's a passenger ferry to it from a tiny place called Gien. Outside the village there are virtually no houses. Annette's *fermette* is isolated on the other side of the island, facing out to the Mediterranean and North Africa. There are no beaches there, just high rocky cliffs. Isabelle's people have made discreet enquiries and found that the house and the vineyard have fallen into disrepair.'

'It sounds ideal if you wanted to hide something. Or someone,' she added.

'Exactly. Let's talk about where we go from here.'

Liz paused to think. She was torn between wanting to send armed police to the island right away, and the realisation that any mistake might alert Piggott and Milraud, and end up with Dave being killed.

Seurat seemed to read her thoughts. 'I was going to propose that my people have a look around, but very carefully—I will supervise the operation. I'll go down to Toulon tonight and we'll look around in the morning. If we do establish that someone is there, then I think we should move in quickly. The longer we wait . . .' He left the sentence unfinished.

'Of course,' said Liz, already making arrangements in her mind. 'In which case I'll want to be there. I'll come down to Toulon tomorrow after-noon. Unless you have any objection,' she added as a formality.

'Of course not. I'll be delighted to have your company. I'll ring you tomorrow, and don't worry: our people are very good. *À bientôt.*'

PIT PAT, PIT PAT, PIT PAT. If the noise didn't stop he'd go mad. The ceiling was too high for him to reach the pipe with its tiny leak causing this infuriating continuous drip of water onto the concrete floor.

You've got to concentrate, Dave told himself. Stop thinking about that bloody drip. He was trying to beat his tired, confused brain into action.

It had been pitch-dark when they'd put him in here, and now he could see sunlight through the slit of a window high up in the wall. It must be afternoon, so he'd been here at least eighteen hours. By standing on tiptoe he could just see trees. By the look of it he must have been brought south, Spain possibly or somewhere along the Mediterranean coast. Near the sea in any case; he could smell it when he put his face to the little window, and hear waves breaking on a shore.

He couldn't remember much about the journey. He vaguely recalled two occasions when they'd transferred him from one boat to another. The second one had been small—probably just a dinghy. He'd had a bag or something over his head—and he'd been pushed and dragged up some kind of steep path. His wrists were tied and he'd fallen several times.

Then the foreign man had forced him into this place. He was Spanish— Dave was sure of that, since he had a dim memory of the man saying 'sweet dreams' sarcastically in Spanish. *Sueños dulces*—that was it. Thank God the Spaniard had taken the bag off his head and untied his wrists. He'd also shoved a mattress and a blanket in before he'd locked and bolted the door.

Dave figured he was in some sort of old wine cellar. A faint aroma still hung in the air. There was a wall of empty bottle racks and two huge oak barrels that sounded hollow when he tapped them.

Why were they holding him and what did they want with him? Think back, he said to himself. He could remember sitting in Milraud's shop. They'd been looking at a derringer and he was just about to proposition Milraud when the Spaniard had burst into the room waving a gun. Then he couldn't remember anything clearly until he was on a boat. Just a lot of what seemed like muddled dreams. There'd been several people on the boat; he'd heard voices but he'd only ever seen the Spaniard.

None of it made sense. If this was some renegade Republican conspiracy aimed at British intelligence, surely they'd have kept him in Northern Ireland. Why bring him on this long journey? Why was a Spaniard involved? He remembered Jimmy Fergus had said something about Piggott bringing in a hit man from the Costa del Sol. Was he in the hands of ETA? Did they take hostages? Why were they operating in Northern Ireland? Did Milraud work for ETA? And if so, what did he want with Dave?

He had no answers. But he kept asking himself the same questions to avoid sinking into despair. He felt ill. His wrists ached from being tied up and his head ached with a dull, throbbing pain that made him feel dizzy.

He remembered Seamus Piggott, the American man who wanted to kill an intelligence officer, questioning him in some sort of library. This would be a good place to put a bullet in his head, thought Dave gloomily, as he surveyed his prison. But they hadn't done it yet, so there must be another plan. Did they plan to ransom him? He almost grinned at the thought of Michael Binding negotiating for his release—he'd probably try to knock the price down—but then suddenly depression settled on him like fog and he crawled back to the mattress and lay down.

Then he heard something outside, quite far away. *Thumpa thumpa thumpa*. It was a helicopter, probably military, by the sound of its base rumble. He opened his eyes. Was it coming closer? 'I'm here, boys,' he found himself saying aloud. He held his breath and waited, but now the noise was receding.

Then silence. *Pit pat, pit pat, pit pat.*

SHE LOVED WINDOW-SHOPPING, so Mireille Vitrin was perfectly happy strolling along the rue d'Alger, looking in the shop windows, admiring the clothes. But Mireille wasn't going to buy anything; her window-shopping was cover. She was waiting for the little device in her hand to vibrate, signalling that the target was on the move ten miles away.

'She's coming out.' The gardener, cutting the grass verge at the top of the hill in Bandol, spoke into a tiny microphone fastened to his collar. He wasn't the usual gardener and anyone who'd watched him closely might have wondered how he got the job. But he wasn't staying. As soon as the white Lexus convertible passed him, he put his mower on the back of his truck and drove away. In Toulon, Mireille's hand vibrated.

Down the hill in Bandol two women sat in a dusty-looking Renault consulting a map. As the Lexus passed, they seemed to make up their minds on the route and drove on, slotting in behind it. The woman at the wheel of the Lexus, wearing a bright Hermès silk scarf, was Annette Milraud.

'On our way,' the passenger in the Renault announced, as they followed the Lexus in the direction of Toulon. A set of traffic lights turned amber just as the Lexus approached, but Annette speeded up and flashed through as they changed to red. The Renault stopped and waited, watching as the Lexus purred off onto the motorway. But a Volvo was already on the motorway, driving cautiously in the slow lane but speeding up as Annette went by. When the Lexus left at the exit for Toulon, the Volvo stayed on the motorway, leaving the job to another team already waiting outside the Musée de la Marine.

Under their watchful eye, Annette drove into the centre of town and parked on the quayside. Carrying a fashionably large designer handbag, she crossed the avenue de la République and turned down the rue d'Alger. As she approached her husband's shop, she may have noticed the woman with strawberry-blonde hair just coming out of the pharmacy opposite. She didn't go into the shop, but continued along the street at a fast clip. Behind her the blonde woman, apparently muttering to herself, passed the target on to colleagues at the end of the street.

Walking briskly, Annette turned into the street where the market was in full swing, and went into a café. She sat down at a corner table and ordered a *café crème*. When her coffee arrived she paid the waiter, left the change on the saucer, and, taking her handbag, got up and retired to the Ladies'.

Mireille Vitrin, who had circled round from the Milraud shop, came into the café and went directly to the Ladies'. Inside, she found one of the cubicles occupied, and quietly went into the next one. When she heard the door of the neighbouring cubicle open she waited several seconds, then opened her own door and emerged in time to glimpse a woman leaving—she wore jeans, trainers and a T-shirt, with her hair tied back in a ponytail. She was carrying Annette's large handbag. Mireille radioed Annette's new description to all colleagues as she went to the door of the café and looked out to see the woman in trainers striding swiftly back to the quayside.

'*Charmant*,' said the old woman to her husband, and it was true that the couple disembarking from the ferry this afternoon and setting off across the Ile de Porquerolles on foot looked madly in love.

The man, Alain, wore a knapsack from which protruded a baguette. Françoise, his companion, had a pair of binoculars on a strap round her neck—the island was not famous for its bird life, but there was a large population of waders on the south side, which justified both the binoculars and the three-mile walk.

The couple were heading for the walking trail that crossed the island and led to a promontory on its rocky southern shore. They took their time, holding hands, and every now and then stopping to exchange a kiss. But once they'd passed the first bend in the trail and could no longer be seen from the village, they picked up pace, walking briskly, no longer holding hands. They were not lovers, but they had worked together many times before. Alain was cautious, thorough; Françoise was wily and inventive.

They stayed on the tree-lined path, passing some deserted holiday homes. Suddenly, as if on cue, they moved off the path and into the woods. Here they walked quickly through pines and acacia trees, stopping often to check their bearings as they neared the island's rugged south coast.

When they heard the sound of waves ahead of them, they split up. Taking the binoculars, Alain moved towards the seaside cliffs in search of the narrow path that went down to the beach. Françoise stayed on the higher ground, looking for a way to approach the *fermette* they knew was there.

Locating the path down to the beach at last, Alain decided to avoid it and instead to work his own way down the steep bank. The cove was exceptional on this side of the island, with its strip of white sand. Alain could see no one on the beach, although the sand looked disturbed. It would be consistent with photographs taken just hours earlier, at daybreak, by the small helicopter that was normally used to chauffeur visiting dignitaries but which also provided low-key reconnaissance. Any boat that had landed here would have to be small—small enough to be lugged out of sight.

Alain was still above the beach, and from behind three eucalyptus saplings he used his binoculars to scan the bushes that started where the sand of the beach stopped. For ten minutes he moved them inch by inch over the dense undergrowth, but eventually, when his eyes were tired with the effort, he let the binoculars hang from the strap round his neck. It was then that a reflection of the sun, now straight ahead of him, briefly blinded him. He realised the flash was coming from the bushes below him—the one place he had not examined with the binoculars. Peering down, he moved his head slowly back and forth, until again a dazzling flash hit his eyes.

There it was. The boat had been tucked deep underneath a large myrtle bush, but a steel corner of its outboard engine was exposed—just enough to catch a glint of sun.

Got you, thought Alain.

Twenty minutes later he was back in the woods above the cliffs, at the place where he had arranged to meet Françoise. He waited impatiently, and then suddenly, soundlessly, she was standing next to him.

'Christ, you startled me,' he said.

'Good. If you'd heard me coming they might have heard me as well.'

'*They?* You've found people?'

She nodded. 'I discovered the farmhouse. Very run-down; I was sure no one could be living in it. But then two men came out; one of them was walking in the yard. He didn't look too good. I'll radio in when we get a bit further away and tell them we've found them.'

Alain hesitated. Always cautious, he did not share Françoise's certainty. He said, 'We shouldn't jump to conclusions. I found a boat—a little dinghy, well hidden. But that could just be to keep it from getting stolen. And the two people you saw might be perfectly innocent visitors to the farmhouse.'

'Trust you and your caution,' said Françoise with a deprecating laugh. 'The man I saw walking in front of the house was being *guarded* by the other fellow.'

'How could you tell?' Alain demanded.

'Because the man on the porch was covering his prisoner with a gun.'

As LIZ EMERGED from the baggage hall at Marseilles Airport, she saw a young man in naval uniform holding a sign reading 'CARLILE'. She introduced herself, '*Bonjour. Je suis* Liz Carlyle.'

'Good afternoon, mademoiselle,' he responded, shaking her hand. 'Follow me.' He led her to a smart black car parked outside the terminal.

Having apparently exhausted their knowledge of each other's language, they drove towards Toulon in silence. Liz gazed out at the Provençal landscape and the Mediterranean glittering in the midday sun, wishing that her first visit to this part of France could have been in happier circumstances.

Martin Seurat had telephoned late the previous afternoon to report the results of the surveillance on Porquerolles—the signs of a landing at the small cove, the dinghy concealed in the bushes and, finally, the sighting of occupants at the *fermette*, with an armed man guarding a prisoner. He was, he'd said, sending a photograph taken by one of the surveillance team. He waited to see if she could identify her colleague. Shortly afterwards, Liz was looking at a hazy photograph on her screen—a man apparently walking in a dusty yard as another man, holding a gun, stood watching him from the porch of a ramshackle house. It was the Spaniard, Gonzales, and Dave Armstrong—she recognised him even with his back to the camera.

Liz had taken the last flight from Belfast to Paris, frustrated that she couldn't be instantly whisked straight to Toulon. Martin Seurat had told her that no rescue attempt could be mounted before the following night, but she still wanted to get there and not hang about wasting time in Paris.

In the airport hotel, Liz had taken a call from Peggy, who told her that she heard from the DCRI that the mobile phone number she'd circulated round the world, the phone that had called Dermot O'Reilly shortly before he'd been killed, had come on the air again that afternoon. The French DCRI had noted it making a call to a number in Algiers, which had been routed through a mast near Toulon. It must be Piggott, thought Liz. So he's on the island, too.

As the car turned through tall iron gates on the coast at Toulon, she dragged her mind back to the present. She was surprised when a sentry saluted smartly as they passed; not sure how to respond, she acknowledged the courtesy with a wave. They drew up in front of a long, elegant, pink building and Martin Seurat stepped out and opened the car door.

'Welcome to naval headquarters, Liz. Come inside and I'll show you your cabin. This place is run like a ship, but you'll soon get used to it.'

Seurat looked reassuringly calm and in his navy-blue polo-neck sweater, ready for anything. Liz felt her anxieties begin to slide away; now she had someone else to share both the worry and the responsibility.

'It's not the Ritz,' he said, opening a door, 'but I hope you'll be comfortable. Not that you are likely to get much sleep, I'm afraid. We're planning to go in at three thirty tomorrow morning.'

Liz looked in at the room. It was spare and functional: a narrow bed, a bedside table, a cupboard and a small desk along the wall. She was pleased to see that it had its own small bathroom.

'I'll meet you downstairs in fifteen minutes and brief you about what we're planning,' said Seurat, closing the door behind him.

After Liz had changed into trousers and a sweater, she went down to find Seurat waiting for her in a comfortable lounge. 'Good,' he said, smiling. 'Let's have a cup of coffee. We've got a little while before we go into the briefing meeting. The teams are all here. Crack commandos from our *bérets verts*, the Commandos Marine. They are good, Liz. If anyone can rescue your colleague alive, they will do it.'

Liz smiled at him. 'It was an immense relief to know that Dave is alive, and we're very grateful for all you've done,' she said. 'I just hope we can get him out of there unhurt. But I'm mystified about why he's been brought here. What is Milraud up to? What do you think he wants?'

Seurat shrugged. 'Antoine will have no interest in harming your colleague. If I'm right, he will be trying to find a way out for himself. Your Miss Kinsolving'—he hesitated over the pronunciation—'has let us know that she thinks that the American Seamus Piggott is also on the island and that the armed guard our surveillance saw must be working for him.'

'Yes. She told me that Piggott's mobile phone came through on the Toulon transmitter.' Liz shook her head with worry. 'We know that Piggott would like to murder a British intelligence officer. This guard of his is a Spanish hit man he hired to work for him in Northern Ireland.'

'Well, as they haven't killed your colleague yet, Milraud may be stopping them,' replied Seurat calmly. Looking at his watch, he announced the time had come, and led Liz to an office upstairs where he introduced her to the base commander, a burly bearded figure called Hébert. Commandant Hébert held Liz's hand and bowed in a disconcertingly formal way, then made a short speech of welcome in French. The formalities over, the three of them walked along a corridor to a conference room. Here, a group of about twenty men dressed in white T-shirts and navy-blue trousers were lounging on chairs talking. They stood up as Liz, Seurat and the commandant came into the room and sat down at a table facing their audience. All eyes were focused on Liz.

Hébert clapped his hands and they sat down. Liz looked coolly back at the men whose job it was to free Dave Armstrong. They were all lean, fit, wiry and agile-looking.

It was a dangerous task the men would embark on, Hébert announced, but he knew they would do their utmost to accomplish it on behalf of France and our good allies the British—here he introduced Liz as 'our colleague from the English MI5', and every eye turned to scrutinise her again. Their task, he continued, had the full authority of the minister and the government was aware of their mission. He knew they would conduct themselves as the professionals they had always shown themselves to be, and for which they were known—he turned in Liz's direction—throughout the world.

She was relieved when the commandant concluded his remarks and left the room, leaving the practicalities to Seurat. On the screen behind him a map of the Ile de Porquerolles appeared.

'You've all had the chance to study the aerial photographs of the island and the plan of the inside of the *fermette*,' Seurat said. 'You should remember that the plan is several years old, but we don't think any significant alterations have been made to the building in recent years.'

Seurat went on, showing photographs of the island and outlining the purpose and plan of the operation. 'You will be in three teams of six. The first will land on the north side of the island at the harbour where the ferry arrives from the mainland.' He indicated the place on the map behind him. 'The second team will stay out at sea, off the south coast of the island, facing the cliffs here,' he said, moving the pointer down the map. 'You will be ready to intercept anyone trying to escape from the south.'

He paused, then looked at one of the commandos sitting in the front row. 'The third team will lead the assault on the farmhouse, landing in the small cove where we believe the targets also landed. Commando Laval, you will be responsible for taking the farmhouse and freeing the hostage.'

Laval nodded sombrely and Seurat said, 'We believe that apart from the hostage there are three people in the house.' Four photographs came up on the screen. 'One is a former colleague of mine.' He pointed to a photograph of Milraud. 'Our English visitor, Mademoiselle Carlyle, can tell you what she knows about the other two hostage takers—and of course the hostage himself. She will speak in English, but I'll translate.'

Liz stood up and began with a short description of the situation in Northern Ireland, pointing to the picture of Piggott. 'This man is American, of Irish descent. He was born James Purnell, but changed his name to Seamus Piggott when he moved to Northern Ireland. He is an expert in missile technology, but in Ireland he has been running an organisation that deals in drugs, extortion, prostitution.' She gestured at the image of the bespectacled man. 'Don't be fooled by his appearance. This man is highly intelligent and very dangerous. He will not hesitate to kill.'

The commandos were listening intently as Liz went on to describe Gonzales, the Spanish hit man. Then she paused, glancing at the alert faces watching her. 'It might be useful if I tell you how my colleague became a hostage.' As she spoke and Seurat translated, describing the circumstances behind Dave's capture at Milraud's shop, she felt a certain hostility growing in the audience. Commando Laval raised a hand.

'Yes?' said Liz, but he addressed his question to Seurat.

'From what I understand, this Englishman Dave must have behaved very recklessly in putting himself into this situation. How can we be assured that he is a genuine hostage? Could he not be a willing captive, perhaps cooperating with this Piggott and Milraud for some unknown reason?'

There was a murmur of assent. Seurat looked at Liz. She had understood the question and was astonished at the suggestion. But of course these men didn't know Dave, and they were about to put their lives at risk to rescue him.

'Let me tell you about Dave Armstrong,' she said. And as she talked, she tried to give a picture of the Dave she knew—recounting his enthusiasm for the job, his honesty and bravery, the key roles he'd played in counter-terrorist operations. Gradually, she sensed the mood changing.

'It is the case,' she said finally, 'that on this occasion Dave Armstrong acted impetuously, even recklessly. But whatever he did was with the motive of serving his country and preventing harm to others. I assure you, you need not fear that he will be cooperating with his captors.'

She sat down, and to her surprise a small ripple of applause came from the commandos. '*Merci, mademoiselle*,' said Laval. 'That is reassuring.'

Another commando raised his hand. He said to Seurat, 'It can be chaotic in the confusion of an assault. If it turns out that there are more people in the house than we expect, will you be on hand to help identification?'

'Yes,' said Seurat. 'Though only Milraud is known personally to me.'

Liz spoke up. 'I can identify the targets, and of course the hostage, too.'

'You are landing as well?' asked the commando in astonishment.

'Naturally,' said Liz simply. 'But don't worry—I won't get in the way.'

THEY WERE RUNNING out of food. There was nothing fresh left—no vegeta-bles, no bread or milk, just a few tins. Milraud reckoned they could hold out for another day and then they'd have to get supplies from the Casino mini-market in Porquerolles village, three miles away.

He supposed it might be safe to send Gonzales over to the village, but it was a risk—Gonzales, with his strong Spanish accent and his tendency to pull a gun at the slightest provocation, was hardly unnoticeable. There was also always the chance that Gonzales might simply get on the ferry with a one-way ticket and never come back. That is, if he managed to get away. Milraud guessed that Gonzales's description would have been as widely cir-culated in France as his own—and Piggott's. As he thought of Seurat's visit to Annette he felt certain that time was running out and that his former col-leagues were circling ever closer.

Food was not the only problem. Piggott was growing increasingly volatile. The night before he had lost his temper when his laptop computer had frozen, and he'd hurled it across the room. The man couldn't seem to sit still, and three or four times a day he walked down the cliffside path to check that the dinghy, buried beneath bushes, was still there.

More worrying still, he was ignoring Milraud's advice not to use his mobile phone. Every few hours he asked if there was any reply from the contacts Milraud said he had emailed with the offer to sell Dave. If something didn't happen soon, Milraud feared he would snap, and that could mean very bad news for Willis in the cellar.

There was no sign of a response from the contacts because Milraud had not actually sent any emails. His original idea had been to convince Piggott that Annette was to be the intermediary with the purchasers. Then somehow she would get Willis off the island and Milraud would find a way of following her, leaving Piggott and the Spaniard to fend for themselves. But this was now out of the question, as the email he had received from Annette this morning made clear: I think it best to postpone my visit for a while. Too crowded, even at this time of year. She was under surveillance and had been unable to shake it off.

Which meant there was now only one way out.

It took Milraud ten minutes to compose the email. He sat at the old pine table in the sitting room, keeping several windows open on his screen as he typed—ready to switch over at a click of his mouse if anyone came in and tried to look over his shoulder. Finally he finished, and hit the SEND button.

Greetings, Martin

    I have in my possession something of value to you and your colleagues across the Channel. I can deliver this package and those responsible for taking it, and I will do so and help to bring the perpetrators to justice on one condition. I need assurance that I have official immunity from prosecution from both the French and British authorities. I have kept the package unharmed but may not be able to do so much longer.

    I await your response. Time is running out.

    Antoine

'THE WIND'S GETTING UP,' said Liz. She was watching the yachts in the marina through the window of the restaurant where they were having an early supper. 'It won't stop us going, will it?' she enquired anxiously.

'It's the mistral. It comes and goes at this time of the year. But don't worry,' said Martin Seurat with a smile. 'It would take a hurricane force ten to stop Laval. It may mean they'll change the plan and load the rigid inflatables onto a frigate rather than sailing them out from the base.'

'When will they decide?'

'Sometime in the next few hours. The weather is very uncertain on this coast at this time of the year. The wind may drop again.'

There was silence as they drank their coffee. Then Liz said, 'The waiting is always the worst part. I feel far more nervous in the run-up to an operation than when it's actually under way. There's always in the back of your mind the thought that things might go wrong.' She thought of Dave and the consequences for him if things didn't work out in the next few hours.

'That's what this job is all about: the excitement, and the fear,' Seurat said. 'But there's also the satisfaction when things do go right. Whatever happens, at least it's never boring. That's a great help when other things aren't going so well.'

Liz looked at him, sensing that he wanted to say more. 'Is there something in your life that hasn't gone well?' she asked gently.

He gave a small shrug. 'Recently there was.' He sighed, then seemed to decide he wanted to tell her about it. 'I think I told you that my wife suddenly took herself off to her mother's house in Alsace last year. It was on a Friday. She said she was going for the weekend. I was surprised because she hadn't mentioned it before. I was even more surprised when the weekend ended and she didn't come back.' He gave Liz a wry look. 'She had neglected to tell me that she was still in love with her first boyfriend.'

'That's awful. I'm so sorry.'

Seurat shrugged. 'I was sorry too at first. But it's history. We're divorced now. And that's where the job came in. However bad I felt at the time, I always felt better the moment I got to work.'

Liz said nothing, but she knew what he meant. When her personal life had seemed especially bleak (there'd been Mark the married *Guardian* journalist, Piet the Dutch banker who'd dropped her, and the tantalisingly unavailable Charles Wetherby), she had always found one consolation. The job. As a cure for heartache it was unbeatable.

'Anyway,' Seurat said, 'that's enough of that. If you've finished, I'll get the bill. I propose we walk back to the base through the town.'

Half an hour later they were back at the gates of the naval base. Liz was hoping to catch a few hours' sleep before the 3.30 a.m. rendezvous. But she had not been in her room for more than ten minutes when the telephone on the desk rang. It was Seurat.

'Liz. I'm sorry to disturb you but there's something I need to show you.'

Her stomach lurched. Was it some bad news about Dave? Seurat was standing at the bottom of the stairs, clutching a sheet of paper, and his face had lost its usual calm expression. 'I've had an email from Antoine,' he said, giving her the paper. 'He says he can hand over your colleague.'

Liz read the email carefully, then looked at Seurat, mystified. 'I don't get it. This can't be what he's been planning all along or he would have been in touch before. What do you think's going on, Martin?'

'There must have been a different plan that hasn't worked out. I think he knows we're getting close; Annette's been sending him emails. Milraud's trying to leave Piggott and his Spanish hit man to face the music, while he cuts a deal to save his own skin. That's typical of him.'

Liz thought for a moment. 'You know Milraud—I don't. But I don't see how he can deliver on this offer.' She waved the print-out with one hand. 'I can't believe Piggott would ever let it happen. And don't forget, Gonzales works for Piggott, not Milraud—I think if Piggott knew about this email he wouldn't hesitate to order Gonzales to kill him.'

'I would imagine Antoine's getting desperate. How would you like to proceed? It is, after all, your colleague who's at risk.'

She said, 'I need to consult my head office. But I also need your view— do you think Milraud can deliver what he's promising?'

'I think he wants to, in part to redeem himself. But whether he can depends on the situation on the island. I would be surprised if even this Piggott could easily get the better of him. But in the end, Antoine will look after his own interests, and your colleague will come second, whatever he's promised us.'

Which would leave Dave at the mercy of the psychopath Piggott and his hit man Gonzales. No, thanks, thought Liz. 'I'm going to recommend we go ahead as planned. Can I use the communications on the base?'

Twenty minutes later, Binding's reply came back:

DG agrees with your recommendation. Please go ahead as planned and good luck.

11

D ave was shivering. When he was first locked in the cellar, it hadn't seemed particularly cold. Now it felt chilly and dank. He must be running a temperature. If someone didn't rescue him soon, it would turn to pneumonia and he'd die in this miserable place, without ever knowing where he was or why he was here.

That was if the Spaniard didn't kill him first. Each time Gonzales unlocked the door to shove in a tray of food, he looked at him with real venom. Food, thought Dave—you could hardly call it that. He was getting less and less of it, too. They must be running out, which was another reason why something had to happen soon.

There had been no further sound of helicopters since the one he'd heard the day before, but he told himself that Liz and the team would be scouring the earth for him, helped by every foreign service they were in touch with. Sooner or later they'd find out where he was, and help would be on its way.

Meanwhile, he had to stay alive until they came, and be ready to help them if he could. For he had no doubt that Piggott and the Spaniard would do everything to resist the rescuers—including shooting him. He needed to find some sort of weapon—any sort, however primitive—which would increase his chances if the shooting started. The problem was, the cellar had been stripped clean: there was his mattress, a bucket that functioned as a disgusting toilet, two large empty wine barrels, propped on their sides on stands, and a wall of empty wine racks.

Moving slowly, Dave systematically explored the rest of the cellar. The thin shaft of light from the slit window didn't reach into the corners, so he had to stick his hand in and feel around, sending spiders scuttling.

After ten minutes he was exhausted and ready to give up. He leaned against one of the two empty barrels for support, and suddenly whatever was propping it up gave way. The barrel rolled off its stand, crashing onto the floor and knocking Dave down.

After a time, he dragged himself up onto his knees and looked at the damaged barrel. It had split apart, its ribs fanning out like an opening flower. Could he use one of the wooden ribs as a weapon? No, they were too big to conceal. What about the circular metal bands? Again they were too big and, anyway, he had nothing to cut them with.

But as he looked at the pile of wood lying on the cellar floor, Dave saw something metallic glinting among the wooden staves. He crawled over and reached out to where he'd seen the glint, only to be rewarded with a sharp prick on his finger. He gingerly felt around again for whatever it was. Got it! He looked at the object in his hand. It was some kind of blade.

Lifting it up to the light, he saw that he was holding a small knife, no more than four inches long, with a worm-eaten wooden handle. The thin, rusty blade had a wickedly sharp point—blood was dripping from his finger now—and was sliver-thin. It wobbled precariously in the ancient handle, but it felt wonderful in his hand and he held it lovingly. He could use it only once and he'd choose his moment carefully.

LIZ WAS WIDE AWAKE when the alarm on her phone went off. It was 3 a.m. After helping Martin Seurat compose a stalling reply to Milraud, she'd dozed rather than slept for three hours, troubled by muddled dreams of Dave, Piggott, and boats rocking in the wind.

Liz dressed in warm clothes and went downstairs to the rendezvous point in the lounge. Seurat was there looking threatening in a black battledress and trousers, with light black waterproof boots. In his hand he held a black balaclava and helmet.

'Put these on over your clothes,' he said, pointing to another set of black garments laid out on a chair. 'They're the smallest size there is, so I hope they won't be too big.'

'Where are the commandos?' she said as she pulled on the suit.

'They're down at the harbour, loading the inflatables onto the frigate. The wind is still blowing, so they've decided not to go out in them.'

The frigate was a long, lean, evil-looking vessel with a stern that was open like a car ferry. Liz and Seurat were welcomed on board by one of the crew and taken up to the bridge to meet the captain.

On the dot of four o'clock the frigate slipped out, sailing quietly past Toulon harbour, where a slumbering flotilla of sailing boats and motor cruisers lined the jetties, then moving towards the open sea. Now the wind began buffeting the ship and spray splashed against the window in front of them. Two lights on the bow cast dual beams across the waves as the frigate swung in a long arc eastwards towards the Ile de Porquerolles.

As they approached the island, Seurat put his hand on Liz's shoulder. 'Laval asked me to make sure you understood the rules for this operation. When we land on the island, he's in charge. You and I are merely here as advisers. I have communications but you haven't, so you must stick very closely to me to avoid getting out of touch.'

Liz nodded. This was not the first military operation she'd been on. '*Compris,*' she said.

The frigate slowed to a stop and with a gentle splash the first inflatable, with six commandos on board, emerged from the stern and, its outboard motor muted, headed off towards the ferry terminal on the island's north side.

'Time to go,' said Seurat, and they climbed down companion ladders to the ship's belly. The twelve remaining commandos were a frightening sight, dressed as they were entirely in black, their faces streaked with black pitch, balaclavas on, night-vision goggles on top of their heads, with their guns and equipment hanging at their sides.

Ten minutes later the frigate stopped again, this time on the Mediterranean side of the island, half a mile out and half a mile down the coast from the farmhouse. The second team climbed into their boat and peeled off rapidly to take their position well back from the cove, covering that exit route.

'Here we go,' said Seurat, smiling at Liz, and her stomach gave such a lurch that she thought for a moment she would be sick. Laval shook hands and they wished each other *bonne chance*. A few seconds later, it was Liz's turn to climb out of the open stern into the rocking rubber boat. Seurat kept a steady hand on her arm as she lowered herself into the boat, where a commando was waiting to help her sit down on the side of the middle pontoon.

'Hang on tight,' said Seurat, joining her on the pontoon, and a moment later Laval sat down in the stern, the outboard whirred and they were off.

At first Liz could see nothing but the white spray of the waves as the boat bumped over them. Then she made out the looming cliffs of the shoreline to her right, and began to get her bearings—they were working their way west to the cove.

Suddenly Laval closed down the throttle and the boat slowed abruptly. The commando in the bow stood up and as the engine cut out he jumped over the side, holding a rope attached to a hook on the prow. Seconds later, the bottom of the dinghy jarred against the beach.

Following Seurat, Liz jumped out into the shallows and waded up onto the little beach. Taking her cue from the others, she pulled on her night-vision goggles, and an eerie monochrome world appeared.

Three commandos stood guard on the beach, facing the path they'd seen on the map of the island, while two others went rapidly off to one side of the beach. A minute later this pair returned; they'd found the boat Seurat's surveillance officers had discovered.

Laval said, 'Pierre, you stay here and guard the boat.'

The commando named Pierre disconsolately kicked the sand, then headed off to his post. Laval said something to the other commandos, and they laughed.

'He seems very disappointed,' Liz said to Seurat.

He chuckled. 'Yes, this is his first mission so he wants to make his mark. Laval said once he had more operations under his belt he'd be less keen.'

Now Laval turned to the other commandos, and pointing to the path just visible on the edge of the beach, announced, '*Allons-y.*'

The path climbed sharply and was wet. Liz was not used to the night-vision goggles and found it difficult to gauge her footsteps. She slipped twice; each time Seurat was there to help her up. At last they reached the clifftop, where she was able to catch her breath as Laval conferred with the other commandos. Then, from further along the cliff, a noise. The commandos moved swiftly and silently into the cover of the wood and Liz, led by Seurat, joined them in the trees.

They crouched in silence, the men with their weapons at the ready. Suddenly a shriek broke the silence—then again, even higher-pitched.

Laval whispered somewhere to their left, and Seurat said in Liz's ear, 'A fox. And now it's got a rabbit.'

They regrouped on the path, which ran through the wood in the direction of the farmhouse. Laval was about to speak when there was another noise, just yards up the path. This is no fox, thought Liz, as they all moved back into the trees. Footsteps. Someone was approaching.

'I AM SURE we'll hear from FARC tomorrow,' Milraud had said before he went up to his bedroom, but from Piggott's absent nod he could see the man wasn't listening. It was then he'd realised that Piggott didn't care about selling Willis any more. He'd decided to do something else.

Milraud lay now on his bed in the dark with his clothes on, listening carefully. It was 4.30. He was tired, very tired, but he'd managed to grab a cat nap in the early evening precisely so he wouldn't fall asleep now, when he most needed to be alert.

He had received an email from Seurat. It said that he needed more time to consult the British before replying to Milraud's offer. Perhaps that was true; equally, though, it might be an effort to buy time while he and his men hunted them down. He had replied tersely, Time is running out.

Piggott's behaviour had, if anything, become more unbalanced—he had begun talking to himself and pacing continuously. He had started complaining of being 'cooped up', and he'd even threatened to take the ferry for a visit to the mainland.

This had forced Milraud's hand—he'd had to tell Piggott then about Seurat's visit to Annette and explain that there was surveillance on the mainland. Piggott had taken this news badly and had started making even more forays out to 'check the boat', which still lay hidden down by the beach. On one of these jaunts, Milraud had taken the opportunity to search through the American's belongings. In the small holdall beside Piggott's bed he'd found a Smith & Wesson .38.

He felt it first, rather than heard it—a slight shuddering of the floor. If it was an earthquake, it was very mild. But then he heard the soft burring noise. What was it? A helicopter some distance away, or something else?

As he listened, he heard a creak from the landing. Silently, he swung his legs off the bed and went to his door, which he had left open a crack. Peering out, he could just distinguish a figure moving cautiously down the stairs. Slim, tall—it was Piggott.

'James,' he said calmly, fully opening his door.

Piggott didn't seem startled. 'Did you hear that?' he asked. 'It sounded like a chopper.' He was moving towards the porch. Was he carrying something? In the dark, Milraud couldn't tell.

'Where are you going?' asked Milraud.

'To check the dinghy,' said Piggott over his shoulder. He opened the screen door and stepped onto the porch. 'That's our only ticket out of here and I'm not letting anybody take it.'

Milraud waited, counting to ten, then went back into his room and picked up a heavy torch. He walked across the landing into Piggott's room. In the torch beam he saw the bed, unslept in, and looked around for the holdall that held the .38. It wasn't there—Piggott must have taken it with him.

That confirmed what he suspected—Piggott wasn't checking the boat; Piggott was going to *take* the boat, to get away. Which would be disastrous—left with a homicidal Spaniard and a hostage, Milraud calculated that he'd either be shot by the hit man when he discovered Piggott had fled, or shot by Seurat's men when they arrived to rescue Willis. If he somehow managed to survive, he'd be in prison for ever after kidnapping a British intelligence officer. None of these options appealed. The only thing to do was to follow Piggott and persuade him not to leave. That would buy enough time to alert Seurat that he must move in fast.

Opening the screen door, switching on his torch and shading the beam, he moved gingerly outside, towards the path that led down to the beach.

THEY WOULD BE here soon—very soon. He didn't stop to wonder who 'they' were—French or British or even the FBI. Any one of them would be intent on arresting him.

That wasn't going to happen. As soon as Piggott reached the woods, he stopped and unzipped his holdall. The .38 lay on top of a folded towel and he took it out and stuffed it into the waistband of his trousers. Then he threw the holdall into the bushes at the side of the path. It wasn't going to help him escape—for that he needed only his wits about him. And the gun.

He moved quickly, ignoring the brambles that scraped his arms and face as he tried to stick to the path. He hadn't dared bring a torch, since that would draw the people closing in on him.

He should never have trusted Milraud and never have let him bring him here. Not to an island, so easy to seal off. The only way out was by boat. Once he got to it now, he'd be free and clear.

Next stop Algeria, he thought. Ahmed there had replied to his email at once, saying Piggott could pick up a consignment of hashish. He could also pick up a larger boat, and he figured a good five days' hard sailing would see him back in County Down, no one the wiser about where he'd been or what had happened.

He supposed it would have been best to silence Milraud before he'd left, or at the very least leave orders with Gonzales to kill both him and the prisoner. Still, Milraud was the one left holding the can, not Piggott. As he began to descend the trail to the beach, he was cheered by thoughts of returning to Northern Ireland and finishing his business there. Soon MI5 would rue the day they'd taken over intelligence duties in the province.

Suddenly Piggott heard footsteps along the trail, coming up from below. He moved quickly into the thick brush, where he crouched down. He waited tensely, hand on his pistol, and listened as several people—at least six, maybe seven—climbed up the path. Then they were above him and he rejoined the path silently and continued his descent.

Take it slowly, he told himself, as he drew to within a stone's throw of the cove. To his right the dinghy lay covered in brush, but he knew better than to go straight to it. These people were doubtless fools, but even fools took precautions, and Piggott expected a sentry to stand guard over the boat.

He left the path again, a good twenty feet above the beach and edged, inch by inch, circling the dinghy. He stared hard at the shadows on the beach cast by the overhanging trees and pulled the gun from his waistband.

THE FOOTSTEPS WERE getting closer. Liz crouched behind the trunk of a eucalyptus tree, waiting for the commandos' challenge.

'*Halte!*' Laval shouted. '*Qui va là?*'

There was silence for a moment, then from the trail a voice called out, 'Antoine Milraud.' He seemed to hesitate. 'I am not armed.'

'Are you alone?' Laval called out.

'*Oui.*'

Seurat interjected, 'You had better be telling the truth, *mon ami*, because it will cost you your life if you're not. Where are the others?'

'In the house. Except for James—the American. Piggott as he calls himself. I was following him when you stopped me just now. He has gone to check the boat.'

'The boat hidden by the beach?'

'Yes. That's the one. And he's armed.'

Laval spoke urgently into his radio, warning the young commando in the cove. He turned to the commandos around him. 'Fabrice. Jean. Go back and help him.'

Two men slipped away through the trees. Then Laval, Seurat and the two remaining commandos emerged onto the path, while Liz stayed behind in the shadow of the woods. She could see Milraud's face now, illuminated by the commandos' lights.

'Where is the hostage?' demanded Laval.

'He's locked in the cellar. I will show you. But be careful: the man guarding him is not likely to hand him over without a fight.'

'Is that the Spaniard, Gonzales?' asked Liz, emerging from behind her tree to stand beside Seurat.

'So. The English are here too,' said Milraud, looking at the slender black-clad figure in surprise. 'You are well informed, mademoiselle.'

'Is anyone else here?' asked Laval.

'No one,' said Milraud. 'Just three of us and Willis. That's all.' He looked at Seurat. 'You know I wouldn't lie to you about that.'

'I don't know what you'd do any more, Antoine.'

'It's been a long time, but some things don't change. I would never have harmed this man. And I offered you my help in my email. Don't forget that.'

Seurat said drily, 'Well, we managed to get here without your help.'

Suddenly there was the sound of a gunshot, a solitary *crack* breaking the predawn silence. It came from the beach.

Seconds later Laval's radio crackled. 'Pierre here—I've been hit,' the voice said in a high-pitched tone of pain. 'I didn't hear the bastard coming. He's winged me in my shooting arm and he's got the dinghy. I can see him.'

The radio crackled again. 'Fabrice here. We were just seconds too late. We're with Pierre now. The target is in the boat, twenty yards from the shore. We're leaving him to Team Bravo.'

'We have him in our sights,' came back from the team waiting offshore.

Led by Laval, the group on the path moved quickly through the trees, taking only a minute or two to cover the short distance to the cliff's edge. A hundred feet or so below, the sea shone grey as the early-morning light began to touch the water. As they looked down, they could see a dinghy moving out into the cove, the puttering of its outboard motor just audible.

'That's him,' said Milraud, and Laval radioed confirmation to Team Bravo. He issued an order: 'Attempt to detain. Otherwise destroy.'

They watched as Piggott picked up speed, heading straight towards the south. *Next stop Algeria*, thought Liz.

But then she saw the commando craft appear at the mouth of the cove. Even loaded down with its team of commandos, it was going much faster than Piggott. As it drew closer, on a line to cut off his escape, Piggott changed course sharply to the east.

Suddenly a long arc of red dots jumped out of the commando boat: syncopated tiny flares, fluorescent against the dark grey sea. They disappeared just ahead of the bow of Piggott's little dinghy. Tracer bullets, thought Liz. Watching in silence, she heard the sharp crack of a weapon. Piggott was returning fire. He must be crazy.

The commandos fired another line of red bullets, this time even closer to the target. And again Piggott fired back, accurately enough to cause the commando dinghy to veer. There was a momentary lull, then the commando boat fired again, and these were not warning shots.

Suddenly flames appeared at the back of the small dinghy. Piggott jumped up from his seat in the stern, his clothes on fire. As the illuminated figure moved to leap overboard, the dinghy wobbled perilously. But before he could jump, the outboard motor burst into flames, and a split second later exploded with a bang that reverberated round the cliffs. The sky above the dinghy lit up like a rosy-pink firework, and the shock wave reached the watchers on the cliff.

'*Mon dieu!*' exclaimed Seurat.

Liz looked in vain for signs of the dinghy. But it had completely disappeared, blown to bits by the force of the explosion.

THEY STOOD IN SILENCE. Then Laval said, 'We must get to the house fast. That must have been heard from there.'

Milraud pointed to a track. 'This way is quickest.'

They moved along as fast as they dared; it was still quite dark in the woods, and the track was overgrown with tangled shrubs and tree branches that hung low. Laval led the way with one of the commandos, while Liz, Milraud and Seurat proceeded in a line behind them. The second commando brought up the rear.

Suddenly Laval stopped and held up his hand in warning. He had reached the edge of the trees. In front of him was an open courtyard and, looming in the background, a long stone building with a verandah up wooden steps to one side. The farmhouse.

Laval gathered the group round him. 'If the Spaniard is still asleep, where will he be?' This was addressed to Milraud.

'That leads into the kitchen,' the Frenchman said, pointing at a door covered by a fly screen. 'There are two doors out of it. The green baize one leads into a sitting room; the other one opens into a corridor running the length of the house. Gonzales sleeps in the first room off the corridor. There's another door to the house at the front.'

Laval nodded and turned to one of the commandos. 'Gilles, you cover the front of the house. Once you get there, wait till you hear my order then move inside and throw the stun grenades into the Spaniard's room. If he comes out your way, don't let him escape. *Compris?*'

Gilles nodded, his jaw clenched.

He turned to the second commando. 'We'll go in through the kitchen door. We will try to flush out the Spaniard before we release the hostage. Seurat, you go in up those steps and watch our backs, and keep Milraud with you. We may need him to talk to Gonzales. Mademoiselle, you keep under cover out here in the trees.'

As she positioned herself behind the broad trunk of a pine tree on the edge of the courtyard, Liz felt her heart beating painfully against her ribs. This was the moment when Dave would either be saved or killed. It seemed to her that Laval had split up his forces far too much. Pitifully few of them were actually here to do the job they had come to do: rescuing Dave. He's left the courtyard unguarded, she thought, her spine crawling at the thought that Gonzales might already be out of the building and in the woods, perhaps creeping up on her, unarmed and unprotected as she was.

She watched as Martin Seurat and Milraud crept up the rickety wooden steps and disappeared into the farmhouse. Then she turned to look at Laval and the commando moving stealthily round the edge of the courtyard, towards the kitchen door, keeping low, holding their weapons ready. They had reached an open-doored barn containing an old car, when suddenly the screen door of the kitchen was kicked open from inside and Dave appeared, staggering as though he was being pushed. Right behind him, clutching Dave's shirt in one hand and holding a 9mm automatic against the back of Dave's head, was Gonzales. He was using his hostage as a human shield.

Laval stopped moving and slowly stood up from his crouch, raising his gun. The other commando had disappeared. Laval hesitated. He couldn't fire for fear of hitting Dave. There was a momentary stand-off. Then suddenly Gonzales pushed Dave to the side, still holding onto him with one hand, and fired at Laval. Then he quickly pulled Dave back in front of him.

Laval fell, dropping his weapon and rolling over on the packed earth until he lay sideways, twitching in obvious agony. As Gonzales took a step towards Laval, Dave suddenly twisted in his grasp and raised his hand. Gonzales lifted a protective arm and tried to bring his gun round, but Dave's hand flashed down and he plunged something into his captor's chest.

'*Ahhhh!*' the Spaniard shouted, flinching in pain and letting go of Dave.

Dave ran for the edge of the yard. He was perhaps twenty feet away from where Liz was standing when Gonzales lifted his gun and fired. Dave went down at once, clutching his side. Simultaneously the commando emerged from behind the car and fired at the Spaniard. He hit him in the leg and the Spaniard fell heavily but held on to his gun.

Lying where he'd fallen, he lifted his hand and pointed his gun at Dave, still alive but groaning and helpless on the ground. He's going to finish him off, thought Liz. Stepping out from behind the tree she ran forward to Dave, shouting at the Spaniard. 'Stop! Stop or I'll shoot!'

Gonzales's head jerked up and he raised his gun to fire at this new target. Liz watched with a growing sense of horror as the black gun pointed directly at her. She tensed, waiting for the shot, but though she heard the flat crack of a gun, she felt nothing. Had Gonzales missed?

She dived flat onto the ground before he could fire again—surely he couldn't miss twice at such short range—but then she saw that Gonzales had dropped his gun; his head had flopped to the ground and she watched with macabre fascination as blood poured from it, staining the ground. The commando and Seurat had fired together and neither had missed.

Liz staggered to her feet as Seurat rushed down the wooden steps and across the yard, kicking away the Spaniard's gun as he passed, though there was not the remotest chance he'd ever use it again. 'Are you all right, Liz?' He put his arms round her as her legs gave way and she fell again.

'I'm so sorry,' she said. 'I did a very silly thing, rushing out like that. But I thought he would kill Dave.'

'No, no. You were very brave.'

But she wasn't listening. She was kneeling beside Dave. He was alive but barely conscious, breathing shallowly. The bullet had hit him low on one side of his stomach and blood was spreading like water through a sponge, gradually turning the blue of his shirt black.

'He's going to die if we don't get him to hospital,' whispered Liz as she helped Seurat gently open up Dave's shirt. Blood continued to flow from the bullet hole in his lower abdomen, as Seurat folded the cotton fabric back against the wound to staunch it.

The commando who had fired at Gonzales had been talking on the radio and was now kneeling beside Laval next to the garage. His colleague Gilles came running from the front of the farmhouse with his gun at the ready. 'It's all over,' Seurat called out to him.

Then almost directly overhead Liz heard the *phut phut phut* of a helicopter, and felt the lightest of breezes stirring her hair. Soon the breeze was a stiff wind, then a gale, and she watched as the chopper settled on the yard and the blades began to slow. Then the side door slid open and an armed man in military fatigues jumped out, followed by two men in whites. Stretchers and medical equipment were unloaded and within thirty seconds the doctor had taken over caring for Dave. Before long the wounded man was strapped to a stretcher, drugged now with a morphine injection, a drip in his arm, and loaded into the helicopter. The doctor quickly turned his attention to Laval, who had been hit high in the collarbone. He too was strapped to a stretcher and loaded on board.

Liz, Seurat and the two commandos stood in the courtyard looking up as the helicopter lifted away. As the noise died down, Gilles spoke to Seurat. '*L'autre, monsieur?*' was all Liz could hear above the whirr of the chopper.

'*L'autre?*' asked Seurat, frowning with incomprehension.

'*Le troisième. Où est-il?*' said the commando insistently.

'He means Milraud,' said Liz, suddenly conscious of what the commando was saying. 'Where is he?'

Seurat froze, a look of anguish on his face. 'He's gone. He slipped away while I was focused on what was happening in the courtyard.'

'Oh, no,' said Liz. 'Just when you thought you'd got him.'

'He can't have got very far,' said Seurat. 'Radio to the team at the ferry and alert them,' he ordered Gilles. 'I'll call for air surveillance. If he can't get off the island I'm sure we'll soon track him down.'

BUT THEY DIDN'T. All day helicopters hovered over the island of Porquerolles and the surrounding sea. Some had heat-seeking equipment that flushed out a couple of cyclists, a walker, and two lovers furious to be disturbed from above. Gendarmerie had been recruited from as far as Marseilles to search the mainland ferry port and the nearby town of Hyères. The CRS had sent a platoon to go through the empty houses and hotels on the island, and the navy had been patrolling a two-mile sea perimeter round it. But so far the same: no Milraud.

As Liz sat in the naval-base canteen in Toulon, watching through the window the daily life of the base going on outside, she gave a silent prayer of thanks for the hundredth time that Dave had survived. She'd been to see him that morning in the base hospital. He was drowsy with morphine but he'd given Liz a weak smile as she came in. 'I'll be fine again sooner than you know,' he'd declared, and Liz had refrained from sharing with him what the doctor had told her the day before—a half-inch higher, and the bullet fired by Gonzales would have killed him. A close call, but Dave would be well enough to be flown back to hospital in London the next morning. Liz wondered if he'd be sent back to Belfast after recuperating, and hoped so. Life there would not be the same without him.

'I suppose I'll be in trouble when I get back,' Dave had said ruefully. 'Judith warned me not to go back to Milraud's shop and she was right.'

'Don't worry, Dave. Everyone will just be delighted you're alive.'

'Do we actually know what Piggott and Milraud were trying to achieve?'

She'd given him a look of mock-sternness, like a ward sister with a recalcitrant patient. 'There will be lots of time for that. Right now, you just concentrate on getting better.'

'OK, OK. But I can't do that till I know what it was all about. Why did they bring me all the way down here if they were going to end up shooting me? Did they have a plan?'

'Hard to say. Our French colleague, Martin Seurat, thinks they panicked and made it up as they went along. His guys found two laptops in the farmhouse. They'd been sending emails to somebody. They may tell us what the plan was, but it will take a bit of time to unscramble it all. And that's all I'm telling you now. Go back to sleep; I'll see you in the UK.'

Now, as she watched some workmen erecting a grandstand on the parade ground, her mind still on the dramatic events of the day before, she felt a hand on her shoulder and a voice asked quietly, 'Where are we now?' Martin Seurat sat down at the table opposite her.

'I was just thinking about our mysterious Monsieur Milraud. How did he get away and where has he gone?'

'There's some news about that. We've heard from the harbourmaster that a resident in the village reported his skiff's been stolen from a small jetty near the harbour. We think Milraud may have taken it some time yesterday, before the cordon round the island was in place.'

'Where would Milraud head for?'

'He could go anywhere, especially since I think he had help once he reached the mainland. I've just come back from his house in Bandol— Annette Milraud has disappeared as well. We had surveillance outside the house but she fooled them. We found her maid tied up in the kitchen. *Mon dieu*, was she cross! Especially as she was in her underwear.'

'What?' asked Liz, laughing.

'Annette made her take her clothes off, then she put them on herself, before driving away in the maid's car. Our surveillance thought she was the maid going home and didn't stop her. They are very embarrassed—I'm not surprised. They should have been onto a trick like that.' He frowned and shrugged. 'But it's too late now. She's gone.'

'Presumably the car will be stopped soon.'

'It's been found already. Parked in Cannes. We think they must have a safe house there. Knowing Milraud, he'll have a set of false documents too.'

'So where do you think they'll go?'

'Somewhere far away—like South America. Or perhaps one of the former Soviet Union states. But Milraud will pop up again—give him time. Annette will grow dissatisfied with life in a backwater, and the lure of the arms trade will have Milraud back in circulation. I would say my hopes of catching him have been deferred, not destroyed.' Seurat brushed his chin thoughtfully with one hand. 'You know, it's a very strange feeling, sitting here talking like this after the *événements* only yesterday. It seems unreal.'

Liz nodded. 'I know. I feel the same.'

'I was considering taking a few days off. If only to readjust oneself to the obvious fact that life goes on.'

Liz laughed. 'That sounds like a good idea. What are you thinking of doing?'

Seurat paused, then said lightly, 'There's a little hotel I know. Not far from here, up in the hills—a beautiful setting, though the hotel itself is nothing fancy. Still, it has excellent food, and the walks are simply wonderful. At this time of year, you're beginning to see the first signs of spring. It starts early in the south.'

He turned and looked at her, and Liz realised it was not his intention to stay at the hotel alone. Her heart began to beat a little faster but she waited until his meaning was absolutely clear. Not that she had many doubts.

Then Liz's mobile phone rang.

It was a London number, which seemed familiar. The name came up on the screen: *Charles*. How funny that she hadn't immediately remembered a number that she used to know so well.

'Liz, it's Charles. Are you all right?'

'I'm fine, thanks. And so is Dave—or at least he's going to be.'

'So I hear. You've all had quite a time of it, I gather.'

'Quite exciting,' she said drily. 'Unfortunately there's one loose end—Milraud, the arms dealer, seems to have got away.'

'I wouldn't worry much about that. Piggott was by far the greater threat, and you've taken care of him—and his organisation. As well as his Spanish hit man. A job well done by any standard.'

That was true, and she wished she could take more satisfaction from it. The cost had been high—and Dave was very lucky to have survived.

'But that's not the reason I'm calling,' Charles was saying, jolting Liz out of these post-mortem thoughts. 'DG wants you to call in at Thames House before you go back to Belfast. He wants a full report on everything.'

'OK,' she said, slightly puzzled. She'd expected to report back to Binding in Belfast.

Liz glanced at Seurat, and found him watching her intently, appraisingly.

She found herself starting to blush like a schoolgirl. How ridiculous, she thought furiously. 'Am I needed immediately?' she managed to say.

'Are there things you have to do there?' Charles paused. He sounded nervous, thought Liz. What about?

'Because it would be very nice to see you over the weekend,' he said suddenly. 'I was thinking we could have lunch. Or dinner. You could come out to the house perhaps.'

Liz didn't know what to say. For years she had hoped for just what she was getting now—a signal that he cared for her and was at last willing to show it. But she didn't feel as excited as she should have done. And that surprised her. She felt oddly detached. How strange, since here she was, hearing what she had wanted to hear for so long. Yet now it almost seemed unreal. Or, if not that, at least something removed from the present, something that belonged to the past. To the days before Gonzales had pointed a gun at her and she had known with certainty that she was about to die.

Was that what was making her feel so ambivalent, as Charles waited on the line for her reply? Perhaps, though, it was also a strong sense that she had to get on with life now, that there was no point in retreating yet again into the patchwork of code that had characterised her relationship with Charles for so long.

She looked up at Martin and smiled, then said to Charles, not unkindly, but in a voice that was entirely certain, 'Actually, Charles, I was thinking of staying on here for a few days. Spring is just about to start in the south.'

stella rimington

RD: Where did you grow up and what are your strongest memories of that time?

SR: I was born in London four years before the outbreak of the Second World War. I avoided evacuation, though, because I moved around the country with my family in early childhood. I have vivid recollections of living in Barrow-in-Furness during the bombing of the Vickers shipyard, spending nights in air-raid shelters and waking up to find my parents sweeping the ceiling off the floor after a bomb fell very near our house.

RD: How would you describe your young self, in a few words?

SR: Anxious, self-conscious, with a big dose of puritan work ethic.

RD: If you hadn't followed a career in intelligence, is there any other field in which you would like to have worked?

SR: My first career was as a historical archivist and, had I not been tapped on the shoulder by MI5, I would probably have remained in that profession and enjoyed it. Archived documents are the raw material of history and I still get a thrill from them.

RD: If you were interviewing candidates for fieldwork in the intelligence service today, would there be one focused question, or area, that you'd home in on, in order to find the best?

SR: No one question, but lots of questions designed to find out about the person, their personality, their intelligence and above all their motivation.

RD: You have often spoken about the clubby, male ethos that prevailed at MI5 when you joined in the 1970s, and have said that condescension towards working women was common. Has that changed?

SR: There's none of it left now. It began to break down at the end of the seventies and during the early eighties, and now women are at the centre of the Service and there have been two female Director Generals.

RD: Does writing fiction set in a world that you know so well pose any special challenges—or just the same ones that every writer faces?

SR: If you write fiction about a world you know well, you have to decide whether to present a realistic picture or one that is totally fictional. Some insiders, like Graham Greene, have either ridiculed the intelligence world, as he did in *Our Man in Havana*, or treated it very cynically, as in *The Human Factor*. I try to make my books realistic, while removing the occasional boring bits that occur even in the intelligence world, and adding enough action to make them exciting.

RD: Was there any particular research that you had to do for *Present Danger*?

SR: Research into places mainly. The book begins on the coast of County Down in Northern Ireland and ends in Provence. I had to research both.

RD: In your years with MI5 were you very preoccupied with the Troubles in Northern Ireland?

SR: When I was working in counterterrorism we did spend a lot of our time working against the IRA, which at that time was actively trying to kill British soldiers in Germany.

RD: You've been out of the intelligence service for over a decade now. Do you miss it or was it a great load off your shoulders?

SR: I think, when you leave a job like that, you have a combination of grief and relief, really. The relief is now dominant because I've done lots of other things.

RD: What else, apart from the writing and public speaking, are you enjoying in retirement?

SR: My five grandchildren, who I love seeing, my garden and having time to enjoy the countryside and relax.

RD: Does being a Dame bring special privileges?

SR: No special privileges. It is a title that some people find quite difficult to manage—is it Dame Rimington or Dame Stella? US Immigration are convinced that my given name is 'Dame' and I have thought it better not to disillusion them.

RD: If you were holding the ultimate dinner party and could invite anyone, alive or dead, who would be on the guest list?

SR: Queen Elizabeth I, Dorothy L. Sayers, Joyce Grenfell, Gandhi, Samuel Pepys and Charles Darwin should make an interesting group.

RD: Looking back at your younger self, what would you advise her if she was starting out in life now?

SR: Seize interesting opportunities when they come along; do your best whatever you are doing; try not to take things too seriously and be kind to others.

RD: And, last but not least, do you have any dreams or ambitions that you would still like to fulfil?

SR: I can't say I have. I feel quite contented with what I have done, and am happy to take up anything interesting if it comes along, but I'm not particularly anxious to go looking.

TERENCE FRISBY

KISSES ON A
POSTCARD

I'd like to dedicate these memories of my wartime childhood to Rose and Jack Phillips—Auntie Rose and Uncle Jack—foster parents to my brother and me during the Second World War, who gave us three rich years of childhood in Cornwall. They live on in our hearts and we will always be grateful to them.

Terence Frisby

CHAPTER ONE

I was the luckiest of children: I had two childhoods.

My earliest memories are of pre-war antiseptic Welling, just in Kent, but really suburban London. The world I first lived in was even younger than I was, street upon street of it, all built since my birth in 1932. This brave new one-class creation consisted of red-brick, pebble-dashed houses—semis or four-in-a-row—bought on mortgages by young couples who had managed to raise the £25 deposit. With their small children they had escaped from the grime of Deptford, Woolwich Docks and New Cross (where I was born) through the newly legislated green belt, to fresh air and gardens.

In spite of the gardens, we kids lived in the street. Children were everywhere, gangs of us on every second corner. Those new-laid, spacious-to-us, concrete streets were our playground. A ball and a bike were essentials from an early age. A motor vehicle was a rarity when it disturbed our games of football, cricket, or 'aye-jimmy-knacker', a pitiless game that involved one team bending over in a line at right angles to a wall, locked together, head between the legs of the boy in front, while the other team, one by one, vaulted heavily onto their backs to make them collapse.

No cars were parked in those streets because none of our parents owned one. In Eastcote Road of nearly a hundred houses there were perhaps three, primly stowed in their garages, or standing gleaming on the garden path of the smug owner. We were interrupted more often by the milkman's or greengrocer's or coal-merchant's horse and cart, and by the occasional steaming pile of manure left behind.

We rode our bikes wildly round our empty streets in a wheeled version of hide-and-seek, then more sedately onto the main roads, with expeditions up

Shooters Hill, into the extensive woods: Oxleas, Jack and Crown. We rode further afield to Woolwich Ferry, Blackheath, Eltham swimming baths and down the A2 bypass to haunted Hall Place, near Bexley.

I was six when I got my first proper bike. As soon as I had it I made my brother Jack's life a misery by following him and his friends everywhere. He was four years, four months, older and regarded me as an embarrassing, unwanted accessory. They could have left me behind, but I could stay with them long enough to get out of our estate and ensure that Jack wouldn't leave me pedalling furiously, alone and at the mercies of main-road traffic. So I was waited for and reluctantly included, happy beyond words to be on my new (second-hand but new to me) bike, out with the big boys.

DAD, LOWER-MIDDLE-CLASS Dad, worked on the railway, a carriage-trimmer, later an undermanager, then, post-war, boss of the carriage and wagon repair depot at Stewart's Lane, Battersea. He had been a successful amateur boxer, a local welterweight champion and contender for national titles. He encouraged us both to box, just to look after ourselves. All of us boys in those streets were in and out of fights constantly. But boxing didn't take with either of us. Dad was a member of the Labour Party, a trade unionist, a physically strong, aggressive, hard-working man who could frighten us by the force of his personality and his occasional tempers. He was also very sentimental, gentle, loved to make us laugh and—as did our mother—made us feel secure and special. This was expressed one day when he came home from work carrying a piece of varnished wood with the word 'JackTer' cut into it and painted gold. This he screwed into the lintel over the front door and every time Jack and I went in and out we were reminded that our house was named after us.

Mum came from a family which had all the appearance, speech and style of the upper middle class—without the income. They were mostly professional musicians, all female by the time I was around. The males had died or disappeared and one great-uncle was in jail in Canada for some white-collar crime. Mum played the piano and would bash out jazz and popular tunes. I loved it when she played: the little rituals of lifting the lid of the piano stool to get the music out, the deliberateness with which she took her seat—no concert pianist did it better—the fiddling removal of her rings, placed carefully at the upper end of the keyboard, and then the house filled with rhythm and joyous noise.

Both our parents came from Brighton. Mum had been a professional jazz drummer there in the 1920s, possibly the only female jazz drummer in this country, unique. At a dance at the Ship Hotel one Saturday night my father stared long and hard at the drummer and, knowing her, she almost certainly glanced back and wielded her drumsticks with extra panache. When the band broke for the interval and records were played, he was the only one with enough nerve to ask the MC if he could dance with the drummer.

They got married and her new husband's job on the Southern Railway took them from the Brighton depot to New Cross in south London. Mum told me years later that she couldn't believe what she had done to her life: from being a local celebrity, playing at dances in the town and glamorous balls in Sussex country houses, she had become a wife living in a Victorian flat on modest wages, with two small sons, in one of the poorer bits of south London. When we moved on to Welling it must have been a bit of an improvement, but the cultural desert of north-west Kent was no replacement for fun-filled, shameless, gaudy Brighton-on-Sea.

Visits to Brighton to see both our parents' families were always exciting. The journey was a thrill enough on its own: a fifty-two-minute, non-stop ride on the Brighton Belle.

Dad's mother lived in an ordinary Victorian terraced house. It was only several minutes' walk from the station, at the back of the town. His father, former chef at the Grand Hotel, was dead. Drink was involved somewhere. As a result, Dad, though not entirely teetotal, was a very light drinker. On the other hand, Mum loved the whole social business of going out for a drink and 'enjoying yourself'. This difference in their tastes did not help an already difficult relationship.

It was the visits to Mum's relatives that were grand, sophisticated occasions. Indeed, it was one of them, her Auntie Molly, who had found the £25 deposit to put down for our house. My great-aunt Molly was the pretty one of the three aunts who brought Mum and her sister up—their mother had been packed off to Canada after some sort of scandal and had a second family there. All three great-aunts (and my absent, possibly disgraced grandmother) had been suffragettes and were very much free feminist thinkers before the turn of the century. They were well educated, cultured and all spoke with beautifully clear Edwardian diction. 'Off' was 'orf' in their language and if they called themselves or someone else 'a silly ass' it had no anatomical overtones.

Molly was a classical double bassist. After one local scandal and more than one *affaire* she married a prosperous furrier so was able to keep her two penniless sisters. The younger one was sweet, vague Auntie Clare, who played the violin and viola and had a lifelong *affaire* with an equally broke violinist. The older penniless sister was crabby Aunt Millicent, a virgin I am sure, who had taught algebra and Greek at Cheltenham Ladies' College and intimidated Mum and her sister throughout their childhood. They all lived in a grand, spacious Edwardian house, 47 The Drive, the best address in Hove, with the sea at the end of the road. Again we could feel special. Molly and husband—who used to hand Jack and me munificent half-crowns when we visited—occupied the main body of the house, with Clare and Milly in the basement flat. The general conclusion among Mum's all-female relatives was that she had married beneath her. Nevertheless, they showed sympathy rather than censure.

A cherished memory of Mum (of so many) is of her standing in the kitchen in Welling with Jack and me sitting at the table, the radio on, Borodin, Rimsky-Korsakov, Stravinsky, Ravel, Debussy or Tchaikovsky playing; she holding a cooking implement, waving her arms and hands about, a faraway smile on her face. She would undulate in her version of a harem-type dance, saying, 'Listen, boys, listen. It's beautiful, isn't it? See? The Russians and the Romantics and the Moderns. Aren't they lovely? Just listen.' And I have, ever since.

THE DAY BEFORE the Second World War started (it was a Saturday), Dad shovelled Mum, Jack and me off to safety in Portslade, near Brighton, to stay with Mum's sister and family in another 1930s house, similar to our own.

During the autumn of the Phoney War we cousins privately started the real thing between ourselves. We brawled incessantly. Auntie Esme and Mum tried to ignore us, while Uncle Walter, tall, gangling, gentle Uncle Walter, decided to bring us all together with a cooperative project. Under his leadership we all embarked on the doomed attempt to build an air-raid shelter in the back garden. This trench, dug with so much effort into the solid clay that was under the garden, was always half full of water and was a glorious place to fight with our cousins and produce quantities of mud that horrified even our hardened mothers. Uncle Walter lived above the squalls and skirmishing in a quiet world of his own from which he tried, with no success, occasionally to remonstrate with an errant child. Dad was absent from Monday to Friday: 'essential war work' on the railway in London was the hushed, reverent explanation. We were—as was promised to the soldiers of the previous world war—home by Christmas.

Back in Welling the Phoney War continued, a few months of a sort of pre-war existence, except that now there were shortages of everything that had been available even in a Britain barely emerging from the Great Depression. In anticipation of air raids, barrage balloons hung over Shooters Hill golf course, great useless bags of gas that were supposed to deter low-level attacks and did absolutely nothing as far as anyone can remember.

Up in Oxleas Wood, a few hundred yards from our house, anti-aircraft guns, searchlights and rockets were hidden in the trees. The long menacing shapes of the barrels of the ack-ack guns poked up through the leaves and branches. The beams of the searchlights waved about, hitting the underside of clouds or continuing to infinity, as the Observer Corps trained at night. But when the rockets were fired the shattering whooshes and roars seemed to open the doors of hell. We cowered in our beds, our stomachs turning to water, even though we knew they were on our side, and pitied any Germans who would dare come near. To have close looks at these alien, thrilling objects we children invaded those parts of the woods that were fenced off and marked 'Private', only to be good-naturedly driven off by the soldiers and chased with less amiability by the park keepers.

One of them caught us one day and gave us a severe lecture. 'Before you kids came here, nightingales sang in these woods. Where are they now, eh?' I went home and reported this to Mum. Her mouth set in a hard line. Never one to take on authority directly, she put on her coat, went and found the keeper and harangued him on the subject of how much disturbance he thought regiments of soldiers created as they erected campsites and tested their guns in comparison to a few kids trying to creep about and not be caught. I don't know what the keeper said in answer, but he still went on chasing us. It wasn't long before those guns and rockets were in nightly use. No nightingales have sung since in Oxleas Wood, to my knowledge.

Then in May 1940, the Second World War broke out in earnest as far as Britain was concerned. German panzer divisions swept through the Low Countries and France, the British and French armies were brushed aside, the disaster-cum-deliverance of Dunkirk happened, and what I call my 'other childhood' began. Jack, aged eleven, and I, aged seven, became evacuees—vackies—and were carried off to another world.

WE WERE ALL UP EARLY that morning, June 13, 1940. Two little brown cases were already packed, sandwiches and pop at the top for easy access. Dad was first to leave, off to work. I don't remember him hugging or kissing us; men didn't go in for that in those days. He may have shaken our hands. What he did do, to demonstrate his authority and reassure us, was to tell us that he knew where we were going, but he could not tell us because it was a war secret—a heavy wink accompanied this—and we would like it there. It would be in the country, fun; perhaps even—dare we hope it?—the seaside. No, he wasn't going to tell: wait and see. We were to be sure to look out on the left just after Wandsworth Road station as our train would go over his office, which was in the arches under the railway there, and he would wave. We knew then that we would be on a train that would leave Welling and cross south London, on to the Western Section: not a scheduled route. We knew our train would be special. We were railway children and proud of it and of our privileged knowledge. And if Dad knew we were taking that route he must be privy to the whole secret evacuation plan.

'It'll be a steam engine.' Another clue that we were going well out of our electrified world, an impressively long journey. We knew the exact stations where electrification terminated in all directions.

'Cor, what? A namer?' we asked, excited. 'Schools class?'

'Don't think it'll be a Schools class,' he said. 'Not big enough for your journey: only a 4-4-0.' He dismissed an engine that pulled the Dover boat trains and one we loved, a compact modern design sitting on its four driving wheels and four bogies. 'Could be a King Arthur.' This was a 4-6-0 express with three drivers a side. 'Maybe even a Lord Nelson.' Another 4-6-0, the biggest engine on the Southern Railway, only used for the West of England runs. We digested this with a sense of importance as he went off to work.

Mum had a tie-on label in her hand with my name and address on it in block capitals. 'Here, let me put this on you,' she said.

'Ah, no. I know who I am.'

'That's in case the Germans capture you,' said my knowing brother.

'Honest?' I was fascinated.

'Don't be silly, Jack. Come here.' Mum was sharp.

'I haven't got to wear one too, have I?' Jack was disgusted.

'Yes, both of you.'

The two labels had our school, class and teacher on the reverse side. I was being evacuated with Jack's school, Westwood, a large secondary school over a mile away, although I was still at Eastcote Road Primary, opposite our house. Whoever had devised the evacuation scheme had the sense to try to keep younger brothers and sisters with their older siblings.

While we objected, she tied them through the buttonholes in the lapels of our jackets. As I look now at all those old photos and films of vackies boarding trains and buses in their thousands in 1940, it leaves a hole in my stomach to consider how our mothers felt, tying labels on the most precious things in their lives and sending them off like parcels to God knows where, with the threat of annihilation from the air or sea hanging over us all. But our mother showed no sign of worry. She had two serious points to remind us of. The previous night at bedtime she had drilled them into us.

'Terry, you've got to do as Jack says. Do you hear me?'

'Oh, no.'

'Oh, yes. And you stay with him all the time. Got it? He's older than you.'

'Four years, four months older,' put in Jack.

'I'm cleverest.'

She snapped at me, 'Cleverer, smart alec, and you're not. You do as he says. Always.'

She was on delicate ground and she knew it. Although I was so much younger, I was a far better reader, coming top of my class regularly in most subjects and regarded as a very bright child, especially by myself. Jack, on the other hand, although no fool, was a very slow starter. He not only had the nuisance of a younger brother to deal with, he also had the humiliation of constantly being bettered by me in lessons and hearing me held up as an example to all. I, as a consequence, was pretty cocky. Getting me safely under Jack's wing must have been tricky for our mother.

'He's your big brother. You stay with him and do as he says. And you, Jack, you see that he does. All the time.'

Jack agreed, but the prospect of the pair of us being together the whole time, his albatross-little-brother round his neck, must have dismayed him as much as it did me. 'Can I bash him?'

Mum silenced my protests. 'There's no need for that but don't you stand any nonsense from him, Jack. And don't you dare leave him.'

I was indignant. 'I can look after myself.'

'All right, all right. You both look after each other. How's that?'

For Jack, the idea of being looked after by me, even partially, held no charm, but as he started to protest Mum threw in her final compromise.

'Just until you get to where you're going. Until you get there. Really there.'

'Where?'

There was no answer to that so she introduced her second point, her game. 'Now listen, both of you. Look what I've got here. It's a postcard. And it's in code. A secret code. Like the Secret Service. Only this is our code. Our own secret code. Read it, Jack.'

This was exciting stuff; the postcard was stamped and addressed to our parents. Jack started to stumble through it. '"Dear Mum and Dad, Arr—arr—arrived safe and well. Ev—ev—every—"'

I snatched the postcard from him and rattled off, '"Everything fine. Love, Jack and Terry."'

Mum was furious with me. 'Give that back at once. I told Jack to read it, not you. He's the older one, you do as he says. Always.'

'I don't see why—'

'*Always*.' The word was flung across the room at me, cutting through my disobedience, telling us both on a deeper level just how serious all this was. Jack completed the reading of the card, uninterrupted. There was a pause.

'But—what's the code?' Jack ventured nervously.

'When you get there,' Mum continued, 'you find out the address of the place where they take you. And you write it on the card there.' She had left a space. 'Here, Jack. Here's the pencil to write it with. You look after it. I'll put it in your case. And when you know the address—'

Jack cut across her. 'I'll give the pencil to Terry and he can write it.'

Mum was momentarily taken aback. She wasn't expecting such help. 'That's right, Jack. Good boy.' I didn't understand then why she gave him a hug that nearly stifled him when all he had done was to suggest the, to me, obvious solution. She continued to both of us, 'Then you post it at once. All right? Now listen, I've only got one card so you've *got* to stay together or I won't know where one of you is.' It was her final shot on the other subject that was eating her.

'But that's not a proper code.' We were disappointed.

'No. Now *this* is the code. Our secret. You know how to write kisses, don't you?' We agreed with 'eargh' noises to brandish our distaste for such things. Mum waited for the ritual to subside. 'You put one kiss if it's horrible and I'll come straight there and bring you back home. D'you see? You put two kisses if it's all right. And three kisses if it's nice. Really nice. Then I'll know.'

CHAPTER TWO

The narrow up-line platform of Welling station was packed with hundreds of excited, chattering, rampant, labelled children with their cases and their teachers and mothers. Teachers were ticking registers, two men were removing the station nameboards.

'Why're you doing that?' asked a pushy bigger boy.

The man who answered him fancied himself as a comedian. 'It's so the Germans won't know where they are when they get here.'

Our special train puffed round the bend into the station and the decibel-level rose sharply.

'It's an N class,' Jack and I saw with intense disappointment. 'A manky old N. It hasn't even got a name.' We were clearly not as important as we thought, even though the N class was a powerful 2-6-0, used for long-distance freight and passenger work. Suddenly we saw it was a corridor train and excitement again took over. Plenty of scope for fun: we could run from end to end of it, from compartment to compartment; lavatories to lock ourselves in; a guard's van to explore.

I don't remember seeing any tears on that platform but there must have been plenty. Jack and I stood at a window, waving and shouting at Mum, who stood in a crowd of waving, smiling mums. She mouthed, 'Don't forget the code,' as though we could have. She told me years later that she went home and sobbed. Like all the other mums, I expect. I still cannot think of her inventiveness and bravery, even now nearly seventy years later, without my eyes filling. Mum and Dad, with her (their?) secret code and his man-to-man confidences about our route and locomotives, ensured that Jack and I left home without a qualm. Perhaps even Mum's success, seeing us shrug them off with such ease, gave another twist to the knife. We have all heard the stories of frightened, unhappy vackies being torn from their parents and shipped off to the unknown, but not Jack and me. As far as either of us can recall we just thought it was an adventure with his classmates and teachers and friends, although I had no difficulty in obeying Mum's instruction to stay close to my big brother. Perhaps I was more anxious than I realised. As one of the youngest I knew practically nobody there; I was the only representative of Eastcote Road Primary; my infant-schoolmates had been sent elsewhere, many of them with their mothers because they were too young to be separated. But Westwood Secondary School, situated too far from my home for me to know any of those children, was kept together, like a gigantic school outing. In any case they were all, except the younger siblings like me, eleven or over—Jack had only just started there—so they were distant, godlike figures to a seven-year-old. None of that made any difference to my feelings; they were a seething, familiar-to-each-other crowd, and I had Jack and was caught up in it all.

The old N class puffed us off to our new lives and to my other childhood.

OUR TRAIN LEFT the usual route to Charing Cross at the Lewisham flyover, as Dad had forecast, and rumbled over the arched workshops, engine sheds and railway offices of south London. Jack and I disagreed about which side Dad had told us to look out of at Wandsworth Road. I looked left and he right. It seemed that all south London was out there waving. Jack said he saw Dad in one place, I saw him in another. Dad later said he saw both of us, but all any bystander could see of that train was that it sprouted yelling, juvenile heads and waving arms from every aperture.

We passed from Victorian, industrial inner suburbs to Surbiton's twentieth-century semis with gardens; like where we had come from but posher. Gathering pace we sped by the huge flower gardens of Sutton's seed factory near Woking. 'A Blaze of Colour' their seed packets used to proclaim, and it certainly was that day, in high-summer June. Then past Brookwood Cemetery, the London Necropolis, the largest cemetery in the country. Jack and I knew that we were on the main West of England line; out beyond the far reaches of electrification; on through Andover Junction, Basingstoke, Salisbury; through a level crossing at Wilton, I think, over streams, under bridges; a wait or two on sidings while more important war traffic roared past (what could be more important to a country than its future?). And everywhere there were people waving, always waving. The whole country seemed to know of the evacuation.

An age further on we pulled up at a major station: 'Exeter Central', it said. The Welling-station-nameboard-remover hadn't got there yet. The stop was only to change engines and pick up a little tank engine that would act as extra brakes as our train dived down the steep incline to Exeter St David's station and the main Great Western Railway line.

The Great Western Railway line ran (still runs) dramatically along the seashore at Dawlish. 'The sea,' yelled hundreds of excited voices in unison, and it is a wonder our train didn't tip over sideways as every child and teacher in it strained to get as close as possible to the waves breaking a few feet from us, as we clanked along. Then Plymouth, the Royal Navy base at Devonport packed with grey, menacing warships, a slow rumble over Saltash Bridge, which had an armed sentry at each end, and we were told we were in Cornwall. Cornwall—it sounded all right: a wall of corn. But the first station we passed through was St Germans. Sainted Germans? Here? The next was Menheniot, which was incomprehensible. We crossed a viaduct, one of several, but this one was high over a deep little valley with a single-track railway far beneath us, and had a station at the end of it. We stopped there, the front of the train in a cutting, so steep were the contours. 'Liskeard', said the boards. We didn't even know how to say it. Was this a foreign country?

THE AFTERNOON SUN shone down the length of the cutting, making bars of gold through the smoke and steam of our engine. We were led away and walked up the road in long crocodiles of twos, past curious local people, to an assembly room where we were given a bun and squash. We were soon packed into buses which fanned out of Liskeard in all directions, breaking up Westwood Secondary School for good—well, anyway, for the duration.

Still going further west towards the sun, our bus followed another down a long winding hill, past a vast railway viaduct, the biggest yet: Moorswater. On, through strange folded countryside with a line of moors in the distance, to a school—granite and slate, small and bleak and Victorian—nothing like the brick-and-tile, airy, modern Westwood Secondary or Eastcote Road Primary in our modern pebble-dash estates. This one sat just outside the village, squat and solitary on a country road. All the buildings we had seen looked so old. Even the people waiting in the inadequate playground seemed older than our parents—the youngish marrieds who made up the adult population of our street at home.

The sixty or so of us were herded into the centre of the main schoolroom and the villagers crowded in after us and stood round the walls. What a scene, this auction of children with no money involved—almost medieval. The villagers slowly circled us and picked the most likely looking. They used phrases strange to us, in thick accents we could barely understand.

'Hallo, my beauty.'

'There y're, me 'andsome. Wha' be your name, then?'

'Don' you worry none.'

'Us'll 'ave 'ee.'

''Er can come wi' I.'

'This one yere'll do we.'

Inhuman as it all could be judged now, I can think of no quicker, better way of dispersing us. I don't know if the other children felt fear or anxiety; some must have. I remember only curiosity. At least our new guardians were given some sort of choice in who was going to share their homes, even if the children were not. Not that anyone in authority in those days would have thought of consulting children about their welfare. One thing would seem to be sure: whoever was running things locally did a good job because, again, no brothers and sisters were split up that day. Some people took three or four children to keep families together.

A female voice said to me, 'What about you, my pretty? D'you want to come wi' I?'

'I'm with my brother,' I said.

'Two of you, eh?'

'Yes, he's with me. We're staying together,' said Jack.

'Two boys is a bit much for we.' And the owner of the voice moved on.

A hand grabbed my hair. There was quite a lot of it and it was fair.

'Yere. I'll have this one yere, little blondie,' said another female voice.

'Ow, that's my hair.'

'I know, boy. Could do with a cut, too.'

I cannot be quite sure about my first reaction to this person, older than my mother, who laid claim to me in such a way. Although the hand that had ruffled my hair had been less than gentle, she herself, looking down at me, did not look intimidating. Her accent was different again, much easier to follow than much of what we were listening to.

'You've got to have my brother, too.'

'*Got* to?' Her eyebrows went up a little in surprise.

'Mum said we've got to stay together. She said so.'

'Did she now?'

'Yes, we're staying together,' said Jack, more firmly than he could possibly have felt.

'Are you now? And you're his younger brother, are you?'

'Yes. We're together.'

'Both of us,' I added, to clear up any possible misunderstanding.

She regarded us reflectively. 'That's right, then. If your mam said. How old are you, boys?'

We spoke eagerly and simultaneously. 'Eleven, nearly twelve.' 'Seven and a half.'

'And what are your names?'

Again we tumbled over one another. 'Jack.' 'Terry.'

'Well, you're a pair, aren't you?' she said and it sounded complimentary. 'I like boys, less trouble than girls. Girls, oh *Duw*. Nimby-pimby, all tears and temper. Can you top 'n' tail?'

'We did that at our cousins' last year,' said Jack.

'Well, that's all right, then. You may be down in the front passage for a bit. We got two soldiers, see? Just for now. From Dunkirk. They'll soon be gone. Come on. Both of you. I like little blondies. Our family's dark, especially my son, Gwyn. He's in the Army, training in Wales.'

We left the vacky market. Outside she called out to someone. 'Here, over yere. We got two.'

'Oh *Duw*, girl. Can we fit 'em in?'

'We'll think of something. Come on, boys, quick, 'fore he changes his mind.' She led us over to a man standing next to an old-looking car.

The man, tiny, bald, tanned, rotund, like a hard rubber ball, had booked the solitary village taxi. He was much shorter than his wife, who was no great height. 'Here, boys, in you get, quick, 'fore someone else gets him. Ever ridden in a taxi?' He didn't wait for any possible reply. 'I hadn't when I was your age.'

And we were in the taxi with this odd couple, heading back up the lane, left onto the main road through the village, Dobwalls, where we passed villagers walking home with their new vacky acquisitions.

Out into open country again, towards the setting sun. The man sat in front with the driver, Jack and I behind with the woman. The man turned round. 'Now then, what's your names, boys?'

Once more neither of us waited for the other. 'Terry.' 'Jack,' we said in unison.

'And how old are you?'

'I'm nearly twelve,' said Jack as I said, 'I'm seven and a half.'

The man pretended to be confused. 'Have you thought of electing one of you to be chairman?'

This, in turn, confused us.

'Leave 'em alone, Jack,' said the woman, already protective.

The man pointed at me. 'So, you're Jack.' He pointed at Jack, 'And you're Terry.' His finger stabbed at me again, 'And you're nearly twelve.' Back to Jack, 'And you're seven.'

We giggled. 'Don't be silly.'

He did it all again but correctly this time.

'That's right.'

'Well, thank God we got that straight.' His grin included us in his joke.

'Only seven, are you?' said the woman to me, as though it were a wonder.

'Yes.' I was confident by now, too confident, and decided to identify myself. 'I'm the clever one.'

'Are you now?' said the man, his grin fading. He turned to Jack, 'And what are you?'

'I'm the older one.'

There was a silent moment during which he glanced at the woman, then looked from one to the other of us. 'Hmm,' was all he said.

The woman came in quickly. 'Well, that's funny, my husband is Jack, too.'

Jack was amazed. 'Is your name really Jack?'

The man grinned again, instantly responding. 'Course it is. What d'you think? We're telling fibs?'

'Isn't that funny?' said Jack, pleased.

'We'll have to make sure we don't muddle you up,' said the woman.

'D'you think you can manage to tell the difference?' The man looked very concerned as we both laughed. 'Well, what's funny?' he asked. 'We look just the same, don't we?'

'He's younger 'n you,' I said.

'No, not much,' he replied.

'I've got hair,' said Jack, and this got a good laugh.

'Oh, cheeky, are we?' was the response.

'And you're redder than him and fatter. And you talk funny.' As always I went too far for my brother, though everyone else laughed.

'Please, I'm sorry. He didn't mean anything,' Jack said, embarrassed.

The woman was all reassurance. 'That's all right, boy. He's only saying what he sees and hears. So. You call him Uncle Jack. And I'm Auntie Rose.'

The driver said something incomprehensible to the man.

He turned back to us. 'Hear that, boys? What he says about the vackies?'

'No,' we answered, mystified.

The driver half turned his head so that we could hear better and repeated whatever it was. We stared in silence.

'Is he speaking English?' I asked at last, and earned a roar of laughter.

'Oh, ar, 'tis English all right,' the driver said. ''Tis Cornish. 'Tis proper English. We'll soon 'ave you talking it, don't you fret, my beauty.' Beauty, as he said it, came out as 'boody'.

'Not living with a Welshman, they won't,' said the man Jack. 'I'll tan it out of them.'

'Hark at them both,' chimed in the woman, defending us from the threatened assault. 'Double Dutch is all either of 'em talk. You take no notice, boys.'

WE SWEPT PAST a farm with a huddle of outbuildings that long-sufferingly showed their backs to the weather and the outside world; they looked into shelter and pungent smells. We topped the brow of a hill with a lone oak tree growing from the hedge, not very tall but stark, only thinly veiled in June leaf, with all the branches blown one way like the fingers in a skinny hand pleading to the north-east for relief.

The man spoke. 'There we are. See? That's where we live. We're the end one. There.' We stared across a field at a terrace of Victorian cottages—more slate and granite. They looked tiny and grim. Seven of them, as it turned out. How could seven families live in so little space? 'That's Doublebois,' he said. He pronounced it 'Double-boys'. He continued, 'Doublebois is French.' Now he tried a French pronunciation on it: '"Doobler-bwa." It means "two woods". Not two boys, two woods. Only we can say two boys now, isn't it?' And he laughed at his welcoming wit.

The taxi pulled up and we got out. We went through a little wrought-iron gate between a warehouse on the right and the row of seven cottages on our left. This area, we learned, was called the Court and all the back doors opened on to it. The Court was the common ground, the thoroughfare. We walked past a pump on the wall of the first cottage, down a narrow courtyard, past a large concrete rainwater tank halfway down on the right, joined to the back of the warehouse. A tap, set over a drain, jutted from this tank. All our washing water came from that; our drinking water from the pump. After this the Court widened a little with a small whitewashed bungalow on the right. We went to the end house of the terrace, which had a wooden wash-house beyond it and some hens in a wire-enclosed run on the right.

Neighbours looked out of doors at us. A woman said, 'Thought you was only getting one.'

'They was on special offer,' said our man.

'They looked too good to leave behind,' said his wife.

Auntie Rose and Uncle Jack all dressed up in the Court

He grabbed my hair. 'This yere's Terry, the uppity one, and'—he patted Jack on the back—'Jack, my namesake, is the nice one.'

She was in quickly again. 'Leave them alone, Jack. They must be tired and hungry.' And she ushered us in.

We entered and stared in wonder at a shining black range with a cat curled beside it; at a canary in a cage; a green velvet tablecloth; a sideboard on which sat a little brass dustpan-and-crumbs brush; a shapeless sofa; oil lamps—no electricity here; at two First World War shells in their cases, over six inches tall, standing on either side of the clock on the mantelpiece. They took our excited attention, beating even the cat and the canary, with their soldered-on army badges that had three feathers and '*Ich dien*' on a scroll. The evening sun lit the room in nearly horizontal shafts full of dust; the room seemed packed with things and smelled of coal smoke and cooking.

But the glory came last: outside, past the hens in their run, right behind the wash-house, tucked down in a cutting, was the main London to

Penzance railway line with Doublebois station practically below us, its goods yard and sidings a couple of hundred yards down-line beyond a road bridge at the far end of the station. In the short time before we went to bed—and even after—the rural silence of Doublebois was occasionally shattered as an express train roared by a few yards below us, steam and smoke belching over the cottages. Local trains chuffed. In the mornings, goods engines shunted and banged and clattered, shouts echoed, the arms of signals clanked from danger, to caution, to go, and bells in the signal box announced the up-train to Plymouth and the down to Truro and Falmouth. We two railway children couldn't have dreamed of arriving in such a place. Even our address, cumbersome but utterly satisfying, was: '7 Railway Cottages, Doublebois, Dobwalls, near Liskeard, Cornwall.'

CHAPTER THREE

The tiny front hall, where we were installed on a borrowed mattress on the floor, was a narrow passage that led to the front door, which was the 'back' door and never used. Everybody who entered Railway Cottages, except strangers, did so via the Court. They ignored the row of front gardens with their little gates, came down the Court and rapped on the back door that led straight into the back parlour or kitchen, the centre of the world in each cottage. If a stranger entered the gardens, walked the length of the terrace and banged on the front door, he was shouted at through the locks and bolts to come round the back, which was always open.

In the privacy of our mini-domain we stared at Mum's postcard by candlelight—a first for us—and considered our code. Jack held the pencil. 'How many kisses shall we put?'

I had no doubts. 'I vote three.'

'Hmm. I'm not sure.'

'Come on yere, you two. What's all this? Up-a-dando, into bed.'

Suddenly our new—surrogate—mother was with us. Jack slipped the postcard under his pillow—too late; she had seen but she said nothing. I think I remember her putting us to bed that first night, at once making us feel at home, secure. But perhaps I am running many bedtimes into one because sometimes we were in the hall on the floor (where we were put when visitors stayed) and sometimes we were upstairs in what became our room. However, whichever place it was, there was always her warmth, her smiling good humour, her tact with two children who were not her own—just the presence of her. 'Come on, then. Who's going at which end?'

I grabbed the corner to snuggle into. But Jack was doubtful.

'Will there be enough air for him in the corner? You see . . .' He trailed off unhappily. 'He won't tell you, but—'

'Oh, no,' I breathed. He was splitting on me.

'I must.'

'Must what, boy?'

'He gets asthma.'

'I don't. Not much.'

'All right, all right, young 'un. I won't tell anyone.' She turned to Jack and treated his concern with careful respect. 'Now listen, you—Jack. We can't open the front door, we'll have God knows what animals and creepy-crawlies in yere, but we'll leave the door to the front room open; there'll be lots of air and he'll be able to breathe there in the corner, you take my word. I know 'bout asthma. Is that all right?'

'Yes, thank you, Mrs Phillips.'

'Did your mam tell you to see about the air?'

'No, I thought of it myself.'

'Did you now? You're a fine boy. Now into bed, go on. No. Wait a minute. Do you say your prayers at night?'

We stared.

'All right, I'll say a prayer for both of you. In you get. My Jack's a heathen, too. Look, boys, if you want to go outside during the night you got this yere instead. D'you see?' She showed us a flowered jerry, hidden under a cloth.

We knew what a jerry was, of course, but her phraseology confused us. 'Why should we go outside?' asked two boys brought up in modern, plumbed Welling.

'To go down the garden, of course. To the privy.'

'Oh, yes. Outside. Sorry, Mrs Phillips.' We had already used the odorous, unattractive privies. There were two cubicles, each a wooden two-seater, making four places in all. Though four people sitting there simultaneously didn't bear thinking about.

'Auntie Rose, I said you call me. Right?'

'But you're not our auntie. Our auntie's in Portslade.'

'I'm not. You're right. You call me Auntie Rose when you want to, is it?'

I wriggled down into the soft feather mattress we were to sleep on. 'Cor, it's ever so nice in here.'

'There. Look at you. As snug as bugs in a rug.'

'What?'

'Tha's what we say. As snug as a bug in a rug. Only there's two bugs in my rug.'

'I'm not a bug,' said Jack, enjoying himself.

'He's a bugger sometimes.'

Her face momentarily showed that I had gone too far.

Jack was in at once. 'I'm sorry, Mrs—um—he didn't mean to say that. He's just stupid sometimes.'

'I'm not. You are.'

'Well, he's young, isn't he? When he gets to your age he'll know better. Now I'm going to put out the candle, if you're ready?'

'Could you leave it, please?'

'Don't you like the dark?'

'No, it's not that. We've got to—um—do something.'

'It's bedtime now.'

'We've got to send a card to Mum and Dad.'

'This one?' She had moved round, sat on the floor and satisfied her curiosity about what we had been up to when she came in by producing the postcard from under the pillow.

We were dismayed. 'Yes.'

'Is that your writing? It's very grown-up.'

'No, it's Mum's.'

'Well, she's already written the card.'

'We've got to put your address on it.'

'Well, you've done it, haven't you? Yes, that's more like your writing. That's not how you spell Liskeard. I'll do you another card in the morning. A nice new one with a picture. How's that?'

'No, no. We got to put something else on.'

'What's that?'

She was met with silence.

'Well?' she asked gently.

'Er—kisses.'

'All right, then. We can do that, too, in the morning.'

'*We* want to do it.'

'By ourselves.'

She stared at us, reading something special and prepared to give us our heads now that she knew that we were up to no mischief. When she spoke again her voice was even more gentle, more reassuring than she had sounded so far. 'All right, then. You do it by yourselves, is it? That's right. You got something to write with?'

'Yes. Here. A pencil.'

'All right, then. I'll leave the candle lit and then come back again and watch you put it out the right way. We don't want a fire, do we? Your mam wouldn't like that.' And she left us.

'How many kisses?'

'I vote three,' I said again, obstinately.

'Perhaps we should take one off cos we're on the floor, not even a bed.' Jack continued to take his older-brother responsibilities seriously.

'I don't care.'

'There's no taps in the house.'

'It's t'riffic here. Trains and everything.'

I am sure he felt the same as I did but wanted to be sure. 'What about no electricity?'

'I don't care.'

'And no lavatory.' It was his last try.

I went on stubbornly, 'I don't care.'

He relaxed. 'Me, neither.' At last he said what we were both feeling. 'It's like being on holiday only there's no sea.'

'We could put four,' I said. 'The more we put, the happier Mum and Dad will be.'

'D'you think so?'

'Yeah.'

We ringed the card with kisses and posted it next morning.

WHEN JACK AND I ringed that card with kisses there was an unintended symbolism: Jack and I were ringed with love, though we didn't know it and would have been embarrassed to have used such words.

Our foster-parents, Rose and Jack Phillips, were Auntie Rose and Uncle Jack to everybody in Doublebois. This was extraordinary: they were not

Cornish; they had only lived in the tightly knit little hamlet for ten or fifteen years (a blink in rural timescales); he was neither church nor chapel, though she occasionally went to church and—even more occasionally—dragged him along. Yet even ancient Mrs Moore next door and Granny Peters, two doors up the Court, a whole generation older than them, always called them, in the broadest Cornish, 'Ahn'ee Rose' and 'Uncle Jack'. It was clearly some sort of tribute to their characters. He was a South Wales miner turned platelayer on the Great Western Railway. Their own two sons and one daughter were grown-up. Uncle Jack had been in the trenches in the First World War, in the Royal Welch Fusiliers, involved in some very heavy fighting. He had been invalided out with shrapnel wounds. Our father had been too young to be conscripted for the First World War and was just too old for this one, while Jack and I were—as yet—too young. We were a lucky family. But Uncle Jack and his sons fell precisely into the wrong age groups.

Two others who were in the wrong age group were a pair of soldiers, privates, who were the reason for Jack and me having to top 'n' tail for a few nights on the mattress in the hall. They were up in the back, or I should say front, bedroom and were direct from Dunkirk, stationed in the grounds of Doublebois House, a large Victorian mansion that stood in its own substantial wooded grounds with two gated entrances just down and across the road from Railway Cottages. It had been turned into an army camp, with Nissen huts up the twin drives to the big house, where the officers were. When we arrived, immediately after the Army's retreat from France, the whole place was overflowing. Soldiers were billeted anywhere and everywhere. I don't know how the local people had found room for us vackies.

One of our two soldiers was bright and nervous, the other had undergone some sort of shock and just sat staring into space the whole time he was there. The bright one smoked a lot and winked at Jack and me about his companion, making light of something that clearly concerned him. He tended his comrade's every need, taking him out to the wash-house to shave him and leading him to the outside privy.

I can see Auntie Rose's concerned, unhappy face when she looked at the benumbed soldier and offered him food and drink. And, even more, Uncle Jack's quiet, respectful movements when he entered his own house with this damaged man in it. He had been there and understood. Then, quite suddenly, they were gone in a roar of army lorries, and Jack and I shared the front bedroom, which was the back bedroom and looked down the gardens, over the outdoor privies behind their discreet hedges, across a cornfield, the railway line in full view on the right as it rose out of the cutting and curved away towards Liskeard, Plymouth and England, where we had come from. Yes, with Welsh foster parents in Cornwall and sentries guarding Saltash Bridge, we soon learned that the River Tamar was a frontier. It was the crossing point back into England.

Me, one week after arriving in Cornwall

THE HAMLET OF DOUBLEBOIS had four local children: to these were added eight vackies, four from Welling—Jack and me, and Harold and Alan Packham, billeted rather grandly across the main road in the solid detached house of the district nurse, Miss Laity—and four from Plymouth—the three Plummer boys, Peter, Eric and Ken; and one girl, Elsie Plummer, a cousin of some sort, who didn't live with the rest of the Plummers but was billeted with Miss Polmanor, the Doublebois Wesleyan zealot.

A few months later, when the summery Battle of Britain, fought in daylight over the Kent and Sussex skies of our former home, evolved into the nightly, autumnal Blitz on London, another vacky joined us: five-year-old Teddy came to 3 Railway Cottages with his mother and baby sister.

On our first morning the four Welling vackies met the four locals— Jimmy Peters and the three Bunney children—in a smallish triangle of land known locally as the Park. The Park was at the crossroads in Doublebois.

This was a five-road crossroads consisting of the main road running east to west, a lane going north to Bodmin Moor or south to Lostwithiel, and Station Approach sloping down to the up-platform and ticket office. When you add to that the two sentried entrances to Doublebois House and the main railway line running down the valley, you had a veritable rural Piccadilly. But little stirred there until a train stopped or the army was on the move.

The Park had several magnificent beech trees, especially one right on the corner from which you could see everything in Doublebois: all of the dozen or so houses, the station, over to the Bunneys' farm, the goods sidings with Blamey and Morgan's mill, and especially the trains panting up the long gradient from the west into the station. We were soon up it day in and day out.

That tree, our tree, also commanded an astonishing view: the Fowey Valley. The main road plunged down on one side of the valley past a quarry into woods; the railway snaked parallel along the other side on a thrilling succession of bridges and viaducts; between them initially was a field, the Rabbit Field, we learned, beyond which the tops of trees waved and swayed into the hazy distance, beckoning.

As we all hung from the branches of this tree one day, Jack voiced the shared, aching longings of the four vackies.

'Let's go down the woods.'

There was a silence while the locals stared at us. Then in broad Cornish from David Bunney, 'Wha' frr?'

It was our turn to stare at them. 'What for? To play.'

'Play wha'?'

'Just play.'

'Wha's wrong wi' yere?'

We stared at the crossroads beneath us and away out over the enchanted valley. '*Can't you see?*' '*Are you blind?*' There lay adventures, endless woods, a rushing river, fish to catch, streams to dam, paths, tracks, the quarry to climb, creatures and things we hadn't heard of. What *for*?

The locals drifted away as we vackies charged down the Rabbit Field and on into the dappled gloom of our vast new empty playground.

A DAY OR SO after I got to Doublebois I was playing with Alan Packham down on Station Approach by the entrance to the up-line. We were throwing the little stones that had worked loose from the tarmac at each other. There was no animosity in this. I threw a handful and one made a tiny hole in the top left-hand pane of the frosted-glass window of the booking office. I tried to claim it was Alan's fault because he had been in front of the window and ducked when I threw. My pleas fell on deaf ears. The matter was reported to Auntie Rose and Uncle Jack. I was ashamed to be in their bad books so quickly. They sent me to apologise to Mr Rawlings, the stationmaster, and to offer to pay for the damage (with what, God knows). He gave me a lecture about shortages of glass and told me the pane couldn't be replaced. It stayed unmended for the duration, rebuking me every time I went down Station Approach. The ticket clerk sat behind it when on duty, and I always wondered if he got a stiff neck from the draught when it was cold. It finally had some paper stuffed into it.

Just a day or two after that incident, I was with some others up our beech tree: vackies and Doublebois children. We had soon found we had enough interests in common to make friends in spite of what we saw as their lack of gumption. School was in shifts. There was nowhere to put all the children at once so some of us were off that afternoon watching army lorries going in and out of the camp. Everything to do with the Army fascinated all of us. We asked the guards on the entrances if we could touch their rifles and generally made nuisances of ourselves. In the first nervous aftermath of Dunkirk we were told to buzz off but, as things calmed down, we were tolerated and then even welcomed by some, perhaps missing their own kids, so that the army camp became another adventure playground, made even more alluring by the element of danger involved in dodging guards and officers.

We watched a train from Plymouth pull into the station, a Hall-class engine drawing it. Jimmy Peters, son of another platelayer, the sub-ganger in Uncle Jack's gang, didn't even need to watch. He could identify a few of the individual engines that regularly drew our trains just by their sound; something I quickly learned from him. One or two people strode up Station Approach. I stared in wonder. My mother—my mother, lugging a heavy suitcase—was actually trudging up from the station towards me. She had received our card all right but had turned up anyway. I did not rush to greet her; instead, I turned and raced up the road, past the stationmaster's house, past Jimmy Peters' house, into the Court, down it and breathlessly indoors.

'Auntie Rose, Auntie Rose, Mum's here. My mum's here. She's outside,' I gulped, excited beyond belief. Having delivered the news I turned and ran straight back to Mum.

My mother has often since reminded me of that moment. Her blue-eyed boy recognised her, turned and ran away. Whatever was wrong with him? It clearly upset her. Nothing was wrong at all, of course. I had simply run to tell Auntie Rose. My mother said that all sorts of anxieties took over in those few minutes before I came back. Had Auntie Rose become, in under a week, the first person in my life to share such things with?

My mother's favourite photo of herself

I have no real idea of how Auntie Rose and Mum got on in that first meeting but it must have been well. When amoral, raffish Brighton met a South Wales mining village there was plenty of room for misunderstanding, to say nothing of the generation and class divides. Mum, with her good looks and classic lines to her face, always looked classier than we actually were. I don't know what Auntie Rose thought of Mum but Mum must have trusted Auntie Rose immediately, because she told her about the kisses code and our judgement of her.

As they settled down over tea, I was driven out. They wanted to talk about us. I went down the main road into the valley, to the bridge over the River Fowey. It was a place of infinite attraction for me all the time I was in Cornwall. There was a pool under the bridge where there were always trout and, seasonally, sea trout. There were rapids below the pool.

I scrambled down a path from the road to a little piece of bank that jutted into the river, just above the rapids. There were magical things to be seen, including dragonflies: the smaller, common green ones, really damsel flies, and larger ones with yellow and black hoops. One of these flew out in front of me and I looked up from my study of the water and reached out to it, not to catch it, I think, just to touch it. Into the river I went and found myself clinging to the bank, up to my chest, shocked, freezing cold and shouting with all my might as the current pulled at me. When I had left the road I had noticed one of Uncle Jack's mates from the platelayers' gang going home. He was pushing his bike up the long hill to Doublebois. Within moments I saw him above me, jumping the wall by the road and slithering down the steep path to where I was. He lugged me out, sat me on his bike and pushed me up the hill. Mum's and Auntie Rose's tea was broken up with the arrival of Uncle Jack's grinning workmate and one dripping, shivering vacky.

''Ee got a proper voice on 'im,' said the platelayer. 'I 'eard 'ee all right. Good job I was there. 'Ee'd 'a' been gone. Swept away.'

THE PLATELAYER'S ASSESSMENT of my situation may have been a trifle lurid but Mum said she constantly worried her two sons would never survive the war. My rescue from drowning within an hour of her arrival did nothing to reassure her. London was unthinkable and the country too unpredictable for her.

But for Jack and me the world was secure; the war was an exciting but unthreatening event; Cornwall was an adventure, with Auntie Rose and Uncle Jack simply there, our 'other parents', taken for granted. That was their achievement. We soon learned that it was Uncle Jack who was colourful, the one who entertained us or riveted us with his actions, stories and views of the world that we were just beginning to discover. But his life, their marriage—and now our lives—were based on the solid foundation of Auntie Rose. She was generally self-effacing, firm and—like him—utterly reliable. Going home to her was in no time as natural as going home to Mum. I believe, in retrospect, that a great part of the self-confidence of these two people and their partnership was that they each knew who they were. They were part of the working-class culture they came from and embodied. And 'working class' was the right definition for them. They knew their jobs and did them, earning their rest as fully paid-up members of the hard-work union. They had their own natural courtesy to each other. Their lives were full of unmentioned demarcation lines and no-go areas that both understood and observed. The unselfconscious way they gave ground or claimed it between themselves was over my head, lost on me at that time, part of the scenery. Each knew their own domain, respected the other's boundaries and didn't stray over them. Well, Auntie Rose didn't, and when Uncle Jack did he was put smartly in his place—something he always meekly accepted without ever losing his masculinity. Uncle Jack had the sense to realise his good fortune in marrying such a woman, and Auntie Rose was equally blessed. She never wanted anything other than their welfare—and now ours. If that is not a description of a love match then I don't know what is. But the word love seems too insubstantial to describe the deep roots, the thick foliage, the hard-wearing warp and weft of their union.

After Mum's first visit they were given express permission—if they needed it—to treat us exactly like their own children and punish us when we deserved it. I can think of no better expression of the trust Mum had in them. And I can still see Auntie Rose's slightly enquiring smile when we pleased her, and still feel the warmth of her body when she held me; and her hands, so much more roughened than my mother's, but just as gentle.

She would grumble when she hadn't slept well. 'Oh *Duw*, I feel like a stewed owl,' and she had a saying that she used on afternoons when she wanted a nap—no amount of mockery from us would make her abandon it—'I'm just going upstairs to throw myself down.'

But Auntie Rose was not just a cuddly mum-figure. We had to live by her standards, and it was not a good idea to forget or flout them. She once gave me a lesson that bypassed the mind, etched itself into me and is still there. It was a while later; I was perhaps eight or nine. Her daughter-in-law, Ethel, wife of older son Len, was staying. The three of us went for a walk up the lane to St Cleer and the moor; each of us had a jam-jar to search for wild strawberries. There weren't many but I persevered and after much effort had a miserable half-jarful, while Auntie Rose and Ethel picked fewer still. They preferred to natter. When we were back home I poured mine on my plate at teatime and planned which of the best ones to save till last.

Auntie Rose looked across the table at me. 'You've got your strawberries there, then, have you, boy?'

'Yes,' I answered, not sure what was wrong.

'Aren't you going to offer them round, then? We've got a guest.'

I flushed, aware of my gracelessness but also of the injustice. 'But you two didn't bother. I mean—I picked these while you were talk—and—'

'Greed I'm bringing up yere, is it? What if I only gave you the food you got yourself?'

'I—sorry—I—er. Would you like some?' I offered my plate to Ethel.

'No, thank you, Terry,' she said.

'Would you, Uncle Jack?'

Uncle Jack was equally unhelpful. 'No, thanks, boy.'

I turned to my nemesis. 'Auntie Rose, would you like some?'

She hadn't finished. 'No, you have 'em, boy. You obviously need 'em most.'

The chickens ate the wild strawberries.

AND THERE WAS UNCLE JACK, with his ferocious, secret scowls, sudden broad grins and his brusque delivery. In spite of these characteristics—or perhaps because of them—he was far less intimidating than Auntie Rose could be when she thought it necessary. One day he caught Jack and Ken Plummer trying to smoke down the garden beyond the privies. I was allowed to watch but not join in and waste the precious single Player's Weight (one genteel, feminine step above the inevitable working man's Woodbine) that Ken had stolen from his mother's packet. Uncle Jack didn't ask us where the cigarette had come from; he knew that unless it was one of his the answer would only involve his having to report the theft to someone else and compound the matter. He regarded us seriously and spoke man to man. 'You don't want to smoke, boys. It'll stunt your growth. I smoked when I was your age and look what happened to me.' As he drew himself up to his full five foot nothing his eyes twinkled in self-mockery and his rebuke floated away like exhaled smoke. To redeem the seriousness of the moment he urged Ken and Jack to take a full drag and inhale. Of course, they both choked and he strode away, knowing that he had done all he could to discourage the habit.

Uncle Jack's 'If I was your father, I'd—' was the start to many a threat that held few terrors for Jack or me. 'Bloody Cornish,' he would say without rancour. 'God-bothering, Bible-punching Tories.' And then the sentence that was applied to anyone who displeased him in some way, 'Send 'em down the mines for a bit, then they'd know they were born.'

I wondered what Tories were and why they punched Bibles. Jack explained. 'It's just an expression. They don't actually punch them. I think they just bang them down hard in church or chapel. I've seen them do it with hymn books.'

'Bloody Churchill' was another of Uncle Jack's remarks that seized our shocked attention. 'He sent the troops in against us at Tonypandy.'

'Us' were his beloved South Wales miners, on strike for a living wage. His complaint, I later learned, was in reference to the government reaction to that strike in 1910 when Churchill was Home Secretary.

'Nye Bevan, there's your man. On the Opposition benches all by himself. Attlee, Morrison, Bevin, they're all in the Government. Part of it. Sold out.' The Labour Party, which he had voted for all his life, had united with the arch-Conservative Churchill to form a coalition government and win the war. They earned only Uncle Jack's contempt. Nye Bevan, Uncle Jack's Welsh, left-wing idol, was the man who stood out virtually alone against the war and coalition.

Then there were the one-sided arguments that Uncle Jack had with the BBC Home Service newsreaders.

'It's no good, Jack, he can't year you, and the boys and me aren't listening,' Auntie Rose would interject.

But we were. It was from these outbursts that Jack and I learned the political and religious geography of our world. I found these attacks on people I had barely heard of, but had been conditioned to hold in esteem, thrilling and subversive. They gave us the references that influenced our lifelong political thinking. One day, I asked Uncle Jack why he came to Cornwall if he didn't like it. 'Work, boy, work. No work there in the Valleys. Come with the Great Western, didn't I? The Company.' This word was spat out in a way that questioned my hitherto benevolent view of all things railway. 'Got the house an' all. Tied. Huh. Tied. Like our lives.' Of course I didn't then understand all that was behind that, but as comprehension grew, so there was a growing awareness of how the world about me worked differently for different people.

In spite of these sentiments, Uncle Jack seemed to like living in Cornwall. I cannot believe that working on the glorious three-and-a-half miles of track that wound westward down the Fowey Valley from Doublebois—and was his gang's stretch—wasn't infinitely preferable to any coal mine, no matter how strong the camaraderie down there. I think he must have been painfully split between his leftist, internationalist, socialist ideals and his patriotism, as were so many. He certainly supported the war effort, going into the underused front room to listen, rapt, to Churchill's speeches on the wireless, which ran from great acid batteries that needed frequent changing and charging. And he went drinking on Saturday nights with his allegedly Tory, church-or-chapel Cornish workmates, singing his way home from a pub in Liskeard—for Dobwalls was dry, the Wesleyans had seen to that. 'Bloody chapel. Bloody hypocrites,' Uncle Jack used to growl, but, like Dad, he was no great drinker, he just liked to have something to beat the Methodists with.

When he went with his workmates to Liskeard for a drink on a Saturday they had to be on the last down-train or it was a four-mile walk home. They would pile out of it, go to the rear end (our end) of the down-platform, cross the line (illegally) as the train left to continue its way west, greet the signal-man in his box just below us, scramble up the narrow, steep footpath that climbed up the cutting between the nettles and bushes, slip through the wire behind the wash-house and there they were, at the end of the Court. I remember one warm, magical night when they stopped at the top of the footpath to relieve themselves. They must have been a bit tight or noisy, probably singing, because Jack and I were awake and quickly up.

They were hissed at by Auntie Rose at the back door. 'Sssh, Jack. Everyone'll year. All up the Court.'

'I should hope so. Half of 'em are out yere with me,' was Uncle Jack's reply, half smothered in his own and others' giggles. 'Four miles to wet your whistle.' He raised his voice to complain to the world. 'It's bloody antediluvian. Bloody Methodists. Bloody Cornwall.'

'Oh-ho-ho. Plenty of time for all that in the morning. Bed now. Shall I wake you for morning service, is it?' Auntie Rose demonstrated her control of the situation with a shaft that brought grins from the others.

Uncle Jack's 'I'll bloody kill you if you do' had no more threat for Auntie Rose than did his other, more sober, threats to Jack and me.

'You couldn't kill a dozy fly with a frying pan. Come on, up to bed. You'll wake the boys.'

'It's all right, Auntie Rose. We're awake.' We were already down at the back door.

'Oh *Duw*. Back inside, you two, before you catch your deaths.'

'Want to splash your boots, boys?' was the far more alluring suggestion from Uncle Jack.

'Yes, yes, I'm bursting, I'm dying to.' And we two whippets were past Auntie Rose and through the wires to join him and splash anything we could. We thought we were men indeed to stand in such a row, barefoot on an enchanted summer Saturday night, as the last train's sounds echoed over the Fowey Valley and left the dozen or so houses of Doublebois to silence.

CHAPTER FOUR

We went to school in the village of Dobwalls, a good mile away, east along the A38 main road. Both schools, the vackies' and the village kids', were at the far end, to add to the yardage. We Doublebois children walked there and back every school day for the three years I was there, in all weathers. Nothing was thought of this. Though I recall that coming home sometimes seemed to be endless. To breast the last rise with the lone oak tree at the top, bent and stunted, growing only one way in the wind, and to see Railway Cottages, with ours on the end, was always welcome. I don't think there was a single fat child in Doublebois— or Dobwalls for that matter—and few, if any, adults. Wartime rationing had little to do with it: the greedy could always find something to eat in the country. It was simply that whatever we put into our mouths was burned away in constant physical activity.

In Dobwalls village, the vackies and the village children took one look at each other, and it was instant war. It wasn't, as far as I remember, that we hated each other, simply that we regarded them with contempt, and they resented the pushy newcomers. Perhaps it started from the very first meetings. They only had to open their mouths to be objects of ridicule to us. Perhaps they were trying to be friendly. 'Whirr be you fram, then?' was greeted with suppressed giggles and 'You talk funny.'

'No, us don't. You do.'

We all stared at each other.

'Wha' be you staring at, then?'

And the usual knowing answer. 'Don't know, it ain't got a label.'

'What be you looking so glum for?'

'There's nothing to do here,' answered the vackies. (A view not shared by us at Doublebois. We had the station and goods yard, flour mill and stock pens, big house, army camp, the valley, the woods and the river. But when in Dobwalls we showed solidarity without even thinking about it.) 'No Woolworth's, no pictures, nothing.'

'Well, go home, then. Nobody asked you to come.'

'We can't. Bombing.'

'There bain't no bombing,' (and there wasn't yet). 'I reckon 'tis cos your mothers don't want you.'

'You haven't even got pavements. It's a dump.'

'No, 'tisn't, 'tis our village.'

'Oh, 'tis it?' All the vackies laughed. 'Well, you can keep it.'

Stung, the village kids' answer was, 'Townies. Slum kids.'

'Turnips. Yokels. Clodhoppers.'

We twelve Doublebois children would walk to school together quite happily but, when we got to the village, we separated, without conscious effort, into vackies and village kids.

Vacky boys soon after arrival in Doublebois—no wonder we intimidated the village kids. I am seated front left, I think

Dobwalls straggled in an undistinguished way for more than half a mile along the A38. There were a few houses down side lanes and that was more or less it; some few hundred inhabitants. The first building we came to at our end was the post-and-telegraph office. Then the Lostwithiel road forked into ours and we were in the village, with Ede's shop on the right and Rowe's garage facing it on the left. Three lanes joined the main road as it forked, one prong leading back to Doublebois and Bodmin and the other diving under the railway line to East Taphouse and Lostwithiel. This six-pronged junction, as complex as ours in Doublebois, had no more traffic than we did.

We split up as we passed the shop, walked on past the main drinking-water tap at the bottom of a little hill and up the other side past St Peter's, the tiny Anglican church. At the far end, the village kids turned right and had the pleasure of going past the forge of Mr Uglow, the blacksmith, where horses sometimes stamped uneasily, aware of the burning smells from within, and all sorts of exciting things could be happening, before continuing a little way down the Duloe road to their school. The vackies turned left into the Methodist graveyard. Our main classroom was in the chapel; our infants' class, my class, was behind the graveyard in a wooden building with a corrugated-iron roof, misnamed the Hall; our playground was the consecrated churchyard, hide-and-seek between the slabs of slate.

We were forbidden to leave the churchyard during the day and the village kids were not allowed out of their school playground. This, of course, led to the more adventurous escaping to taunt the other lot over their wall and then run away. After school there would be more taunts and scuffles. Of course, once we Doublebois lot had got clear of the village we joined up and continued on our amicable way home.

The vackies had one song, favourite among the many that were used:

> The turnips are thick, the turnips are dumb,
> They use stinging nettles for wiping their bum.
> They eat mangel-wurzels and live in a shed,
> They're dotty and spotty and soft in the head.

The village kids' song had, in my view even then, more style:

> They come down yere from London so swanky and stuck up,
> They challenge us to take them on and say they'll duff us up.
> So we'll blow away them vacky kids to kingdom come,
> We'll blow away them smarty-pants and kick them up the bum.

Perhaps the last five words let it down.

Efforts were made to improve relations. They were futile. Some well-meaning person suggested a cricket match: we walloped them. A football match followed: the score was vackies thirty-odd, village kids nil. Our contempt for them was confirmed. Westwood Secondary School—no great shakes academically, consisting almost entirely of grammar- and technical-school rejects—was streets ahead of Dobwalls village school. We younger brothers and sisters soon saw that we were equally superior to their infants. As we came from the suburbs with woods and greenery, even their strengths, the mysteries of the countryside, were partly known by us, though we had much to learn. When it came to street wisdom the gap was unbridgeable. They didn't seem to have heard of scrumping; if they wanted an apple they either asked or took one. Or of stealing from Woolworth's— for obvious reasons that we vackies made no allowances for. Although it soon became apparent to even the most hardened of us that you couldn't possibly steal from Ede's, the village shop; not because it was too danger- ous, but because it was too personal. It was unthinkable to take things from Mr Ede and his brother. The anonymity needed for petty crime was gone.

We arranged our own private group fights—more confrontation and insults than violence—in the dinner break, and returned to our separate classes late and dishevelled, to get our knuckles rapped with a ruler—more painful than the fights. And our leader, Frank Emmett, and their leader, Sam Finch, fought in single combat to wild cheers and a disputed result.

The whole village divided. Those with their own children and many others regarded the vackies as a pestilence to be endured or resisted. But there were those who suddenly found themselves with new families: ener- getic, bright children who won their hearts and brought a new vitality to their village, trebling the under-fourteen population. And, of course, there must have been the unfortunate misfits, vackies who were too difficult to manage for one reason or another and villagers who just couldn't handle the children dumped on them. But, although the stories of cruelty and abuse abound and resound even now, I remember none among my fellows who was mistreated. Though there was one little boy in Junior Vackies who often wet himself, so at least one of us was unhappy.

Prominent among the pro-vackies faction was the Reverend Clifford Buckroyd, the Wesleyan Methodist minister, a pleasant, good-looking, fortyish man (my mother told me years later that every time she visited us she always fancied him, which surprised me as much as an adult as it would have done had she told me at the time—he was a *minister*, for goodness' sake), who worked hard to make us vackies feel at home and the village accept us. He was a popular man and lives clearly in my memory. If person- ality had dictated where people worshipped, his chapel would have been overflowing and the Anglican church empty. I can barely remember its vicar, the Reverend R. O. Oatey, though I attended it for three years, taken there by Auntie Rose. But denominations and places of worship were ingrained, only marginally decided by such ephemeral factors.

THERE WAS ONE Wesleyan Methodist woman, the anti-vacky Miss Polmanor, the one with whom Elsie Plummer had the misfortune to be billeted, who seemed to personify all the traits of uptight bigoted Christianity that made Uncle Jack so angry. It abounded in the country in those days. When I say country I don't just mean countryside, I mean the whole country. Miss Polmanor lived in one of a pair of houses some yards from the Court, up the road towards Dobwalls. But her religious convictions meant that there was more to her than mere narrow-mindedness. She was harder on herself than on anyone. She seemed to make her own life something to be endured rather than enjoyed. There was not, no matter what Uncle Jack might have thought, the faintest whiff of hypocrisy about her. Whatever she demanded of people she first drew from herself. I became, soon after my arrival in Cornwall, her unwilling confidant, though I did not understand much of what I was privy to till much later. I certainly did not like her or wish to be near her, but was obliged to talk to her alone regularly.

It all happened by chance. To eke out what must have been a frugal existence, Miss Polmanor had acquired the Doublebois concession on Corona. Corona made fizzy drinks that were the favourite of all of us children. If you wanted a bottle you had to go and knock on her back door. She had crates of full bottles in her cool little cellar and crates of empties ready for collection outside the back door. Our favourites were cherryade and ginger beer.

Every Sunday dinner in summer Jack and I were allowed to have a glass each with our meal. But there was a difficulty. Miss Polmanor would not trade on a Sunday. That was against her strict Methodist religious convictions. The same widespread convictions that had ensured, to Uncle Jack's frustration, that there was no pub in Dobwalls and that most of Wales was shut on a Sunday. So we had to buy our bottle the day before during normal shopping hours. On a Saturday morning, with Jack and with last week's empty, worth a penny or ha'penny back, it was an enjoyable errand. We could choose the flavour—if there was a choice—and carry the new full treasure carefully home for Sunday. But the errand was sometimes forgotten on a busy Saturday and disappointment stared us in the face on Sunday morning. On one such morning Auntie Rose cannily sent me alone on what looked like a pointless mission.

Acting on instructions I said, 'Sorry, Miss Polmanor, but Uncle Jack was working on the line yesterday, war work. Auntie Rose was ill and Jack and I were at choir practice. Could you let us have a bottle of pop, please?'

'I can't sell you anything on a Sunday,' she said in the shocked tones of one who was appalled at even being asked. 'Mr and Mrs Phillips know that.' She was one of the few who did not call them Auntie Rose and Uncle Jack. ' 'Tis against the Scriptures. I'm surprised at them sending you.'

Somehow I had the wit to say, 'Oh, but they didn't, Miss Polmanor. I thought it by myself. I thought you might make an exception.'

She must have liked that because I saw a rare faint smile on her face and she sounded more gentle. ' 'Tisn't for me to make exceptions, young man. ' 'Tis for God. Be you worth an exception?'

I couldn't handle the problem of thinking how God might make an exception for me, so gave up. 'Sorry to bother you, Miss Polmanor.' I turned away, looking into a Corona-less Sunday lunch.

'Just a minute, young man. Did you say that you were at choir practice?'

I was too honest by far. 'Yes, Miss Polmanor. But it was Church of England choir practice, at St Peter's, not at Mr Buckroyd's.'

'That don't matter, boy. You was doing God's will as you saw it.'

Is that what I was doing, I thought to myself.

'I can't sell you anything on a Sunday. That's for sure. But, if you're very good, I could *give* you a bottle to take with you and you could pay me tomorrow. Not a word to anyone, mind, or my life will be a misery. And only because you was singing to the glory of God. This is just between you, me and Him.' She gestured upwards. 'Promise?'

I did so fervently.

'And will you be good if I do?'

Another ardent assurance.

'There you are, then. And give thanks to God when you drink it.'

I took it, thanked her and God and ran for it.

Of course, the minute I was home Auntie Rose had to know how I had drawn ginger beer from that particular stone. When I told her, she quietly smiled and I was made to promise to take the money straight after school. Uncle Jack's eyes lit up when he heard the story. 'A chink in God's armour,' he laughed. 'Who would've thought it.'

Unfortunately this led to a further intimacy: when I took the money, Miss Polmanor asked me in. Her house was more old-fashioned than anything I had seen, packed with bric-à-brac, mementoes, religious texts and biblical pictures. There was one item that stood centre on the sideboard that was unmissable: a silver-framed photo of a man. It was turned into a modest shrine, standing on a little tapestry with candlesticks on either side.

'He was a saint,' said Miss Polmanor, as she saw me look at him. 'He died abroad for me and Jesus, and now I live for both of them.'

Realising that I was some sort of favourite, Auntie Rose usually saw that Jack was working on our vegetable patch in the garden with Uncle Jack, something Jack enjoyed and I didn't, and sent me to buy the Corona on my own. I think she did it as a kindness—to Miss Polmanor, not to me. Objections from me were overridden: it became my job. Miss Polmanor gave me texts and talks and even the occasional glass of Corona along with oblique references to the 'saint' that were lost on me but which left me uncomfortable. I got the impression that he was a missionary who had died of something or other in darkest somewhere or other. She liked to open herself, no matter how slightly, to me and even patted my head once and gave me a half-hearted hug, which enveloped me in a two-level, sweet-and-sour sickly smell that nearly caused me to run for it. But we were used to being the recipients of unwanted embraces or cuffs and were skilled at dodging them. After that I generally managed to keep the plentiful furniture between her and me. Somehow I had slipped through the net of her disapproval of all things young—and especially vacky—and had her bottled-up affection.

I used to hope for Elsie to rescue me from all this if she was in, but when Miss Polmanor answered the door to me with my sixpence and empty bottle, Elsie was gone in a flash and I am sure that Miss Polmanor was glad to see her go in spite of her constant denunciations of Elsie's unwillingness ever to stay in—probably to avoid yet more futile, pious indoctrination.

Miss Polmanor rode her bicycle into Dobwalls to shop and do her good works, often, so Auntie Rose said, to the exasperation of Buckroyd. She was soon round the Wesleyan minister's neck about us vackies playing in the Methodist graveyard at dinner break. ''Tis sacrilege, Mr Buckroyd. Disturbin' the dead like that.'

'I don't think the dead mind too much, Miss Polmanor.'

'They make up profane words to hymn tunes. I've heard they.'

'So do our children, Miss Polmanor.'

'But not so profane as they.'

'Well, they're more—er—inventive.'

'More sinful.'

'There's a war on, Miss Polmanor.'

And, in the rumour and gossip that always rides in tandem with war—

I mean our private war—stories abounded of vackies who behaved outrageously or were treated with cruelty.

'Have you ever heard? Over to Tremabe they chopped off the chickens' heads. Every living one o' 'em. Two little savages, only seven years old.'

'No. Is that so, my dear?'

'And down to Warleggan they slaughtered lambs in the fields, fired a rick. 'Tis bloody mayhem, I'm telling you—sorry, missus, I didn't mean to—but 'tis terrible.'

''Tis like a plague: the eleventh plague of Egypt, the plague of children.'

'Oh, no. We got two. They'm nice. I like 'em. My missus dotes on 'em.'

And, after their gossip, villagers strode off down the road along which Dobwalls was strung, tut-tutting or doubting, according to their views.

There was one story that was ubiquitous, told in every village in the county. 'You know that farmer up the edge of the Moor, Penmalligan. He had two vackies billeted on he.'

'Ar. Boy 'n' a maid.'

'Well, he locked they in the linney all night, then took his strap to 'em after breakfast. His breakfast. They din' get none. They was nine and ten years old. Well, their father got to year. In the Guards, he is. Grenadiers. Back from Dunkirk. Well, he went AWOL, went to Penmalligan's farm, punched he all round his own farmyard, then took his kids off with him back to Lunnon. 'Twas a proper job.'

'Have you heard of anyone else giving they vackies what for?'

'No. Everyone round yere be giving it up for Lent.'

And though such events always took place in the next village but one, the mythical guardsman was a famous and cautionary figure.

Uncle Jack took Jack and me in hand. 'Who started it all?'

'They called us slum kids.'

'And what did you call them?'

'Turnips.'

'What else?'

'Yokels. Clodhoppers.'

'Hmm. Who called who names first?'

This was lost in the mists of time.

He put his arms round us confidentially. 'Listen, boys. You can't call people names when you're living in a village full of self-righteous, God-bothering hypocrites. So don't do it.'

'No, Uncle Jack. Sorry, Uncle Jack.'

'I know they're a lot of Bible-punching Tories, but try to make friends with 'em. We're fighting the Germans, not each other.'

Vacky boys in the graveyard of the Wesleyan chapel, Jack far right

QUIET BUT INTENSE excitement in the Phillips household: Gwyn, the younger son, was coming home on leave. He was training somewhere. When he was called up he managed to get into the Royal Welch Fusiliers like his father had. The Welch, with its archaic spelling, was a top regiment. Uncle Jack must have been pleased in that schizophrenic way he had of both hating the military and being proud of being Welsh. Auntie Rose's political views were simple: she distrusted anything or anyone that put her loved ones in jeopardy. She had suffered the First World War with Uncle Jack being at the front and invalided out. She didn't need any of that again, and Gwyn was her youngest and most vulnerable. Her daughter, Rose, was relatively safe in Barry, South Wales. Older son Len was ground crew in the RAF, which seemed as good as she could hope for. Both of them were married, something that gave a feeling of danger shared, of security, no matter how false. But Gwyn was single, all hers, and anything could happen to him. He was already a corporal, another source of unspoken pride for Uncle Jack but of no comfort to Auntie Rose.

She was on the platform to meet the train; Uncle Jack was working on the line in the valley; Jack and I swung on the wire fence behind the wash-house and looked down on the station. The train blocked our view at first but as it pulled away we saw Auntie Rose in the arms of a soldier, his back to us, her head buried in his shoulder, then raised to look into his eyes; we could see hers shining from fifty yards away. He was dark, not very tall, had a kitbag and rifle. Instead of taking the usual route, walking to our end of the platform, crossing the line and climbing the little track that many feet had worn, then ducking through the wires, they walked away from us, the long way round, down the platform to greet the porter and Mr Rawlings the stationmaster, over the bridge, up the road and down the Court. I think she wanted to show him off to anyone who was about.

We soon discovered that Gwyn was extrovert, carefree and seemed to like the world as much as we quickly grew to worship him. When I say carefree, his humour had a black, graveyard edge to it, always visible, like Uncle Jack's. He never stopped singing, a nice tenor or light baritone, I am not sure which. The reason for his musical leaning was not just the cliché of being Welsh. Uncle Jack had encouraged it, trained it since Gwyn's treble days, as a possible escape from a life of drudgery down the mines, on the railway, or in some factory. He had seen a way to help his son escape from what had been his life. He had the right pupil, with a ready unselfconscious voice and easy invention. Every popular hymn and Welsh song was sung to us in snatches with Gwyn's (and other soldiers') subversive or filthy lyrics.

'How did you become a corporal, Gwyn?'

'I kissed the sergeant major.' He cleaned up the usual saying for us, although kissing the sergeant major face to face seemed more shocking than kissing his arse.

'Are you going to fight the Germans, Gwyn?' I asked him when his leave was drawing to a close.

'No. More training in the mountains, boy. Bloody cold. The Brecon Beacons. It's not much fun but it's better than getting killed. They're saving us Welsh. In reserve. After the Germans have wiped out all you English, we'll go in and sing 'em to death.' And he let out a burst of a Welsh patriotic tune with very unofficial English lyrics.

The popular song 'We'll Meet Again' was constantly on the radio, gener-ally delivered by Vera Lynn. Gwyn loved to parody her. He would emote extravagantly, arms thrown wide, and sing, 'We'll meet again, when they've blown up Big Ben,' holding 'Ben' for ever with massive vibrato.

I wondered about those mountains, unknown things to me. Our train rides to Brighton took us through the South Downs; but mountains? And the Brecon Beacons? What were they? And why were they cold in the summer? Uncle Jack soon had his atlas out from the shelves of Serious Books that filled the bookcase in the rarely used front room. I was in it for hour after hour when it was too wet or cold or hot or dark to go out. And often when it wasn't. There were cities with exotic names that became battlegrounds in the war; mountains, seas, oceans, plains, deserts and rivers that were being fought over; the shapes of the continents fascinated me; the outlines of the countries, each with its own individual colour; the vast amount of pink where the thin red line had passed, nearly half of the world, it seemed, was the British Empire. I swelled with pride: our empire.

Some evenings in Gwyn's week's leave, Uncle Jack went for a drink in Liskeard with him and, on Sunday morning after Auntie Rose had put the roast in the oven, we all walked down to Halfway House—our nearest pub down the main road into the valley, halfway to Bodmin Road station (now, prissily, Bodmin Parkway), the next stop on the line—for drinks before Sunday dinner: beer for the men, shandy for Auntie Rose, pop for Jack and me, crisps for all of us. Then back with bottles in the men's jacket pockets. We learned to value our pleasures: it was three-and-a-half miles there, three-and-a-half miles back, mostly uphill, singing all the way, led by Gwyn.

'Gwyn's going to be a singer after the war,' Uncle Jack had told us and anyone who would listen.

'Going to be? He never stops,' Auntie Rose complained insincerely.

She was a different person with Gwyn there, like an opened flower. Uncle Jack quietly glowed instead of his usual half scowl. The place was lit up, full of Gwyn's song and laughter. And then he was gone.

THE WOODS, IN SUMMER, became our playground. They were as good as they promised when we first saw them: trees to climb; little streams everywhere, some of which dried up in hot weather and others that only appeared when there had been a lot of rain. Even these were often, to our surprise, full of minnows or sticklebacks, which you could catch in a jam-jar and take home. But they soon died so we gave that up. These streams we dammed or re-routed; we collected watercress from them and took it home for the table. I saw a kingfisher that had built its nest far from the river and was raising a family on one of these tiny, gurgling flows.

But it was the River Fowey that was the magnet to us. It hurried along in its dappled cavern, with deep pools that swirled mysteriously, could suck you down, and held fish of giant size in our imaginations. It splashed over rapids that it seemed no fish could negotiate. There were little sandy beaches with backwaters where you could examine the water insects and trout fry in close proximity, making a pool that they could not escape from until you dug a channel with your hand and watched them swim away. Tree trunks lay across it, felled or left to make bridges for the more agile. Further upstream, beyond the Doublebois House estate, the woods thinned and the river flowed through meadows until you traced it back to open moorland where the buzzards soared and the wind always seemed to be blowing too much. But that was quite a walk, rarely undertaken.

Of course, when they visited, our parents were taken to our magic playground. Mum, hobbling along the riverside path in unsuitable shoes—high heels if my memory is correct—was soon stuck over the middle of the river on one of the tree trunks, sitting down, legs astride in a very undignified manner, while we ran back and forth, climbing over her to show off our skill, offering advice that she couldn't take and laughing and yelling with glee. She would appeal to Dad, 'Billie, help me, I can't . . . I'm slipping . . .' but Dad played to the gallery of his agile sons and joined in the masculine taunts. Mum laughed, too, in that hopeless way she used when she couldn't do anything about a situation, though I suspect she was really hating it, just making acquiescent noises and glad to be with us.

ONE OF THE FIRST THINGS we vackies did was to build a hut in the woods. Most of the forest in the Fowey Valley was deciduous but there were plantations of firs, standing in military rows. We drove in some stakes between four of these trees, cut branches for mainstays, found ferns and wove the fronds into four walls and a roof. More ferns and pine needles made a dryish floor. It was dark and womb-like in there, exciting when with someone else, frightening when alone and the sounds of the forest outside became menacing. The smell of resin was everywhere; we would go home sticky with the stuff. Jack and I, Ken, Eric and Peter Plummer, and Harold and Alan Packham created this place. It was our secret, jealously guarded.

Ken and Eric from Plymouth lived in the cramped little whitewashed bungalow across the Court with their mother. Their older brother Peter soon left, I think to join the Army, and there were four more brothers, grown-up, who showed up occasionally, and a father who was sometimes seen. They were probably all serving somewhere or other. My mother would have called them common—and they probably were. How would a family of seven brothers, brought up in one of the tougher parts of Plymouth in the Depression, be anything else? Welsh, working-class Auntie Rose found them 'a bit rough', but they were our friends across the Court: such distinctions didn't matter. Their urban attitudes resonated with us vackies from London more than the rural ones of the Doublebois children. We, like them, were outsiders, although to us Londoners their accents were at first indistinguishable from the local children's, something both parties hotly denied.

Elsie Plummer, their cousin, ripe with imminent puberty, was certainly 'a bit rough'; even Mrs Plummer thought so. One of Elsie's regular games was executing high kicks whenever we were playing together, generally at the entrance to the army camp. She was very proud of the height she could kick, would demonstrate it whenever possible and afforded every child, and most of the soldiers on guard duty, frequent glimpses of her knickers. When the ground was dry she would also demonstrate the splits to anyone interested, lifting her skirt to show that her knees were straight and her knickers touching the ground, providing us with a more protracted view. There wasn't room in the bungalow for a girl, she and her male cousins were approaching puberty, so Elsie was billeted out. With Miss Polmanor.

Elsie was into the bungalow and our house whenever possible. Auntie Rose half disapproved of her and half sympathised. Miss Polmanor regarded Elsie as her cross to bear for the duration; she made it her mission to convert Elsie to godliness. 'I'll save that maid's soul or die in the attempt.' A hopeless cause. It must have been one of the most mismatched billetings of the whole war, and I wonder if some malicious officer was settling a score with Miss Polmanor. The trouble was that, besides foisting Elsie on Miss Polmanor, he inflicted Miss Polmanor on Elsie, though I think Elsie was the more resilient of the two.

When Elsie first met us London vackies we'd thought she was a local. She had vehemently denied this and faced us squarely with her direct stare and burgeoning body. 'Well, you talk like they do,' we said.

'I don't. I talk ever so different. I be from Plymouth.' She pointed vaguely. ''Tis over to there. My dad's in the Army and my mum's gone off with a sailor, so they sent me yere. I don't like it yere.'

'We do,' someone ventured.

Elsie continued on her own tack. 'I've held the hand of a dead person.'

We just stood and stared at this revelation, imaginations racing.

'Whose?' challenged a disbelieving voice.

'My granny's. I was holding her hand and she died.'

We learned later from the Plummer boys that this story was often trotted out. 'If she was holding my yand I'd've been glad to die,' said Peter Plummer contemptuously.

But Elsie was in my head, indelibly. Months later she and I were playing together and went off into the woods to explore. Anxious to impress her I took her to our secret hut and swore her to secrecy. We crawled in through the low doorway; she looked round. 'Cor, 'tis lovely and dark. Smells of resin. No one would ever know we were yere.' She settled herself. 'D'you want to play doctors?'

I was mystified.

She looked at me speculatively. 'How old be you?'

'Nearly eight.'

'I'm nearly thirteen. I'll be doctor first.'

'All right.'

'You got to take all your clothes off.'

I was flabbergasted. '*All* of them? My pants too?'

'Yes. Then you lie down and I examine you. I say, "What seems to be the trouble, Mr Smith?"'

'The school doctor just combed my hair for nits.'

'Do you want to play or not?'

'No.' But I did, desperately.

'You shy?'

'Yes.'

'So be I. Let's undress together.'

Clever Elsie calmed the fears of both of us. We solemnly started to remove our clothes. Before we had got far: 'You know boys and girls 're different?'

More new territory. 'I think so.' I knew so, thanks to our cousins.

'D'you know why?'

'No.' This seemed like the safest answer. 'Hazily' would have been more truthful.

''Tis to make babies. You put your widdler in my twinkle.'

I giggled nervously. She was insane. 'Don't be daft. It wouldn't go.'

'No, I thought that. I don't think it works till you're married. Or grown-up.

Tiny little babies come out the end of your widdler. All swimming.'

I let out an 'eeargh' of disgust.

But she was relentless. 'The husband has to lie on top of the wife, then it works. All husbands and wives do it. Your mum and dad did it to get you.'

'Shut up,' I muttered sullenly, not wanting to imagine such an event.

'The baby grows for nine months in yere, then comes out.'

'Babies are too big.' I had caught her on a practical level.

But even that was no good. She just agreed. 'I know. I don't get it. The woman screams, so it mustn't half hurt. I don't think I want babies.'

We were both out of our depth. 'You made it all up.'

'The animals do it, too. You watch. I have. Nobody saw me. Crago's bull. His widdler. You should see. They all laughed.'

I was shocked into protest. 'We're not animals,' and searched for an argument to refute her. Sunday school came to mind. 'We got souls. The vicar said we've got souls and animals haven't.'

'What does he know? Be you going to play doctor, then?'

'No. I don't like you.'

'Yes, you do.'

And she was right. I did. I, sort of, loved her. She spoke with a calm authority that was thrilling and disturbing. Like every other child learning the facts of life unofficially as we did, I thought of my parents doing it: no. It was all too grotesque. I went home, stared at Auntie Rose and Uncle Jack and tried to imagine them engaged in something so rude and unlikely. No, not possible. I cornered Uncle Jack in the garden where we wouldn't be overheard. 'Uncle Jack, have we got souls?'

He was always glad to hold forth on this subject. 'Nobody knows, boy, though they say they do.'

'Nobody in the whole world?'

'No. But if you ask me, it's all tripe. All of it. All religion. Rubbish.'

'So we *are* just like the animals?'

'I wouldn't say that, boy. We got *minds*.' And he grinned with satisfaction at this opportunity to make his prime, anti-religious, point.

Auntie Rose was feeding the hens.

'Auntie Rose, have we got souls?'

'Course we have, my love. What d'you think we are, animals?'

'Uncle Jack says we haven't.'

'What does he know? Heathen.'

There appeared to be nothing but confusion on the subject in the adult world, so how could Elsie know? But the assurances of her still childish but swelling body against mine, the changes in herself she pointed out so proudly, the persistent rumours of the truth that I encountered among the older children and the overwhelming evidence in the countryside all round us soon undermined my disbelief. So, when the other boys were busy elsewhere, the promise of a breathless, dry session of doctors with Elsie—full of intimacy yet reserve—created a trembling, inexplicable excitement that was quite fulfilled by the cool, clinical little scenes we acted out in our pine-scented surgery in the woods.

CHAPTER FIVE

Autumn introduced me to different new pleasures in the countryside. Blackberrying with Auntie Rose on the Slates came first. The Slates was the embankment beside the stretch of railway just below Doublebois before it disappeared into the woods. This embankment sloped down into the Rabbit Field, the long narrow field that lay between the main road and the railway and eventually merged into the woodland. The Slates was made up of the slate blasted from the side of the valley when the railway was cut into it. Nothing but brambles and thistles would grow there. On the far side of the line was the goods yard, Blamey and Morgan's mill and the animal pens. Auntie Rose, with bowls and jugs in a basket, led us out of the Court, through the crossroads and very quietly through the gate into the Rabbit Field. This was the moment for Jack and me to take off, hullooing and yelling down the slope. It was only then, among the thistles and hummocks of this not very fertile field, that you realised how aptly it was named: it came alive with rabbits scattering in every direction.

Next, the Slates: steeply sloped, dark grey Cornish slates sliding under your feet. Don't fall over, they cut. Bushes in clumps all round you, big fat blackberries. Pick four or five, eat one, pick some more, eat some more, fingers and lips stained purple. Stop and stare while a train that has stopped at Doublebois gathers speed just above your head, huge and threatening from where you stand below its wheels. Sometimes an express would roar by just above you, thrilling in its power and noise, belching smoke if it was labouring up the gradient on its way to Plymouth, or rattling happily, only a thin plume of steam, as it virtually freewheeled going west, down the valley. And waving, always waving at the drivers, firemen, passengers, guard. Then back to the business in hand until Auntie Rose said, 'All right. These yere'll do. We'll come back next week, there'll be a new crop ripe by then.' She always picked more than Jack's and my efforts put together.

Auntie Rose turned those blackberries into jam for the winter—all the jam she could make on our meagre sugar ration—and blackberry and apple pies for Sunday dinner, with custard usually, or rarely, if we were very lucky, with clotted cream: the best pudding in the world, hot or cold.

The other riveting activity of autumn was the harvest. As the binders went round and round the fields, leaving a diminishing stand of oats or barley in the middle—no wheat was planted in wet, windblown Cornwall—we would stand the cut sheaves into little stooks. Generally two children would work with a man, the children gathering the sheaves, the man expertly stooking them so that they wouldn't fall over in any wind or rain that might come before we gathered them onto carts and built ricks ready for the threshing, the next excitement to come. Everyone turned out for the harvest, a country tradition. We children, promised payment for our time, set to with a will as we eagerly worked out how much we had earned at so much an hour. We would turn up at the farmer's door a few days later for our money and find out it was always less than we thought we had been promised; probably another country tradition.

But the real fun for most of us was the rabbits. As the tractor cut more and more corn the rabbits would retreat into the centre of the field, frightened inwards by the noise. As the climax drew near, the rabbits would break with increasing frequency, but now they had to thread their way through many clutching hands, past stabbing pitchforks and—generally their doom—the dogs. As each rabbit broke, there was a mad hallooing and barking, generally ending in a growl, a sudden death and a warm furry body swiftly disappearing into a capacious pocket.

Uncle Jack was a master at rabbit-catching. Into the field straight after his day on the track, he would arrive as cutting was nearly finished. That tiny, round figure could cover a few yards in a flash. Jack and I were always racing him down the Court and never won. A rabbit would break, a dive, a quick twist with his hands, and he would wink at us as the little bundle went into the pocket inside his jacket. When he had got two or three he would whistle to us and off we went home for tea to discover he generally had another one he had caught when we weren't looking. I find it almost unbelievable now that round little Uncle Jack could snatch at and catch a passing rabbit, quicker even than the dogs. But he could. And he was not unique.

We were always on at him to let us kill one, and I can remember experimenting with tentative, inadequate rabbit punches as I held up some poor creature by its hind legs and chopped tentatively away at the back of its neck with the side of my hand until Uncle Jack took it from me and ended its pain and fear. At first I was the squeamish young townie, half afraid of anything living and wild, and not really wanting to hurt it. Quite soon that was buried under my wish to demonstrate my—what? Manliness? Competence? I don't know, but thus are many sorts of killers made, out of wishing to belong. We caught rabbits all the time in the gins and snares that were in constant use all round us, and, as the rabbits were often still alive when we came to inspect the traps, we had plenty of opportunities to improve our techniques. I became adept, preferring to hold the neck in one hand and hind legs in the other. Then a stretch and sharp twist. Apart from the centuries-old farmer/rabbit war, they were a welcome addition to our wartime meat ration, but that was just an excuse for my willingness to kill.

When threshing time came, a tractor would tow the threshing machine round the local farms: a clanking, smelly thing, driven by a belt fitted onto a tractor, that produced clouds of chaff that made you sneeze. We would gather at each farm to join in. Then it was the turn of rats and mice to be the quarry. There were always some who had made the newly built ricks their home and larder in just a few days. But as the sheaves were dismantled and forked into the thresher it was slaughter. The bigger boys loved to spear them with pitchforks as they appeared and the dogs made short work of those that were missed.

And then, as the leaves started to fall, I can remember standing at the crossroads in Doublebois looking out over the valley and watching flocks of birds heading south; I don't know what they were but they were big and small birds, in big and small groups, and in vast numbers. The biggest and most spectacular flocks, though, were the starlings just finding their roost for the night. They wheeled and dived and rose and spread, bunching up and thinning out from dense black clouds into long wisps before sinking down into the woods and disappearing.

The climax of autumn was the harvest festival when the church was full of donated fruit, vegetables—principally marrows, which people were glad to get rid of—and sheaves of corn, and we all belted out 'We Plough The Fields And Scatter', and 'Come Ye Thankful People, Come'. After this celebration the fields were bare, tractors criss-crossed the cornfields, ploughing-in the stubble, followed by squabbling crowds of seagulls, crows, lapwings and starlings. And the world turned brown.

WHEN THE FURIOUS WINTER of 1940–1 took hold, the village pumps were encased in ice and the wind whipped snow down off Bodmin Moor, making six-foot drifts in the middle of Dobwalls. Snow was a rarity in the south-westerly airstreams of Cornwall. For the Doublebois children, the mile-and-a-half walk to school became an ordeal involving red ears and noses, chilblains, chapped fingers, soaked woollen gloves with icicles on them, and wet feet and necks from the melted snow that spilled into every gap in our clothing, especially over and into our hobnail boots. We had cold feet all day. Not one of us had wellies as I recall; there was no rubber to spare to make such things for children.

When we walked home was the time for games: slides in the village street that annoyed the grown-ups, snowballs thrown at each other as we ran and trudged the mile and a half back. We waded into snowdrift after snow-drift until we were frozen, soaking and bored with it. Then, oh then, the warm range in the kitchen of the Phillips' cottage, fingers and faces going red in the heat, hot drinks, cosiness and Auntie Rose presiding.

Going to bed was the next ordeal. Undress downstairs into warmed pyja-mas, no heat up there, but a lovely stone hot-water bottle in the bed to put your feet on as, shivering, you scrambled in to snuggle down into a billowy mattress, pillows, blankets and eiderdown. In the morning the windows were an etched miracle of frost patterns, often with the ice on the inside, condensation from our night-time breathing, which you could pick at or draw on with your fingernail before reluctantly getting out and diving into clothes that Auntie Rose had left warming by the range all night.

The children arranged a mass snowball fight one dinner break; vackies versus village kids. It included every child in the district between the ages of five and fifteen and got utterly out of hand. Schoolchildren surged up and down the road between the village school and the Methodist chapel, hurling ice and snow or just shouting. When the bells sounded, while law-abiding souls went in to school, the rest of us spilled over into fields and chased each other to Duloe Bridge. The climax was a snowball shoot-out as the wan winter daylight faded. We swaggered back into class in front of the admiring looks of the more timid kids to have the smirks wiped off our faces by Mrs Langdon, our Junior Vackies mistress, normally the kindest of women, and Miss Shepherd of the village school, a tiny, bird-like creature, who laid their rulers mercilessly across our chapped and tingling fingers.

And once, when Mr Evans, the elderly village-school headmaster, was absent, tiny Miss Shepherd was forced to bring out their school cane and wield it on several of the bigger boys—vackies and village kids—for a group transgression: chanting blasphemous versions of *Hymns Ancient and Modern* in public. Miss Shepherd was halfway down the row of proffered backsides when the cane, groaning under its excessive burden, gave up the ghost and snapped in two. Miss Shepherd burst into tears and the row of unyielding bottoms returned to their seats.

A WEEKLY ORDEAL was the letter home. Auntie Rose was adamant. We were never allowed to miss. I regarded it as a chore to be endured; it must have been torture for Jack. One winter evening I sat at the table chewing a pencil while Auntie Rose mended socks with a letter from Gwyn on her lap. She was upset and not inclined to be indulgent to my whinges.

'I can't think of anything to write.'

'You say that every week.'

I was as foolish as ever. Walking in where I should never go. 'You've read that letter from Gwyn hundreds of times.'

'And I shall probably read it hundreds more. They said he was only going training back home in Wales. Now they've sent him abroad. Abroad. Where? Haven't they ever heard of embarkation leave?' Her voice had risen to a querulous high and she stared at me as though I had the answer.

Intimidated, I offered, 'Uncle Jack said they didn't give them leave because they didn't want to warn the German submarines. Careless talk costs lives.' This was a wartime slogan, which I piously trotted out.

'What does he know about it?' she growled.

'That means the Army were protecting our soldiers,' I tried.

'The Army? Protecting our soldiers?' She raised her head again from her mending. Her eyes were hollow black bottomless holes as she looked at me. Her voice slashed across the room. 'When did that ever enter their heads?'

I stared at this apparition, a moment ago sober, comforting Auntie Rose, now someone looking out of hell. I think she must have seen my dismay because her eyes and voice returned to normal. To my relief she went on. '"Address, care of the War Office". Care of. Huh.' She changed again, lost in her own world; I wasn't there. 'Like they took care of the boys from Jack's pit in the last lot.'

I was too curious to keep silent. 'What's the last lot, Auntie Rose?'

She was still lost. 'The last war. Jack was the only one who came back alive to our village in Wales. The only one. It's why we left: every woman staring at me as if it was my fault.' She shuddered and returned to the present, waving Gwyn's letter accusingly at me again. 'Ink on paper instead of a person here in your life. That's all there is: letters. And every letter from Gwyn is one page long. That's all he can manage. One page.'

'Two sides,' I tried helpfully.

'It's not enough. You write two pages home to your mam and dad this week. Two. D'you hear?'

'That's *four* sides. I've never written four sides.'

'You can this week.'

The awful injustice of this made me reckless. 'That's not fair. We shouldn't have to write at all. It was her sent us away.' As soon as I had said it I wished I hadn't. I tried not to catch Auntie Rose's eye and muttered, 'Well, she did.'

'What?' she said quietly.

'I didn't mean it.'

'Don't you ever say anything like that again about your mother. Or your father, for that matter.'

'I was only moaning about writing letters.'

'Never. D'you hear?'

'Yes, Auntie Rose. Sorry, Auntie Rose,' I muttered miserably. 'I didn't mean it.'

'I don't care what you meant. Never.' It was the first time I ever saw her really angry with me, even though she must have known it was only child-ishness on my part. 'I have to stop myself writing *fifty* sides to Gwyn, and I can hardly spell my name. You're supposed to be clever.'

I was trying not to cry. 'Just because you're upset about Gwyn, I've got to write four sides, a whole blinking book. It's not fair.'

'I know it's not fair, boy. Nothing is. Listen. Who did your shoelaces up for you before you could do your own?'

'Mum, I suppose. And Dad sometimes.'

'Your mam and dad. Exactly. And do you think they minded?'

'Dunno.'

'No, my Terry, they didn't mind. You can be sure of that. Because they love you. And your brother. They love you both . . . and your shoelaces . . . and your first teeth when you lost 'em . . . and the locks they cut from your hair. I've still got some of Len's and Rose's and Gwyn's. Even the clippings when they cut your toenails.'

'Ergh.'

'Yes. Everything about you. So. You write them four sides about your shoelaces, is it?'

'Nobody can write four sides about shoelaces.'

'I would jump for joy if I got four sides from Gwyn.'

'If they were about shoelaces you'd think he'd gone barmy.'

So, Gwyn was abroad, in North Africa, the only place the war was really going on at that moment, except over London. Perhaps his embarkation leave had been when we met him and he had kept quiet about it. We looked at pictures in the papers and during our rare visits to the cinema at the newsreels, which showed Italian soldiers surrendering in their tens of thousands, long columns of them walking across the desert guarded by the occasional casual Tommy with a rifle slung over his shoulder. We searched to see if it was Gwyn, our hero. We seemed to be winning. It was all an illusion: the Germans led by Rommel hadn't even arrived there yet.

JACK AND I used to go shopping with Auntie Rose once a week in Liskeard, four miles away, the next stop on the train. There, with pocket money supplemented by our parents, we bought our weekly treats: for Jack it was generally an army cap badge, for me a Dinky Toy.

Jack's cap badges, mounted on a green baize cloth, were quite something. He must have got most of the regiments of the British Army: the Sphinx of the Gloucesters, for their service in Egypt, the little badge worn on the back of their caps because they fought a heroic rearguard action; the many variations of the cross of St Andrew of Scottish regiments, some with exotic names: the Argyll and Sutherland Highlanders, the Black Watch. We loved the rearing white horse of our own Royal West Kents; romantic names like the Green Howards from Yorkshire; the hunting horn of the Duke of Cornwall's Light Infantry, now our local regiment. The skull and crossbones of the 17th/21st Lancers with 'Death or Glory' scrolled under them easily imprinted themselves into the imaginations of romantically bloodthirsty boys; Uncle Jack's Royal Welch Fusiliers with its curious mis-spelling and motto of '*Ich dien*' ('I serve' in German). I think Jack had over a hundred and I learned the geography of the country from those badges and much of our military history, all seen in a heroic glow. We were in the middle of a war for our survival and these were our saviours.

Auntie Rose, Jack and me by the never-used front door

My Dinky Toys were just as important: we had sea battles with HMS *Hood*, *Valiant*, *The Prince Of Wales*—all sent to the bottom in the real war with terrible loss of life even as we played our games. We had aerial dog-fights, Spitfires and Hurricanes shot Messerschmitts, Heinkels and Dorniers out of the sky. We raided Germany with Wellingtons, Blenheims and Halifaxes. With Sunderland flying boats we saved our convoys from U-boats. Panzer tanks were blown apart by Churchills. Foot soldiers, firing lying down, or running, were placed behind table legs, some in historic cos-tume, but all involved in this war. There were Bren Carriers, machine guns and some artillery that actually fired. Even German soldiers were there, to be knocked over and killed again and again as they lost battle after battle in the front room out of Auntie Rose's way, or in the hall, where they were laid out for us to admire without anyone ever likely to tread on them. Jack sold his wonderful collection years later to help pay for the conversion of the very nice coach house he and his wife had bought. But even then, when I was well into my twenties, it seemed like an act of vandalism to me. My Dinky Toys disappeared over the years in a much less useful fashion: I lost them or swapped them for other things now long forgotten.

The trips to Liskeard were regular weekly outings. But the great events that filled us with excitement were the much rarer twenty-two-mile train rides to Plymouth. Onto the 9.40 a.m. stopping train, over Moorswater Viaduct and some spectacular views, especially down onto the Looe branch line that went right beneath us like a model; out of Liskeard station on another viaduct. At last, the Royal Albert Bridge, known to us all as Saltash Bridge. 'Built by Isambard Kingdom Brunel', it announced at either end. What a name. It was the crossing point back into England.

There followed the slow rumble over the bridge, guarded by a sentry at either end. Local legend said that it moved a foot every time a train crossed. I multiplied the number of trains each week by the number of weeks since the bridge was built in 1859 then wondered why it hadn't either edged itself up the Tamar or sidled miles out to sea.

The sight of the warships, low, grey and stark, indescribably menacing, lying in the Tamar estuary, and Devonport Docks; then Plymouth and the Hoe; the statue of Drake with his bowls, a stylish reminder of how to reduce the enemy to size; pasties that tasted of potato and pepper but had never seen meat. Jack and I saved pocket money for these trips for more Dinky Toys and army cap badges, ones too rare to be found in rural Liskeard.

Over these expeditions presided Auntie Rose with two shopping bags that became loaded and that we all struggled with as she led us first from queue to queue then, when the serious business was done, from shop window to shop window. A cameo brooch was pinned to her best blouse and a silver-and-blue enamel butterfly brooch to her lapel. She wore a shapeless hat that required hatpins to hold it onto her long, thick brown hair, done up in a bun.

We were waiting one evening in Plymouth North Road station buffet for a train that was very late. 'Bombing up the line' was the dark rumour. Jack had bought a miniature sheath knife in its leather sheath, something he had been coveting and saving for for ages. He kept taking it from the shopping bag, unclipping the press-stud fastening round the handle and half withdrawing the glistening blade. It was a formidable purchase. The date was March 20, 1941. It was a Thursday, the first of the two nights on which the

Luftwaffe wiped the centre of Plymouth from the face of the earth.

'Come on, boys,' said Auntie Rose. 'Put that knife away till the proper time. When you get home you play with that, not in yere. You'll lose it.'

She was interrupted by the sound of a distant siren. The whole buffet went silent. 'Oh *Duw*, what was that?' she breathed.

'An air-raid siren,' said Jack superfluously.

'They're a long way—'

She drew in her breath as the heart-stopping, low-pitched whirr and whine that develops into the shattering wail of a siren started up close by. The voices broke out again into a hubbub and a Devon accent rose above them all to say, 'All passengers in the subway, please. At once. Come along now, my lovelies. Let's be 'avin' you.'

We all hurried out onto the platform and headed down the ramps into the subways under the tracks. The sound of gunfire was clearly audible some way off. Auntie Rose gathered us on either side of her on a bench, shopping bags on the floor before us.

'Are they bombs?' I asked Jack.

'No, they're our guns, shooting the Jerries down. Bombs whistle.' He was rooting about in the shopping bags. Suddenly there was panic in his voice. 'My knife. Where's my knife? My new sheath knife is gone.'

Auntie Rose grabbed a bag. 'Perhaps it's in this one. Yere, let's see.'

But Jack was gone, racing down the subway. 'I left it in the buffet.'

Auntie Rose was distraught. 'Come back, come back, boy, you can't . . .' Her voice faded into disbelief. 'He's gone.'

I had been searching in the first bag. 'Here's the knife, Auntie Rose. It's in this bag. I've got it here. Jack, I got it. Come back. Come back.' And I set off after Jack, ignoring Auntie Rose's agonised voice as the tumult outside grew louder. I flew between the huddled groups of people, turned a corner and stared up the slope towards platform-level. No Jack; he had already gone. As I started to run up the slope there was a loud bang and bits of glass and debris flew about above me. I stopped, terrified, and stood bawling near the bottom of the slope, afraid to move, when hands grabbed me and pulled me back round the corner.

' 'Ere, boy, come yere. I got you. You can't stand out there.'

I sobbed, 'Let me go. My brother. My brother's up there. He lost his knife. We've got it.'

'What you talking about?'

Before I could say more I heard Auntie Rose's voice. 'Here, Terry. Here he is. With me. He came back.'

And there stood Jack. His courage, like mine, had failed at the sight and sound of the real war. Auntie Rose led us back to our bench, sat down and enfolded us both. 'Oh, boys, come yere. You give me heart failure, you did.'

God knows what hell we had put her through in those few moments. How do you explain to their parents that your two charges ran up into the bombing and were blown to bits looking for a sheath knife that was in your shopping bag all the time?

'I was going to go,' Jack assured me. 'It was only that you stopped me.'

'So was I,' I affirmed, equally inaccurately.

We spent the night sitting on the bench while the inferno raged above us. My principal memory was that, no matter how I shook with fright, the bench, which seated about ten people, always quaked at a different rhythm, and I couldn't get my bottom synchronised to the common tempo of terror.

The next morning was the first day of spring. We stood among glass and bits on the platform till a train took us across the miraculously unscathed Saltash Bridge. Plymouth was ablaze, smoke hung everywhere; a high proportion of the bombs had been incendiary. The warships still lurked, apparently intact, in Devonport Docks and the Tamar estuary, out of the way. Or perhaps their fire had been so intense that it was easier for the bombers to unload onto the undefended civilian centre of the city.

At each station groups of people met the train to ask for news or just to stare at us. And there at the end of the platform at Doublebois stood Uncle Jack looking ridiculously small and vulnerable till he saw the three of us waving wildly from a window. Then his shut face burst open into a grin that threatened to tear it in two. He hurried down the platform, took Auntie Rose's shopping bags from her, put them on the ground and hugged her. It was a rare enough event to see them touching, let alone this display. He just said, 'Oh *Duw*, girl. There you are. There you are.'

'Of course I am. What d'you think? Let me go, you fool. People are watching.' She was flushed and pleased.

'You looked after her, boys, did you, for me?'

We couldn't wait to tell him about it. 'It was t'riffic, Uncle Jack.'

'I was ever so scared.'

'I'll bet you were, boy. I thought I'd got rid of you all at last. But there's no peace for the wicked, is there?'

ALL OF THAT DAY in the sky to the east hung a pall of smoke, which turned to a red glow at dusk. Then the bombers returned.

A small crowd of us gathered in the gardens of the cottages to watch. In the distance there were flashes and crumps while the searchlights reflected off the smoke pall. The glow under the clouds, which was Plymouth burning, grew brighter.

'Oh God, 'tis not possible.'

'Will anyone be left?'

Miss Polmanor had the explanation for it all. ''Tis hell here on earth. 'Tis the inferno come to punish us.'

'Not us.' Someone pointed at the pyre in the distance. 'Them.'

'Let us pray to God to strike Hitler dead.'

'If God wanted Hitler dead he wouldn't wait for *her* to ask,' muttered someone softly.

The Plummers, joined by Elsie, stood silently and watched their city being destroyed. Elsie didn't know if her mother, who had run off with the sailor while her father was away in the Army, was there or not.

'Are you sure my mum's not there, Auntie Rose?'

'Course not, my lovely. Don't you worry.' Auntie Rose sounded convincing.

A neighbour added quietly, ''Er's crying for her mother; 'er mother never gave 'er a moment's thought.'

'Is that what's happening in London to our mum and dad?' asked Jack.

Uncle Jack was stumped for a moment. 'No, it's not nearly so—London's enormous, Plymouth's small—it just looks—worse . . .' he trailed off feebly.

'It's why we'm all vackies,' said a Plummer boy.

And Auntie Rose held me tighter than before.

The fires could not be put out; they were beyond the scope of the fire services of several cities to deal with. Most of East Cornwall and South Devon watched Plymouth burn for nearly a week, under that pall of smoke all day and that red glow at night, like a false dawn.

The Germans returned for three successive nights a month later, and the whole business was repeated. This time, with shopping trips cancelled, we watched the destruction from the safety of our bedroom window.

Auntie Rose told us that she had spent that entire night when we were under the bombers worrying about how, if we were killed, Uncle Jack could possibly explain to our parents why she had taken us into danger in Plymouth.

CHAPTER SIX

U ncle Jack didn't take long to get Jack and me singing. His success
with Gwyn, and his natural inclinations, led him. I am not so sure
about Jack's enthusiasm for it but he went with it, anyway. On the
other hand, I was a willing pupil and soon heard Uncle Jack's views on
many subjects as a result. One day he was taking me through a hymn, trying
to get me to make sense of it. I sang without thought, breathing automatically at the end of each line:

> Time, like an ever-rolling stream,
> Bears all its sons away.
> They fly forgotten, as a dream
> Dies at the opening day.

Having listened he said casually, 'That's right, boy. Not bad. If we got to
bother God this Sunday let's bother him with a bit of sense, eh? Not all that
slop about living eternally in heaven with Him, eh? There's nothing cosy
about time bearing its sons away. Pretty agnostic, really, innit, for a hymn?'

'What's agnostic, Uncle Jack?'

'It's halfway to good sense, boy. Atheism says there's no God; agnostic
says I'm not sure. I don't suppose the chap that wrote any hymn's a real
atheist, so we'll have to do with a halfway house. Now, let's have it again
but we'll hit 'em with a bit o' clever phrasing this time, so they listen. Look
yere, take your breaths where I marked the page. See? Then they'll have to
think a minute. Not that any of 'em do in church, but you never know.'

'There is only one God, isn't there, Uncle Jack?'

'At most.'

'Then why are church and chapel different?'

I had got him on to one of his favourite rants. He leaned in confidentially.
'Well, you see, boy, church is a lot of lying, hypocritical, God-bothering,
sinful Tories.' He paused, hoping I would ask the question. I did.

'And what's chapel?'

'Chapel is church without the poetry.' Having got that one off his chest,
he returned with vigour to the matter in hand. 'Come on now, with sense

this time. Breathe where I marked it and start off with a big 'un.'

I gave it to him as instructed, one breath for the first two lines. I could just make it. ' "Time, like an ever-rolling stream, Bears all its sons away." ' Big breath. ' "They fly forgotten," ' a quick breath, the remainder smoothly rolled out in one, "as a dream Dies at the opening day." ' I let the last word hang and fade as my breath ran out.

There was a moment before he spoke. 'There is lovely, my Terry. There is a beautiful voice you do have there. Makes me cry to year you. A scruffy little cockney with a voice like an angel.'

But I was learning his language. 'You don't believe in angels.'

He grinned and made to cuff me. 'Only when I hear them sing.'

I dared to be too intrusive in this cosy atmosphere. 'Why don't you believe in God, Uncle Jack?'

He leaned back. 'Perhaps I should ask you why you *do* believe.'

Like so many of his remarks this was too fundamental for an eight-year-old. I thought and stared at him, my head in a whirl. 'Everybody does.'

'Do they? I'm not so sure about your dad and mam.'

More things to grapple with that I hadn't thought about.

'You know, boy, I was a Christian once. Brought up into it like all of us. Then, when I was in the trenches in the last war—the one before this one, two before the next—we went through no-man's-land one night and captured some German dugouts. D'you know what was written on the wall? Three words. In German. *Gott mit uns*. It means "God's on our side".' He smiled at me. 'Well. And all the time I had thought he was on ours. There was silly of me. He was backing both sides. Or neither.'

Suddenly I was on firmer ground. I came in hotly, 'Those Germans were wrong. He was on our side. We won that war.'

Uncle Jack was unperturbed, continuing to smile sadly at me. 'You're right. So we did. I forgot for a moment.'

'And we'll win this one too.'

'I'm sure you're right, boy. Let's hope so.'

'Can I go out to play now? The soldiers are back from manoeuvres.'

'Have you written to your mam and dad this week?'

'I was going to.'

'Mam and dad first.' He winked at being able to get both the last word and the last joke in: 'You don't want them thinking we're all heathens down yere in Cornwall, do you?'

ON THE MANTELPIECE over the range in the living room of 7 Railway Cottages sat the two little brass shells in their cases with their soldered-on badges of the Prince of Wales: the three feathers and '*Ich dien*' on a scroll beneath, part of the cap badge of the Royal Welch Fusiliers. These shells, standing some seven or eight inches high, were treasures to Jack and me. We were fascinated by them. I can remember handling them again and again, feeling their weight, their shape, their menace. They were from the First World War, we knew, something to do with Uncle Jack's past, but he would not tell us. At some point, however, we had made some sort of deal with him about practising singing and the shells. One evening we sang 'The Ash Grove' in harmony for him and Auntie Rose. She was, as always, full of praise.

'That's lovely, boys,' she said, glowing.

Uncle Jack was more cautious. 'That's right, both of you. Not bad. You sound as though you're thinking about what you're singing as well as making a beautiful sound.'

Jack was in at once. 'You going to tell us now, then, Uncle Jack?'

'You promised when we got "The Ash Grove" right,' I chimed.

Auntie Rose was instantly alert. 'Promised what?'

Uncle Jack squirmed more. 'I didn't say it was right. I said it's not bad.'

'He said he'd tell us the story of the army badges on the two shells on the mantelpiece. And "*Ich dien*",' we clamoured.

She looked upset. 'Oh, Jack, what do they want to year that old history for? Horrible war stories. Isn't this one enough? Our Gwyn's out there, you know.'

Uncle Jack was surprisingly mild. 'They're boys, Rose, not wurzels.'

Auntie Rose got to her feet. 'To the chickens, me. Get the eggs. The hens do talk more sense than you.'

And we were left to hear the stories of Uncle Jack's war. 'I was in the bantams' battalion, see. If you was under five foot you weren't accepted at first. Good enough to dig coal, too small to fight, they said. Then, after our High Command had let the Germans slaughter most of the good men, they needed more cannon fodder so they took us titches. We made a whole battalion: the Welsh Bantams. We was in the line-up against the Prussian Guards, fine fellers, all of 'em over six foot tall. How 'bout that?'

'Cor, that's not fair.'

He smiled, having caught us, an easy thing to do. 'Oh, no. Not so silly. Every man's the same height when a bullet hits him. He's horizontal.'

'That's brilliant.' His views of generals and others in charge were already well known to us. 'Our High Command weren't so stupid, Uncle Jack. They thought of that.'

He changed at once, growling angrily. 'Don't let me catch you saying any good of our leaders, boy. Especially that particular lot. They were just men, like you will be sooner than you think. What were we doing fighting at all? Ernie Bevin tried to stop it with a general strike but they called him a traitor. Now, in this lot, he's in the Govern—'

Politics had got him again and he needed to be rechannelled. 'But the shells and the badges. What happened in the Great War?'

His response was sharp. 'Great War, eh? Who taught you that?'

'It's on the war memorial in the village.'

'Huh. Great, indeed.' He gathered himself again. 'First we was up against the Saxons. They was all right. They didn't like the war no more 'n we did. We used to put up a tin helmet on the end of a rifle for their snipers to take potshots at. Then they did the same for us. The officers stopped that. Said it was giving them practise. Practise? Huh. Nobody needed it.'

'But what does "*Ich dien*" mean?'

'It's Welsh for "I serve". The Prince of Wales's motto. It's funny, "*ich*" is like German. It's more German than English. But we're Celts, dark and small, different from you Anglo-Saxons, fair-haired like them buggers.'

'Are Jack and me Saxons?'

'Were the Prussian Guards fair, too?'

'Some of 'em, yes. A thousand of them were in this wood near the Somme. There was a thousand of us, too. Our artillery started shelling them. Their artillery started shelling us. Everyone got blown to bits. Who killed who? I don't know. Bloody fools. Trees like used matchsticks stuck in the mud. Then it got cold. German and Welsh dead frozen together, bayonets in each other. Next morning the frost had made them all white; it didn't look real, like some hellish wedding cake. Seventeen of us came out alive. We got one of those insignia each.'

'But you've got two.'

'One is my mate's, Ifor Davies. Faceman from Ystrad, even smaller 'n me.'

'But if Ifor Davies was one of the seventeen why didn't he keep his badge?'

'There were plenty more battles, boy.'

'You were lucky, weren't you, Uncle Jack?' Jack said.

'That's right. Lucky. Survival is an accident, boy. Chance. We learned that in the trenches but it applies to everything. It's not destiny; it's not bravery, nor cowardice; it's not God paying you back because you're good or bad; it's not even survival of the fittest. It's an accident.'

'But you lived through it. I bet you were clever and kept your head down,' I said, clinging to some certainty or other in this bleak assessment of the world by our diminutive soldier philosopher.

Uncle Jack's voice rose with a bitter tang. 'No one was clever, boy. The clever ones weren't there at all. No matter what happens to you in your life, remember this: there's no justice. There never was and there never will be. But you've got to pretend there is. We call that being civilised.' He looked at our dismayed faces and relented a little. Anyway, he could never resist a final twist to anything he said, and though his expression remained serious, he paused, betraying his lighter intent. 'Just remember two things: it's not fair . . . and don't be late. Live your life like that and that's all you can do.'

I turned the massacre in the woods over and over in my mind. I acted out the scene in our woods below Doublebois. I hid behind trunks as shells ripped through the foliage, tearing the boughs off; splintering the green wood, uprooting forest giants, converting trees and men to blackened stumps. Why did the thousand of our men go in here? And why did the Germans? Who wanted to capture a wood anyway? All those little Welshmen hugging the ground, getting blown to pieces in spite of their lack of inches. The event had horror, fascination and mystery, which I could leave only briefly behind as I emerged into the Rabbit Field, one of seventeen sur-vivors going home to tea and the polished mementoes on the mantelpiece.

Uncle Jack, when pressed by us, had other stories. 'It was raining. Raining. Raining. The soaking summer of 1916. Everything was sodden. Your boots rotted on your feet. Mud, there was mud everywhere; chest-deep sometimes. Men disappeared in it.'

I held my breath. 'What do you mean? Disappeared? They can't just *go*.'

'Oh, couldn't they? You had to make sure you didn't follow them. Stay on the boards.'

The acceptance of death in so casual a way was harder for me to swallow than bangs and bullets.

He continued. 'But there was no clean water to drink, of course. I had to draw ours from a shell hole near by. Then it stopped raining. The water went down and we saw there'd been a dead Frog in there. Just as well I boiled it.'

I was puzzled. 'What's so terrible about a dead frog?'

Jack knew. 'Stupid. A Frog is a Frenchman. A French soldier.'

I was horrified. 'Uragh. Oogh. I feel sick. Ergh.'

'There's lots of ways to die,' Uncle Jack reflected, looking back into his war. 'The only ones who don't die are the generals . . . except of old age.'

Auntie Rose came in. 'Now stop that, Jack. Filling the boys' heads with all that rubbish. That war's over twenty years ago.'

Uncle Jack was unabashed. 'This one's on now, isn't it? D'you think it's any different? If it goes on long enough Jack could be in the Army easy. Home by Christmas, we was told. How long is it since we've seen Gwyn? Over a year he's been out there.'

Our war took on a new, dreadful fascination for me. It was no longer an imaginary, 'Bang-bang, you're dead,' with sanitary corpses—mostly German—and bandaged, tidy wounds. It became bloated, covered in mud, disembowelled, like the rabbits we snared then gutted with our penknives.

ONE MORNING I stood in the Court unable to believe my eyes. I stared up the railway line towards Plymouth and raced in to Auntie Rose. 'Auntie Rose, Auntie Rose. There's a German plane coming. Look. It's ever so low.'

She came quickly out. 'Where, boy? Oh, don't be daft. It's Red Cross. Look.' She pointed at the crosses on the plane. The plane was barely above us, limping slowly along. The crew in their bubbles were clearly visible.

'It's not. It's a Dornier 17.' I knew precisely from my Dinky Toys what plane it was. 'They're German crosses. See?'

She wasn't listening. 'Look, you can see him, plain.' She waved.

'He's the gunner. Look, one engine's not working.'

'He's waving back. Wave, boy, wave. Woo-oo.'

'I think he's going to crash.'

'If they're Germans they'd shoot us.'

We watched it fly over the station and down the valley.

'Look, it's coming down.'

And it did. A distant explosion and a plume of smoke.

Auntie Rose put a hand to her face. 'D'you think they were Germans?'

'Course they were.' I was annoyed at her naivety.

'Why didn't they parachute?'

'I think they were too low.'

She was most upset. 'Those poor boys. I saw them. Young, like Gwyn. Why didn't he shoot us if they was Germans?' She clasped me to her.

'I think he must've been a Saxon, one of Uncle Jack's friends.'

SPRING UNFOLDED into our second summer in paradise, the summer of 1941. The drift of vackies back to London had begun in spite of continued heavy air raids. The worst of the Blitz was over but there was still plenty of bombing, and more to come. Things were still going badly for our forces. We were very much in reverse. Rommel had arrived in North Africa and was driving us back to Cairo. That was the campaign that we followed avidly, poring over the maps in our atlas and in the *Daily Mirror*: Gwyn was there.

My life now was that of a country boy. Of course many things were different from Welling but surely most different of all was our relationship with animals. In Welling there was the odd pet and the tradesmen's horses. Here we were surrounded by all sorts of creatures: wild, farm and domesticated.

The fish migrations were part of the rhythm of the year. When we fished for trout we would walk the banks or lie on the fallen trees over the river, spot them and—rarely in daylight and with our basic equipment—catch them; they were there all year. But the salmon peel—the local name for sea trout, bigger and rarer—were visitors, nosing upstream to breed, and even harder to catch. Most spectacular and rarest of all, was the migration of the eels, elvers about an inch long, filling the river and turning the shallow pools near the banks into flashing green-and-silver kaleidoscopes. They came in on the spring tides. Glass eels, they were called when very small. If you laid one on your palm you could see its organs through its flesh. There was a fish run, a channel some eight feet wide, with sluice gates, that made a bypass round the rapids just below the road bridge. We lay on our stomachs in the grass and stared into the clear water filled with millions of these tiny creatures swimming from—so I was told—the Sargasso Sea on the other side of the Atlantic Ocean. I went home and looked at the world atlas in the front room in wonder. How could those tiny things swim from there to here? Virtually the only other time you saw an eel was when a full-grown one all too frequently took your trout bait and you cursed the twisting, knotted, furious thing you had to get off the hook without it biting you. It often ended with your having to saw its head off and throw the two bits back into the river. We didn't eat eels, though the river was full of them, nor elvers.

We would occasionally see an otter in the river, flashing elusively through the water. 'That's the end of fishing for the day,' locals used to say.

There was even, rarely, a salmon to be seen in the river. When we learned of one, if we could, we would hurry the mile down to the pools near the road bridge to catch a glimpse. 'Well, it was there yesterday,' the platelayer or labourer or fisherman who had seen it would tell us disappointed kids.

In summer we would go looking for adders in the woods, sometimes finding one and keeping our distance behind long sticks as we tormented it till it slid away.

We saw rabbits daily, foxes and badgers occasionally. Moles were everywhere, but you didn't see them, only their runs and molehills, cursed by farmers and gardeners. My teacher, Mrs Langdon, decided she would make a moleskin coat for herself so we were offered sixpence a skin. I couldn't catch a single one, though I set snares on their runs in our gardens and surrounding fields. Neither, I believe, could any vackies. For once the village kids, especially the bigger boys, showed their superiority: during dinner breaks a stream of them came to our class with skins and claimed their sixpence. I don't remember ever seeing the finished coat.

But the domestic and farm animals were the ones that engaged our attention daily and were part of our lives.

Peter, Auntie Rose's canary, brightened the day with his singing, especially when the sun got round to the window in the afternoon and struck his cage, an event he always greeted with a burst of song. On some evenings the doors and windows were closed and the canary was given a free fly round the room, fluttering in a trail of feathers from picture frame to picture frame to the top of the dresser. I am not sure the canary enjoyed these outings as much as we did. He always seemed in a panic and it was never a great problem to usher him back into its cage. Sometimes we would hold him gently in our clasped hands, his anxious head darting this way and that, his tiny warm body so light and fragile-seeming, with a heart that beat fit to burst.

The cat was always locked out for these outings. The tabby that lived with us led a schizophrenic life. I loved just to touch it but it had to be constantly on guard; as far as cats were concerned Auntie Rose was unpredictable. It wasn't fed too much as it was encouraged to be a good mouser. As a result the canary was the subject of some pretty hungry glares when it sang. The cat would rub itself against Auntie Rose's leg, hopefully purring for food or milk, but if she was busy or tripped over it you would hear, 'Oh Duw, get out of it,' and a kick sent the cat running. Or she would pick up a broom, in which case it became a blur as it shot out of the back door. One day I found our cat in one of the fields over the other side of the railway with a young rabbit in its mouth. It growled a warning at me as I approached in case I meant to take its prey, but I had no such intention.

Our cat had, I suppose, an idyllic life compared to one unfortunate animal, victim of a vacky with an experimental turn of mind. He used to make parachutes out of handkerchiefs, tie them onto a cat and throw it out of the upstairs window. We watched fascinated as this cat hurtled through the air with the handkerchief having no effect on its descent. It would land with a thump on the grass and shoot off into the bushes.

'I can't get the parachute to open properly, that's the trouble. I will. You'll see,' said the boy as he hunted for the animal for another try.

The hens in their run were something that fascinated us for only a short while on our arrival. But to collect their eggs was always a good moment. A squawking and fluttering often announced the fact that there was one to be had, or we would just have a speculative look in the coop. And there in the straw, often with bits sticking to it, still warm, better than a shop egg, was a perfect white or brown ovoid with its smooth hard shell.

Auntie Rose, holding the cat, with her neighbours beside the whitewashed bungalow in the Court

Occasionally a chicken was eaten: a young cockerel, one too many in the run, or a hen that no longer laid. When they went broody they were put in the woodshed. They stood in there for a day or so on the logs and then were returned to the run. It seemed to work. But if one permanently stopped laying she ended up in the oven. Then it was a fight between Jack and me: we both wanted to be allowed to kill it. I cannot believe now what blood-thirsty creatures we were, but killing rabbits, chickens, any small living thing, seemed to be part of us, a treat almost. I don't think it was cruelty. We just wanted to do what the grown-ups did. It certainly involved curiosity. Anyway, Uncle Jack always did it quickly, so quickly that we barely saw it happening, though we were watching. Then the chicken was hung up on the clothes line to bleed. When Auntie Rose cleaned out its innards I remember marvelling at the tiny, half-formed, soft-shelled eggs it contained.

At one point, we had a pig in the linney. Uncle Jack brought the little piglet home one day, its head sticking out of a sack inside his jacket. It thrived and reached a good size, living on bran and kitchen waste that Auntie Rose would boil in a huge pot on the kitchen range to make swill, which smelled frightful and drove us out until the windows had been opened. Then it was time to eat the pig, a big treat in the war. A permit to kill it was required, all to do with meat rationing, and when all the red tape was done Uncle Jack prepared to hang it up by its hind legs in the linney, slit its throat and let it bleed to death. Jack was allowed to help string it up but I was considered too young. I sat seething with disappointment in the house with Auntie Rose while Jack helped in the preparation, then he was thrown out and Uncle Jack and the Bunneys' Uncle Ned, who came over from Taphouse especially, did the deed. Auntie Rose was salting and cutting the carcass on the kitchen table for what seemed like weeks; sides of bacon seemed to hang everywhere. 'No more pigs,' she said.

ALL ROUND US were the farms, exciting places full of activity. There were three I visited often: the Bunneys', Crago's and Treburgie, owned by the Tamblyns and where the Burfords—four siblings who had been on our vacky train—were billeted. At the Bunneys' we were often allowed to help, to become part of that strong-smelling world, to shovel, gather, carry, round up, milk, just *do* things until you were tired, hungry and glad to go home. 'Old Bunney been getting some free labour again, has he?' would be Uncle Jack's greeting. But at Treburgie with the Burfords, I remember that we played: in barns, where we could hide-and-seek and slide down chutes of straw and hay; round the pungent dung heap, which we turned over with pitchforks to envelop ourselves in the overwhelming stench of rotting straw and cow dung cleared from the milking sheds; on the tractor, whether still and silent as you pretended to drive it into battle against the Germans, or when you rode with Mr Tamblyn, bouncing across lumpy, bumpy fields to the roar of the motor.

But best of all were the animals. We helped drive the cattle in for milking and learned how to do it, grasping the long warm teats as instructed, pulling and squeezing. I remember the fleshly feel of them, the massive size in my hands, almost embarrassed at the intimacy of the contact. The cow gave nothing, then little squirts of milk followed by regular full jets as you got the idea and she decided to put up with your incompetence and release her udderful, probably as relieved as you were. Mechanical milking was just coming in but even where a farm had it fitted the cows had to be finished off by hand, and we were keen to do it.

There were sheep to be rounded up with a companionable dog, and pigs pleased to have their backs scratched in their evil-smelling sties. Tractors had mostly replaced horses on the farms but we got the occasional ride on Crago's big farm horses.

To watch the various ponies and workhorses being shod at Uglow's in Dobwalls was thrilling. Each new shoe was heated in the furnace till it was red-hot, then, while malleable, beaten and bent to the right size, plunged into cold water to cool it just enough before it was fitted to the hoof, hissing and smelling of burning hoof and horsehair as it was nailed on. Although this was painless for the horses, they stirred uneasily and laid back their ears as they smelled themselves scorching. Occasionally the more spirited or nervous ones would lash out. Mr Uglow would dodge the kick, swear, pick up the red-hot shoe with tongs and start again.

On Saturday mornings we could earn pocket money from local farmers by herding pigs, sheep and cattle into the pens in Doublebois goods yard. The thrill of being partially responsible for getting the animals down a mile or two of lanes without them diving through a hedge or running off somewhere was enormous. The difficult bit was when we left the road and had to get them into the pens without them escaping across the goods yard and onto the main line. We stood in a row with arms spread, holding sticks and making noises, yet still some independent-minded animal would dash through our line and make a break for it. Difficult to stop a full-grown cow, or even a pig, once it has made up its mind. The sheep you could grapple with, hanging onto their wool. Once, a goods train coming up the line from the valley was brought to a halt as the main line was dotted with men and boys trying to usher a lowing, terrified steer away from a very messy end and back to the one planned for it. One Saturday we had a very randy pig who tried to mount every other pig of whatever sex that was in its pen. We boys were delighted and urged it on, amazed at its pink wriggling corkscrew penis. The pig finally made the mistake of climbing onto one of its companions at the wrong end and got its penis bitten. It ran squealing round the pen, barging the others aside in its agony while we chortled with glee. Once all the animals were in, we swung on the rails round the pens, slapping the pigs and cows like knowledgeable farmers, complacent in the skill we had shown and each with a sixpence in his pocket.

CHAPTER SEVEN

One day Jack and I joined Ken and Elsie Plummer behind the row of privies that sat across the foot of the gardens of Railway Cottages, preparing ourselves for a raid on Granny Peters' gooseberry bushes. Scrumping was to us vackies an occupation of our childhood, to the village kids it was unknown. It didn't seem to have occurred to them, or perhaps they were used to taking what they wanted. Nor did we vackies do it because we were hungry for fruit, or greedy. There were all sorts of wild fruit and nuts in the woods, fields and hedgerows. No, it was simply something we did. Granny Peters was Jimmy Peters' grandmother, which might explain why he didn't feel inclined to rob her. She was, to us, half funny, half witch and lived in the Court at number 4.

Jack and Ken were in charge of our raiding party, planning it with military precision. 'Look, Ken, it's best if Elsie keeps watch here and we crawl across the paths.'

Ken agreed, holding just enough reserve in his tone to show that he was joint leader, not second-in-command. 'Yes. I vote for that.'

Elsie had her own ideas. 'I want to come with you.'

'You can't,' Ken said.

'Why?'

'Because you're useless.'

'You're mean you are, you sod.'

'You always make a noise or get seen or something.'

'I can't help it if people notice me.'

Ken sighed. 'She makes me sick.'

This routine family spat over, Jack resumed. 'Well, Terry's the smallest. He can get right in under the prickles and pass out the goosegogs.'

I was glad of my important role. 'Yeah, no one will see me.'

'And Elsie can stay by the corner and see all the windows and if anybody comes to the bogs.'

Elsie was indignant. 'I'm not staying here, it smells.'

'Stop moaning or we won't give you any,' Ken threw in.

'Don't want any.'

I suppose any plan that included an unwilling Elsie in a vital role was doomed, but Jack ignored this. 'All right, come on. Terry first.' We wriggled round the odorous privies on our stomachs. We boys slid in among the bushes while Elsie kept watch and communed with her changing body.

In the cocoon of the gooseberry bushes it was both cosy and painful. No matter how careful I was, they pricked.

Jack whispered, 'Come on, Terry. Pass 'em out.'

Ken could see me. 'He's eating 'em.'

They were delicious. 'I only had a few,' I said.

Suddenly there was a distant female voice calling, very Cornish, very old: Granny Peters. 'Hey, you. You boys. What you to?'

Jack turned on Ken. 'Where's your cousin?'

'She's gone.'

Granny Peters was on top of us now. 'Why be you lying down there?'

In my anxiety to get out, my clothes were impaled on the barbs. Gooseberries in my pockets were squashed as I struggled. Ken ran for it; Jack stayed with me. Granny Peters stood over us, a figure to frighten you from sleep.

THAT EVENING in 7 Railway Cottages Jack and I were standing in the dock, in the court of Auntie Rose and Uncle Jack. Uncle Jack opened the proceedings. 'So you two tried to steal Granny Peters' gooseberries, did you?'

'We were only scrumping,' I mumbled miserably.

'What's that, then? Cockney for stealing?'

'Scrumping is when it's apples and things,' said Jack helpfully.

'I know what it is.'

Auntie Rose joined in. 'I'll never hold up my head in the Court again. Ashamed, I am of you both. Poor old Granny Peters.'

Our heads drooped further.

Uncle Jack stared at us. 'What are we going to do with you?'

We didn't know, but Auntie Rose did. 'You're going to go in to her and say you're sorry, to start with. And you take her in some of my rock cakes. You know she do make jam from all her fruit and she earns her money from it and she do give us a jar every Christmas. And then you steal 'em.'

Uncle Jack was as unforgiving. 'If you wanted some gooseberries why didn't you ask? Were you hungry? Don't we feed you?'

More shuffled feet.

'You take my rock cakes and you ask her what jobs you can do for her.'

We knocked timidly on Granny Peters' door. No answer. 'Perhaps she's out,' I said hopefully to Jack, ready to run.

'She's never out.' He knocked louder. 'Granny Peters? Granny Peters?'

Suddenly she was there before us. I am not sure how old she was, certainly the oldest inhabitant of Doublebois, though the trio in 1 Railway Cottages at the opposite end from us, an elderly man and his two sisters about whom there were incestuous defamatory rumours, must have run her close. Her voice was cracked, barely of this world, and she wheezed; she wasn't really there in one sense, though with the support of her relatives near by and the neighbours she managed. 'Who's tha'?'

'Jack and Terry, Granny Peters, the boys from Auntie Rose's.'

'Oh, the vackies. Aaah. Hallo, my boodies.'

'We brought you some of her rock cakes.'

Granny Peters took us in, talking wheezily all the time. 'Ahn'ee Rose. Oooh. Her rock cakes. Aaah. Give 'em here. I'll soak they in my tea. You boys be from Lunnon, eh? I was there once, with my Arthur. Too many 'osses. Everywhere. 'Osses all round you. Worse'n Plymouth, 'twas.' She gestured to me. 'Come yere, my pretty. Come closer.'

I was rigid. 'Oh, no.'

'Go on,' urged Jack, in no danger.

'She smells funny,' I whispered as I submitted to an embrace of old person's smells.

'Oh, you'm pretty 'n no mistake. Don't wriggle, I won't hurt 'ee. You mind me o' my Billy. Ginger, they call 'ee. All down Dobwalls Street they chanted, "Ginger, you'm barmy, you oughtta join the army," 'n he did.'

To my horror she started to cry. 'Oh, Billy, my firstborn, my pretty, where you to now? South Africa, he went, and the Boers shot 'ee. There's his medals. He warn't simple. The Army took him. So he couldn't a' bin, could 'ee? They maids led him on. 'Twas they fault, not 'ee. He didn't hurt they. You wouldn't hurt a fly, would you, my pretty?'

I struggled in folds of enveloping cloth. 'She won't let me go.'

'His father, he was the simple one. I 'ad eight from 'ee. All gone to God. He took 'n all: three in the war; two when they was little like you, my boody. Henry, he went on the railway. Working on the line. Down the valley. They threw a bottle from a train and it hit his lovely face. Oh. The 4.12 to Snozzle, 'twas.' (All locals pronounced St Austell like that.) 'Oh, I outlived all my own children. 'Tis not natural. 'Tis wonderful lonely.'

'Isn't Jimmy Peters' dad your son?' asked Jack.

'Oh, yes. Yes. I forgot 'ee. Huh. I don't count 'ee. He's still here.'

I tried a new tack. 'If you let me go, I'll take your jug and get some water.'

'Wha' for? 'Tis half full.'

'Auntie Rose said we got to.'

'Oh, Ahn'ee Rose. Yes. Her rock cakes: they'm well named.'

Jack got to the point. 'We're sorry we tried to steal your gooseberries.'

'You want some gooseberries? Go on, then. They be yansome now. Take that bowl and bring me some. I'll make you some jam. Yere, come yere, little one. Let me touch your hair.'

'I got to go. Auntie Rose is calling.'

'Give me a kiss, Billy. Henry, give your mam a kiss 'fore you go to work.'

But we were out of the door with jug and bowl.

'We'll bring you some gooseberries in this bowl, Granny Peters.'

And we were gone, her ethereal, quavering voice floating behind us, still echoing in my head to this day.

IN OUR TINY community we all knew each other's characters very well:

> Elsie Plummer was a very good girl.
> She went to church on Sunday,
> To pray to God to give her strength,
> To kiss the boys on Monday.

There was no escape. Elsie had her reputation; she had worked hard enough for it. With my first winter in Cornwall over we met again and again in the house in the woods as I grew more and more jealous of her and confused about my own feelings. I was nowhere near puberty.

'Terry, let's play families.'

'No.'

'Oh, go on. You be Dad and I'll be Mam.' By now she had learned from the cinema what to say and how to say it. She threw herself into the scenarios she had invented for us. 'I love you, Dad. You can tell. Listen to my heart.' She paused at my lack of response, entirely due to inhibition. 'Feel it.' I could do it only halfheartedly. 'No, inside. Undo them, can't you?'

'Don't want to.'

'You do.'

'You're older'n me.'

'I'm fourteen.'

'I'm eight. Boys should be older'n girls.'

'Mrs Kitto's older'n Mr Kitto. By miles. So's all right. I like you best.' She tried her seductive tone again. 'Have you seen my new knickers?'

'Everybody has.'

She was indignant. 'When?'

'When you do high kicks.'

'Like this?' She lay back and demonstrated, foot high in the air.

I was noncommittal as I covertly looked.

'Want to see 'em now?'

'I just did.'

She leant close to me. 'Want to touch?'

I was routed. 'Don't know.'

'You knew the other day.'

'Shut up.'

'You want to, really.'

'I'm going.'

'You're scared.'

At last it burst out of me. 'Just stop talking about it all the time.'

She understood at once. 'Sorry,' she said quickly. 'Sorry, sorry. Yere. Lie down. By me. I won't speak again. Promise.'

I did as she asked.

'That's right,' she breathed in relief. 'Give me your hand.'

THE SOLDIERS STATIONED in Doublebois House were always being replaced. When we first arrived in Cornwall it was occupied by men shocked after the Dunkirk debacle. They moved on and the place was taken over by a succession of different regiments, generally training for some event or other. At one point Canadians were there and suddenly left. We read in the papers a few days later of the ill-fated raid on Dieppe in which so many Canadians died. Doublebois seemed to go into unofficial mourning for a while.

Every time we got wind of a change of personnel, if we weren't at school we children would all run into the Park and hang from the beech tree, cheering and waving, excited by all the activity. The soldiers always waved back and were often singing—dirty songs if we were lucky. Sometimes they were marched out to the station and boarded a waiting train. Then we would all run back down the Court and hang over the wire fence behind the wash-house, waving them out of sight up the line. Generally the movement was by road. Soldiers we knew, guards who had let us see their rifles and examine their equipment, went riding away in lorries, waving and smiling. Sometimes the replacements came riding in at the same time as the previous incumbents were leaving, so there seemed to be a frenzy of activity with a military policeman directing traffic at the crossroads. As convoys of lorries roared past the end of the Court, it became hazardous even to venture onto the normally empty A38. Nevertheless, we always dashed across it to the Park to watch the newcomers drive in through the left-hand gate of the twin drives, as the others departed by the right.

But most often and gloriously, one contingent would leave and there would be nobody there for a few days or weeks. The whole estate became an empty adventure playground for us children, vackies and locals. The two drives up to the big house were lined with rhododendrons and other shrubs. Between the drives was a monkey puzzle tree, beloved of the Victorians who had built this place. We couldn't climb it and soon gave up trying. There were woods and empty Nissen huts to explore; there was an abandoned swimming pool, beside which I spent hours watching tadpoles and newts in spring, and water boatmen making lazy circles on the still surface during summer afternoons. We pushed out little boats made of leaves and twigs with ants as the crews, we trailed our hands, we saw a snake trapped in there one day, swimming round and round looking for a way out, keeping us at bay, but it was only a grass snake, I think, gone the next day.

Our glittering prize in the middle of all this was the big house. Easy entry through a broken window and there was an unoccupied, echoing manor for our playground. We made full use of it, crashing and banging about until the owner of the estate, old Mr Steer, known to us as Old Man Steer, would appear to drive us briefly out. But his heart wasn't in it after the soldiers' destructive occupation. We soon returned. He lived in Home Farm, behind the big house, looking out over the valley; alone, I think, or with a housekeeper, because he still worked the farm.

In the lodge by the right-hand entrance lived Mr and Mrs Holman. Mrs Holman was the daughter or granddaughter of Old Man Steer. Mr Holman was a solicitor who commuted daily to Plymouth. They were a gentle, childless couple in their late thirties or early forties who made a point of befriending us vackies. They formed a mixed scout or cub group for all the children of Doublebois and we met in their house and played Kim's Game, did first aid, read books on tree, bird and insect recognition and went on patrols round the estate.

Best of all, Mr Holman, a keen fisherman, took Jack and me on all-night trout-fishing trips on the river during the holidays. The thrill of being allowed to do such a thing, of staying awake all night, was considerable. The actual event involved a walk in the late-evening light; we were full of anticipation, following a footpath down the hill from the back of the estate to the river, loaded with a borrowed rod each, bait, sandwiches, wet gear, a blanket, drinks and a torch. This was followed by long hours of just sitting on the bank in the dark with rod and line, often bored, often frightened of the noises in the pitch-black woods that surrounded us. Sometimes these noises came, mysteriously, from the river itself, sudden splashes that could not have been caused by the flow: perhaps fish, perhaps an otter, perhaps something else in our overheated imaginations.

We broke the night up with sandwiches and hot drinks from a Thermos. Occasionally your line jumped from a bite and all was excitement. It was generally an eel to throw back or kill if the hook was too far down. By torchlight we pushed squirming worms longways onto the hooks for bait and caught the odd trout which went into our keep net. I never worked out how the fish saw the worms in the dark; perhaps they smelled them. Up we would trudge in the early-morning light, leave Mr Holman, go home to gut our catch, watch Auntie Rose fry them for breakfast, eat them and fall into bed as Mr Holman got the morning train to his office in Plymouth. In spite of all the fright, cold and boredom I was always eager to be asked again.

Another all-night thrill was to be allowed—again in the holidays—to do the night shift in the signal box of the next section down the line. The signalmen in the box on Doublebois station were local and permanent. Jimmy Peters' dad was one at some point. Three miles down the line, controlling the next section, was a box in the heart of the Fowey Valley, deep in the woods, a few yards from the river. These signalmen were not local, only temporary, often taking lodgings in one of the Railway Cottages. The shifts were 10 p.m. to 6 a.m., 6 a.m. to 2 p.m., 2 to 10 p.m. We were often allowed in the box on the station but it was an event to be allowed to go down to the other box. It was far enough to demand that we had to be accompanied there and back on the line. So it meant an entire shift with the signalman. One evening I went down and spent from 10 p.m. to 6 a.m. in the box.

It was quite different from the fishing experience. The noise of the nearby river was a soothing background outside the safety of the dimly lit box. On that warm summer's night it became a focus for every moth in the woods. They fluttered in and flopped down round the oil lamp and hovered and mated and died by the hundred. The few trains, nearly all goods, were in mid-rush down the valley or trying to gain speed for the climb, so clattered swiftly past the box with a wave from the driver and fireman, who you could see in the light from the locomotive's furnace. Another wave from the guard, who could see us but who was just a shadow. I was allowed to heave on the heavy signal levers, nearly as tall as me, and to ring the warning bells to the next section. In the long silences between the trains we saw owls float soundlessly down the line. Sometimes, with their eyes turned towards us, gleaming yellow in the far limits of our light, we saw foxes and badgers— lions and tigers in my imagination—crossing, vulnerable for a few yards on the rails before the undergrowth swallowed them. After the sun rose there was the three-mile walk in the early-morning light, straight into its beams, back up the track to Doublebois, breakfast and bed.

AFTER ONE of the empty intervals, soldiers once more descended on Doublebois. The big house was requisitioned and overflowed. The Nissen huts were reoccupied. Girls took to walking the lanes near by with increasing frequency; Elsie, now abundantly fifteen, lost interest in me. If the vackies had shocked nearby Dobwalls, the soldiers stunned it. As lorries trundled along the main road their bawdy songs rang out:

> Hitler has only got one ball.
> Goering has two but very small.
> Himmler has something similar
> And poor old Goebbels has no balls at all.

The Miss Polmanors of the village rushed to the Methodist minister. 'Mr Buckroyd, Mr Buckroyd, have you heard—'

'Yes, yes,' and then wearily, 'There's a war on.'

CAMP CONCERTS were huge events. Entertainment was at a premium in our backwater. The locals—especially the children—did their best to get places. Professional entertainers and the Looe Fishermen's Choir performed in the long Nissen hut that was the camp canteen. I remember one concert in particular. After the choir, came a sing-song: 'You Are My Sunshine'. Rows of soldiers and not enough girls sang with a sudden, rolling, bellowing roar and swayed as they sang. The force and enthusiasm of all those open male throats gave that song an emotional power the composer could only have dreamed of. Oh, my wartime childhood: the stinging smoke and sickly beer smell; the distant light on the stage; and here in the comforting dark, rows of soldiers and the meagre ration of girls.

It was my childhood but it was their youth: hands tight round willing waists; male fingers pressing into thin summer frocks; female cheeks against harsh army tunics; bawling out their fervour with a passion I could sense but not comprehend. Their passion was not to get at the Germans, of course, but to stay—for ever if possible—in the warm half-dark, in the promise of a smile and against the pressure of another body that might be snatched away. They had the threat of extinction to sharpen their senses.

WE KIDS HUNG ROUND the soldiers constantly, cadging rides, holding their rifles, wearing their forage caps and, when the sentries allowed us to, swinging open the big iron gates at the entrances to the drives of Doublebois House so that cars, lorries and even Bren Carriers could rumble in and out. We were then allowed to swing the twelve-foot-long things closed again with a satisfying clang. Then the gates were deemed by the military too much of a bother constantly to open and close so were taken off their hinges and leant against the wall to be removed. Instead of swinging them we just sat on them.

The smallest of us all was Teddy Camberwell, a five-year-old, evacuated with his mother and baby sister. He was not one of us Welling crowd. I call him Teddy Camberwell, but I don't remember his surname, just that he was bombed out from Camberwell in the Blitz. Teddy, his mother and little sister were billeted at 3 Railway Cottages and he tagged along with us in most of our play. On this day he was at the end of a row of us sitting on the gate when a lorry came round the corner, caught the gate, tipped it forward and left us falling backwards into the bushes—except for Teddy. He was thrown forward and went under the gate. And the gate went under the lorry.

I clambered out and looked at the scene before me: the driver, staring aghast at the result of his tiny error; the unbelieving sentry; three other children, one with his hand in his mouth, all beyond tears; Teddy's crushed body under the gate, leaking blood and other things. I turned and ran for the only help I trusted. 'Auntie Rose, Auntie Rose. Come quickly, Teddy's dead. He's dead. Teddy's dead.'

I arrived at our house at the far end of the Court as Auntie Rose emerged. She stared at me, shocked. 'You're covered in blood.' This was nothing, just scratches from the bushes I had landed in.

'Teddy's dead. A lorry went over the gate.'

We ran back up to the main road. The sentry, accompanied by the bemused driver and three children, was walking up the main road carrying Teddy's tiny, crumpled body to his home at 3 Railway Cottages.

Auntie Rose shouted, 'What are you doing? What are you doing, man?'

'Are you the mother?' asked the sentry, probably dreading the answer.

'No, where are you taking him?'

'The boys said he lives in the cottages, here.'

'What are you trying to do? Give his mother a present, you bloody fool? Take him back to the camp.'

The sentry, no more than a teenager, was hopelessly out of his depth. 'I didn't know where to—'

Auntie Rose practically pushed him. 'Go on. Take him to your medical officer. His mother'll be out any minute.' She turned to me. 'You, into the wash-house and get that blood off you.' She turned to the others. 'You lot, home and tell your mams. Alan, go home and get Miss Laity to come to my house.' Alan was billeted with the district nurse.

I next saw Auntie Rose taking Teddy's mother into our house, where she lay collapsed and sobbing on the sofa, watched by Jack's and my detached, curious eyes until we were driven out. So much emotion seemed more than one person could contain. Her body jerked and heaved as her grief tore its way out of her.

Next day a soldier appeared in the Court: a private, Teddy's father. He was accompanied by an awkward-looking padre, an officer, and stood mutely, arms pinned to his side by his wife as she clung to him and sobbed anew. What guilt she must have suffered besides her simple agony. To have brought her son to Cornwall for safety and then to have this news for his father. Auntie Rose had washed, dressed and laid out Teddy, something she was experienced in from her days in the mining village in South Wales.

One day later, Jack and I, Jimmy Peters, Brian Bunney, Harold Packham and Ken Plummer were to carry Teddy's coffin to the station to put it on the 9 a.m. Cornish Riviera express to Paddington: a farewell gesture from us all. The train was stopped especially. A makeshift military band from the camp was to lead us. The whole of Doublebois came out to watch. A funeral march was considered inappropriate for so small a child, so some genius of military bandsmanship used his discretion and 'Early One Morning' rang tinnily out as we carried the tiny coffin from 3 Railway Cottages to the station, followed by Teddy's father and mother carrying his baby sister.

Because I was the smallest boy, I was one of the two in the middle. My shoulders weren't high enough so I had to hold my hands up to reach the coffin. The couple of hundred yards to the station seemed endless. Teddy's coffin was not long enough to accommodate three boys a side and nobody had taught us to walk in step and, as we tripped and shuffled along, my heels and calves were skinned by the hobnail boots of the boys behind as I inflicted similar injuries on the boy in front, whose heels were meanwhile gashing my shins. Mr Rawlings the stationmaster, stout and self-important, held the train as we filed down the slope of Station Approach between two rows of soldiers presenting reversed arms.

Passengers stared from the train as we clumsily put Teddy in the smelly guard's van, on to straw that was laid for some tethered creature, a calf or goat, which stirred uneasily at the activity round it.

The train departed and we turned and ran hard to our schools in Dobwalls over a mile away, each to our different classes. I was the only one in Junior Vackies. Because I was good at my lessons I was one of Mrs Langdon's favourites. But my habit of arriving late in the morning and returning late from lunch because of games and digressions with the bigger boys had gone too far this time.

She stared sternly at me. 'Terry Frisby, you're late again.'

All I could produce was heavy breathing.

'What is your excuse this time?'

I couldn't utter a word.

'Look at the time. And your legs. All scratched and bloody. What have you been doing? Fighting? Climbing?'

'No, Miss,' I managed.

'Forty minutes you're late. This is a record, I think.'

One of the vackies who lived at Treburgie Farm near Doublebois put her hand up. 'Please, Miss. Miss.'

'Be quiet, June Burford. Terry, come here.'

The dreaded ruler was produced. God knows how such a failure of communication had occurred in our gossip-ridden little community but Mrs Langdon in Dobwalls somehow knew nothing of the Doublebois farewell ceremony. I got six whacks across my knuckles, and broke into breathless sobs. It had all finally got to me.

Mrs Langdon was not a liberal wielder of the ruler and probably didn't feel that happy herself. 'Now go to your place and don't be late again.'

June didn't give up. 'Please, Miss.'

'Be quiet, June.'

My sobs grew louder.

'And stop snivelling, Terry. You've had that much before and earned it.'

'*Please*, Miss.' June's arm was straining for the ceiling.

Mrs Langdon turned rattily to her. '*Yes*. What *is* it, June?'

'Please, Miss. He's been carrying Teddy's coffin. They put it on the train this morning at Doublebois.'

CHAPTER EIGHT

The Bunney children's uncle Ned drove a lorry for Blamey and Morgan. In school holidays, Blamey and Morgan's mill was a magnet for us. You could slide down chutes built for sacks of grain, rope them together and help wind them out of first-floor loading bays into the lorry, sit in piles of loose grain or cow cake and run it through your hands as you sank into it. There were a hundred other ways we could supposedly help in this busy workplace as long as we behaved ourselves and the men tolerated us, or until we were ordered out by authority, or—sad days—not allowed in at all.

Trips with the Bunneys' Uncle Ned were the best of all as he delivered produce to the farms in the area. The Bunney children had priority; he could get two, or perhaps three, in the cab with him, so we others had to hang about and hope. Occasionally, depending on the load, the bigger boys could ride in the back, clinging to the sacks as the lorry wove its way through the empty roads and lanes. Meeting another vehicle was rare, just tractors, district nurse Laity—she had a car and a bike—and the occasional piece of military hardware: a Bren Carrier, a dispatch rider, a Land Rover and, later, jeeps. After the loads were delivered we could all stand in the empty back, holding on to the frame attached to the cab, the wind in our hair, shouting and singing, waving madly at anyone we saw.

One day Ned took a bend a bit sharply, hit a bump and the oldest Bunney, David, shot into the air, out of the lorry and over the hedge. Frightened, we beat on top of the cab and shouted. The lorry pulled up, we told Ned and all of us raced back to the bend. We peered through and over the hedge. No David. As we searched we heard a shout from down the road beyond the lorry and there was David clambering over a gate. He had run across the field after us, afraid he would be left behind. A bush had broken his fall and he had nothing more than the scratches we could see and the odd bruise. I don't remember his uncle's reaction but he must have been mightily relieved. We all crammed into the cab for the rest of the journey home and later boasted madly about the incident, exaggerating whenever possible. Lorry rides ceased for the remainder of that holiday, to be continued later.

The lorry took us to many farms that merge into one in my memory, except when we went across the moor. Bodmin Moor in its many moods I remember with clarity, almost awe. We went as far as Jamaica Inn on the A30; we expected to see smugglers and excise men, disappointed with the farm labourers and occasional travelling salesmen who were in the bar while Ned had a pint and we stood outside with crisps or pop, if we were lucky. We stopped at Dozmary Pool, supposedly bottomless, and stared at its surface, dark under the scudding clouds, and at the sedge, the gorse, the tufty grass that made up the forbidding landscape round it.

Dozmary Pool had a legend that we all knew well: Giant Tredegar had made a pact with the Devil. He sold his soul in exchange for riches in his lifetime. After his death, the Devil gave him the task of emptying Dozmary Pool with a limpet shell with a hole in it. This task to last until he succeeded or for eternity. Every so often Giant Tredegar grew fed up with this and tried to run away across the moor. The Devil would send his hounds after him to bring him back and if you listened carefully you could hear them howling. You could recognise this howling, we were told, because it sounded like the wind moaning in telephone wires—only there were no telephone wires on the moor. When we were out of the lorry we listened and, sure enough, there was the sound we had been told to expect. It must have been the wind soughing through the grass and round the rocks. We would climb back into the lorry, enjoyably scared, and look back at the cheerless stretch of water, glad to be leaving.

We were also told that Dozmary Pool was the place where King Arthur threw Excalibur and the hand came up, caught it and waved it three times before disappearing. But looking at the place I couldn't really make that connection; it was simply too bleak, free of Arthurian or any sort of romance. It was Giant Tredegar running from the Devil's hounds that caught my imagination.

The moor was generally lowering, always menacing, or when low sullen clouds reigned, even dreary—it caught every weather front coming in off the Atlantic. But on a rare fine day it could be magnificent. The horizon stretched away, wild flowers blew in the eternal south-westerlies, the grass welcomed you to lie down in the sun. On such days there were plovers and lapwings, ravens, rooks and buzzards wheeling, distant rabbits who disappeared before you could blink, even shyer than the farmland rabbits we were always hunting. And, especially, there were larks everywhere, rising from the heather before us with their hysterical, cascading song. There was a story, often repeated to us complete with accent, about a cockney vacky, who, on first seeing and hearing a lark hovering and singing, pointed to it and said to his teacher, 'Look, Miss, there's a sparrer up there. He can't go up and he can't go down and 'ee ain't 'arf 'ollering.'

I wasn't aware then how much it all affected me. But when I returned to the moor years later I could feel my former childish joy rising in me again.

IN OUR FIRST SPRING in Cornwall, I am sorry to say, we often went bird's-nesting, unlike the local boys, although I don't remember that we were a terrible scourge of the local avian population. Often broken eggs lay on the ground under the nests: lovely, tiny, delicate, shattered worlds. That was how you and, more seriously for the birds, cats found them.

What appealed to me was to find a nest with eggs and return to see them hatched: scrawny, bald, ugly chicks with gaping beaks into which we put worms or insects while the anxious parents fluttered and scolded us from nearby bushes. We were soon told not to do that as the parents would abandon their chicks if they were fed by someone else. The wild, naked, vulnerable scraps had none of the appeal of the day-old chicks that appeared in our chicken run every spring: fluffy, Disney objects that touched all hearts before they grew big enough to lay if they were hens or go into the pot if they weren't. The wild-bird chicks developed down, then feathers and were soon perched on a twig or on the clothes line in the garden, or on farm buildings in a row before they challenged gravity. Songbirds were all round us; we didn't need to go down to the woods to find their nests—although we sometimes did—they were in every bush and hedgerow.

But buzzards were different. Buzzards were big, nested in inaccessible places and their eggs were prized. If you got one it proved that you had dared and achieved something.

Ken and Eric Plummer, Jack and I set off one day for the quarry. A buzzard had been seen circling there. It was the right time of year, there must be a nest somewhere. The quarry was down the main road, past the Rabbit Field and on the right, just where the woods started, a great chunk which had been blown out of the hillside bit by bit to get the slate. When they were blasting, which wasn't often, we were forbidden to go near it; notices were put out on the main road and traffic was held up until a satisfying boom was heard and vehicles could continue through.

We crouched in the quarry and searched the sheer faces and steps of slate above us. A buzzard wheeled in and settled on the bough of a stunted tree near the top. There was the nest, a ramshackle affair of sticks and bits, in the tree. The other bird was sitting. It took off and the first took its place. We set off round the quarry and up the hill through the woods until we were near the nest. We crept through the undergrowth to the edge of the quarry and peered about us. There was the nest with the bird on it. One of the Plummers found a broken branch and we stripped it of twigs. We crept nearer. The sitting bird, the female, saw us and stirred uneasily.

Ken, the older Plummer, crept forward with his long stick and prodded at the bird. He could barely reach her. The tree hung out over the quarry. The bird briefly pecked at the stick, but was soon intimidated. Reluctantly she shuffled to her feet and took off, falling away on a glide before she languorously flapped her way up and out of sight. In the nest, snugly lined with moss and leaves, lay three glorious buzzard's eggs, white with brownish veins or marks, a little smaller than hen's eggs.

The problem was: how to get them? The tree bent alarmingly when we tested our weight on it; we didn't want to tip them out; the ground was a long way below for either eggs or boy to fall to. As always, I was the smallest and lightest. We made a chain, Ken anchored himself to a tree and I slid out along the branch, which creaked beneath me. I reached out with one hand but couldn't make it. Bits of earth and loose stones rattled down the slates below me. I looked down into the quarry and clung tighter to the tree. I tried again and could just reach an egg by all of us moving forward in our chain. I heard the slithering of heels in the ground behind me as I strained for the nearest egg. I got it and was passing it back when there were shouts. The furious buzzards had returned together, mewing and flapping. Nearly dropping me and the egg into the quarry the others dragged me back and we all fled. You don't realise it until you are close up, but a buzzard's wingspan is about a yard and a half and its beak looks enormous when coming at you.

We proudly showed our prize to Uncle Jack. He was unimpressed. 'Oh, what did you want to do that for? They're not harming you. They're on our side, the buzzards. They eat rabbits and moles and rats. Put it back and leave 'em alone in future.'

Abashed, we wondered what to do. Uncle Jack's disapproval meant less to the Plummer boys than to us but nobody prized the egg any more. The Plummers shrugged the matter off and walked away. As for Uncle Jack, he couldn't possibly have known what risks his casual 'Put it back' involved Jack and me in. We made our resolution: the next day we went down to the quarry, frightened away the sitting bird and, once more, I slid out along the tree, insecurely held by Jack, and replaced the egg. Just as well I didn't slip; he would have had to let go or come with me. I don't believe the egg could possibly have hatched; we probably knew that at the time, but it seemed like atonement.

We went and watched out for the buzzard chicks to hatch but couldn't really be sure as we were soon back to school after the Easter holidays, chastened and cured of bird's-nesting.

PUTTING HA'PENNIES on the rail before a train went through was something we all tried; the incentive, apart from experimental curiosity, was to turn a ha'penny into a penny. After the train had gone over it, it was certainly twice the size but you could never pass it off as a penny or use it again as a ha'penny. We soon desisted from this expensive pastime.

Shunting in the goods yard went on all the time. We often tried to join in. We knew the porters, guards and the men on the footplate of the various tank engines. If they were in the right mood, we could throw the points levers, run beside the rolling wagons, pull the brakes on and even go on the footplate. But the sight of the stationmaster walking towards us meant that we quickly vanished and the men wouldn't let us near again for a while, clearly having been told off. When there was no shunting and the stationmaster was off duty we played among the stationary goods wagons at will. If we could find one that was well down the siding out of the way, we took turns to lie down under it between the rails and, using a shunting pole, roll it over the boy on the ground to prove the point that a train could go right over you without hurting you. There were many stories of people having saved themselves from being killed by doing just that, hurling themselves down under sixty-mile-an-hour expresses and walking away unscathed. Our games with the goods wagon were a preparation for one of us to do that on the main line one day. We stood beside the line and, with heightened senses because of our project, examined at close hand the massive rush and roar that a speeding train makes as it thunders by. Nobody volunteered to go first. The thought of the major trouble you would be in if you survived was as much a deterrent as the prospect of a mangled death.

During the war all road signposts and signs identifying stations were removed so that, in the words of the man on Welling station, 'The Germans won't know where they are when they get here.' Mr Rawlings would promenade up and down the platform whenever a train pulled in saying, 'Doublebois,' with an upward inflexion, followed by, 'Doublebois,' on a downward. He did this very quietly. When a 4-6-0 Hall-class or Grange-class engine was letting off steam, having climbed the bank from the valley, his little melody, 'Doublebois,' up, 'Doublebois,' down, was completely inaudible. People would lean out and ask where they were when only a foot or two from him. This gave great pleasure to Dad when he visited, who compared him to the man at Eltham Park, two stations from Welling, who, over a silently arriving electric train, would bawl, with the second word on two wavering notes, 'Elt-ham Pa-a-rk,' so that he could be heard across the whole of Eltham in the blackout.

DURING OUR SCHOOL HOLIDAYS we were taken by Auntie Rose—and some-times Uncle Jack if he was on his fortnight summer break—on outings, always with packed lunches and bottles of pop. The trips I remember best were to Looe, the most frequent destination. After that came Polperro, Newquay and Padstow. All were by train, with our privilege tickets reducing the cost because Auntie Rose and Uncle Jack were a railway couple and we were railway children.

Dad would sign vouchers and send them to Auntie Rose and we would go down to Doublebois station and present our Southern Railway credentials to the ticket clerk in this heart of the Great Western Railway empire, always a moment to savour. Occasionally these outings were with Mum and Dad when they came down to see us, some four or five times in the three years—Mum more than Dad—were all they could manage.

The branch line to Looe was my favourite. First, it left Liskeard station at right angles to the main line, going due north, the wrong direction for Looe, curved to the right in a semicircle and dived underneath the main line before continuing to circle back to Moorswater, once more facing north, where the engine changed ends and the train reversed to continue its journey directly south to the sea. The branch line was shaped like a giant question mark with Looe the full stop at the bottom. It went under the main line twice on the circular part. Out at Looe station, we walked along the quayside, with all sorts of fish in crates for us to examine curiously. They looked nothing like the fish, or bits of them, that we had on our plates to eat. These had more detail, often an iridescent beauty, but mostly to our igno-rant eyes were far more ugly, more from another planet than merely another familiar element. The lobsters and crabs in baskets had more character, more foreignness when seen here, tentacles and claws waving, sightless eyes staring, still alive, just out of the sea.

Occasionally a Royal Navy motor torpedo boat with a gun on its bow and torpedo tubes with torpedoes lashed on the deck would cruise menacingly in from the sea or be berthed. Inspecting them from the quayside, we imagined those tubes unleashing hell at U-boats out in the Channel, though I think they were all in the Atlantic sinking our convoys.

As the Looe river reached the sea it was contained by a high hill to the west and a long jetty to the east. This jetty ensured that the entrance to the port was navigable. It also helped to create the sandy beach that stretched away eastwards and on which we could play and bathe in specified areas between the tank traps, pill-boxes and barbed wire, there to repel the Germans. We spent most time in the rock pools—I once caught in a toy bucket a cuttlefish the size of my hand, to me a weird, alien creature that I wanted to take home but was persuaded to put back.

After a day on the beach if it was fine we wandered round the town, looking fruitlessly for an ice cream, having fish (now reassuringly white and flaky) and chips with pop, or tea in a café and—the highlight before we took the train home—an hour on the boating lake, rowing round and incompetently round.

Mum, Jack and me in the Court outside 7 Railway Cottages

To get to Polperro we took a bus from Looe. Polperro was Mum's favourite. 'Quaint' was the word I most often heard used to describe it. Now a tourist trap, packed with Cornish ephemera, it was then utterly deserted, bereft of its pre-war trade. Only the port produced income—from the fishing. There was the odd newsagent's which had unsold picture postcards, and I first learned the word 'piskie'—Cornish for 'pixie'—from those cards in Polperro. Even I, not yet ten, succumbed to the charm of the place as I followed Mum and Dad from one chocolate-box view to another.

Newquay was a much more adventurous journey. Three stops down the main line to St Blazey, then a branch line that had exotic halts called Luxulyan, Bugle, Victoria, Indian Queens and Mount Joy. Unfortunately the landscape we rode through did not match the place names. A large area of undistinguished, low, flattish moorland dotted with vast, melancholy china-clay tips, alternated with the great gashes in the ground from which they had been dug. It always seemed a very dreary place in my mind.

The little tank engine finally pulled us into Newquay on the north coast. The railway had made Newquay. Once the line had been opened it had grown from Victorian times into the famous seaside resort that we all knew of, packed all season. It was now deserted in high summer. There was a story that circulated the railway community of Doublebois—and no doubt much wider—of the porter on Newquay station who saved all his tips from the pre-war holiday seasons and bought a row of cottages, which he let out during the summer, enjoying a well-heeled retirement on the rents.

We always made straight for the glorious beaches, unscarred by barbed wire as I remember, perhaps because nobody imagined the Germans would sail round Land's End and attempt a landing there. If the tide was out there was mile upon mile of empty, clean sand with streams to dam. Shrimps and lots of little creatures came out of the sand to greet the wavelets as the tide flowed swiftly in, all preyed on by sea birds and waders and examined by me. Above all there was the surf. We never dared go into the big stuff but it was the first time I experienced the fun of standing up to my thighs in freezing water with a foaming wall bearing down on me, to knock me over and carry me back onto the beach spluttering, choking and exhilarated. Shivering to pieces, you towelled yourself down or, better still, had Mum or Auntie Rose do it for you. All in all, Newquay was always the most exciting trip.

Another journey that Auntie Rose took us on, only once, I think, was to Wadebridge and Padstow. We went through a village on the branch line with the glorious name of Washaway. At Wadebridge, the Great Western Railway met the Southern Railway line which came down north of Bodmin Moor from Launceston and Okehampton. It was a measure of our estrangement from home that the green livery of the Southern Railway coaches looked drab after the Great Western chocolate and cream, and the un-Great Western shape of their engines with the numbers painted on instead of on fitted metal number plates looked alien—even inferior—to our eyes.

Wadebridge, with its arched bridge over the river, I remember only as being granite and dull. We trailed after Auntie Rose looking at the uninteresting shops, then onto a Southern Railway train to trundle along the ravishing Camel Estuary to Padstow, another 'quaint' fishing village that tumbled in down the hills on all sides onto the port. The only item of interest to us boys was that the railway line went onto the quay to get the fish directly from the boats and then away non-stop to Billingsgate. My principal memory of Padstow is the smell of fish, not unpleasant but very strong.

Dad, Jack and me on Newquay beach

Jimmy Peters and I went to Bodmin one day, I think to visit a relative of his in hospital. We managed to buy a *Beano*, quite an event, and read it together on the train back. One of the comic strips, about Mussolini, the Italian Fascist dictator, was called 'Musso Da Wop, He's A Bigga Da Flop', which we found uncontrollably funny. We were overcome by giggles that we could not contain as we sat in the full compartment. People stared, then smiled and soon were chuckling with us. The better their humour, the more hysterical we got. Perhaps playing to the audience, we speechlessly pointed to the drawings and captions, the reasons for our incontinence. The adults' good humour grew and we all got out to change at Bodmin Road with grins on our faces and said goodbye like old friends. Then the fun evaporated, everything went flat. We stood spaced along the platform waiting for our train, once more back in our own separate worlds. The whole group of us embarrassed, it seemed, by our former exuberance.

A CIRCUS CAME to Liskeard. The children were told to bring money to school to book a seat if they wanted to go in a party. I was left out. Somehow or other Jack and I failed to ask Auntie Rose for the money. Or

Jack was doing something else (what else would a boy be doing when the circus was coming to town?) and I was too shy to ask—an unlikely prospect. Anyway, I was alone, didn't have a ticket and felt very hard done by when most of the children crowded onto the bus and left school early.

'You're early. What's up?' asked Auntie Rose when I got in.

'Everybody's gone to the circus early from school.'

'Well, why haven't you gone?' she said, surprised.

I was near tears when I realised I could have been on that bus. It was all a misunderstanding. Now there was no bus and the next train would be too late. Auntie Rose gave me the entrance money, a shilling and sixpence, plus the fare home from Liskeard in case I couldn't get on the bus coming back, a sandwich, and pushed me out to thumb a lift from one of the rare passing cars or lorries. Actually, I needed no pushing. I ran towards Dobwalls. I ran through Dobwalls, still no cars. Out of Dobwalls, down the winding hill and up the long drag past Moorswater. Still no lift. Four miles I covered and arrived at the circus, pitched in a field between Liskeard station and the town, to find that the show had started and the marquee was full. I stood there with no breath, gasping with exhaustion and frustration, only just holding down my sobs.

My heartbeats and breathing slowed down as I wandered about listening to the laughter and applause from inside, more gall to my soul. Someone was selling candyfloss, unheard of during the war. It tasted filthy even to my eager tongue. I went round the back and saw some dejected-looking ponies, which I tried to pat until abruptly told to leave them alone. I moved resentfully away among the circus people who were bustling about.

Just as I was about to give up, a baby elephant came out of the marquee, having done its stuff for the moment. This creature, with its huge ears and searching active trunk, seemed like a miracle. I swear it glowed. It stood shorter than I did and must have been very young. I stared at it in wonder, then sidled up to it and was allowed to pat it. I felt the sensitive top of its trunk explore my clothes, searching for my sandwich, I suppose. This was no mirage but a wonderfully solid, magical, gigantic pet. I asked its handler, an unbossy woman, if I could give him some sandwich. She inspected it and said yes, adding, 'She's not a him.' So, breaking my sandwich into the smallest pieces I could, I fed it bit by bit to the elephant, who stood there waiting for more, its trunk running over my clothes and hands, thrilling me with its touch, not always gentle, always demanding. When my sandwich was finished I asked the woman what else the elephant liked. 'Apples,' she said.

I raced out of the field to the nearest greengrocer's, still just open, bought a pound of apples and tore back. The elephant was gone. Lungs again bursting, I nearly cried with frustration but she reappeared from the tent, having done another turn. She headed straight for me; I nearly died with joy— elephants, apparently, do remember—and I fed her the apples until told by the woman that that was enough, she had to take her away. I patted my new best friend goodbye, tried and failed to hold her trunk for a moment, watched her amble away, spent my remaining pennies on a bag of chips, had my last apple and, penniless, walked contentedly home.

CHAPTER NINE

Uncle Jack's antipathy to all things religious turned a minor incident involving Miss Polmanor into a comic and shaming episode. It was their polarised attitudes that caused it and I am certain that he, at least, regretted it. His atheism was founded on or confirmed by his experiences in the First World War. Any faith he may have had was—like the faith of many others—blown to pieces in the trenches along with the thousands of their comrades and nominal enemies. His real enemies were not German soldiers, of course, but all people with civilian power over him: bosses, owners, all officers above a certain rank, staff officers perhaps, who ordered the soldiers into danger as opposed to sharing it with them. Bestriding all of his world was religious authority, then so much more important than now. So a woman like Miss Polmanor, who, though she paraded her faith, was in reality a sad lonely figure (as Auntie Rose recognised), was a red rag.

Some Saturdays Uncle Jack would take Jack and me into Dobwalls to visit the barber. There, in a glass-covered annex to a house on the right just as we entered the village, sat a barber's chair that looked across the road at Rowe's garage opposite. A smaller road and three lanes joined the main road here; it was as near to a focal point that a village which straggled along one road for over half a mile could have. The house was a few steps above street-level so the barber's chair was a splendid place from which to watch the world—or Dobwalls, anyway—go by. Uncle Jack sat there chatting to the barber while his little ring of hair was cut even shorter and shaved at the neck. Jack and I—and all the other children in the village—were seated on a board set across the arms of the chair and given haircuts in spite of our wriggles. Up the back of the neck and over the crown went the clippers—short back and sides it was called but it was very nearly short back, sides and top. This haircut was thought to keep nits to a minimum. A forelock was all that was left of my former fair-haired tangle; my mother hated it when she visited: her boys in hobnail boots and cropped hair like hobbledehoys.

One Saturday, with newly shorn heads, we left the barber's to see if there were any sweets or comics in Ede's. It was a busy morning: there were several vackies and village kids in the road, some villagers were chatting and Miss Polmanor arrived on her bicycle with its shopping basket.

In the shop children were pestering Mr Ede. 'Haven't you got the *Beano*?' 'No *Dandy*?' 'Any gobstoppers?' 'No sweets at all?'

He was a pleasant man who got on with most people. 'No, no, no, us don't have naught.'

'You said you'd have the *Beano* today.'

'Us can't do naught about the paper shortage.'

'You've got the *Farmers Weekly*.'

'That's vital for the war effort.'

And the children would make a ragged chorus of that ritual answer to all complaints: 'Oh, yeah. There's a war on.'

'Go on, you children, off you go. Don't block up the shop. What can I do for you, Miss Polmanor?'

She was rummaging anxiously. 'I can't find my purse.'

Mr Ede addressed Uncle Jack. 'Morning, Mr Phillips, what can I do for you?'

Before Uncle Jack could answer, Miss Polmanor spoke loudly. She was getting agitated. 'My money. 'Tis not yere. I must have been robbed.'

'Perhaps you dropped it,' said Mr Ede helpfully.

'No, I can't have. 'Twas in my purse, which was in my handbag, which was in my shopping bag, which was in my basket.'

Uncle Jack couldn't resist such an opening. He chipped in with a friendly smile. 'Must have been Dick Turpin to get that off you.'

Miss Polmanor's temperature went up. ''Tis not funny, Mr Phillips.'

'Did you leave it in the off-licence?' His concerned expression looked quite real.

'How dare you!' She was quite rattled by this and went too far. 'They children jostled I just now. One o' they must have taken it.'

Uncle Jack took this seriously. He rounded on us. 'Have one of you got Miss Polmanor's purse?'

Fervent denials all round.

'There.' He spread his hands to her as though the matter were concluded.

Mr Ede was genuinely helpful. 'Look round on the floor, my dear. 'Er must be yere somewhere.'

Everyone started looking.

'There's more than two pounds in there,' wailed Miss Polmanor.

We all redoubled our efforts, some of the children overdoing it a bit. 'Wow.' 'Quick. Where is it?' 'Do I get a reward?'

A vacky called John White started to leave the shop. Miss Polmanor jumped on him. 'Where be you going?'

'I was gonna look outside,' said John, upset at the implications.

'Escaping, were you? You'm hiding it somewhere.'

John, a gentle boy who later became a Methodist minister, was near tears. 'I haven't got your rotten purse.'

'Us should search all of 'em. One of 'em has it, 'tis sure,' continued the distracted Miss Polmanor.

Uncle Jack strolled to the door, seething. 'I don't think I can stand it in yere.' He raised his voice. 'I suppose I can leave, can I? Without being searched?' and added to me, 'I'll be outside, boy, when you're released.'

Miss Polmanor pointed at me. 'You stand guard by the door, boy.'

Mr Ede, too, was upset. 'Well, how's us gwain to search they?'

'The boys can empty they'm pockets to start with.'

The boys reluctantly started to do this as, outside, I saw Uncle Jack meet Jack, who had been talking to a friend. 'Look, Uncle Jack, I've just found this purse over by Miss Polmanor's bike.'

Uncle Jack gave a thin, bitter laugh. 'Take it in the shop. She's in there having kittens. Tell her where you found it.'

Inside, the melodrama continued. I had no chance to open my mouth. Mr Ede looked at the girls in their flimsy summer dresses. 'How's us gwain to search they maids? They bain't got nowhere to hide naught.'

One boy pointed at Elsie. 'You'll have to look in her knickers. She puts everything in there.'

Elsie coloured up as all the children except me giggled. To have searched her would have been ludicrous: she lived with Miss Polmanor.

At which moment Jack came in. 'Is this your purse, Miss Polmanor?'

She grabbed it triumphantly. 'There. One of 'em has it. I told you.'

Mr Ede protested that Jack had just come in.

Jack said, 'I found it on the ground by your bicycle.'

Miss Polmanor left, trying to gather the shreds of her dignity. The moment she was outside, excited giggles and chatter burst out among the children. 'She blames us for everything.' 'Blinking old bat.'

Mr Ede wasn't having that in his shop and we were all driven out to where Uncle Jack was in conversation with Miss Polmanor. He was chewing a matchstick and grinning. 'So the vackies didn't steal your purse after all, then?'

She turned away to her bicycle. 'Oh. Look at this. I've got a puncture.'

'Oh, bad luck,' said Uncle Jack. Then an even bigger exclamation of sympathy. He pointed at her back wheel. 'Look at that. Both of 'em. That's terrible. Where have you been riding it? In the quarry?'

Miss Polmanor stared at her bike. '*Two* flat tyres. It's they vackies again.'

'But they was all in the shop with you,' said Uncle Jack. 'You kept 'em in there. Remember?' He looked away down the road to Doublebois and the army camp. 'I reckon it was one of those two soldiers who were here just now. I saw them fiddling about by your bike.'

Miss Polmanor was near tears. 'Soldiers. Vackies. I've left my pump at home. I'll have to push it all the way.'

Uncle Jack called the biggest vacky over. 'Hey, Frank, wheel Miss Polmanor's bike over to the garage and pump her tyres up and she'll give you sixpence.'

She grabbed the bike. 'Don't worry. I can do it myself.'

'No, no, you mustn't. There's help here aplenty.' He turned to Frank again. 'You do it and *I'll* give you sixpence. We can't leave her to do it on her own, can we?' He reached into his pocket. 'Miss Polmanor will just say, "Thank you very much. You're a good boy."'

'I shall do no such thing,' she said firmly and pushed her bike away.

'Cor,' whispered Elsie. 'How did she get two punctures?'

'I reckon somcone let her tyres down,' said Frank.

'I told her. I think it was those two soldiers.' Uncle Jack again pointed vaguely towards Doublebois. 'D'you know how they did it?'

'Easy,' boasted Frank. 'You can do it with a matchstick.'

Uncle Jack took the matchstick from his mouth and gestured with it. 'That's right, boy. You just use the matchstick to push the valve in and . . . psssss . . . there you are.' He gave the matchstick to Frank. 'But don't you ever try it on my bike or I'll tan the hide off you.' He winked at Jack and me. 'Come on, boys. Home for some dinner, is it?'

ONCE MORE THE SOLDIERS piled into their Bedford lorries with their kit-bags and rifles and rode away, waving to us kids and singing bawdy songs. The district just had time to heave a corporate sigh of relief before the roar of different motors was heard. Vast, high-bonneted, high-sided lorries that the occupants called trucks, with names like Dodge and Chrysler, and jeeps, a stylish updating of the English Land Rovers. It was the Americans.

A year earlier Hitler had declared war on them to show solidarity with his friends the Japanese after they attacked Pearl Harbor. Now England was being flooded with American soldiers prior to the invasion of Europe.

In our part of Cornwall, people from the next village were strangers; Englishmen from across the Tamar were foreigners; Americans might have been from Mars. And that wasn't all: to cap everything, they weren't just Americans, they were black, a whole regiment of them. Many in the village had never seen a black man; I don't think I had.

'They'm BLACK,' some squawked at each other.

'What? All over? All the way up and down?'

'They got white palms to their hands, I saw when I shook 'ands wi' one.'

'It wears off, that's why.'

'Does it wash off?'

'They can see in the dark.'

'They'd have to, wouldn't they.'

'And their lips!'

The men lowered their voices. 'They got John Thomases like Crago's bull.'

It's no good thinking in terms of colour prejudice. The village wasn't prejudiced—it was astounded. Although we were at the centre of the British Empire, populated with millions of every size, shape and colour, this was a remote part of Cornwall in 1943.

We kids in Doublebois loved them. They made our soldiers seem drab. Their uniforms, their equipment, their cigarettes, their sweets and their very colour. We wore their hats, chewed their gum, held their strange hands and ate their candy. Rides on army vehicles doubled. Jeeps were the big treat: tooth-loosening, rebounding joy-rides across the fields. We drilled with their rifles and learned their slang. I had a tap-dancing lesson on a sheet of plywood at the army camp gates from a man from New Orleans itself.

I was in Ede's shop with some other people, when a couple of them strolled in. They politely took their caps off and greeted us.

Mr Ede was always kindly, but perhaps he sensed trade. 'You'm welcome to Cornwall. 'Taint much but 'tis home to us.'

'This is paradise. You should see where we come from.' The deep voice and Southern accent astonished me. It wasn't like the voices in the Westerns we had seen every Saturday morning before the war.

A man asked the question all Americans got asked. 'Where you been to these last three years? 'Tis nearly all over.' But it was lost on these two and somehow seemed scarcely fair. All of our images of America were white— with blacks occasionally being goofy or loyal in the background.

The second GI asked, 'Excuse me, ma'am, but we see you have two churches in your city. Is one all right for coloured folk to worship in?'

'They be Church of England and Wesleyan Methodist. Which be you?'

'We're Baptist.'

'I reckon that's the same as Methodist, don't you, Miss Polmanor?' someone asked maliciously.

There was another camp concert given with the ubiquitous Looe Fishermen's Choir performing and us kids singing traditional and patriotic songs for our guests. Then their own jazz band played for us. It was sensational; the whole room was soon rocking. I had never heard music like it. But when GIs started jitterbugging there and then in the aisles with each other and the few girls who were present—their dresses swirling up above their waists—it went too far for most. Opinion about our guests' behaviour divided between those who couldn't wait to join in—mostly girls—some who didn't mind, and most—or possibly the most vocal—who were shocked rigid. The arguments to support the shocked-rigid view became wider and wilder. A dance at the army camp, always an attraction for the younger females in entertainment-free Doublebois, Dobwalls and wider, became a must for all who could or dared.

And these smiling, flamboyant, gentle men who came from God knows what hells in the Deep South of the segregated USA let us pull their hair, rub their skin to see if it came off, examine their pink palms, marvel at their very existence—and then they were gone as suddenly as they had appeared and were replaced by other Yanks, white ones, no less friendly, no less generous, but with not a tenth of the exotic appeal of their black comrades.

FIGHTING WAS A PART of living for most boys in those days. I know that I was always willing to defend myself or my position or my rights even if the other boy was a bit bigger. And not just to defend myself. I was willing to attack, too. If he was too big I would hit him and run. I don't think I was brave; we just thought like that. It established pecking orders and settled disputes. At first the vackies fought the village kids. When that calmed down and many vackies had returned home—quite a few simply turned fourteen, left school and went home to work—so that we were outnumbered, we fought each other. I remember having a strolling casual fight with Alan Packham all the way home from school one day while his older brother Harold walked with us and looked on. We were evenly matched in age and size; we walked a bit, punched a bit, walked and skirmished, breathing heavily from emotion as much as exertion. When he reached his house, the district nurse's house across the road, he went in and I walked the few yards to the Court. I crept into the wash-house, washed the blood off and bathed the scratches from where we had fallen into the hedge as we grappled, before going in for my tea.

There was one fight, though, that was serious. I was just ten, we had been in Cornwall for nearly three years and had just been given our end-of-term reports for Easter term 1943. By this time in the war the bombing seemed to be over so most of the vackies had already gone home. We few who were left had been incorporated into the village school. I was top of my class and, indeed, the whole school, which had pupils up to the age of fourteen. This was no great academic achievement, the bright kids over eleven were already creamed off to Liskeard County School. Jack, having reached fourteen, was going to go back home to Woolwich Polytechnic. I was soon to sit the entrance exam for grammar school. Coming top must have made me insufferable, certainly to my brother. I don't remember precisely what happened but perhaps I crowed once too often.

Anyway, he who had shown a whole childhood's forbearance to his uppity young brother, hit me on the way home from school. This was a huge shock. I was surprised and hurt, not necessarily physically, and I furiously ran at him to hit him back. He defended himself easily and we had a long trail back to Doublebois, walking apart, punctuated with futile rushes from me and flung insults—I was good at those—between bitter sobs and recriminations. The other children kept well ahead, walking briskly on and staying out of this family squabble.

At home Auntie Rose quickly got to the bottom of who we had been fighting: each other. She was shocked. 'You hit your little brother?' she demanded of Jack in a voice that frightened us both and had him in tears of guilt and shame. I was sent out to the wash-house to clean myself up and put cold water—as though there was any other sort to wash in—on the back of my neck to stop the nosebleed. She was closeted with Jack and the two reports. I listened outside the window.

Jack on the parapet of the River Fowey bridge

To my surprise I heard Jack receive no telling off for hitting me—though he cried from time to time and I could hear the indrawn sobs as he tried to stop himself. Instead, Auntie Rose paid him strings of compliments about how he had taken on the responsibility of me when we were evacuated, how he had looked after me, what a good boy he was, how he was always helpful and hard-working, utterly trustworthy, how he looked after his allotment and produced food for us all, how much she admired him because he was so like Uncle Jack, who had looked after her and their children through the Great Depression. And, biggest surprise of all, how clever he was. Not just book-and-sums clever like me, but really clever and

Wise about Life. When he was back in London and at the Poly he would soon overtake me and then we would all see. Then she called me in and sent me on an errand.

When I returned Uncle Jack had arrived home from work. He and Auntie Rose were closeted together briefly. He went out to the wash-house. She handed me my report and told me to take it out to him. 'There,' she said. 'Surprise him. See what he thinks about that.' Auntie Rose, impressed by learning, was normally very pleased by my reports.

No matter what my report and the teachers said, I was clearly pretty slow in some departments because, as I took it to him, pride reasserted itself; I was expecting praise. 'I've got my report, Uncle Jack.'

'Oh, yes?' He said noncommittally. 'Get me a bowl of water from the tap, there's a lad. I'll wash some of this muck off.'

I couldn't go fast enough. But Uncle Jack stripped off his jacket and hung it up, then his waistcoat, rolled up his sleeves, sluiced his arms, hands, face and bald head. He dried off, got dressed, took me into the house, removed his boots, put on his glasses and sat in the armchair to read the golden report.

I was bursting. 'I got all nines and tens. I only lost five marks in the whole exam. Every subject.'

'Five marks?' He was sharp. 'Five? What d'you lose them for?'

I gaped at the question, breathless. My world turned upside down. It's not what you achieve, but how far you fall short that matters. 'Er—well—um—well—I—er—two were silly mistakes, I really knew the answers, and three were taken off for untidiness.'

'Carelessness, is it? I'm bringing up carelessness yere, am I? That won't do, will it, boy? Let's see all tens next time.'

'But I came top of the whole school. Some of them are nearly fifteen.'

Uncle Jack was contemptuous. 'Bloody yokels. Clods. Cockneys and farm labourers. What do they know? Tens, boy, next time. Tens. And remember: when you're top dog no one likes a clever Dick. That often results in losing friends, the ones you might call thick. And if you think I'm being hard, well, life's never bloody fair. Pass me the newspaper.'

We had our tea. The meal seemed to be finished and only Jack and I sat, still subdued, at the table. Auntie Rose put a bowl in front of each of us. 'Yere you are, your favourite: blackberry and apple pie, over from Sunday. But I'm not sure you deserve it.'

She left us to get on with it. I had an idea. 'I'm not hungry, Jack. Would you like mine?'

He stared at me and then at my plate. 'D'you mean that?'

'Yes. Honest.'

'OK. No. I'll tell you what: I'll have half.'

I carefully cut mine into halves and spooned one of them onto his plate, watched by him. He looked at my plate, then at his full one. 'There's too much there. I can't eat all of that. Would you like half of mine?'

'All right.'

Jack cut his portion, picked up his plate and carefully spooned half of his pie onto my plate till both were equally charged. 'That's fair, isn't it?'

I nodded.

We ate our blackberry and apple pie in the peace brokered by Auntie Rose and Uncle Jack.

JACK AND I were doing our homework one evening. Auntie Rose was listening to something on the radio so we were banished to the front room instead of the cosiness of the kitchen table in the middle of the life of the house. Uncle Jack came in from work. The radio was turned up but we easily heard why we had been sent out. Auntie Rose said, quite quietly, 'Elsie's pregnant.'

'There's a surprise,' said Uncle Jack, showing none whatsoever.

'Three months gone.'

'Who knows?'

'Miss Polmanor, for one.'

'Everybody, then.'

There was a silence broken by Auntie Rose. 'I wonder if she knows who the father is.'

Uncle Jack's footsteps were taking him to the back door and the washhouse. They stopped. 'If you eat a tin of baked beans, how do you know which one made you fart?' And his steps receded before she could answer.

I found Elsie down the gardens beyond the outside privies. She was crying. This upset me terribly, no childhood outbreak of tears but something grown-up and important. 'Elsie, Elsie, don't cry. I love you.'

'Oh, shut up,' she sobbed.

'I'll stay here with you.'

'Bugger off.' I didn't move. 'Go on, bugger off. Leave me alone.'

I ran back to the house. 'Auntie Rose, Auntie Rose.'

'Calm down, boy. What's up?'

'Elsie's crying,' was all I could think of saying.

'She'll do a lot more of that.'

'Have I got to marry her?' I blurted out.

'What?' Auntie Rosie stared at me.

'I'm the father.'

She laughed, an entirely unexpected event. 'Don't be silly, boy.'

'But I am. I—I—I kissed her.'

'If you've finished your homework you can go out and play. Go on.'

I started to cry, not sure why. 'But I love her. She said she loves me.'

'It's not what she said to you that matters. It's what she did with someone else. Go on. Out.'

Elsie and I met frequently in spite of her telling me to bugger off. I was someone she could share things with, after all. Life must have been a bleak business with Miss Polmanor. I have no idea what Auntie Rose's views were on the subject of unmarried pregnancies—I cannot believe she condoned them—but her natural compassion asserted itself. Elsie was a girl she was fond of who needed help. That was that. Uncle Jack, equally kind, would always go along with his wife in such matters, anyway. So Elsie was an even more frequent visitor to 7 Railway Cottages. The rest of Doublebois more or less accepted it: 'There's a war on.' Pregnant girls were becoming more numerous everywhere—especially since the Yanks had arrived. Although on that score there were those who thought girls who went with Yanks were not only tarts but also traitors to 'Our Boys'.

When everyone else was out, Elsie and I giggled over her round tummy. 'That's the baby. Remember when you didn't believe me about babies?'

'I was young then.'

'Feel it. It moves.'

I did and was startled, repulsed, I think. 'Erggh. 'Slike a frog squirming.'

'I hope 'er's a Yank. They was best,' was a remark she often made to my shocked ears.

I hadn't seen her for a while when I saw her walking down the road from Dobwalls. 'Cor, Elsie, your stomach's enormous.'

She was in no mood for childish pleasantries. Her face was set. Her mood angry. 'They're going to send me away to a home, they said. Where I'll be looked after, they said.'

I was desperate. 'I'll look after you, Elsie. I love you.'

She ignored me, looking into her own hell. 'This home'll be full of girls what have had babies from soldiers. They'll all be adopted. We'm "fallen women", somebody said in the village.'

'We can go to our hut in the woods, Elsie. We can live there together.'

'Don't be simple,' and she strode furiously away to Miss Polmanor's, leaving me shattered in the road.

CHAPTER TEN

Singing became part of my life in Cornwall. It seems that I sang all the time. We sang at school: a hymn in assembly and all the well-known folk songs and children's songs in music class, plus the occasional more serious piece. We played singing games in school breaks; as I have said, the vackies and village kids even sang our antagonism at each other, and when that was over we sang children's chants, games and popular songs together. At home the Light Programme was always on the radio with Auntie Rose joining in through the day and encouraging us to do the same: 'Come on, boys, I sound like a crow. You can do better than that.' So we sang not only the current hits but songs from previous years back to Victorian ballads and the music hall. We sang in church on Sundays and carols at Christmas.

I said how our mother introduced us to the Russians, the Romantics, Ravel, Debussy, serious twentieth-century music starting with Stravinsky and lots of popular music and jazz, which she played to us and for her own pleasure. Well, Uncle Jack introduced us to a different range. There were the Welsh songs that he loved and the folk songs and children's songs that we knew from school, but the surprise was that atheist Uncle Jack showed us the beauty and majesty of the harmonies in *Hymns Ancient and Modern* and other ecclesiastical choral music. He never objected to our attending church on a Sunday—not that he would have dared cross Auntie Rose on the subject—indeed, he often came himself, turning the old 'Why should the Devil have all the best tunes?' into 'Why should God have all the best music? He's not listening anyway, so we might as well.'

Jack, like me, was a member of the choir at St Peter's church. But when he reached fourteen, voice wavering between alto and croak, he preferred to have his turn on a Sunday, like all the older boys, pumping the organ for sixpence; I was never big enough. All sorts of naughtinesses were indulged in by those on duty, out of sight behind the organ between hymns; their whispers and stifled giggles were given black looks by the vicar and others. Occasionally it would get out of hand when the boys did not pay attention to the service and forgot the few pumps necessary to get the organ primed. The organist would touch the keys and, instead of the opening chord, the instrument would let out a dying, groaning sigh that made you have to struggle not to let out a snort of laughter into the solemn Sunday silence. The boy would be given the dreadful punishment of being forbidden to pump and having to sit in the congregation each week with no sixpence.

Although I regretted not being a part of the bigger-boy fraternity that actually got paid for doing such a desirable job, I loved being in the choir. I have long since been an atheist but I remain grateful and glad that I have a Church of England background. It gave me so much and it was Auntie Rose who set us on the road by insisting that we went to church and Sunday school, and Uncle Jack who made us listen to the beauty, both musical and verbal. I still use my King James Bible and *The Book of Common Prayer* presented to me in September 1940 and September 1942 for Sunday-school attendance, and inscribed by the shadowy Reverend Oatey. Unfortunately I have lost my *Hymns Ancient and Modern*, which probably has 'September 1941' written inside it. The best of religions, full of glory and utterly ineffectual.

I used to go and play with the Burfords at Treburgie Farm. An avenue of magnificent beech trees led to the farm. As soon as I reached it I would start to sing. This avenue formed a natural nave that sent my voice echoing back to me. Alone in my beautiful cathedral I used to let rip with all my being into whatever we were rehearsing at the time and into my favourites. 'Jerusalem', of course, was one of them and I would send it soaring up into the branches to come back at me. My voice never sounded better and it gave me the confidence to stand up and sing it in the East Cornwall Silver Voice competition one anti-acoustic day in Liskeard cattle market, where sound was shredded by lowing cattle, bleating sheep and a gusting wind. The marketers stood in respectful silence while we children entertained them but it must have been thin gruel. I won, possibly because I was the loudest, and was presented with a half-crown's worth of National Savings stamps and a bucketful of pride for Auntie Rose and Uncle Jack.

One Christmas, towards the end of my time there, another vacky, Betty Cormack, and I, sang the carol 'Good King Wenceslas' in costume to the school, indeed the whole village. She was the King and I was his/her page. Auntie Rose sat beaming at me from the audience and Uncle Jack looked suitably critical.

CORNWALL IS PROBABLY the warmest county in the country but when the wind swung round the wrong way and came down off the moor, it used to cut through you like a knife. One year had a brief, very cold snap. There was more than a smattering of snow on the ground that was blown into your face by a biting northerly wind. Under the snow were sheets of ice, which had fallen as rain and frozen before the snow came. By Boxing Night we children must have been driving our parents and foster-parents mad because we were all let out to play. The Plummers, Jack and I huddled in the Court. We hit on the idea of going carol singing, unusual, as far as I remember, in our world. We collected Jimmy Peters, the Bunney children, Harold and Alan Packham. Eight or ten of us gathered. Someone found an old tin and we punched a slot in the lid. We had our collecting box. We wrote: '*Mrs Churchill's Russian Red Cross*' on the side of the tin, so it must have been 1942, by which time the Russians had been invaded by the Germans and were on our side. We started singing in the Court, were given some money and set off into the blackest of nights. Half a mile up the road to Dobwalls were some cottages down a lane. We sang and knocked, were given some money, sang some more and went to Crago's farm. The same story. Across another half-mile of frozen field to the houses on the Lostwithiel road, where a party was in progress. We were asked into the glorious warmth and stood in rows, singing to the householders and their guests, who smiled. They applauded us, gave us food, drink and money, and off we went. Another trek across fields and down lanes. More coins clanking into our tin. We stopped at a crossroads, crouched in a circle and emptied it onto the icy tarmac to count it by the light of a torch. On through the bitter dark night with tingling fingers, ears and toes to other isolated houses and finally triumphantly home. Fifteen shillings, we raised. We got a postal order, sent it off and proudly showed everyone our letter of acknowledgement signed by Mrs Churchill herself.

SOME SORT of a Silver Voice competition was held every year in many villages. Jack and I were to sing a duet, coached by Uncle Jack: 'Sheep May Safely Graze' by Johann Sebastian Bach, Jack singing the alto line, me the treble. Uncle Jack wanted us to win this for many reasons: his Welsh pride in singing; his previous work with Gwyn; his desire to beat the 'God-botherers' in their own backyard. It must have been in 1943 because Jack was due to go back to London to the Poly. The competition was to be held in Dobwalls Methodist Chapel, the largest space in the village—someone had realised that the cattle market was no place for children's voices. Jack kept complaining to Uncle Jack that his voice was 'going funny'.

'Don't you dare let it break till after the competition,' Uncle Jack said.

We arrived at the Methodist chapel along with most of the district. I had tried to persuade Elsie to come but she had refused. She was too shy or ashamed to go to such a gathering with her burgeoning stomach and, had she asked, Miss Polmanor would have refused permission for her even to leave the house in such shape: literally publicising her sin. We all sat in a state of excitement as the chapel filled. Auntie Rose pulled my sock up, straightened Jack's tie, ineffectually smoothed our cropped hair. 'There. You look a pair now, both of you.' Her favourite compliment.

'Nervous, boys?' asked Uncle Jack.

'A bit.'

'Good. You should be. Take good big breaths, you'll see 'em all off.'

The Reverend Clifford Buckroyd welcomed us all while the Reverend R. O. Oatey sat beside him and smiled vaguely: joint denominational events were rare. Buckroyd led us in a prayer that beseeched God to give the children tuneful voices and the judges clear minds. Like all prayers of whatever denomination it finished with '. . . bless all our forces, army, navy and air force, wherever they may be', followed by a fervent 'Amen.'

During the prayer, while everyone's head was lowered, someone slipped onto the bench beside me, nudging me along. It was Elsie. She grinned, proud of her own daring. I was both glad and embarrassed to see her there.

Uncle Jack had no such qualms. 'Hello, Elsie,' he said, none too quietly. 'You decided to support us, then, is it?'

Elsie grinned briefly as I was aware of something else going on. Miss Polmanor was on her feet. 'Mr Buckroyd. Mr Buckroyd.'

'Yes, Miss Polmanor?'

'In view of the fact that most of the children of the village are here this evening, I wonder if you fully approve of the congregation?'

Buckroyd was confused. 'I don't quite understand, Miss Polmanor.'

'This is a children's occasion. We should be protecting them. From corruption. From lewdness.'

The penny was dropping all round the chapel. There were murmurs and a muttered, 'Hear, hear'.

Elsie squirmed beside me. 'Oh, no. Oh, no.'

I must say, no matter what I thought of Miss Polmanor, she had guts, the conviction of her beliefs. She had already reported Elsie to the authorities, sparking off the decision to have her sent away to a home, but she hadn't kicked her out; that would have been un-Christian. And now she was prepared to stand up in public and make a fuss about Elsie attending this gathering when she should have been invisible at home. 'While our men-folk are away fighting God's holy war, we womenfolk should be setting an example, not pointing the way down the primrose path to damnation. I think you all know to whom I refer.' She didn't even need to point at Elsie.

There were more murmurs, a louder, 'Hear, hear'. Elsie got to her feet.

'Sorry, Mr Buckroyd. Honest. I only came to hear the boys sing. I'll go—'

A hand came across me and grabbed her. 'You bloody sit down and don't move,' growled Uncle Jack.

Elsie was crying. 'No, no, I—'

Everything started to go very fast. People were talking as Buckroyd said, 'Please, Miss Polmanor, I am sure there is no need—' and Uncle Jack topped it all with, 'What's she supposed to have done then, eh, missus?'

Auntie Rose pulled at Uncle Jack's sleeve without much conviction. 'Oh, Jack, don't make a scene,' but I am sure she was on his side; it was only her natural aversion to public display that prompted her to object.

Miss Polmanor's voice rose above the hubbub. 'Sinned. As well you know, Mr Phillips. Sinned again and again.'

Buckroyd managed to get in with, 'Please, please, this is a house of God.'

'Durst we not mention sin in the house of God now?'

'Elsie may have transgressed—' began Buckroyd.

Uncle Jack had the best pair of lungs there. He used them now. 'Let him or *her* that is without sin cast the first stone.'

'I was about to use those very words,' said Buckroyd.

'Then what's all this "transgressing"?' said Uncle Jack. 'She did what come natural.'

'I intended no censure,' said Buckroyd.

'Then why *not*?' Miss Polmanor was indignant.

Poor Buckroyd was under attack from two directions. Oatey, as far as I remember, wisely stayed out of it all. The place was seething by now.

Uncle Jack continued without pause. 'And if anyone should leave this house, you should order *her* out . . .'

Buckroyd chimed in, 'Mr Phillips, I'm not ordering anyone out. That—'

' . . . for the sin of envy. We all know she'd like to have been in this state years ago only no one'd touch her, bloody dried-up old haybag.'

Buckroyd showed dismay. 'Oh, now, Mr Phillips, that is not Christian.'

'Well, I'm not one of them, thank God. Come on, Rose, boys, let's breathe some clear air outside. Elsie, you want to walk home with us, is it?'

As far as I know, East Cornwall never did get its Silver Voice for 1943.

THE VOICE OF PROPRIETY, the voice of conformity, had a strength then that went far beyond the outbursts of frustrated old maids, as we all discovered when the vackies' billeting officer came a few days later. Though what followed seems antediluvian as well as inhuman to us now, I suppose all one can say is that millions of children were sent away from their parents in the evacuation and someone, somewhere had to make some rules. I was not allowed to hear what he said and he missed Uncle Jack, which was just as well. He had an order: I was not to associate with Elsie again for my 'moral welfare'. She was unmarried, fifteen, underage and pregnant; I was ten. Breach of this could result in my being taken away from Auntie Rose and Uncle Jack, again for my 'moral welfare'. By the look of him when I saw him walking away up the Court, the billeting officer had not enjoyed his mission.

'Has the world gone mad?' Auntie Rose asked me rhetorically.

Uncle Jack got home from work. He was predictably purple. 'God save us all from the clutches of the bloody Holy Ones,' he spat. 'The sooner they all join Him in heaven and leave us down yere in peace . . .' He threw his jacket across the room.

I was coming out of school a day or so later when I met Mr Buckroyd. He greeted me as usual but got a surly response. 'What's the matter, Terry?'

'They're taking Jack and me away,' I blurted accusingly.

'Who are? Your parents?'

'No. You. The Holy Ones. And you're sending Elsie away.'

The Reverend Buckroyd took a swift hand in our affairs. A phone call from him to Welling police station sent a constable to call on Mum and Dad—frightening the life out of them into the bargain. A return phone call from Dad soon settled where we should stay. But Buckroyd couldn't wave his wand over Elsie. Miss Polmanor would not tolerate an illegitimate baby in her house. Elsie's father had become a prisoner of the Japanese; her mother was nowhere to be found—whether through enemy action or Allied attraction, I don't know. Elsie was bound for a home. Homes for unmarried pregnant girls appeared all over the country during the war. Somehow or other they seemed to be compulsory. Incarceration of the mother was followed by adoption of the child.

And alongside the trivia of our lives, great events were taking place in the world. After the entry of the Americans in the war the tide had turned. North Africa was taken from Rommel; the Russians were turning defeat into triumph. British forces under the command of General Montgomery—the former Desert Rats—landed on Sicily. The invasion, of what Churchill mistakenly called 'the soft underbelly of Europe', had begun.

OUR THREE-YEAR 'other childhood' came to a swift climax. With air raids more or less over, Jack was to return home to go to Woolwich Polytechnic and I was awaiting the results of the entrance exam to see if I would go to Dartford Grammar School. The postman saw me in the Court one morning; our summer holidays had started. He handed me two envelopes and rode quickly off on his bike. The top one said 'Kent Education Committee' on it. I didn't even look at the one underneath, but turned and ran indoors shouting, 'Auntie Rose, Auntie Rose, the letter's come. Look. It's come.'

She was as excited as I was. 'Well, open it, boy. Let's see.'

As I separated the two letters to open the top one I saw the one underneath was a telegram. I stopped dead, my voice changed. 'It's a telegram.'

Her voice, indeed every angle of her body, became tense. 'Telegram? What's it say on it?'

I faltered. 'It just says "Telegram. War Office".' Any telegram was a rare enough event to send out warning signals in those days. Even I, at ten, knew the dread import of one from such a sender. The postman had shirked his duty in handing it to me. I looked at her. 'Shall I open it?'

She looked shattered, her head moving about as she looked vaguely for something. 'Where are my glasses?' There was no answer. She knocked something over. 'Oh *Duw*. Yes, open it—no—you can't—yes, open it. Read it. I can't—' She sank into a chair.

I opened it and started banally from the top. 'The War Office, Whitehall, London SW1. 8.30 a.m., 14 July 1943. We regret to inform you that your son Gwyn has been—' The word glared up at me from the telegram tape stuck onto the yellow paper. The world was reduced to that one word filling my vision. All I could manage was, 'Oh, oh.'

Auntie Rose didn't look at me. She said, almost inaudibly, 'Does it say it, boy? Does it say it? Say it doesn't.'

I just stood there staring at the word. I didn't dare look up at her.

She held an arm out. 'Come yere, boy. Put your arms round me. Hold me for a minute.' There was no sign of weeping. I did as she asked though she scarcely seemed to notice that I was there. 'Oh Gwyn, Gwyn, my little— I was always afraid for you. Oh Gwyn, Gwyn, Gwyn.' She started to rock back and forth still saying his name every few rocks.

After a while I said, 'Shall I go down the line and find Uncle Jack?'

'No. He'll be up from work later. Time enough for his world to end then.'

JACK AND I watched Auntie Rose and Uncle Jack for two days. They didn't cling to each other or sob but their palpable misery was a bond between them that excluded us. He touched her more often than usual as they moved about the room and once she laid her head against his bald one in a weary, hopeless way that seemed to fill the room with a sigh. When Auntie Rose and I were alone for some moments I took her hand, too awkward and the wrong height to embrace her properly. She put her arms round me and buried my head fiercely in her bosom. We stood there, motionless, while I tried not to suffocate, the only time I ever remember her needs taking precedence over mine. Jack and I crept about not knowing what to do till we went outside, over the road to the Park, and climbed up into the big beech tree to discuss it. We wrote to our parents with the result of our deliberations:

Dear Mum and Dad,

Just a line to let you know Auntie Rose and Uncle Jack's son Gwyn has been killed in Sicily. They are very unhappy. Auntie Rose keeps crying and Uncle Jack keeps going to the bottom of the garden and just sitting there instead of going to work. We thought it would be a good idea if only one of us came home and one of us stayed here with

them and became their son. Then you've both got one each. That's fair.
We were going to toss for it but Jack said I've got to go back to
Dartford Grammar School. Jack doesn't mind not going to the Poly
and he can stay here and work on the track with Uncle Jack. He says
he would like that. He could come and visit with a privilege ticket.
  Love, Jack and Terry xxx

PS: I passed my entrance exam.

Another day passed. Our letter was in the post. I watched Uncle Jack at
the bottom of the garden, beyond the privies. He was right at the bottom, out
of sight of the houses, by the vegetables, with a cornfield beyond and the
railway line rising out of its cutting and snaking towards Liskeard, Plymouth
and London. I hadn't made a sound. He was sitting on an old bench set there
to rest on when gardening. He had his back to me, in his own world.

'Can I come and sit with you, Uncle Jack?'

He patted the bench at once as though he had already heard me. 'Yes,
come by yere, boy.' As I sat by him he ruffled what little there was of my
hair. 'Time you had a haircut, is it?'

''S not that long.'

He was in the quietest of voices. His voice with its sharp South Wales
cutting edge and its rumbling undertones was at its most gentle. 'Little
blondie Anglo-Saxon. Gwyn was dark, like me: a Celt. "The soft underbelly of Europe." The mud was soft in Flanders, too. Didn't save anybody.
Remember, boy: never, never, never, never, *never* trust your leaders.
Montgomery's a hero. Churchill's a hero. Gwyn is dead. And it's not just
this war or the last. It's all history. "Into the Valley of Death rode the six
hundred." Who sent 'em there, eh? Don't *ever* trust 'em, not any of 'em.'

Jack came round the hedge by the privies. 'Uncle Jack, Mr Buckroyd's
with Auntie Rose. He'd like to see you, too.'

'Oooh, no, not the bloody minister,' sighed Uncle Jack. 'They don't just
kill you, they send someone to tell your next of kin it's all for the best.'

Mr Buckroyd came diffidently down the garden. 'Good afternoon, Mr
Phillips. Boys.'

Jack and I greeted him.

Mr Buckroyd went and stood by the fence, looking out. He continued,
'I can't tell you, Mr Phillips, how sorry I—'

He was gently cut short. 'Then please don't try.'

Mr Buckroyd thought for a moment. 'I know that your wife is Church of England and that you are . . . neither, but I suggested to her a memorial service in the chapel because it is bigger there than the church and I think there would be many indeed in the village who would want to come.'

Uncle Jack sitting on a wall, feet not reaching the ground

'What did she say?'

'She would like it.'

'Yes, yes, she must have it.' Uncle Jack gave the briefest of snorts, remembering his last performance in the chapel. It says much for Buckroyd that he was even here giving this invitation. 'Don't worry, I'll behave myself.'

'Yes, of course.'

'Only nothing about souls in heaven. Eh? Or eternal life. Or any of that. A memorial service: let's just remember him.'

'I'll vet everything myself.' Mr Buckroyd smiled uncertainly, not sure how to close this meeting. 'I'm sure he died a hero, Mr Phillips.'

The cliché brought a sharp edge to Uncle Jack's voice. 'Are you, now? I seen a few o' them die. Ashes to ashes and mud to mud.' He paused and added, 'About what you did over Terry and Elsie. We're very grateful.'

'I'm doing my best about Elsie but it's not always straightforward.'

'Yes, yes. You're a good man . . .' Uncle Jack paused. He couldn't resist it even in his agony, '. . . in spite of being a Christian.'

Buckroyd started to leave. He was stopped by Uncle Jack's raised voice.

'One other thing. I'll apologise to Miss Polmanor when I see her.'

Buckroyd turned, surprised. 'What?'

'For calling her names. Even though she asked for it. She's just another casualty, you know. Like all of us. A million men didn't come home from the first war.' He paused. '*My* war. Huh. That left a million spare women. She was engaged, wasn't she? To a corporal in the Duke of Cornwall's Light Infantry. Killed on the Somme.'

'That's right.'

'A whole generation of leftover women. A lot of them got a bad attack of God. I suppose it's better than emptiness. She didn't want to be a dried-up old haybag. She just found out that, one day, that's what she is.'

Mr Buckroyd was poised to go. 'You're a good man, Mr Phillips . . .' He too paused, '. . . in spite of being an atheist.' And he was gone.

There was silence for a while. Uncle Jack's arm was thrown round me.

Then he spoke. 'I like it yere, boys. Look at the wind on that barley field. And the valley. And the compost heap, there, to remind us what we're coming to.'

I tried to think of anything I could. 'And the railway. That's good.'

Uncle Jack hugged me. 'Yes. That's good.' He changed tack. 'Let's have a service here. For Gwyn. Us three, eh? An Anglo-Celtic service. You remember that song you learned last year, "Barbara Allen"?'

We did.

'Sing it, both of you. Go straight to the third verse. That's suitable.'

And we sang, in two parts, me treble and Jack alto, into the summer's day, to the haunting tune of 'Barbara Allen', while Uncle Jack looked away from us into his own wounded life.

And death is printed on his face
And o'er his heart is stealing;
The pain of love he bravely bore,
So far beyond the healing.

He turned his face unto the wall,
And death was with him dealing . . .

TWO DAYS LATER we faced Auntie Rose in the living room. She looked drawn and stern. 'I've got a letter yere from your mother.'

Jack spoke for us, ruefully. 'So've we.'

'You don't want to go home, is it?' she said.

I was shamefaced. 'It's not that.'

'Whose idea was it for you to stay here, then?' she pursued.

Jack was the braver of us. 'We thought it together.'

I joined in. 'We were going to toss for it, but Jack said I've got to go back to Dartford Grammar School.'

'Did he now?' She looked at both of us with an expression I could not read. 'Come yere, both of you.' She held us close. 'You're a pair, aren't you? I thought so when I first set eyes on you.' And she held us in a vice-like grip until I had to complain.

'Ow, you're hurting.'

She released us. 'But, you see, boys, you can't stay with us. As it is you both have to sleep down in the front hall there together till you go. Top 'n' tail. We must have your room at once. Don't look so pained. Guess who's going up there? Elsie and her little one.'

'Elsie's going to stay here?' I said, unbelieving. 'Can I go and tell her?'

'She knows, silly.'

'Well, can I go and tell her I know, too?' And I was off up the Court shouting, 'Elsie, Elsie. You're coming here, Elsie.'

A WEEK LATER, Jack and I lay in terror on our mattress on the hall floor listening while Elsie, up in our room with Auntie Rose and the district nurse, gave me another lesson on the facts of life. We crept into the kitchen and there was Uncle Jack, with a glass in his hand. 'Hello, boys, too much of a racket to sleep, is it? She always was a noisy girl. Now's her chance.'

'Is Elsie all right?' I asked.

'Right as rain. Here, have a sip of this. Drink to the baby's health. Say "Good health and long life to you."'

Jack tried a sip and had to run outside to spit it out.

'Don't waste it,' Uncle Jack called after him.

I was concerned. 'Is it a boy or a girl?'

'A boy. Black as pitch.' Uncle Jack smiled but without his former twinkle. That, so much a part of him, was gone. It was like an amputation. 'Well, sort of greyish really, but same difference. Pretty little thing. I'll have to learn some Negro spirituals to teach him for the Silver Voice competition, eh? They're good singers, those darkies. That Paul Robeson, he made that film with us, didn't he: *Proud Valley*. He sang with the South Wales miners in the Depression. Great bass voice.'

The whole thing was beyond me. 'Is he black—I mean, grey—all over?'

'Just about. He'll do a lot for Rose, being yere.' His good humour faded into bitterness. 'The Lord giveth and the Lord taketh away—as the bloody minister would say.'

A FEW DAYS LATER on Doublebois station we boarded the Cornish Riviera for Paddington. I was ten and a half when my 'other childhood' ended, Jack was nearly fifteen. We had fewer people to see us off than poor Teddy Camberwell, but there were enough: Elsie with her baby and Auntie Rose and Uncle Jack.

Oh, Auntie Rose and Uncle Jack! Ten shillings a week per vacky was the official allowance, and in return they had given themselves without stint. Was there ever such a bargain? Yes, they were about to give Elsie the same, for nothing. They were without guile and without self-interest: 'The salt of the earth' is the saying. And if ever the earth needed salting, Auntie Rose and Uncle Jack were there to do it.

Amid the huffing and puffing of the engine and the stationmaster we said our farewells.

'Give my respects to your mam and dad. Write soon. Oh, we'll miss you, boys,' Auntie Rose repeated.

'Bye, Terry. See you in London one day,' said Elsie. She held up her baby's tiny hand with its pink palm. 'Say goodbye, Louis. Say bye-bye.'

'Bye, Elsie. Bye, Louis.'

Doors were slammed, flags waved, a whistle blew.

'Goodbye, Auntie Rose, Uncle Jack,' we shouted.

'Goodbye, boys. Look after your—you be—' He choked, stopped, tried to grin at us and failed miserably. Unheeded tears ran down his cheeks.

Auntie Rose cut in. 'Oh, now don't cry, Jack, for God's sake. You'll start me off.' And she started to cry.

The train moved forward.

'Remember what I said, boys,' called Uncle Jack. 'Two things: it's not fair and don't ever trust 'em. Your leaders. Never. You never know what they'll do. And whatever it is, it won't be for you.'

We hung out of the window, waving furiously, and the train went past Railway Cottages above us, where neighbours were waving at the wire fence. We began to round the curve in the line so that we could only just see the platform on which Auntie Rose and Uncle Jack were still waving back: last sight of our own Rock of Ages and her bloody-minded bantam.

The train took us over the Lostwithiel road, past Dobwalls, over the Moorswater Viaduct. It stopped at Liskeard, Menheniot, St Germans, Torpoint, rumbled over Saltash Bridge—presumably moving it another foot one way or the other—and we were in Plymouth, England, and on our way back to our half-forgotten home.

UNCLE JACK AND AUNTIE ROSE. Auntie Rose and Uncle Jack. Aunt and uncle. Not father and mother but not distant either, just in-between relatives. In fact, of course, they weren't even that; they were our foster mother and father, not relatives at all. But even now, sixty-six years later, I still cannot say their names without a full heart and a lump of gratitude in my throat.

terence **frisby**

RD: *Kisses on a Postcard* **was published to mark the 70th anniversary of the evacuation of city-dwelling children to the country at the outbreak of the Second World War. Did you attend the special service at St Paul's Cathedral in London?**

TF: I did, and on September 1st, 2009, there were 2,000 white-haired people, like me, blubbing into their hankies. Of course, that date in 1939 was two days before Chamberlain declared war on Germany. My mother sent my brother Jack and me to live with our cousins near Brighton. It was the time of the Phoney War, when Britain wasn't under attack, and so children drifted back to the cities. In May 1940, after Dunkirk when war broke out in earnest, Jack and I and thousands of other children became 'vackies', sent into the unknown.

RD: There are many very sad stories, but your experience was a good one. Did you manage to keep up with 'Auntie Rose' and 'Uncle Jack' after the war?

TF: Yes, we certainly did. But we were boys getting on with life and we were probably not assiduous enough. Some years later, they came to my brother's wedding. Not long afterwards, Uncle Jack died of a heart attack and Auntie Rose eventually left Cornwall and went to live with her son, Len, in Weston-super-Mare.

RD: At the end of *Kisses on a Postcard* **you say that your home in Welling was 'half forgotten'. Was it hard to adapt to living there again?**

TF: I don't think it was. As a kid, you just get on with the way things are. My mother worked, and I do remember not enjoying coming back to an empty house after school. But a much greater shock was discovering that there were an awful lot of boys at the grammar school who were much cleverer than I was. I was ten and I'd been top of the school in Cornwall. Now I was in the 'B' stream. I did well in my final exams, though.

RD: You've had a long career as an actor, director, producer and scriptwriter. Was this the life you'd set your heart on?

TF: No. First I wanted to be a journalist and then to be elected as a Labour politician and do some good, but there were no jobs in journalism. I ended up, by chance, in Men's Tailoring in Selfridges. Over the course of six years I gained a diploma in cloths and learned to cut a suit. At twenty-two I met an actor who filled my head with tales of the theatre and that was it. I went to the Central School of Speech and Drama.

RD: What was your first big theatrical breakthrough?

TF: Actually, there were two big breakthroughs, On the critical level, my first play, *The Subtopians*, was very well received. On the financial level, it was *There's a Girl in My Soup*. After a chaotic tour in the provinces it ran for years in the West End.

RD: You went on to write the film script. Did you have a say in the casting?

TF: No. Peter Sellers played the middle-aged male lead and we became good friends, but he wasn't really right for the part. Goldie Hawn was the girl; she was American, essentially a rich man's girl, a princess, but the role required a sixties chick—mini-skirted, blonde-haired, downmarket—someone who you'd find walking down the King's Road on a Saturday morning. The cast of the stage play was terrific, but people remember the film.

RD: What made you want to write your 'vacky' memories as a radio play?

TF: I wrote twenty-two pages of reminiscences just for myself. I then showed them to a producer of radio drama at the BBC, who asked me to turn them into a ninety-minute play for Radio 4. *Just Remember Two Things: It's Not Fair and Don't Be Late* aired in 1988. One of the letters I had came from a listener in Coventry: 'I'm the granddaughter of Auntie Rose and when she came to live with us she had a photo of herself with you and your brother.

She used to tell me bedtime stories about you. You feel like the brothers I've never met.' The letter was from Len's daughter!

RD: That's extraordinary. Did you contact her?

TF: We kept in constant touch after that, but I didn't actually meet her until the 2009 book launch of *Kisses on a Postcard*. I told her: 'This book is a tribute to your grandparents. Wouldn't it be wonderful if it makes them posthumously famous!'

RD: Your next plan is to stage a musical version of *Kisses* in a West End theatre.

TF: Yes, it's ready to go. All we need is the necessary funding. It was first performed in Barnstaple in 2004 as *Just Remember Two Things*, where it played to packed houses. This production is called *Kisses on a Postcard* and www.kissesonapostcard.com is worth a look. My son designed the site and you can watch and listen to video clips.

RD: If you could turn the clock back, would you still choose the stage?

TF: Definitely. I've loved everything I've done in the theatre, especially the acting and writing. If I had another chance, I'd start at sixteen. I wasted six years in the rag trade.

COPYRIGHT AND ACKNOWLEDGMENTS

NINE DRAGONS: Copyright © 2009 by Hieronymus, Inc.
Published at £18.99 by Orion Books, an imprint of The Orion Publishing Group Ltd.
Condensed version © The Reader's Digest Association Limited, 2010.

THE MURDER OF KING TUT: Copyright © James Patterson, 2009.
Published at £12.99 by Century, an imprint of The Random House Group Limited.
Condensed version © The Reader's Digest Association Limited, 2010.

PRESENT DANGER: Copyright © 2009 by Stella Rimington.
Published at £14.99 by Quercus.
Condensed version © The Reader's Digest Association Limited, 2010.

KISSES ON A POSTCARD: Copyright © 2009 by Terence Frisby.
Published at £14.99 by Bloomsbury Publishiing Plc.
Condensed version © The Reader's Digest Association Limited, 2010.

The right to be identified as authors has been asserted by the following in accordance with
sections 77 and 78 of the Copyright, Designs and Patents Act, 1988: Michael Connelly, James
Patterson and Martin Dugard, Stella Rimington, Terence Frisby.

Spine: © National Geographic; page 5 (top) © Getty Images/Jim Watson/AFP.
6–8 images: © National Geographic; illustration: Narrinder Singh@velvet tamarind;
184 (top) © Wendy Werris, bottom © Alamy/dbimages; 185 © Alamy/Danita Delimont.
186–8 images: © Photodisc, Flickr; illustration: Curtis Cozier; 304 © Rankin; 305 © Getty
Images/Hulton Archive; pages 306–9 images: © iStock; illustration: Rick Lecoat@Shark
Attack; 454 © Jamie Hughes. 456–7 image: courtesy of Terence Frisby; Illustration: Darren
Walsh@velvet tamarind; all other photographs courtesy of Terence Frisby; 574 © Ronnie
Laughlin; 575 www.picture-desk.com.

All rights reserved. Unauthorised reproduction, in any manner, is prohibited.

Reader's Digest and The Digest are registered trademarks of
The Reader's Digest Association Inc.

Printed and bound by GGP Media GmbH, Pössneck, Germany

020-264 DJ0000-1